T5-AFV-244

HUMAN GROWTH AND DEVELOPMENT

HUMAN GROWTH AND DEVELOPMENT

By

ROBERT W. McCAMMON, M.D., *Director*

and the Staff of the Child Research Council
University of Colorado School of Medicine
Denver, Colorado

With a Foreword by

Albert Damon, M.D.

Harvard University
Cambridge, Massachusetts

CHARLES C THOMAS • PUBLISHER

Springfield • Illinois • U.S.A.

Published and Distributed Throughout the World by

CHARLES C THOMAS • PUBLISHER
Bannerstone House
301-327 East Lawrence Avenue, Springfield, Illinois, U.S.A.
Natchez Plantation House
735 North Atlantic Boulevard, Fort Lauderdale, Florida, U.S.A.

Library of Congress Catalog Card Number: 71-113793

With THOMAS BOOKS careful attention is given to all details of manufacturing and design. It is the Publisher's desire to present books that are satisfactory as to their physical qualities and artistic possibilities and appropriate for their particular use. THOMAS BOOKS will be true to those laws of quality that assure a good name and good will.

Printed in the United States of America
RN-1

To

Alfred Hamlin Washburn, respected teacher,
unfailing friend and inspiration to all, this
book is dedicated with gratitude and affection.

FOREWORD

ONE approaches a monument with a feeling of awe. With this volume the Denver group begins to unveil a monumental body of scientific data, unexcelled in duration and detail – frequently repeated observations, biological and behavioral, of a few hundred persons from birth to adult life. Some participants have now been followed for forty years, while a number of their children have entered the study. The whole project, directed for many years by Dr. Alfred H. Washburn, was made possible by a fortunate combination of investigators, research support, and of course the subjects themselves. Only those engaged in multi-disciplinary longitudinal research can fully appreciate the skill, industry, and devotion that have produced these data.

It has long been recognized that only longitudinal research can answer questions of individual growth, maturation, and aging. For the human biologist as basic scientist, such research has three main aims – description (of events, products, processes, rates, and their variability); correlation (of observations from various disciplines with one another and with time); and prediction. The applied human biologist, whether clinician or public-health practitioner, obtains a set of norms by which to evaluate the status of patient or population, the need for intervention, and the results of intervention.

Dr. McCammon and his associates here describe their population, their methods, the data obtained, the form in which the data exist, and their accessibility to interested workers. Since the number of subjects in long-term longitudinal studies is small, certain problems can be investigated only by combining data from several studies. Detailed description is prerequisite to this kind of collaboration.

Most of the book comprises summaries of data analyzed

cross-sectionally. (Height and weight increments by age – Table E-29 and Figure E-6 – are however truly longitudinal data, providing "velocities" rather than the "distances" otherwise presented.) The authors are well aware that incremental velocities, or growth rates, are the crux of their long and costly research program. They promise a later volume, eagerly awaited, which will contain longitudinal analyses from the several disciplines as well as the correlations and interpretations largely omitted here.

Some workers question the value of cross-sectional analysis of longitudinally gathered data. In my view, cross-sectional data are indeed useful. We need distances as well as velocities. National surveys like the United States National Health Examination Survey or the earlier Canadian one are by their very representativeness less suitable for some normative purposes than surveys of defined ethnic, geographic, or socio-economic subgroups. The World Health Organization specifies that the proper standard for evaluating nutritional status for an individual or group is a well-nourished group of the same racial and ethnic background. The Denver subjects, mainly upper-class "Old Americans" of northwest European descent, provide just such standards for a sizeable percentage of the United States population.

As the authors state, the end-point of longitudinal research on the human life cycle has moved from early maturity to include the total life span. For obvious practical reasons there are even fewer longitudinal studies of aging than of growth. The subjects of growth studies who can be followed throughout life are priceless scientific resources. Only they can provide answers to such basic questions as the relation between rates of growth and maturation and rate of senescence; or the life course, reproduction, health, longevity, and cause of death of slow and fast maturers or of lean and obese (or large and small) children. Here is the real payoff for growth studies. The vision and efforts of the pioneers in human growth research have put this goal on our horizon; the contribution of the Denver Child Research Council brings it closer.

Harvard University ALBERT DAMON

ACKNOWLEDGMENTS

THE authors wish to acknowledge the invaluable and unfailing assistance of Lois B. Dotson and Ada M. Harrison for their many years of assistance in keeping the research program running smoothly and for the typing and preparation of the manuscript; of Carleta Yarian in many roles of data preparation; of all former members of the research staff, who contributed so much to the data collection; to the statistical and computer personnel who assisted in creating and using the data system; and particularly to the subjects and their families. Without their cooperation there could have been no research program.

This work was supported by contract PH-43-68-634 from the National Institute of Child Health and Human Development.

CONTENTS

HUMAN GROWTH AND DEVELOPMENT

INTRODUCTION

THE data presented in this volume represent descriptive statistical summaries of selected segments of measurements of physical growth and maturation, health records, nutritional intakes and biochemical and hematologic variables collected by the Child Research Council in a longitudinal study of healthy growth and development between October 1, 1927 and January 1, 1967. These measurements, while sometimes representing data on more than a hundred subjects of each sex during the childhood years, were developed by repeated periodic measurements of the same individuals followed from early infancy or childhood through the childhood and adolescent years and into early adult life rather than being taken from different subjects at successive ages. The purposes of this publication are three: First, it is designed to make available statistical summaries of measurements and methods of measurement on a group of subjects whose health and socioeconomic status are documented. Second, it provides a statement of the specific measurements that have been done longitudinally and the number of subjects on whom such measurements have been recorded for workers who have use for longitudinal data on healthy growth and development. Third, it describes the data system in which the complete, individual measurements have been organized and which makes it possible for individual seriatim records to be provided for anyone with valid need of such data.

The purposes for conducting longitudinal studies are to trace the course of change in the individual subject over time and to identify as many as possible of the events that occur during growth and development in the belief that they may have significance for the individual as determinants of his future course. This publication does not serve these basic purposes, since the necessary analyses are still in progress. A volume of such longitudinal analyses will follow when they are complete. The present volume presents cross-sectional analyses of data for a number of measurements that change as the result of growth and development. The grids which may be constructed from them are appropriate backgrounds for comparing individuals with the range characteristic of growing, healthy children. Since the group of subjects studied probably represents a large segment of the population of this country, such reference standards should prove useful to others taking similar measurements.

The Child Research Council was one of several longitudinal programs that were founded in the 1920's and early 1930's. While these programs varied to some extent in the subject populations studied, the specific measurements made, and in the intensity of investigations carried out, they shared the common purpose of attempting to learn more about the individual during the growing years. They were not the first longitudinal studies undertaken, having been preceded in this country by the well-known studies of Shuttleworth and the Brush Foundation earlier in this century and by less widely known programs dating back to the study of his own son's growth carried out by Montbeillard, whose measurements were published by Buffon in 1776.

As signified by the name, the original intent of the Child Research Council was to follow individual subjects from birth to maturity. However, by the mid-1930's it became obvious that much potential information would be lost if studies were terminated at the end of physical maturation. Since one of the long-range goals of such a program is to connect events of early life with function and health of the individual in later life, study of the mature subjects as they advanced in years was strongly indicated(1,2). Accordingly, the length of proposed study was extended to include the entire life span.

A brief history of the evolution of the Child Research Council program may clarify reasons for variations in the duration of studies reported in later sections. Incorporation of the Council in 1927 was preceded by a longitudinal program devoted to research in methods of detection of disease in children which started in 1923 to enroll children who were thought to represent high risk of disease development. They were selected from the practices of a group of participating physicians in Denver. Dr. W. W. Wasson was founder of both programs and transferred the subjects of the initial study to the Council. In 1930. when Dr. Alfred H. Washburn became Director of the program, emphasis was shifted to the study of health rather than disease, and subjects were admitted at or before birth so that the infancy period could be included.

Methodology and research goals were different to some extent in 1930 from later years of research. For example, micromethods of blood analysis were not available in 1930, so study in infants was not feasible. Protein separation methods have changed and expanded through the years to a very considerable degree, and while the older methods gave useful information, newer techniques greatly enhanced the specificity of possible determinations. An even more fluid area has been the field of psychological investigation. These data, while not included in this volume, have been developed through the years since 1930 in ever-increasing variety and detail as both the theory of emotional development and the instruments for evaluating it have changed and improved. Sacrifice of absolute continuity of data was compensated for by the increased potential for understanding complex processes in development that resulted from the incorporation of more modern techniques. In addition, whole new areas of research, such as nutritional intake and cholesterol chemistry, were added in later years when it became apparent that information in these areas was essential to the purposes of the program.

The Study Population

The study population in a longitudinal research program must necessarily be small relative to that which is possible in cross-sectional studies. Repeated measurements eventually lead to a large mass of data, and sampling at adequately short intervals together with necessary concurrent analyses of the data require extensive staff time. In addition, the requirement that the subjects remain available for follow-up limits the total population from which such a study group may be drawn. Experience, together with sociological investigations, indicates that the middle and upper middle socioeconomic groups are significantly more stable within a community than either the poor or the wealthy. In addition, since emphasis in a program such as that of the Child Research Council is on healthy growth and development, certain uncontrollable variables are eliminated by selecting from a group that is not economically deprived. For example, none of the subjects was limited in food intake by finances and all received private medical care. A further advantage in selecting from this socioeconomic group is the relatively high intelligence and educational level they represent. In order for a subject to remain within a program for a lifetime he must be able to understand the need for the research and the value of his contribution, even though there is little chance that he himself will benefit directly from the findings.

The above considerations have led to the criticism that such a study population is representative only of itself. A more reasonable position is that this study group probably represents a large segment of middle-class America and does not differ significantly from the population comprising the private practice of medicine in this country.

Selection of subjects after 1930 was made with the primary objective of permanence within the Denver area. Second in order of importance was the family's understanding of the purposes of the program and willingness to cooperate for the entire life span. Finally, the families had to be able to obtain their medical care and advice from private physicians so that the Council staff would constitute as small an influence as possible. All subjects were volunteers and no rewards or bribes were offered. The only promises made were that we would report such data as height, weight and significant physical findings following each examination to the parents and to the physician designated by them. In the event that a condition was found which, in the judgment of the staff, represented an immediate or long-range threat to the health of the subject this would be reported at once to their physician and we would cooperate with him in any way that he requested in the care of the subject.

A total of 334 subjects have contributed measurements used in one or more segments of the descriptive statistics given in the tables in this volume. Of these, 78 were born before 1930 and most were not followed from birth; however, 19 of these were still being actively followed at the end of 1966 and measurements on them are in every way comparable to similar ones made on children born after 1930. Of the 78 subjects born before 1930, 17 were referred either by the National Jewish Hospital at Denver or by the Denver Junior League as close contacts of tuberculous patients. Data collected from the study of these children are included in the anthropometric and roentgenographic measurements and, for two children, in the basal pulse data.

Of the 256 subjects born after 1930, 24 were lost to follow-up after a period of less than 5 years. Reasons for loss of these subjects were varied, but most of them left the Denver area. Forty-one additional subjects may be described as having withdrawn from the program. These people remained within the Denver area for longer or shorter periods but declined to come in. Reasons for loss varied from a group who had understood their commitment as continuing only to age 18 and refused to come in after that to a few who left the program because they objected to one or more of the procedures that were part of the research program.

Ten subjects, 8 males and 2 females, were born prematurely and their growth, nutrition and roentgenographic data are so identified in the data system. The definition of prematurity used was the combination of birth weight less than 2500 grams and less than 36 weeks gestation as determined from the menstrual history of mothers.

At the end of 1966, 179 subjects were being actively followed. One hundred sixty-three of these had been seen for examination in 1965 or 1966 and, for the remaining 16, who no longer lived in Denver, there was no doubt of their commitment to the program or their willingness to be examined when they were in the area.

The following tables give dates of birth by decades and ages of last examination of the 334 subjects who comprise the group from whom data were drawn:

Date of Birth	Male	Female	Total
	Number of Subjects		
1915-29	40	38	78
1930-39	54	52	106
1940-49	27	42	69
1950-59	27	25	52
1960-66	16	13	29
Total	164	170	334

Age at Last Examination			
Age (yr)	Male	Female	Total
	Number of Subjects		
1-5	25	29	54
6-10	22	27	49
11-15	28	28	56
16-20	23	39	62
21-25	23	17	40
26-30	11	14	25
31-35	11	6	17
36-40	14	7	21
41-45	6	3	9
46-50	0	0	0
51-55	1	0	1

Enrollment of related subjects resulted from at least two identifiable factors. First, policy of the program was to enroll first-born children in preference to later-born children when new families were accepted and then to try to enroll all subsequent siblings. This policy was founded on an attempt to limit the genetic pool from which the subjects were drawn as much as possible, and while it did not succeed in enrolling all members of all families, it did produce many sibling groups within the study population. Second, and probably equally important, was the fact that subject families recommended the program to relatives with the result that there are many cousins, nieces and nephews included among the subjects. Finally, the policy of admitting only second-generation children during the late years of the study enhanced the trends originated by the above factors. Charting of the resulting kinships is the only way that a complete picture may be presented, and pedigrees are presented as Appendix A. A summary of these data is as follows:

Number of subjects 334

Number of families (parents + enrolled children) 215

Number of related families (in 34 kinship groups) 83

Number of subjects with relatives as close as first cousin 240

Number of subjects with no enrolled relatives 94

Educational attainment of the subject population was higher than that of the general population. For 59 of the subjects who were born in earlier years of the program and lost to follow-up, no information was available on final educational attainment. An additional 105 of the subjects were still too young to have completed their education. For the remaining 170 subjects, educational attainment by years is given in the following table:

Years of School	Male	Female	Total
		Number of Subjects	
Not old enough	52	53	105
Unknown	27	32	59
11	0	2	2
12	10	17	27
13	2	6	8
14	6	8	14
15	1	4	5
16	39	33	72
17	3	5	8
18	12	9	21
19	1	0	1
20	11	1	12
Total	164	170	334

Education of the parents of subjects is as follows:

Years of School	No. of Fathers	No. of Mothers	Total
Unknown	6	7	13
8 or less	0	1	1
8-11	23	16	39
12	43	54	97
13-15	31	50	81
16	52	71	123
17 or more	60	16	76
Total	215	215	430

Economic level of the families for most of the period of study was of the middle- and upper middle-class level. There was upward mobility economically in many of the young families as they established themselves, and in a few instances economic circumstances showed some decline. No attempt was made to get specific information about the level of family income. A general indication of the economic level as indicated by the occupations of the fathers at the birth of the first child enrolled is given below:

Occupations of the fathers:*	No. of Fathers
Professional, technical, managerial	123
Clerical, sales	57
Service	3
Farming	2
Machine trades, structural work	11
Laborer	14
Student, unemployed, unknown	5
	215

*Based on U. S. Department of Labor: Dictionary of Occupational Titles, 1965, Vol. II. Occupational Classification, 3rd edition.

Of the 170 families for whom religion was known, 122 were Protestant, 15 Catholic, 17 Jewish, 1 atheist, 10 mixed and 5 stated they had no affiliation.

Nationality of the parents was of mixed European stock, with the majority of northern European extraction. Actual nationality as stated by the parents was presumably pure national extraction in 17 families, a mixture of 2 nationalities in 34 families and a mixture of 3 or more in 127 families. There were 38 of the 215 families for whom no information was available about national extraction.

The majority of the subjects were at least second-generation residents of the United States and slightly more than three-fourths of all the grandparents for whom place of birth was known were also born in this country or were U. S. citizens at birth as indicated in the following tables:

Nationality at Birth

Parents	Fathers	Mothers
U. S.	200 (94.8%)	203 (96.2%)
Not U. S.	11 (5.2%)	8 (3.8%)
Unknown	4	4
Grandparents	**Paternal**	**Maternal**
Both U. S.	145 (71.1%)	160 (75.8%)
One U. S.	22 (10.8%)	25 (11.8%)
Neither U. S.	37 (18.1%)	26 (12.3%)
Unknown	11	4

Schedule of Examination

The purpose of the program was to obtain detailed documentation of the events of growth, development and adaptation in a group of healthy subjects. The policy of the program was to sample measurement of each variable on the most frequent schedule possible within limits of staff time and the subject's tolerance. As data accumulated for each variable they were examined for rate of change and for the possibility of sampling less often without significant loss to the accuracy of the description of the course of change. The final schedule of examinations reflected both the general velocity of growth and development and the rate of change of each variable. The schedule was not identical for all parts of the program.

A further scheduling problem arose from the fact that infants, young children, and even adolescents are subject to fatigue if too many procedures are carried out at the same visit. Two hours of intensive procedures are about the maximum that can be tolerated by the subject at a single time. Further, special requirements of such determinations as the basal metabolic rate or the nutrition history made it inadvisable if not impossible to do them during the same visit with the physical or psychological studies. Finally, since many of the subjects were in school, examination time was frequently limited to after-school hours. As a result, each contact was actually multiple contacts, sometimes with one deliberately separated by as much as a month from the appointment for physical examination, measurements, x-rays, blood sampling, exercise tolerance testing, and similar tests which could be grouped in a single visit.

A basic schedule of examinations as modified by the considerations above describes only the schedule of physical examinations with accuracy, but since the other procedures were grouped around these appointments it does represent scheduling in general. Subjects were examined on the first day of life as soon as possible after delivery. Since they were private patients of physicians within the community, they were born at hospitals throughout the area and examinations were arranged in the newborn nursery of the hospital involved. All other examinations and measurements were made in the quarters of the Child Research Council or in the homes. During the first year of life, examinations were at monthly intervals as close to the monthly birth date as possible. From one year to the end of rapid physical growth in adolescence, examinations were done as close to the birthday as possible and at each 3-month interval between birthdays. The end of rapid growth was assumed to occur 6 months after the menarche in girls and after beginning fusion of the long bone epiphyses in boys. After adolescence was completed, examinations were done annually except for nutrition studies, in which sampling continued each 3 months.

Certain general considerations may help to clarify what might otherwise be confusing elements in the data presented. Numbers of subjects vary considerably from one area of the data to another. Even in places where there should logically be correspondence in numbers differences exist. An example of this is the pulse and blood pressure data from physical examinations. Ideally these data would have been recorded at each visit, but actually this did not happen. Pulse rate, which is simpler to obtain, was recorded considerably more frequently and from earlier ages than was blood pressure. Another example, occurring for a different reason, is differences in numbers of height measurements as compared with weights and other anthropometric measurements. Discrepancies in numbers occur throughout the age span presented but increase after adolescence. This resulted from the fact that sometimes subjects, particularly older ones, did not come in for examination at their birthdays but were seen at some other point during the year. A stable measurement such as adult height or one that changes in one direction and in a fashion that may be considered linear over short periods could be interpolated to the birthdate age from data obtained before and after that actual time. However, measurements like weight and circumferences which are subject to increases and decreases in rather short intervals could not be interpolated. Such measurements, though recorded on the tape at the actual age taken, were not used in computing the group statistics, resulting in fewer – sometimes many fewer – measurements of one variable than of another. Finally, even where a unitary record must exist in order for any measurements to be taken, such as in the ECG interval measurements, it was occasionally impossible to measure one or more intervals with acceptable accuracy. This produced only small variations in numbers, but variations nonetheless. In all tables, only actual numbers of measurements included in the calculations are stated.

A further potential source of confusion results from the fact that numbers of subjects decline as age advances. This resulted from recruitment of the subjects at an average rate of 5 to 6 per year since 1930 as described in the next section. However, once a subject was entered in the program he continued to be followed as long as possible. Thus, all subjects at later ages are included in the data for earlier years. No effort has been made to identify which specific subjects are included in data at any one age. Occasionally the N for a variable rises briefly as age advances, signifying that some subjects who had missed a visit were seen at a later age. However, data obtained from them were always included in previous ages since no subjects were admitted except in childhood, and after 1930, no subject was admitted after infancy.

The Data System

Major effort by the senior staff after June, 1967, has been directed to organization of the physical and physiological measurements into a data system suitable for use with current computer equipment. During the years since inception of the research the data have been stored in multiple forms for safety and for ease of use in hand computations. Anthropometric measurements, for example, were kept on the original measurement sheets for each subject, on a typed copy of that sheet in a central record devoted to the subject, and on tabulation cards representing measurements obtained on a single visit, which facilitated such procedures as sorting measurements for age on all subjects. In addition, such original data as the x-ray films and the film output from free-cell Tiselius analyses of serum proteins were also available. Between 1960 and 1962 all available records were transferred to punched and verified IBM cards and measurements thereafter were periodically brought up-to-date in that form.

It was necessary to complete the files of measurements, to design an electronic-access storage system and to insure that data recorded agreed with original measurements.*

A Control Data Corporation 6400 computer was available for

*Major assistance in system design and computer-related operations was provided by Datametrics, Inc., Boulder, Colorado, the University of Colorado Medical Center Computer Services and the Division of Biostatistics, Department of Preventive Medicine, University of Colorado Medical Center.

data conversion from cards to a high-density storage medium. Magnetic tape was chosen for data storage because of its low cost and easy storage. Since the volume of data was large, a file format was chosen to allow blocking of the data into groups. These groups kept all measurements for one subject within two or more logical blocks, and kept all measurements for a particular age for an individual together. The magnetic tape record was written in machine binary format to provide processing without data conversion from BCD code to binary. A usual pass on the data to prepare a work tape can be accomplished in less than 30 seconds of computer central processor time.

The CDC computer handles data in 60-bit words. Using packing routines the format for each word consisted of two 5-digit measurements, so in reading a block of 200 words, 400 measurements were placed into core storage for processing. There are two types of block formats:

A. Topic header blocks identify the measurements which follow and describe the length and word configuration of the blocks which follow.

B. Data blocks are of two types:
   1. Subject identifier blocks give identification number, date of birth, number of data blocks and number of measurements.
   2. Subject data blocks give age and measurements taken at that age, followed by the next age and its respective measurements.

The header block is always 512 words in length and describes the number of words in each block to follow. Each general topic is a complete file separated by file markers. The files are written on two reels of magnetic tape in the following order:

1. Heart measurements)
2. Long bone lengths) from roentgenograms
3. Bone, muscle and fat widths)
4. Nutritional intake
5. Anthropometry
6. Skull measurements

7. Ossification, fusion and skeletal maturation
8. Circumpuberal growth and development
9. Heights and weights at 1/4 and 3/4 year ages
10. Ergometry
11. Blood pressures and pulse after basal metabolic determinations
12. Blood pressures and pulse during physical examination and ergometry
13. Serum cholesterol (total, free, alpha- and beta-lipoprotein)
14. Hematology
15. Plasma and serum protein
16. Electrocardiograms
17. Health history
18. Demographic data

The most useful and reliable system for checking data recorded on the magnetic tape proved to be proof-reading of the print-out by the computer against the original data records. Computer operations for data cleanup were useful mainly in flagging missing measurements and occasionally in locating widely deviant measurements. However, the changing magnitude of measurements characteristic of growth data precluded setting realistic limits for identifying outlying measurements. In addition, it was apparent quite early that the majority of wrong measurement records were not outside reasonable limits for the measurement for age. They would not have been detected by any available machine program for data cleanup. By a process of proof-reading, correcting and re-proofing the final record was achieved. No claim is made that it is error-free, but errors were reduced to a minimum before any statistical procedures were applied to the data.

The total volume of data recorded on magnetic tape considerably exceeds the material presented in this volume. In order to avoid excessive length of tables it was often possible to eliminate ages without altering the basic picture of group changes with age. Anyone working with data related to the individual might very well want measurements as frequently as possible, but group statistics do not require the same frequency as individual records in order to provide valid pictures of change. In addition, certain less commonly used measurements, such as physiologic measurements after exercise, were not included. An effort has been made to indicate the availability of these data in each section so that potential users interested in a particular growth problem would know these data exist. Unfortunately, as is the case with the basic longitudinal records for each subject, reproduction costs of these records must be borne by anyone requesting them.

Measurements Not Included in the Data System

In addition to the data included on the tape there are a few large masses of data and several less extensive accumulations of measurements in the primary records that are not included in the data system. The longest longitudinal records of this group are the basal metabolic studies which recorded energy production as oxygen consumed and carbon dioxide produced under true basal conditions from infancy to adult life in many subjects and under asleep-fed conditions in infants. The only data from these records presented in this volume are the basal pulse rates.

Psychological studies are not truly longitudinal because of changes in methodology. However, a large accumulation of tests of intelligence, personality factors, social development, perception and cognition does exist and represents a resource which would be difficult to duplicate.

Orthodontic studies of cranio-facial development were carried out from 1930 to 1966. Basic data in this study consisted of A-P and lateral cephalometric roentgenograms of the head, dental casts of the full mouth, and orthodontic records of teeth, caries, fillings, etc. Because there were intervals during which no orthodontist was on the staff, only the x-rays were taken regularly.

In the area of functional testing there are long-term records of vital capacity, work stress responses of the cardiovascular system, reaction time and eye-body coordination. Less extensive data are available for grip strength, maximum ventilatory capacity, critical flicker fusion and decision time.

Serial electroencephalographic records were made on all subjects born after 1950. These are in process of analysis, and studies of their relationships to physical and psychological variables are planned.

Serial determinations were made for approximately 10 years on a variety of vitamins in blood. These included plasma vitamin A and carotene, red cell niacin, and plasma and red cell riboflavin. Alkaline and acid phosphatase studies were also done for most of the interval after 1950.

Finally, there were over two hundred total body counts of potassium-40 on children from birth to 10 years of age during the last 2 years of the program.

Program for Calculation of Descriptive Summary Statistics

The means, standard deviations and percentiles for the data were calculated from the individual measurements recorded on magnetic tape by a general program modified to fulfill requirements for each variable except where the data were so skewed that such an approach would not be meaningful, as in eosinophil counts and incidence of illness. This program was designed to determine the recorded maximum and minimum values for any age and use them as the limits of the data. The range was divided into ten equal parts (cells) and each measurement placed in its appropriate cell. Frequency and percentile distributions were calculated, and interpolation made to obtain the 10th, 25th, 50th, 75th and 90th percentiles.

Standard equations were used in the program to calculate the mean and standard deviations. No statistical computations were done for ages where less than 10 measurements were recorded for the variable.

Method of Calculating Technical Error

A uniform method was employed for calculation of technical error for all data for which this is stated except when specifically noted otherwise. The formula used for these calculations was published in *Statistical Methods in Research and Production with Special Reference to the Chemical Industry* (edited by Owen L. Davies, Hafner Publishing Co., New York, 1957, page 35). "The procedure is to calculate for each sample the sum of squared deviations from the sample mean- - -, add these for all samples and divide by (N-k) where N is the total number of observations and k the number of samples.

$$V = \frac{\Sigma (x_1 - \overline{x}_1)^2 + \Sigma (x_2 - \overline{x}_2)^2 + \Sigma (x_k - \overline{x}_k)^2}{N-k}$$

The estimate of the standard deviation from the sample data [Technical Error] is given by $\sqrt{V}$. If each sample contains only two measurements, the equation can be simplified to $V = \frac{\Sigma W^2}{2k}$ where W is the range, or difference, of the two results."

If the mean of the two determinations is the recorded value, the technical error becomes $\sqrt{V/2}$; if the mean of three is the recorded value, the technical error is $\sqrt{V/3}$; etc.

REFERENCES

1. Washburn, A.H.: The child as a person developing. I. A philosophy and program of research. Amer J Dis Child, 94:46, 1957.
2. Washburn, A.H.: The child as a person developing. II. More questions raised than answered. Amer J Dis Child, 94:54, 1957.

Section A

HEALTH HISTORIES

ROBERT W. McCAMMON

THE HEALTH RECORDS

DATA comprising the health records were collected from the beginning of the program in an effort to record the frequency, duration, severity and type of illnesses and injuries that occur in well-fed and generally well-cared-for children and young adults. Unlike other data presented in this volume, these are not objective or nearly objective measurements. They should be regarded as similar to carefully collected clinical records such as might be obtained by a well baby clinic, but extending through the lives of the subjects up to January 1, 1967. One significant factor is that subjects were rarely seen when they were ill with anything other than minor respiratory infections. Examiners were, for the most part, dependent on histories for much of the information, so this aspect of the health record was done with particular care and in considerably more detail than is usually characteristic of clinical records after the first year of life.

History and physical examination records were all evaluated by one investigator (R. McCammon) and coding for the magnetic tape was carried out by two others (V. Trevorrow and A. Meyers). Coding is such that it permits selection of specific diagnoses of a wide variety of conditions but is not sufficiently detailed to give anatomical locations or specific therapeutic procedures. For example, it is possible to select out all fractures of long bones, ribs or skull but not to differentiate the specific site involved. Treatments were coded but were not as specific as would be the case in clinical records. Antibiotic therapy was coded but specific antibiotics were not rated or coded. Within the limits of the records, duration and intervals between the illness or other incident and the time of examination of the subject are also coded. For purposes of this volume it was impossible to record the group frequencies of the more than 300 separate diagnostic conditions that occurred in at least one subject during the study. The most commonly occurring conditions were analyzed age by age for frequencies and are presented in Tables A-1 through A-4. The data are all so markedly skewed that only the mean and range are given.

Health records of 255 individual subjects were rated, coded and used in developing the group statistical summaries. The 79 excluded subjects represent individuals who were seen in the early days of the program and then lost to follow-up so that health record data were too meager to warrant inclusion. Each individual is not included at all ages, but in general the records are quite complete for each subject over the age range through which he was followed. The number of individuals represented for each 5 year age span is as follows:

Years of record	Male No.	Female No.
1 - 5	130	125
5 - 10	109	112
10 - 15	99	91
15 - 20	79	75
20 - 25	63	61
25 - 30	49	45
Over 30	35	30

Mild respiratory infections represent more than half of the total illness recorded. The mean frequency and range of frequency of these conditions are presented for males and females in Table A-1. Since all types of illness are relatively rare in the first six months of life, this period is treated separately. The second half year is also summarized separately. After that, the numbers represent infections per child per year of life. This eliminates the seasonal variation that is quite apparent in the frequency of these infections.

More severe respiratory infections are presented in the same summary manner in Table A-2.

Allergic symptoms constitute a very large percentage of the residual illness total after respiratory infection has been subtracted. The summary statistics for these conditions are presented in Table A-3 with the same time intervals used as for respiratory infections. Since the allergic child presumably remains continuously allergic through periods of symptoms or freedom from symptoms, these data are presented as percentages of the study population showing one or more allergic symptom complexes for each year of life for males to age 37 and for females to age 34.

Figures A-1 and A-2 graphically represent the mean values for minor and more severe respiratory infections and for allergy.

Gastrointestinal disorders are summarized in Table A-4, again using the same time intervals as for respiratory illness.

The numbers of subjects for all aspects of the health records are the same. Data for the male sex include more than 10 subjects to age 37 and for female subjects through age 34.

Presentation of data for tonsillectomy and adenoidectomy (T & A), for appendectomy, and for the childhood infectious diseases represents a special problem because any subject is susceptible only once. This material does not reduce to tabular form with meaning because the number of subjects at risk changes with each incident. However, since these conditions represent a significant part of the health problems of the subjects, the following description of occurrences is given.

Except for nearly universal circumcision of male infants (89%), T & A is the most frequent surgical procedure. In males, total incidence of T & A was 70. The age range over which T & A was done was from the third year of life to the twentieth year. Mean age of surgery was six years (5.97). Distribution of frequency peaked in the year from 4 to 5 and was nearly symmetrically distributed from the third through the ninth years. Only six subjects had T & A after nine years. In female subjects the total incidence of T & A was 47. Mean age was seven and three quarters years. The earliest age of surgery was in the second year of life and the latest in the nineteenth year. Modal incidence was between the ages of four and six years and distribution was essentially symmetrical between age two years and age ten years. A single operation was done in the second year of life and ten were done after ten years.

Appendectomy was performed on 12 males between the ninth and twenty-fifth years and on 15 females between the seventh and thirty-fourth years with apparently random age distribution in both sexes.

Chicken pox was the most frequently occurring exanthem in both sexes. It was recorded in 84 of the males and in 94 of the females. It occurred earlier in life than any other exanthem, with three subjects of each sex having the infection in the first six months of life. Maximum incidence occurred in the years up to nine in males and to eleven in females, but sporadic cases were diagnosed in males through the twenty-seventh year and in females through the seventeenth year.

Measles was the second most prevalent exanthem. It was diagnosed in 77 males and 79 females. It first occurred during the second half of the first year in both sexes. There was no measles diagnosed in males after age twelve and only three scattered cases in females occurred after age eleven years.

German measles was diagnosed in 49 females and 42 males. It was encountered initially in the second half of the first year in a single male subject and continued to occur at low incidence through the sixteenth year. In females the first diagnosis appeared in the second year of life and the last between twenty and twenty-one years. There was no apparent peak age of incidence for either sex.

Mumps occurred in 41 males and 53 females. It was diagnosed earliest in the second year in both sexes. Concentration of cases in both sexes was in the third through the twelfth years of life, but single cases were noted in males as late as the twenty-eighth year and in females in the thirtieth year.

Pertussis was not present in subjects born after 1940, when pertussis vaccination became routine. Prior to that time it was diagnosed in 26 males and 26 females between the second half of the first year and the twelfth year of life.

Other specific diagnostic categories occurred only sporadically and in few subjects. For example, scarlet fever was diagnosed in only twenty subjects during the years of study.

The Histories

Methods of recording histories varied considerably through the years, reflecting efforts to improve the accuracy and detail available. During the early years of the program primary responsibility for historical data rested with the technician who made appointments. This was supplemented by brief notes about illness obtained by one or more of the physicians who saw the child at each visit. In 1934 this system was replaced by a more detailed historical note recorded by the pediatrician responsible for the general physical examination. In mid-1939 a history sheet was devised which was appropriate to the age and sex of the subject and asked questions regarding illness, injuries, operations, therapy, developmental landmarks, etc. These sheets were sent home with the subject after each physical examination visit and the mother or older subject was asked to fill in details at the time of occurrence and return the record at the next visit. In January, 1964, these sheets were replaced by 8½ x 11 inch calendar pads in which each monthly sheet was followed by a page listing the types of information desired and providing space to record it for all members of the family. It was requested that these be filled out as events occurred and returned each month.

The other major source of data was interval histories taken by the examining physicians at the time of the physical examinations. After 1934 these were generally quite detailed notes that indicated illnesses reported, questions answered negatively, and the physicians' appraisal of the accuracy of the information given. The impact of illness on nutritional intake, basal metabolic state, or psychological performance made investigators in these areas sensitive to illnesses in subjects and when they observed or were informed of them, notes were made in the central record.

Finally, office records of physicians and hospital records were occasionally used to augment detail and ensure accuracv of parental reports. For example, all private physicians' immunization records to which access could be obtained were checked against the records provided by the parents and subjects.

The Physical Examinations

Prior to 1930 physical examinations were done by teams of specialists with no single physician responsible for a general examination. The records contain reports of ear, nose and throat, cardiovascular, respiratory system and orthopedic examinations done by different doctors at each visit. Since at least two of the examiners were practicing pediatricians, it is doubtful if any major condition not included in the specialty reports was overlooked. However, the lack of any specific statements about gastrointestinal, neuromuscular, genitourinary, cutaneous or lymphatic systems and the frequent absence of any statement about the behavior of the subject during examinations made evaluation of these reports some 30 years later difficult. In 1930, general pediatric examinations were started to augment specialty examinations. After that there was always a detailed report of the birth examination and there was an increasing tendency for general examinations to contain details of what was found rather than terse clinical appraisals of the presence or absence of abnormality. This recording of detailed observation increased abruptly in 1934 and again at the time of introduction of the written interval history reports in 1939. After that date only a rare physical examination report failed to start with the examiner's over-all appraisal of the size, activity, behavior and general psychological state of the subject and progress through statements of what was observed in each part of a complete physical examination. In 1942 the specialty examinations were discontinued.

Evaluation of the Records

Evaluation of clinical records is necessarily subjective. Efforts to impose rigid criteria for the presence of a specific diagnostic entity serve only to increase the size of a wastebasket category called "miscellaneous." The liberal though often arbitrary and always scientifically unsatisfying use of clinical judgement is necessary. The desire to limit the inevitable biases produced by this procedure as much as possible led to the decision that final judgements would all be made by the same evaluator.

These limitations do not preclude setting up certain general rules which make it possible to judge whether or not the individual biases of the evaluator distort the data unacceptably. For example, major difficulty in assigning a diagnosis was found in minor respiratory illnesses. Confusion arose about whether allergy, infection, or both were present, and in older subjects it was difficult to differentiate between irritation produced by smoking and that which was produced by a mild viral invasion of the pharyngeal membranes. The fact that the subjects were seen at 3-month intervals for most of childhood and annually after adolescence resulted in dependence on reports of many colds. The variations of degree of concern between mothers and by the same mother with different children were reflected in the adjectives used to describe otherwise similar conditions. To resolve these problems as far as possible, the following basic rules were established:

1. The mother's word would be accepted for the occurrence of common colds.

2. In order to classify a respiratory illness as other than a cold it was required that a temperature of more than 101° orally be recorded and some evidence of more than minor illness be given. Twenty-four hours of confinement to bed was accepted as such evidence, as were missing school for more than 2 days and cancellation of other usual activities for a similar period.

3. Diagnoses made by attending physicians were accepted if the doctor actually saw the subject.

4. In chronically allergic children, the finding of edema of the upper respiratory membranes without moderate to marked inflammation was regarded as allergic in nature. The same was true for seasonal allergy when the respiratory edema occurred during the known allergic season.

5. Inflammation as a primary finding was considered infectious in origin.

6. When reporting of respiratory infections was done in terms such as "many," "continuous," "recurring" and similar words, an arbitrary frequency of 2 colds was assigned if the interval was 3 months and a frequency of 3 was assigned for intervals of a year.

By use of these rules it was possible to get good agreement between diagnoses and frequency records for respiratory infections between the primary evaluator and the pediatric residents and fellows who rated randomly selected subject records. However, an effort to separate respiratory infections more severe than common colds into moderately severe and severe illnesses on the basis of location (pneumonia) or pus production in a confined area (purulent otitis) as opposed to purulent, febrile illnesses not meeting these criteria (tonsillitis) failed. The fact that as many as 3 to 5 pneumonias diagnosed on physical examination and confirmed by chest roentgenograms were found in a single year in subjects who were attending school and perceived themselves as well except for a little cold illustrates the problem that led to final grouping of respiratory infections as "colds" and "more severe respiratory tract infections."

Other diagnostic categories presented less frequent but similar problems. Measles represents a good example of such problems. Eventual treatment of this diagnosis resulted in four possible codings, depending upon other information available. One diagnosis was "measles" when the condition was classical in its symptoms and course and ideally involved more than one family member. A rash that followed gamma globulin administration for measles exposure within 2 weeks was coded as modified measles. A similar rash occurring more than 2 weeks but less than 4 weeks after gamma globulin prophylaxis was coded as "possible modified measles." A condition diagnosed as measles but not seen by a physician and preceded or followed by classical measles was placed in a diagnostic group called "exanthem of unknown etiology." Similarly, second and subsequent attacks of "mumps" were called non-specific parotitis unless they occurred at the same time as definite mumps in a sibling, in which case the initial attack was so classified. In one subject two illnesses diagnosed as chicken pox were coded as this condition because it was impossible to select between them. Even so manifest a symptom complex as vomiting and/or diarrhea left questions open about whether the etiologic agent was infection, irritation or psychologic disturbance. They were etiologically differentiated in the ratings and coding as far as possible but have not been separated in the group statistical data reported in Table A-4.

The above examples illustrate the problems encountered in retrospective diagnosis and the methods of resolving them. However, two other factors, severity and duration, have sometimes been used in evaluating serial illness in individuals. With the exception of severity of respiratory infections, these do not appear in the data presented, although they were rated and coded for the taped data.

In connection with severity, it is known that almost any condition varies widely in the severity manifested within the individual. However, unless an experienced observer, preferably the same one, views the entire course of the illness in each patient, such assessments are arbitrary. No experienced clinician would regard pneumonia as less than a severe infection, yet the example given above strongly suggests that many cases of pneumonia occur in individuals who are not subjected to regular, periodic examination and that these infections can go on to resolution unrecognized and without significantly limiting the persons who suffer them. Any of the exanthems can produce either a critically ill child or one whose greatest distress arises from confinement to avoid spreading his disease. When the rater is dependent on the perception of a third party such as the mother to evaluate severity he must also consider such imponderables as her personality, how tired she was at the time the child became ill and her own memories of similar infection in herself. Even such time-honored criteria as whether a doctor was consulted or the child was hospitalized for the condition will not withstand critical appraisal. In selected instances, where the subject was critically ill or incapacitated for long periods the decision is relatively easy, but in the age group considered these represent only a small proportion of illness. Although an effort was made during evaluation and coding to flag severe illness, confidence in the results does not warrant publication of these ratings.

The problem of determining duration is equally complex and elusive of solution. The difficulties involved may readily be understood by anyone willing to attempt to decide for himself exactly when his last respiratory infection started and ended. The best that can be achieved is approximation of the time when clinical symptoms became severe enough to be bothersome and when this was no longer true. This ignores the incubation period and the period when the subject no longer feels ill but may, for example, still have inflammation of the tonsils and visible pockets of exudate on them signifying that the disease process is still active. Similarly, a remarkable number of perons state that they are never entirely free from respiratory symptoms during the winter months. They have periods when symptoms are more marked followed by periods when they feel better. The decision about whether this represents repeated exacerbation of a single infection, overlapping discrete infections, or infections separated by irritation from atmospheric contaminants would require prohibitive costs in time and equipment.

Subjects were repeatedly urged to record durations of illnesses in spite of growing misgivings about such a demand on the part of the staff. Resulting replies record durations of colds varying from 1 day to 3 months and chicken pox infections lasting from 3 days to 3 weeks. They again illustrate the problems involved without providing any solutions. Qualitative estimates are possible and these suggest that there are significant differences in the time it takes individual subjects to recover from similar infectious conditions. Such estimates are of interest only when contrasting individual health records and are not presented for the group.

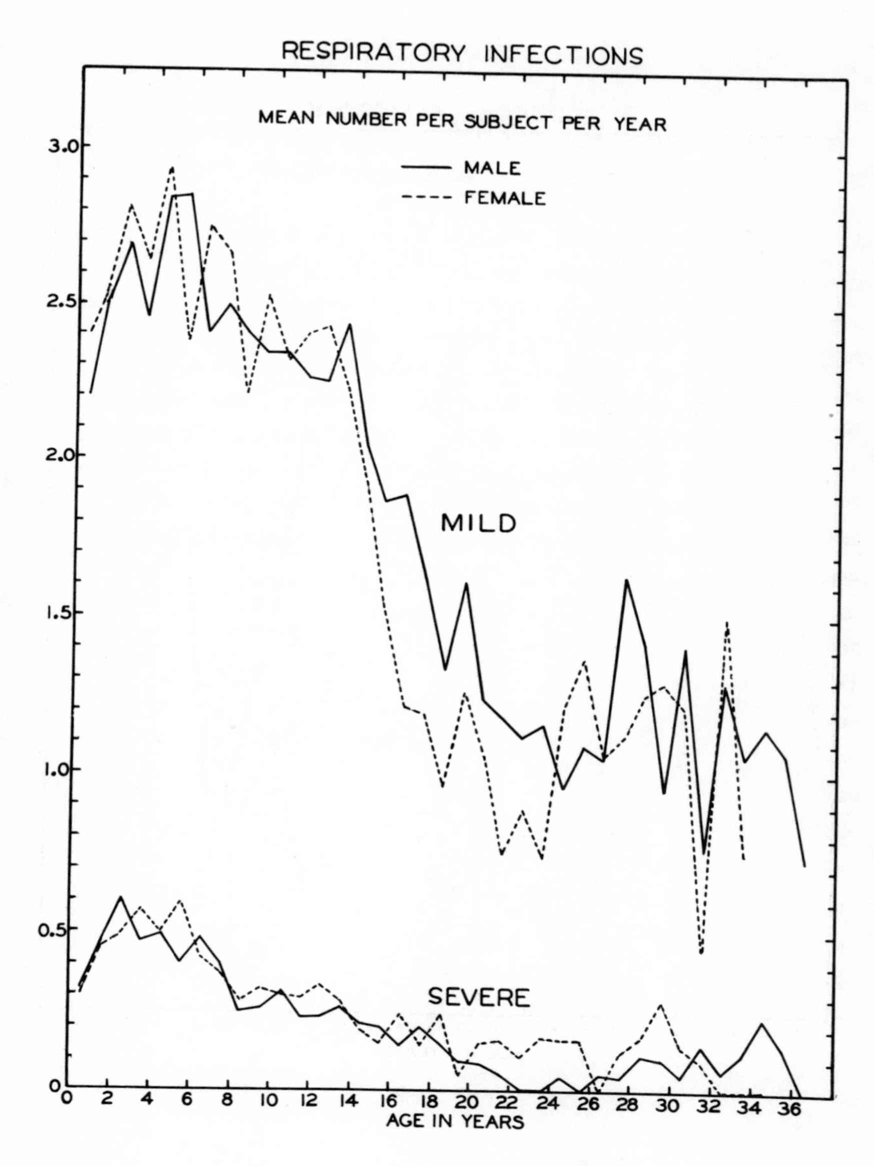
RESPIRATORY INFECTIONS
MEAN NUMBER PER SUBJECT PER YEAR
MALE
FEMALE
MILD
SEVERE
3.0
2.5
2.0
1.5
1.0
0.5
0
0 2 4 6 8 10 12 14 16 18 20 22 24 26 28 30 32 34 36
AGE IN YEARS

FIG. A-1

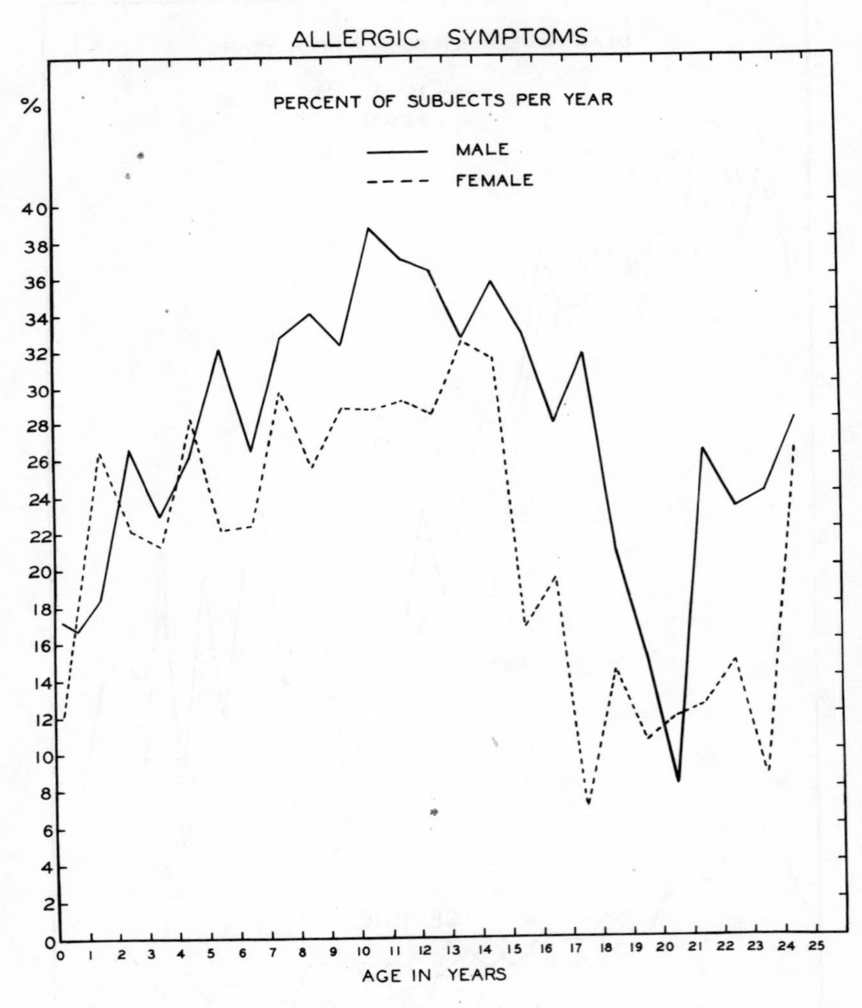
ALLERGIC SYMPTOMS
PERCENT OF SUBJECTS PER YEAR
MALE
FEMALE
%
AGE IN YEARS

FIG A-2

HEALTH RECORDS

TABLE A-1

Frequency of Mild Respiratory Infections

Age Years	Male					Female				
	All subjects			Subjects with no infection		All subjects			Subjects with no infection	
	N	Mean	Max.	N	%	N	Mean	Max.	N	%
0 - 1/2	122	1.0	4	47	38.5	116	1.0	6	47	40.5
1/2 - 1	126	1.2	5	39	31.0	117	1.4	6	31	26.5
1 - 2	124	2.5	8	13	10.5	121	2.6	9	12	9.9
2 - 3	121	2.7	8	9	7.4	113	2.8	8	5	4.4
3 - 4	118	2.5	8	13	11.0	113	2.6	6	7	6.2
4 - 5	111	2.8	7	8	7.2	110	2.9	9	3	2.7
5 - 6	109	2.8	9	6	5.5	104	2.4	6	7	6.7
6 - 7	106	2.4	7	8	7.5	103	2.8	6	10	9.7
7 - 8	101	2.5	8	6	5.9	101	2.7	8	7	6.9
8 - 9	97	2.4	6	11	11.3	98	2.2	7	10	10.2
9 - 10	99	2.3	8	7	7.1	94	2.5	7	4	4.3
10 - 11	93	2.3	7	7	7.5	91	2.3	6	9	9.9
11 - 12	92	2.3	8	10	10.9	86	2.4	6	5	5.8
12 - 13	91	2.2	7	12	13.2	81	2.4	7	8	9.9
13 - 14	89	2.4	6	6	6.7	79	2.2	7	6	7.6
14 - 15	84	2.0	7	12	14.3	73	1.9	5	8	11.0
15 - 16	76	1.9	8	14	18.4	66	1.5	5	14	21.2
16 - 17	72	1.9	7	14	19.4	62	1.2	5	22	35.5
17 - 18	60	1.6	5	11	18.3	57	1.2	8	22	38.6
18 - 19	48	1.3	4	10	20.8	49	1.0	3	20	40.8
19 - 20	46	1.6	5	11	23.9	38	1.3	8	11	28.9
20 - 21	37	1.2	5	11	29.7	34	1.1	3	11	32.4
21 - 22	38	1.2	3	15	39.5	32	0.8	3	18	56.2
22 - 23	26	1.1	4	10	38.5	27	0.9	4	13	48.1
23 - 24	25	1.2	4	10	40.0	23	0.7	3	11	47.8
24 - 25	25	1.0	4	10	40.0	19	1.2	3	6	31.6
25 - 26	22	1.1	4	9	40.9	19	1.4	6	6	31.6
26 - 27	21	1.0	3	10	47.6	17	1.1	4	5	29.4
27 - 28	24	1.6	4	6	25.0	17	1.1	3	5	29.4
28 - 29	19	1.4	3	5	26.3	12	1.2	5	4	33.3
29 - 30	20	1.0	4	10	50.0	14	1.3	4	6	42.9
30 - 31	22	1.4	4	5	22.7	14	1.2	6	6	42.9
31 - 32	21	0.8	3	11	52.4	11	0.4	2	8	72.7
32 - 33	17	1.3	3	3	17.6	10	1.5	12	4	40.0
33 - 34	17	1.1	4	6	35.3	12	0.8	2	5	41.7
34 - 35	13	1.2	3	5	38.5					
35 - 36	14	1.1	3	4	28.6					
36 - 37	11	0.7	2	5	45.5					

HEALTH RECORDS

TABLE A-2

Frequency of Severe Respiratory Infections

Age Years	Male					Female				
	All subjects			Subjects with no infection		All subjects			Subjects with no infection	
	N	Mean	Max.	N	%	N	Mean	Max.	N	%
0 - 1/2	122	0.10	1	110	90.2	116	0.09	2	107	92.2
1/2 - 1	126	0.21	3	107	84.9	117	0.21	2	98	83.8
1 - 2	124	0.45	2	82	66.1	121	0.45	3	78	64.5
2 - 3	121	0.60	4	72	59.5	113	0.49	4	74	65.5
3 - 4	118	0.47	4	80	67.8	113	0.57	4	65	57.5
4 - 5	111	0.49	3	72	64.9	110	0.50	3	71	64.5
5 - 6	109	0.40	2	72	66.1	104	0.59	3	63	60.6
6 - 7	106	0.48	3	71	67.0	103	0.42	5	70	68.0
7 - 8	101	0.40	4	71	70.3	101	0.37	2	69	68.3
8 - 9	97	0.25	2	76	78.4	98	0.28	3	76	77.6
9 - 10	99	0.26	2	75	75.8	94	0.32	3	70	74.5
10 - 11	93	0.31	3	70	75.3	91	0.30	3	72	79.1
11 - 12	92	0.23	3	74	80.4	86	0.29	3	71	82.6
12 - 13	91	0.23	2	71	78.0	81	0.33	3	61	75.3
13 - 14	89	0.26	2	70	78.7	79	0.28	2	58	73.4
14 - 15	84	0.21	3	69	82.1	73	0.19	2	60	82.2
15 - 16	76	0.20	1	61	80.3	66	0.15	1	56	84.8
16 - 17	72	0.14	1	62	86.1	62	0.24	2	48	77.4
17 - 18	60	0.20	1	48	80.0	57	0.14	2	50	87.7
18 - 19	48	0.15	1	41	85.4	49	0.24	2	38	77.6
19 - 20	46	0.09	1	42	91.3	38	0.05	1	36	94.7
20 - 21	37	0.08	1	34	91.9	34	0.15	4	32	94.1
21 - 22	38	0.05	1	36	94.7	32	0.16	2	28	87.5
22 - 23	26	0	0	26	100.0	27	0.11	1	24	88.9
23 - 24	25	0	0	25	100.0	23	0.17	2	20	87.0
24 - 25	25	0.04	1	24	96.0	19	0.16	1	16	84.2
25 - 26	22	0	0	22	100.0	19	0.16	1	16	84.2
26 - 27	21	0.05	1	20	95.2	17	0	0	17	100.0
27 - 28	24	0.04	1	23	95.8	17	0.12	1	15	88.2
28 - 29	19	0.11	1	17	89.5	12	0.17	1	10	83.3
29 - 30	20	0.10	1	18	90.0	14	0.28	2	11	78.6
30 - 31	22	0.05	1	21	95.5	14	0.14	1	12	85.7
31 - 32	21	0.14	1	18	85.7	11	0.09	1	10	90.9
32 - 33	17	0.06	1	16	94.1	10	0	0	10	100.0
33 - 34	17	0.12	1	15	88.2	12	0	0	12	100.0
34 - 35	13	0.23	2	11	84.6					
35 - 36	14	0.14	2	13	92.9					
36 - 37	11	0	0	11	100.0					

HEALTH RECORDS

TABLE A-3

Frequency of Allergic Symptoms

Age Years	Male			Female		
	All subjects N	Subjects with symptoms N	%	All subjects N	Subjects with symptoms N	%
0 - 1/2	122	21	17.2	116	14	12.1
1/2 - 1	126	21	16.7	117	21	17.9
1 - 2	124	23	18.5	121	32	26.4
2 - 3	121	32	26.4	113	25	22.1
3 - 4	118	27	22.9	113	24	21.2
4 - 5	111	29	26.1	110	31	28.2
5 - 6	109	35	32.1	104	23	22.1
6 - 7	106	28	26.4	103	23	22.3
7 - 8	101	33	32.7	101	30	29.7
8 - 9	97	33	34.0	98	25	25.5
9 - 10	99	32	32.3	94	27	28.7
10 - 11	93	36	38.7	91	26	28.6
11 - 12	92	34	37.0	86	25	29.1
12 - 13	91	33	36.3	81	23	28.4
13 - 14	89	29	32.6	79	24	30.4
14 - 15	84	30	35.7	73	23	31.5
15 - 16	76	25	32.9	66	11	16.7
16 - 17	72	20	27.8	62	12	19.4
17 - 18	60	19	31.7	57	4	7.0
18 - 19	48	10	20.8	49	7	14.3
19 - 20	46	7	15.2	38	4	10.5
20 - 21	37	3	8.1	34	4	11.8
21 - 22	38	10	26.3	32	4	12.5
22 - 23	26	6	23.1	27	4	14.8
23 - 24	25	6	24.0	23	2	8.7
24 - 25	25	7	28.0	19	5	26.3
25 - 26	22	3	13.6	19	5	26.3
26 - 27	21	0	0	17	2	11.8
27 - 28	24	1	4.2	17	0	0
28 - 29	19	2	10.5	12	1	8.3
29 - 30	20	1	5.0	14	1	7.1
30 - 31	22	3	13.6	14	5	35.7
31 - 32	21	1	4.8	11	2	18.2
32 - 33	17	1	5.9	10	1	10.0
33 - 34	17	1	5.9	12	2	16.7
34 - 35	13	0	0	9	0	0
35 - 36	14	1	12.5	8	0	0

HEALTH RECORDS TABLE A-4

Frequency of Gastrointestinal Disturbances

Age Years	Male					Female				
	All subjects			Subjects with no infection		All subjects			Subjects with no infection	
	N	Mean	Max.	N	%	N	Mean	Max.	N	%
0 - 1/2	122	0.39	3	87	71.3	116	0.58	5	74	63.8
1/2 - 1	126	0.82	5	78	61.9	117	0.63	8	73	62.4
1 - 2	124	0.87	5	69	55.6	121	0.74	5	62	51.2
2 - 3	121	0.44	4	72	59.5	113	0.58	5	71	62.8
3 - 4	118	0.60	3	68	57.6	113	0.59	4	69	61.1
4 - 5	111	0.52	5	73	65.8	110	0.55	5	72	65.5
5 - 6	109	0.37	4	81	74.3	104	0.50	4	67	64.4
6 - 7	106	0.42	4	71	67.0	103	0.73	5	58	56.3
7 - 8	101	0.43	4	71	70.3	101	0.47	4	69	68.3
8 - 9	97	0.35	3	69	71.1	98	0.46	4	67	68.4
9 - 10	99	0.39	5	74	74.7	94	0.55	4	57	60.6
10 - 11	93	0.37	5	71	76.3	91	0.35	3	63	69.2
11 - 12	92	0.46	4	70	76.1	86	0.56	3	50	58.1
12 - 13	91	0.49	6	62	68.1	81	0.31	3	64	79.0
13 - 14	89	0.34	5	67	75.3	79	0.41	3	55	69.6
14 - 15	84	0.29	3	66	78.6	73	0.18	2	62	84.9
15 - 16	76	0.14	2	67	88.2	66	0.18	2	55	83.3
16 - 17	72	0.19	2	59	81.9	62	0.21	3	51	82.3
17 - 18	60	0.23	2	49	81.7	57	0.11	3	53	93.0
18 - 19	48	0.12	3	44	91.7	49	0.04	1	47	95.9
19 - 20	46	0.13	1	40	87.0	38	0.29	3	31	81.6
20 - 21	37	0.19	3	33	89.2	34	0.21	2	29	85.3
21 - 22	38	0.16	3	34	89.5	32	0.12	2	29	90.6
22 - 23	26	0.15	3	24	92.3	27	0.07	1	25	92.6
23 - 24	25	0.16	1	21	84.0	23	0.04	1	22	95.7
24 - 25	25	0.04	1	24	96.0	19	0.12	1	16	84.2
25 - 26	22	0.14	2	20	90.9	19	0.32	1	13	68.4
26 - 27	21	0.14	1	18	85.7	17	0	0	17	100.0
27 - 28	24	0.12	1	21	87.5	17	0.18	1	14	82.4
28 - 29	19	0.21	2	16	84.2	12	0.08	1	11	91.7
29 - 30	20	0.30	3	16	80.0	14	0.36	2	10	71.4
30 - 31	22	0	0	22	100.0	14	0.21	1	11	78.6
31 - 32	21	0.05	1	20	95.2	11	0.36	3	9	81.8
32 - 33	17	0.06	1	16	94.1	10	0.70	3	6	60.0
33 - 34	17	0	0	17	100.0	12	0.33	3	10	83.3
34 - 35	13	0.15	2	12	92.3					
35 - 36	14	0	0	14	100.0					
36 - 37	11	0	0	11	100.0					

Section B

ELECTROCARDIOGRAPHY

ROBERT W. McCAMMON

THE ELECTROCARDIOGRAMS

ELECTROCARDIOGRAMS were instituted as a routine procedure early in the program and have been recorded routinely since. Tracings were obtained with a Victor Electrocardiograph machine from 1927 to 1952. From mid-1952 until January 1, 1967, they were recorded by means of a Cambridge Instrument Company Eden Electronic Electrocardiograph. From 1927 to 1952 the standard limb leads were the only records. When the instrument was changed a 13-lead record was made routinely, including the limb leads, AV leads and precordial leads V_3R through V_6.

Measurements from the records were pulse rate, P-R, Q-S, and Q-T interval durations and calculation of corrected Q-T intervals by the square root method of Taran ($Q{-}Tc = \frac{Q{-}T}{\sqrt{R{-}R}}$). A longitudinal analysis of these measurements through mid-1960 was published in 1961(1). All measurements were made by the same investigator (R. McCammon). Limits of accuracy on interval measurements were found to be 0.01 second. Three tests were carried out to determine this. First, all records from 1950 to 1959 were measured independently by the investigator and by a series of pediatric fellows and the measurements compared. Second, the investigator remeasured lead II in 1/3 of the records at least 5 years after the original measurement and compared the sets of measurements. Third, arbitrary intervals including two or three of the standard intervals were measured and compared with appropriate sums of interval durations. Results in all tests agreed that 0.01 seconds variations occur in approximately 15 percent of the measurements. Magnification and use of calipers did not improve the accuracy. Measurements were recorded to the nearest 0.01 seconds.

Included in the present data were a total of 5794 records from 129 male subjects and 122 female subjects.

REFERENCE

1. McCammon, R.W.: A longitudinal study of electrocardiographic intervals in healthy children. Acta Paediat, vol. 50: Supplement 126, 1961.

ELECTROCARDIOGRAMS

TABLE B-1

The P-R Interval - Lead II

Age	Male						Female					
	N	Range		Percentiles			N	Range		Percentiles		
Yr. Mo.		Max.	Min.	10th	50th	90th		Max.	Min.	10th	50th	90th
0 - 1	66	.13	.08	.090	.107	.119	73	.14	.08	.098	.104	.120
0 - 2	56	.13	.09	.099	.108	.127	63	.15	.08	.090	.100	.118
0 - 3	55	.14	.08	.099	.108	.130	66	.15	.09	.096	.111	.120
0 - 6	99	.16	.08	.101	.114	.135	96	.17	.09	.099	.113	.129
0 - 9	84	.16	.10	.107	.121	.138	76	.16	.09	.100	.120	.142
1 - 0	80	.15	.09	.109	.118	.139	68	.16	.09	.102	.121	.143
1 - 6	49	.17	.10	.110	.121	.152	60	.19	.09	.104	.117	.138
2 - 0	56	.16	.10	.111	.126	.151	73	.16	.10	.107	.123	.141
2 - 6	68	.18	.10	.117	.128	.152	76	.16	.08	.108	.129	.147
3 - 0	70	.17	.10	.115	.133	.158	74	.18	.09	.111	.126	.154
3 - 6	50	.18	.11	.120	.140	.164	42	.18	.08	.110	.127	.157
4 - 0	42	.16	.11	.116	.130	.156	47	.18	.10	.115	.131	.160
4 - 6	37	.18	.12	.126	.142	.160	34	.16	.11	.114	.129	.156
5 - 0	38	.21	.11	.119	.135	.164	40	.18	.08	.112	.128	.156
5 - 6	37	.18	.11	.116	.143	.165	32	.17	.11	.116	.134	.161
6 - 0	32	.18	.12	.122	.143	.173	33	.17	.12	.123	.139	.158
6 - 6	29	.19	.11	.126	.140	.170	27	.17	.12	.123	.138	.159
7 - 0	37	.18	.10	.125	.151	.169	29	.18	.12	.123	.140	.168
7 - 6	39	.19	.11	.121	.142	.170	24	.18	.12	.125	.144	.161
8 - 0	26	.18	.12	.128	.147	.169	29	.18	.12	.124	.145	.161
8 - 6	30	.19	.12	.130	.154	.172	18	.20	.10	.109	.143	.176
9 - 0	26	.17	.12	.137	.149	.160	30	.18	.11	.124	.145	.166
9 - 6	18	.18	.14	.142	.158	.171	14	.19	.12	.130	.153	.182
10 - 0	19	.18	.12	.131	.156	.161	18	.18	.12	.128	.148	.172
10 - 6	26	.19	.13	.134	.156	.181	14	.18	.12	.124	.144	.176
11 - 0	21	.18	.12	.129	.156	.162	16	.18	.12	.123	.144	.175
11 - 6	19	.21	.12	.137	.159	.184	15	.17	.12	.122	.149	.168
12 - 0	23	.19	.12	.134	.154	.175	16	.18	.13	.132	.146	.176
12 - 6	24	.19	.12	.132	.154	.180	25	.25	.11	.122	.148	.173
13 - 0	18	.17	.12	.127	.156	.168	21	.18	.12	.128	.148	.174
13 - 6	18	.19	.12	.130	.153	.177	21	.19	.12	.131	.155	.182
14 - 0	26	.18	.12	.127	.145	.171	23	.19	.12	.129	.154	.174
14 - 6	26	.20	.12	.139	.152	.186	18	.18	.12	.125	.157	.175
15 - 0	24	.19	.12	.135	.156	.178	35	.26	.12	.135	.155	.183
15 - 6	31	.22	.13	.139	.160	.188	9	-	-	-	-	-
16 - 0	29	.18	.12	.128	.157	.173	42	.26	.11	.127	.153	.174
17 - 0	39	.20	.12	.138	.156	.182	42	.24	.12	.126	.154	.176
18 - 0	31	.21	.12	.130	.160	.183	33	.20	.12	.131	.153	.187
19 - 0	23	.20	.14	.146	.162	.180	35	.22	.11	.116	.155	.185
20 - 0	31	.23	.12	.137	.158	.182	30	.26	.12	.127	.158	.190
21 - 0	31	.23	.13	.138	.157	.180	29	.20	.11	.130	.154	.179
22 - 0	32	.21	.13	.146	.161	.191	27	.22	.12	.124	.142	.178
23 - 0	28	.21	.13	.142	.164	.198	24	.20	.11	.129	.159	.193
24 - 0	28	.22	.14	.146	.166	.190	18	.18	.12	.128	.147	.169
25 - 0	25	.20	.12	.134	.158	.183	20	.28	.12	.128	.162	.192
26 - 0	21	.20	.12	.139	.170	.184	17	.19	.12	.126	.151	.178
27 - 0	23	.20	.12	.126	.157	.183	14	.22	.12	.125	.152	.168
28 - 0	23	.22	.13	.143	.161	.198	14	.16	.12	.123	.150	.159
29 - 0	16	.20	.14	.143	.159	.181	12	.18	.12	.127	.157	.162
30 - 0	19	.19	.12	.133	.158	.183	13	.18	.12	.123	.141	.172
31 - 0	18	.20	.14	.142	.159	.195	11	.19	.14	.141	.156	.170
32 - 0	16	.20	.13	.145	.160	.182	8	-	-	-	-	-
33 - 0	20	.20	.12	.136	.155	.188	10	.17	.12	.125	.140	.165
34 - 0	13	.18	.12	.128	.157	.172	11	.18	.10	.117	.154	.176
35 - 0	10	.17	.12	.125	.147	.165	9	-	-	-	-	-
36 - 0	13	.20	.14	.148	.161	.168	10	.18	.11	.124	.162	.176
37 - 0	10	.18	.15	.159	.161	.177	8	-	-	-	-	-
38 - 0	10	.19	.14	.145	.157	.185	4	-	-	-	-	-

ELECTROCARDIOGRAMS

TABLE B-2

The Q-S Interval - Lead II

Age	Male						Female					
		Range		Percentiles				Range		Percentiles		
Yr. Mo.	N	Max.	Min.	10th	50th	90th	N	Max.	Min.	10th	50th	90th
0 - 1	66	.08	.04	.043	.052	.068	74	.07	.04	.041	.050	.060
0 - 2	56	.08	.04	.048	.057	.070	63	.08	.03	.037	.049	.060
0 - 3	55	.08	.04	.048	.058	.070	68	.08	.03	.037	.048	.060
0 - 6	100	.08	.04	.050	.059	.076	96	.08	.04	.043	.056	.069
0 - 9	84	.08	.04	.050	.059	.078	77	.08	.04	.043	.057	.070
1 - 0	80	.09	.05	.053	.061	.079	68	.08	.04	.048	.057	.060
1 - 6	49	.08	.04	.051	.059	.077	59	.08	.03	.045	.057	.066
2 - 0	56	.08	.05	.059	.062	.078	73	.09	.04	.046	.057	.069
2 - 6	68	.09	.05	.058	.062	.079	76	.09	.04	.046	.058	.076
3 - 0	70	.09	.04	.055	.060	.077	74	.09	.04	.045	.057	.070
3 - 6	50	.08	.05	.059	.069	.079	42	.08	.04	.049	.058	.077
4 - 0	42	.09	.04	.055	.067	.078	47	.08	.04	.050	.060	.072
4 - 6	37	.09	.05	.059	.067	.081	34	.06	.05	.053	.064	.076
5 - 0	38	.09	.04	.055	.060	.078	40	.09	.05	.053	.061	.080
5 - 6	37	.09	.05	.059	.067	.081	32	.09	.04	.047	.058	.078
6 - 0	32	.09	.04	.055	.066	.079	33	.08	.05	.052	.061	.078
6 - 6	29	.09	.04	.055	.066	.078	27	.09	.05	.054	.067	.081
7 - 0	37	.08	.05	.060	.069	.079	29	.08	.05	.052	.061	.078
7 - 6	39	.08	.04	.056	.070	.079	24	.08	.05	.059	.068	.079
8 - 0	26	.08	.06	.061	.069	.079	29	.09	.05	.058	.066	.078
8 - 6	31	.09	.06	.061	.071	.080	18	.09	.05	.058	.062	.081
9 - 0	26	.09	.06	.061	.072	.081	30	.09	.05	.058	.067	.081
9 - 6	18	.08	.06	.061	.070	.080	14	.08	.06	.060	.062	.070
10 - 0	19	.09	.06	.061	.071	.087	19	.08	.06	.061	.069	.079
10 - 6	26	.10	.06	.062	.072	.080	14	.10	.06	.068	.071	.080
11 - 0	22	.09	.06	.069	.072	.088	16	.08	.06	.060	.068	.079
11 - 6	19	.09	.05	.066	.078	.086	15	.10	.05	.054	.066	.079
12 - 0	23	.09	.06	.062	.079	.088	16	.11	.06	.061	.065	.079
12 - 6	24	.09	.06	.062	.079	.088	25	.11	.06	.062	.068	.087
13 - 0	19	.10	.06	.068	.076	.088	21	.08	.05	.060	.069	.079
13 - 6	19	.10	.07	.071	.080	.090	21	.10	.06	.062	.071	.080
14 - 0	26	.09	.06	.070	.079	.081	23	.08	.05	.060	.071	.079
14 - 6	26	.10	.06	.069	.078	.091	18	.10	.06	.062	.071	.096
15 - 0	24	.09	.06	.069	.079	.088	35	.12	.05	.059	.070	.101
15 - 6	31	.11	.06	.065	.077	.096	10	.10	.06	.068	.078	.096
16 - 0	30	.09	.06	.069	.079	.088	42	.12	.06	.062	.070	.084
17 - 0	39	.11	.06	.066	.078	.097	44	.12	.05	.062	.080	.090
18 - 0	30	.10	.07	.071	.080	.097	33	.12	.06	.065	.079	.099
19 - 0	23	.10	.07	.071	.081	.091	35	.10	.05	.056	.069	.087
20 - 0	31	.11	.06	.075	.079	.096	30	.10	.06	.068	.077	.080
21 - 0	33	.10	.06	.068	.078	.097	29	.11	.05	.057	.073	.090
22 - 0	32	.12	.06	.069	.082	.100	28	.10	.05	.057	.075	.080
23 - 0	28	.12	.06	.067	.081	.100	24	.11	.05	.058	.074	.079
24 - 0	30	.11	.06	.066	.078	.097	19	.11	.05	.058	.076	.090
25 - 0	25	.12	.06	.067	.082	.111	20	.10	.06	.068	.072	.096
26 - 0	21	.11	.06	.068	.079	.099	18	.12	.05	.063	.085	.110
27 - 0	23	.12	.07	.072	.078	.099	14	.12	.06	.067	.082	.101
28 - 0	23	.12	.06	.078	.086	.102	14	.12	.05	.065	.082	.110
29 - 0	16	.10	.06	.070	.079	.097	12	.11	.06	.062	.076	.080
30 - 0	19	.12	.06	.069	.083	.114	13	.12	.06	.067	.082	.116
31 - 0	18	.12	.07	.074	.080	.098	11	.12	.07	.071	.077	.090
32 - 0	16	.11	.06	.066	.079	.098	8	-	-	-	-	-
33 - 0	20	.12	.06	.066	.083	.116	10	.12	.07	.075	.080	.115
34 - 0	13	.13	.07	.072	.079	.122	11	.10	.07	.072	.081	.091
35 - 0	10	.12	.07	.072	.080	.115	9	-	-	-	-	-
36 - 0	13	.12	.06	.078	.085	.112	10	.12	.07	.071	.075	.115
37 - 0	10	.12	.07	.072	.080	.115	8	-	-	-	-	-
38 - 0	10	.10	.07	.079	.089	.099	4	-	-	-	-	-

ELECTROCARDIOGRAMS

TABLE B-3

The Q-T Interval - Lead II

Age	Male						Female					
		Range		Percentiles				Range		Percentiles		
Yr. Mo.	N	Max.	Min.	10th	50th	90th	N	Max.	Min.	10th	50th	90th
0 - 1	64	.31	.21	.221	.249	.279	72	.31	.20	.214	.250	.282
0 - 2	56	.30	.22	.237	.256	.283	62	.32	.22	.228	.256	.286
0 - 3	54	.32	.22	.233	.256	.293	66	.34	.20	.234	.264	.306
0 - 6	99	.32	.22	.236	.259	.285	96	.30	.22	.238	.259	.293
0 - 9	84	.32	.22	.237	.270	.296	76	.32	.22	.235	.262	.291
1 - 0	79	.32	.22	.240	.272	.297	67	.31	.22	.243	.269	.294
1 - 6	49	.34	.22	.241	.275	.316	60	.34	.20	.256	.278	.317
2 - 0	55	.36	.24	.266	.292	.322	73	.36	.23	.266	.284	.320
2 - 6	68	.34	.26	.277	.296	.324	76	.35	.24	.274	.299	.326
3 - 0	70	.38	.24	.275	.308	.344	74	.36	.24	.269	.296	.337
3 - 6	50	.38	.27	.279	.313	.339	42	.40	.25	.275	.307	.337
4 - 0	42	.36	.27	.285	.315	.341	47	.37	.28	.292	.317	.353
4 - 6	37	.40	.28	.289	.319	.353	34	.36	.32	.275	.313	.347
5 - 0	38	.40	.28	.294	.324	.357	40	.38	.27	.299	.321	.354
5 - 6	37	.38	.28	.298	.326	.357	32	.38	.28	.288	.315	.358
6 - 0	32	.40	.29	.297	.328	.363	33	.40	.28	.293	.330	.351
6 - 6	29	.39	.30	.309	.337	.361	27	.41	.29	.310	.327	.359
7 - 0	37	.38	.28	.306	.331	.364	29	.42	.28	.300	.334	.379
7 - 6	39	.44	.30	.311	.335	.366	24	.40	.30	.308	.330	.359
8 - 0	26	.42	.30	.310	.351	.383	29	.39	.28	.312	.341	.382
8 - 6	31	.38	.31	.324	.347	.365	18	.41	.32	.328	.347	.394
9 - 0	26	.40	.31	.320	.348	.379	30	.42	.30	.320	.350	.384
9 - 6	18	.42	.32	.331	.350	.377	14	.42	.32	.323	.345	.366
10 - 0	19	.38	.31	.340	.363	.377	19	.42	.32	.325	.341	.391
10 - 6	26	.42	.32	.341	.357	.398	14	.41	.32	.333	.361	.399
11 - 0	22	.42	.32	.325	.357	.399	16	.40	.31	.324	.359	.379
11 - 6	19	.44	.32	.331	.354	.393	15	.42	.32	.325	.365	.397
12 - 0	23	.44	.34	.343	.356	.393	16	.42	.31	.334	.351	.395
12 - 6	24	.42	.32	.341	.360	.399	24	.42	.32	.331	.362	.395
13 - 0	19	.40	.32	.328	.359	.385	21	.42	.34	.346	.371	.411
13 - 6	19	.40	.32	.338	.357	.385	21	.44	.32	.333	.373	.421
14 - 0	26	.41	.32	.334	.374	.398	23	.47	.33	.338	.370	.424
14 - 6	26	.41	.32	.328	.369	.398	18	.44	.35	.358	.397	.406
15 - 0	24	.42	.33	.342	.378	.399	35	.44	.31	.350	.387	.431
15 - 6	31	.44	.33	.339	.384	.417	10	.42	.32	.330	.365	.410
16 - 0	30	.44	.34	.346	.377	.417	42	.44	.34	.350	.374	.414
17 - 0	37	.44	.34	.345	.371	.399	44	.46	.34	.351	.388	.418
18 - 0	31	.44	.32	.340	.377	.424	33	.46	.32	.339	.380	.437
19 - 0	23	.48	.33	.346	.379	.418	35	.44	.30	.335	.383	.410
20 - 0	31	.42	.32	.334	.359	.412	30	.42	.31	.332	.381	.409
21 - 0	33	.42	.32	.343	.377	.412	29	.46	.34	.349	.392	.437
22 - 0	32	.48	.34	.351	.376	.423	28	.44	.34	.352	.390	.416
23 - 0	28	.44	.33	.357	.397	.430	24	.41	.34	.344	.376	.403
24 - 0	30	.44	.32	.344	.374	.402	18	.42	.35	.360	.385	.414
25 - 0	25	.44	.31	.351	.391	.422	20	.42	.36	.363	.387	.416
26 - 0	21	.42	.32	.350	.385	.413	18	.44	.34	.349	.387	.412
27 - 0	23	.41	.35	.356	.387	.405	14	.43	.36	.363	.395	.420
28 - 0	23	.44	.32	.359	.386	.420	14	.42	.33	.343	.384	.410
29 - 0	16	.44	.36	.373	.395	.422	12	.43	.34	.351	.385	.411
30 - 0	19	.43	.36	.363	.378	.422	13	.44	.37	.373	.401	.431
31 - 0	18	.45	.35	.359	.385	.432	11	.41	.36	.375	.395	.400
32 - 0	16	.45	.38	.384	.397	.439	8	-	-	-	-	-
33 - 0	20	.44	.35	.362	.395	.431	10	.46	.33	.343	.369	.447
34 - 0	13	.45	.37	.379	.397	.440	11	.42	.39	.399	.401	.411
35 - 0	10	.44	.38	.386	.404	.434	8	-	-	-	-	-
36 - 0	13	.44	.36	.392	.397	.422	10	.43	.36	.363	.398	.423
37 - 0	10	.42	.34	.356	.398	.416	8	-	-	-	-	-
38 - 0	10	.42	.34	.364	.392	.416	4	-	-	-	-	-

ELECTROCARDIOGRAMS

TABLE B-4

The Q-Tc Interval

Age	Male						Female					
		Range		Percentiles				Range		Percentiles		
Yr. Mo.	N	Max.	Min.	10th	50th	90th	N	Max.	Min.	10th	50th	90th
0 - 1	64	.4660	.3238	.3671	.4032	.4397	72	.4729	.3246	.3667	.3965	.4378
0 - 2	56	.4636	.3443	.3670	.4054	.4455	62	.4835	.3584	.3759	.4112	.4539
0 - 3	53	.4616	.3396	.3707	.4029	.4462	66	.4766	.3488	.3708	.4069	.4470
0 - 6	99	.4661	.3323	.3733	.4092	.4376	95	.4672	.3546	.3715	.4053	.4439
0 - 9	84	.4666	.3166	.3777	.4093	.4497	76	.4693	.3226	.3701	.4070	.4429
1 - 0	79	.4582	.3237	.3680	.4081	.4464	65	.4660	.3160	.3639	.3952	.4416
1 - 6	49	.4818	.3504	.3633	.3964	.4261	60	.4835	.3150	.3622	.3964	.4414
2 - 0	55	.4604	.3552	.3789	.4045	.4367	73	.4852	.3520	.3704	.4037	.4391
2 - 6	67	.4571	.3611	.3759	.4075	.4327	76	.4684	.3380	.3671	.3991	.4393
3 - 0	70	.5484	.3587	.3803	.4048	.4373	74	.4729	.3520	.3717	.4044	.4359
3 - 6	50	.4853	.3706	.3788	.4071	.4371	42	.4537	.3744	.3827	.4081	.4442
4 - 0	42	.4468	.3578	.3716	.3978	.4233	47	.4600	.3646	.3800	.3976	.4273
4 - 6	37	.4717	.3328	.3756	.3996	.4415	34	.4625	.3600	.3750	.4027	.4338
5 - 0	38	.4557	.3674	.3865	.4057	.4369	40	.4848	.3676	.3754	.4038	.4379
5 - 6	37	.4720	.3435	.3737	.4023	.4316	32	.4554	.3535	.3616	.3968	.4391
6 - 0	32	.4533	.3535	.3740	.4034	.4274	33	.4590	.3674	.3779	.4075	.4308
6 - 6	29	.4807	.3554	.3717	.4043	.4375	27	.4688	.3512	.3671	.4002	.4294
7 - 0	37	.4600	.3500	.3704	.4055	.4255	29	.4415	.3718	.3821	.4004	.4279
7 - 6	39	.4491	.3489	.3637	.4048	.4361	24	.4450	.3530	.3686	.4045	.4376
8 - 0	25	.4468	.3624	.3751	.4137	.4398	29	.4692	.3665	.3807	.3986	.4389
8 - 6	31	.4610	.3718	.3808	.4030	.4369	18	.4544	.3646	.3727	.4140	.4463
9 - 0	26	.4289	.3331	.3676	.3980	.4227	30	.4538	.3731	.3852	.4134	.4417
9 - 6	18	.4405	.3601	.3794	.4043	.4333	14	.4457	.3689	.3743	.4054	.4403
10 - 0	19	.4518	.3744	.3835	.4015	.4371	19	.4624	.3672	.3762	.4029	.4443
10 - 6	26	.4360	.3665	.3814	.4134	.4324	14	.4676	.3768	.3800	.4071	.4458
11 - 0	22	.4351	.2942	.3791	.3985	.4205	16	.4580	.3638	.3713	.4046	.4335
11 - 6	19	.4473	.3763	.3830	.4065	.4338	15	.4507	.3403	.3872	.4121	.4424
12 - 0	23	.4502	.3285	.3662	.3954	.4251	16	.4482	.3698	.3740	.4090	.4419
12 - 6	24	.4463	.3671	.3782	.4027	.4400	24	.4526	.3541	.3850	.4132	.4420
13 - 0	19	.4561	.3791	.3820	.4035	.4415	21	.4579	.3660	.3848	.4081	.4362
13 - 6	19	.4359	.3530	.3770	.3936	.4280	20	.4652	.3741	.3923	.4151	.4470
14 - 0	26	.4360	.3509	.3620	.3878	.4286	23	.4469	.3821	.3914	.4152	.4439
14 - 6	26	.4502	.3484	.3667	.4044	.4414	18	.4469	.3858	.3913	.4072	.4414
15 - 0	24	.4506	.3650	.3718	.3935	.4360	35	.4650	.3804	.3920	.4151	.4460
15 - 6	31	.5049	.3564	.3715	.3997	.4274	10	.4474	.3831	.3895	.4217	.4410
16 - 0	30	.4573	.3536	.3640	.3925	.4366	42	.4581	.3570	.3752	.4032	.4374
17 - 0	37	.4450	.3362	.3509	.3970	.4282	44	.4700	.3643	.3770	.4081	.4478
18 - 0	31	.4320	.3340	.3546	.3887	.4269	33	.4646	.3511	.3749	.4135	.4390
19 - 0	23	.4516	.3617	.3720	.4022	.4223	35	.4684	.3643	.3778	.4052	.4502
20 - 0	31	.4200	.3428	.3513	.3833	.4140	30	.4544	.3602	.3696	.4073	.4473
21 - 0	33	.4497	.3406	.3599	.3959	.4372	29	.4506	.3566	.3839	.4106	.4415
22 - 0	31	.4542	.3570	.3645	.3967	.4344	28	.4560	.3704	.3858	.4115	.4440
23 - 0	28	.4571	.3660	.3724	.3933	.4334	24	.4688	.3593	.3746	.4140	.4425
24 - 0	30	.4409	.3634	.3680	.3970	.4351	18	.4636	.3678	.3946	.4109	.4502
25 - 0	24	.4442	.3251	.3632	.4025	.4290	20	.4739	.3900	.3942	.4152	.4382
26 - 0	20	.4388	.3679	.3750	.4034	.4341	18	.4700	.3968	.4034	.4290	.4568
27 - 0	23	.4590	.3615	.3671	.4017	.4366	14	.4672	.3987	.4019	.4284	.4508
28 - 0	23	.4411	.3510	.3704	.3946	.4136	14	.4457	.3998	.4030	.4250	.4359
29 - 0	14	.4551	.3835	.3885	.4086	.4501	12	.4561	.4060	.4080	.4210	.4351
30 - 0	18	.4420	.3660	.3728	.4078	.4374	13	.4789	.4047	.4127	.4288	.4618
31 - 0	18	.4507	.3653	.3730	.4114	.4313	11	.4516	.4000	.4028	.4181	.4459
32 - 0	16	.4629	.3726	.3870	.4132	.4512	8	-	-	-	-	-
33 - 0	20	.4411	.3634	.3789	.4074	.4307	10	.4507	.4010	.4109	.4258	.4457
34 - 0	13	.4515	.3770	.3818	.4105	.4344	11	.4479	.3960	.4017	.4297	.4422
35 - 0	10	.4667	.3852	.3934	.4137	.4586	8	-	-	-	-	-
36 - 0	13	.4397	.3787	.3927	.4107	.4357	10	.4513	.3984	.4143	.4248	.4460
37 - 0	10	.4431	.3800	.3863	.4021	.4368	8	-	-	-	-	-
38 - 0	10	.4552	.3825	.3898	.4152	.4479	4	-	-	-	-	-

Section C

VITAL SIGNS—BLOOD PRESSURE AND PULSE

ROBERT W. McCAMMON

VITAL SIGNS

Blood Pressures

BLOOD pressure data presented are based on readings obtained by the examining physicians using the auscultatory method during routine physical examinations. All recordings used in these computations were made with the subjects lying quietly on their backs on the examining table. The cuff size varied with the size of the child with 6, 10 and 14 cm cuffs available. A Becton-Dickinson mercury manometer was used throughout. Height of the column was recorded to the nearest whole number of millimeters of mercury. Systolic pressure was accepted as the pressure at the first sound heard in the antecubital space and diastolic pressure was recorded as the break between the third and fourth sounds. In more than half the recordings the disappearance of sound was also recorded, but this was not uniform enough to warrant inclusion in the statistical summaries.

Blood pressure data were recorded at the birthday visit and at quarterly intervals between birthdays from age two years six months to the end of the adolescent growth spurt, each six months thereafter until physical growth in height had stopped and then annually. No subject had blood pressure recorded for all examinations at all ages. A total of 4544 blood pressures on 117 boys and 132 girls were recorded. The largest number for one individual was 40 records and the minimum was 1. In computing the summary statistics, age limits were set in such fashion that all readings were included in the computation. The stated ages plus and minus 45 days were included at each age interval through adolescence and plus and minus 6 months in adults. Tables C-1 and C-2 present data at semiannual intervals through the childhood years; similar statistics are available for the 3- and 9-month intervals between birthdays through adolescence, but inclusion of these data does not alter the trends established by the semiannual recordings.

Blood pressure measurements taken on the same subjects in the sitting position are also available but do not vary significantly from those taken supine. Basal condition blood pressures taken at the end of the basal metabolism test are available in too limited a number to warrant descriptive statistics. Blood pressures before, immediately after and 5 minutes after severe physical exertion on the bicycle ergometer were also recorded but have not been included because they represent unusual examining conditions for measurement of this physiological variable and because total numbers of recordings are relatively small.

Figure C-1 represents mean systolic and diastolic pressures for males from 2½ through 33 years and for females from 2½ through 27 years. The differences between the means of diastolic pressures for the two sexes are not significant except at age 24 years, which is presumed to result from chance selection in a small group of subjects rather than a physiological dissimilarity occurring at a single age. Mean systolic pressures are not significantly different before age 15 years, but thereafter they are significantly different ($P = 0.01$) at all ages except 25 and 27 years, where failure of significance is again reasonably associated with chance selection in small groups rather than physiological similarity.

Pulse Rate

Pulse rates vary markedly depending upon the circumstances under which they are recorded. For this reason pulse rates recorded under three different circumstances are reported. Basal pulse rates were recorded at the end of the basal metabolism tests immediately after the metabolism chamber had been opened and before the subject had moved or been moved. Infants were tested under modified basal conditions while asleep and fed and pulse rates were taken while they were still asleep. The rate was determined by a 30-second count of the radial pulse in older children and by auscultation of the heart sounds in infants. There were 5710 counts recorded.

Physical examination counts were recorded on the basis of

30-second counts of the radial pulse or the heart sounds during the physical examination. There were a total of 8172 counts on 129 male and 140 female subjects. No record was made of the body position of the subject at the time the pulse was recorded and the counts therefore represent a mixture of supine and erect body postures.

ECG pulse rates were calculated from the supine records of standard limb lead II. There were a total of 5794 pulse rates recorded on 122 female and 129 male subjects. The average duration of the cardiac cycle was determined from strips of record averaging 9 inches in length, and the pulse rate was calculated by dividing 60 by the average cycle duration. The rate was recorded as the nearest whole number.

Age limits used in computing the descriptive statistics were the same as those for blood pressure except during the first three months of life, when the ages include intervals of 15 days on either side of the stated age.

Pulse rates were recorded each three months between birthdays but inclusion of the data for the 3- and 9-month visits did not change the trend represented by the semiannual data and were therefore excluded from the tables. Pulse rates in subjects from 7 years to the early adult years were recorded by tachometer tape before exercise on the bicycle, at peak rate during exercise and after 5 minutes of rest following exercise; these were not included in the normative data because they represent unusual circumstances of measurement.

Figure C-2 represents mean pulse rates in males from 1 month through 33 years at physical examination and from ECG records, and 1 month through 22 years under basal conditions. There are no significant differences between the pulse rates for males and females but the significance of differences for the same sex under different conditions of measurement are apparent. The change in pulse rate at physical examination from levels similar to basal pulse in the neonatal period to levels similar to the ECG level from 1 to 2 years agrees well with the behavior of infants during this interval. However, no explanation is apparent for the fact that physical examination pulses are consistently higher than ECG record pulses after 2 years of age.

Tables C-3, C-4 and C-5 contain the pulse rate data from basal metabolism, ECG, and physical examination records. Data for basal pulse are more limited in the age range covered because subjects were not followed after age 21 years.

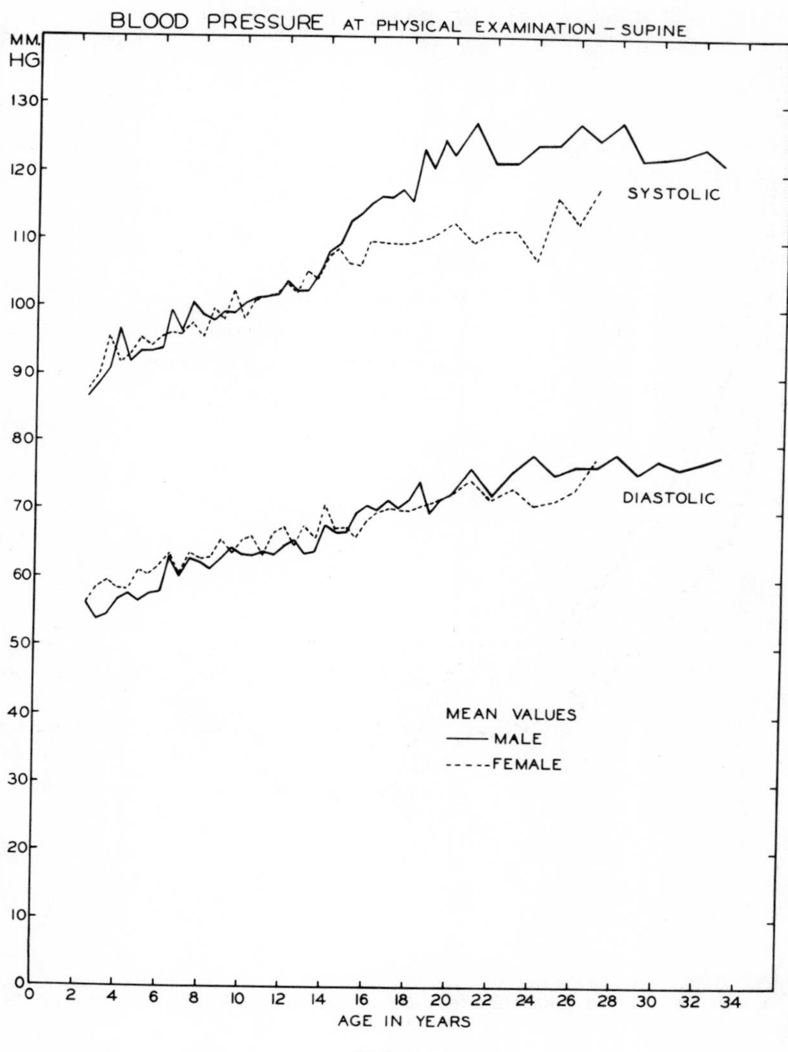
BLOOD PRESSURE AT PHYSICAL EXAMINATION – SUPINE
MM. HG
130
120
110
100
90
80
70
60
50
40
30
20
10
0
SYSTOLIC
DIASTOLIC
MEAN VALUES
—— MALE
- - - - FEMALE
0 2 4 6 8 10 12 14 16 18 20 22 24 26 28 30 32 34
AGE IN YEARS

FIG. C–1

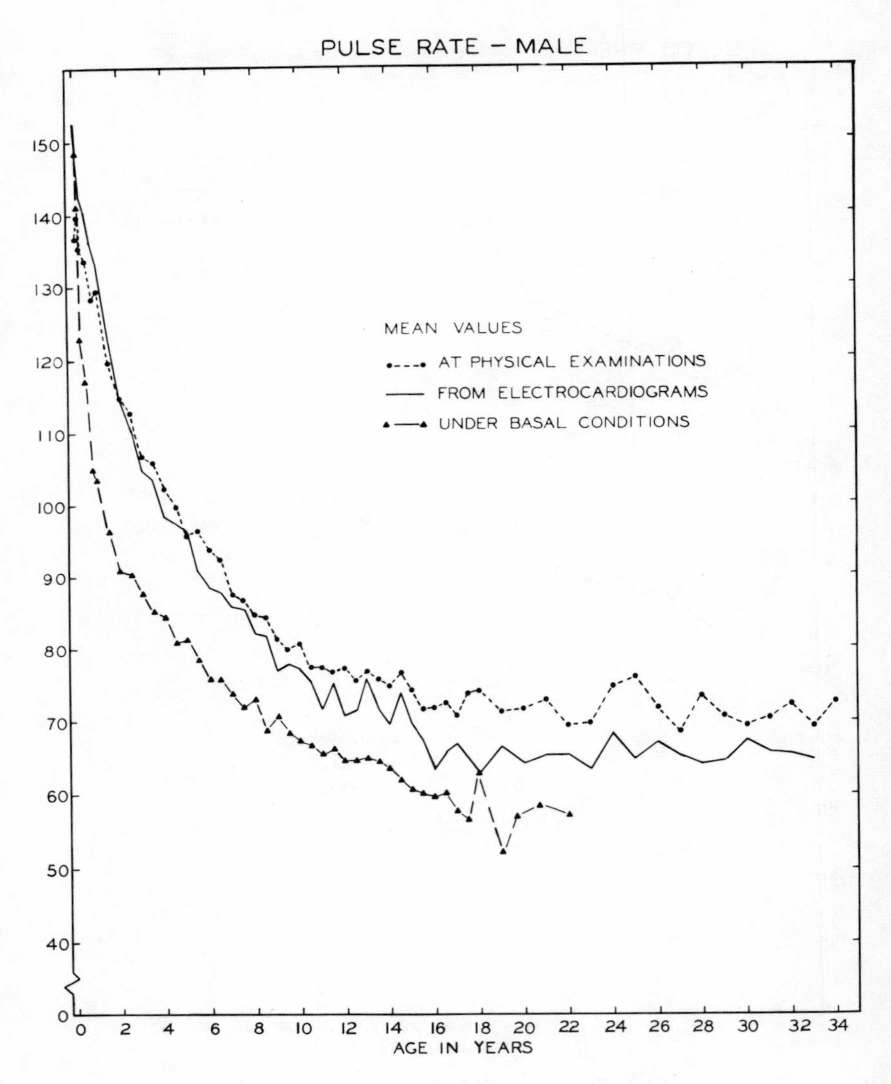
PULSE RATE – MALE
MEAN VALUES
AT PHYSICAL EXAMINATIONS
FROM ELECTROCARDIOGRAMS
UNDER BASAL CONDITIONS
150
140
130
120
110
100
90
80
70
60
50
40
0
0 2 4 6 8 10 12 14 16 18 20 22 24 26 28 30 32 34
AGE IN YEARS

FIG. C-2

ITAL SIGNS

TABLE C-1

Blood Pressure at Physical Examination - Male

Age	N	Systolic									Diastolic								
						Percentiles									Percentiles				
:. Mo.		Max.	Min.	Mean	S.D.	10th	25th	50th	75th	90th	Max.	Min.	Mean	S.D.	10th	25th	50th	75th	90th
ıpine																			
2 - 6	12	94	78	87	4.8	80	83	86	90	91	70	44	56	7.4	49	52	55	60	68
3 - 0	30	112	72	89	9.0	75	83	88	92	99	70	38	54	7.5	40	50	54	59	60
3 - 6	23	110	69	91	10.2	72	88	93	97	105	70	28	54	10.9	38	50	55	63	66
- 0	22	110	82	96	7.4	88	90	95	102	104	74	40	57	8.3	44	54	57	60	67
- 6	29	104	80	92	6.7	83	86	91	97	101	72	36	57	8.8	46	51	58	63	69
- 0	32	106	72	93	8.1	81	88	96	100	102	74	36	57	9.0	46	50	56	64	69
- 6	28	112	72	93	8.5	79	90	94	98	100	76	27	57	10.8	47	52	57	66	70
- 0	31	108	80	94	6.3	86	88	94	97	102	70	46	58	7.0	48	51	57	63	68
- 6	27	120	84	99	7.7	90	95	97	104	109	74	48	63	8.2	49	57	65	70	72
- 0	44	110	82	96	7.1	85	91	96	101	104	70	45	60	7.1	49	55	59	65	69
- 6	38	122	84	100	8.3	91	95	101	104	110	80	38	63	7.9	53	58	62	69	71
- 0	39	122	82	99	9.1	88	91	96	102	112	92	40	62	8.7	52	57	62	65	69
- 6	40	124	80	98	10.2	86	91	98	103	110	76	40	61	8.8	49	55	61	68	72
- 0	44	120	84	99	7.5	90	93	99	102	110	80	34	63	8.2	54	58	62	67	71
- 6	43	118	86	99	7.8	90	93	97	103	112	80	48	64	7.8	53	59	64	69	72
- 0	51	130	90	100	8.0	91	94	99	105	109	90	32	63	10.2	52	58	65	70	72
- 6	44	120	86	101	8.5	91	94	101	106	115	80	50	63	7.6	54	57	62	68	73
- 0	47	122	80	101	8.5	90	97	101	105	113	86	44	64	8.5	53	58	66	70	74
- 6	44	114	78	102	7.6	93	96	102	107	110	80	45	63	7.5	52	59	63	70	72
- 0	39	128	82	104	10.3	91	97	104	111	119	80	46	65	7.0	54	60	65	71	73
- 6	48	134	82	102	9.8	90	96	101	107	116	82	48	66	7.9	54	60	66	71	74
- 0	39	124	84	102	8.9	90	95	102	108	112	84	46	64	8.7	53	58	63	70	73
- 6	41	122	92	105	7.0	95	99	104	109	114	82	50	64	8.7	52	59	64	71	74
- 0	46	144	80	108	11.8	95	101	106	114	123	84	36	68	9.6	56	60	71	74	79
- 6	38	130	98	109	8.0	100	104	108	114	120	90	50	67	9.1	55	60	67	70	78
- 0	44	140	100	112	7.5	103	107	111	115	120	80	46	67	7.7	60	63	70	73	75
- 6	45	154	95	114	11.7	102	105	111	121	128	90	52	70	8.6	59	65	69	74	81
- 0	45	168	94	115	14.0	102	107	113	120	128	90	50	71	8.4	58	65	70	76	82
- 6	35	140	100	116	8.4	106	[illegible]	[illegible]	[illegible]	[illegible]	[illegible]	[illegible]	[illegible]	[illegible]	[illegible]	65	69	74	81
- 0	41	150	98	116	11.3	104	109	117	122	124	100	50	72	10.3	57	65	69	77	83
- 6	26	130	102	118	7.0	109	113	117	122	128	88	50	70	8.6	59	64	71	76	80
- 0	26	140	100	116	9.5	104	108	114	119	130	86	58	72	7.0	64	67	70	78	80
- 6	11	170	108	123	17.8	110	114	118	128	138	82	70	74	4.5	70	71	74	80	81
- 0	24	150	102	121	12.2	106	112	120	128	137	90	48	70	11.7	53	59	71	79	85
- 6	16	150	108	125	13.2	110	114	125	133	147	82	60	72	7.0	61	69	70	79	81
- 0	25	146	100	123	13.4	107	113	124	131	142	90	56	72	10.0	60	65	71	81	87
- 0	26	176	106	127	16.1	110	114	120	135	149	90	50	76	9.3	66	68	77	82	88
- 0	24	150	105	121	10.8	111	113	119	129	135	95	56	72	9.1	62	68	71	79	84
- 0	19	158	108	122	14.6	109	111	119	134	142	96	60	76	9.6	63	69	75	81	89
- 0	22	154	110	124	11.9	112	119	123	129	132	94	68	78	6.4	69	74	78	81	86
- 0	20	164	108	124	14.3	110	112	123	130	142	106	60	75	10.1	65	71	74	81	85
- 0	25	170	100	127	15.4	108	116	127	137	141	95	60	77	9.6	66	69	76	84	91
- 0	18	146	104	125	13.3	108	112	125	137	143	100	64	77	10.5	66	69	73	87	92
- 0	19	180	110	127	14.6	117	120	126	130	139	88	70	79	6.4	71	74	79	85	86
- 0	14	140	112	122	8.6	114	117	120	126	131	94	70	76	6.4	71	71	75	79	82
- 0	19	150	96	122	14.0	101	112	121	132	140	96	60	78	9.9	63	70	78	81	91
- 0	17	154	106	123	11.7	112	116	119	125	146	92	65	77	7.2	68	69	77	80	90
- 0	15	150	108	124	12.6	110	115	119	132	144	90	65	77	7.6	67	69	78	83	86
- 0	16	150	100	122	12.6	107	112	118	129	134	92	65	78	7.8	68	70	79	81	90

TABLE C-2

VITAL SIGNS

Blood Pressure at Physical Examination - Female

Age Yr. Mo.	N	Systolic Max.	Systolic Min.	Systolic Mean	Systolic S.D.	Systolic Percentiles 10th	25th	50th	75th	90th	Diastolic Max.	Diastolic Min.	Diastolic Mean	Diastolic S.D.	Diastolic Percentiles 10th	25th	50th	75th	90th
Supine																			
2 - 6	14	108	60	88	12.9	67	82	90	95	101	78	28	56	11.9	45	53	56	62	71
3 - 0	22	100	66	90	8.8	80	84	91	97	99	76	30	58	10.3	49	54	59	64	71
3 - 6	19	110	84	95	8.1	86	90	96	101	108	76	48	59	7.1	50	55	60	63	69
4 - 0	29	104	76	92	5.6	84	88	92	95	98	72	48	58	7.1	49	53	57	65	70
4 - 6	28	110	80	93	6.6	84	88	93	97	101	68	48	58	6.3	49	50	59	61	65
5 - 0	24	110	85	95	6.3	88	89	95	99	101	72	40	61	7.1	52	59	61	67	70
5 - 6	37	110	64	94	8.5	84	89	94	99	104	80	30	60	9.3	47	55	61	65	69
6 - 0	40	112	80	95	7.6	85	90	95	101	105	80	42	61	8.0	51	57	62	67	71
6 - 6	34	116	78	96	9.3	85	90	95	100	111	80	39	63	9.2	52	58	65	70	75
7 - 0	32	120	80	96	9.3	86	89	92	99	110	86	38	60	9.7	50	54	58	65	73
7 - 6	40	110	84	97	6.8	89	92	96	102	108	88	40	63	9.7	51	60	63	69	77
8 - 0	35	134	78	95	9.7	86	91	95	99	105	80	46	63	7.6	52	60	62	70	72
8 - 6	34	124	84	100	9.0	90	93	96	102	111	80	25	63	11.9	45	58	65	72	76
9 - 0	37	124	80	98	9.0	89	92	97	104	109	78	48	65	6.4	57	59	65	70	71
9 - 6	34	122	86	102	10.2	90	94	101	109	117	80	34	63	8.9	51	59	64	69	71
10 - 0	42	116	84	98	7.3	87	94	97	101	108	80	50	65	8.5	54	59	67	71	75
10 - 6	35	120	82	101	8.7	91	95	100	105	114	80	48	66	7.8	56	60	68	70	75
11 - 0	36	120	86	101	7.8	91	94	102	108	112	80	48	63	7.6	53	58	62	68	72
11 - 6	38	124	86	102	8.4	92	98	101	105	113	80	52	66	6.7	58	60	66	71	76
12 - 0	33	120	84	104	8.4	90	99	104	110	113	80	50	67	7.3	59	61	67	71	78
12 - 6	34	130	82	102	9.2	93	97	101	105	110	82	50	65	7.3	55	61	64	70	72
13 - 0	38	128	90	105	8.6	95	99	104	111	117	84	50	68	8.5	55	62	68	74	79
13 - 6	29	118	84	104	7.2	94	99	104	110	112	80	50	66	7.8	53	61	67	70	74
14 - 0	30	138	94	107	8.8	98	101	106	111	116	80	50	71	7.5	61	66	70	77	79
14 - 6	18	130	90	109	9.3	97	101	107	115	119	78	50	67	6.7	58	64	67	72	74
15 - 0	31	128	90	107	9.2	98	100	104	113	119	90	50	67	7.2	59	62	67	70	74
15 - 6	10	122	88	106	9.3	98	101	104	113	119	74	52	66	8.1	53	57	70	72	73
16 - 0	24	124	92	110	8.6	99	103	110	114	121	84	50	68	8.2	55	67	69	70	77
16 - 6	7	-	-	-	-	-	-	-	-	-	-	-	-	-	-	-	-	-	-
17 - 0	22	130	92	110	7.9	101	105	109	113	118	90	48	70	10.0	57	67	71	76	83
17 - 6	1	-	-	-	-	-	-	-	-	-	-	-	-	-	-	-	-	-	-
18 - 0	19	130	94	110	9.4	99	104	109	117	123	90	50	70	9.5	59	62	69	77	81
18 - 6	4	-	-	-	-	-	-	-	-	-	-	-	-	-	-	-	-	-	-
19 - 0	17	124	98	111	7.0	100	106	111	115	120	90	58	71	8.2	61	68	70	76	80
20 - 0	23	140	95	112	10.5	100	103	112	119	122	100	50	72	11.5	57	61	71	78	83
21 - 0	12	134	94	110	10.7	98	102	106	116	121	90	60	75	7.8	69	70	72	79	81
22 - 0	20	126	100	111	7.7	102	104	110	117	123	84	56	72	7.5	64	67	69	78	81
23 - 0	17	128	100	111	8.2	102	105	110	116	123	86	54	73	7.8	59	68	74	80	82
24 - 0	12	120	90	107	7.6	100	103	106	111	116	80	60	71	7.6	61	64	69	78	79
25 - 0	12	134	100	117	10.1	104	108	117	124	130	90	58	71	10.0	59	61	71	77	86
26 - 0	15	126	102	112	7.9	103	106	111	119	123	90	54	73	9.4	59	69	72	81	82
27 - 0	10	144	105	118	10.8	109	111	117	120	140	102	64	78	10.7	66	73	77	82	98

VITAL SIGNS

TABLE C-3

Pulse Rate/Minute under Basal Conditions

Age	Male										Female									
						Percentiles										Percentiles				
Yr. Mo.	N	Max.	Min.	Mean	S.D.	10th	25th	50th	75th	90th	N	Max.	Min.	Mean	S.D.	10th	25th	50th	75th	90th
0 - 1	13	176	132	149	12.2	137	140	147	157	161	26	190	128	148	16.0	131	135	142	156	168
0 - 2	12	160	115	141	14.5	120	124	145	150	157	12	164	100	134	18.1	108	126	132	145	160
0 - 3	12	148	96	123	18.3	99	106	122	138	146	15	156	52	124	26.7	95	103	133	144	151
0 - 6	35	148	88	117	20.0	91	98	121	133	141	33	162	86	117	21.0	94	101	110	139	145
0 - 9	30	142	84	105	16.9	86	91	101	115	133	37	144	82	104	16.6	86	95	99	115	133
1 - 0	28	150	84	103	18.0	86	89	104	110	132	25	154	68	102	21.6	81	88	97	110	141
1 - 6	23	140	64	96	16.0	80	86	93	103	120	27	132	75	96	14.2	79	83	91	107	112
2 - 0	35	120	70	91	10.9	76	83	90	98	103	49	114	70	92	11.0	79	85	91	100	108
2 - 6	53	120	60	90	11.2	77	82	88	97	101	63	152	70	91	12.4	77	81	89	98	104
3 - 0	44	104	70	88	8.0	78	81	87	93	100	55	118	68	88	9.1	76	81	86	94	100
3 - 6	41	102	72	85	7.2	75	80	84	89	93	53	104	70	86	9.3	74	79	85	93	100
4 - 0	44	100	66	84	7.5	77	81	84	89	95	49	114	70	85	9.1	73	80	85	90	99
4 - 6	40	96	68	81	6.3	72	77	80	84	89	40	98	70	83	7.4	76	78	82	88	96
5 - 0	36	96	62	81	8.2	69	76	81	86	92	47	100	68	82	7.0	72	77	82	86	89
5 - 6	41	100	66	78	8.3	68	72	77	85	89	44	92	60	78	7.9	66	71	79	84	87
6 - 0	44	88	60	76	6.8	66	72	76	81	84	40	92	62	79	7.7	67	74	78	84	88
6 - 6	45	94	60	76	7.0	66	70	76	80	86	47	88	63	76	7.3	65	68	76	82	85
7 - 0	31	90	56	74	9.0	61	66	74	81	86	45	100	62	75	8.3	66	69	74	81	84
7 - 6	39	92	56	72	8.2	62	66	71	78	81	44	88	62	74	7.0	65	69	72	80	83
8 - 0	44	90	60	73	7.6	64	66	71	79	83	42	90	60	74	7.6	63	67	72	77	84
8 - 6	45	84	54	69	7.7	57	64	68	74	79	32	86	60	70	7.4	61	64	69	76	82
9 - 0	42	84	60	71	6.5	61	65	71	74	79	40	88	58	70	7.8	60	64	69	73	81
9 - 6	45	92	54	68	8.3	59	63	68	72	79	36	86	56	69	7.4	59	64	68	74	79
0 - 0	43	88	54	67	8.2	58	62	65	73	79	50	84	56	69	7.2	60	63	68	75	79
0 - 6	50	82	55	67	6.8	59	61	66	70	78	49	84	56	69	7.6	60	63	68	74	81
1 - 0	44	78	52	66	6.1	58	61	66	70	73	44	82	58	66	6.6	59	61	67	70	76
1 - 6	46	80	54	66	6.9	57	62	64	72	76	39	82	56	68	6.6	61	64	67	73	78
2 - 0	50	80	52	65	7.0	58	60	63	70	76	41	86	54	67	6.5	59	62	67	70	75
2 - 6	[illegible]	[illegible]	[illegible]	[illegible]	[illegible]	[illegible]	[illegible]	[illegible]	70	72	39	84	54	66	7.4	57	60	65	70	77
3 - 0	52	82	48	65	6.2	57	62	65	68	73	40	80	54	66	6.6	58	62	66	71	77
3 - 6	40	84	54	64	7.8	56	58	62	70	77	41	80	54	66	7.7	57	62	64	72	78
- 0	43	80	52	63	6.5	55	58	64	67	71	34	84	54	65	7.5	57	59	63	68	76
- 6	39	78	50	62	6.0	55	57	62	64	69	34	92	56	65	8.2	58	60	63	68	77
- 0	44	80	46	61	7.2	52	56	61	65	71	35	84	54	65	7.9	56	59	63	69	77
- 6	40	82	48	60	7.4	51	55	59	64	68	25	82	52	65	6.7	57	61	63	68	75
- 0	42	76	46	60	6.0	52	56	59	63	68	26	76	50	60	6.1	52	57	60	63	67
- 6	27	72	50	60	6.2	51	54	61	66	69	24	82	50	63	7.6	54	56	63	69	72
- 0	29	82	42	58	8.1	46	53	56	60	68	19	66	52	60	3.8	55	58	62	63	64
- 6	16	76	44	57	8.0	48	50	56	60	66	18	74	54	63	5.3	56	57	61	65	69
- 0	10	82	54	63	8.6	55	58	61	67	79	11	72	50	61	7.2	51	57	62	68	70
- 0	13	58	44	52	5.1	46	47	52	56	57	0	-	-	-	-	-	-	-	-	-
- 0	14	68	46	57	5.9	48	54	58	61	63	0	-	-	-	-	-	-	-	-	-
- 0	14	72	48	58	7.2	49	51	59	62	69	0	-	-	-	-	-	-	-	-	-
- 0	13	64	50	57	5.0	51	52	58	61	62	0	-	-	-	-	-	-	-	-	-

VITAL SIGNS

TABLE C-

Pulse Rate/Minute from ECG Tracings

Age	Male										Female									
						Percentiles										Percentiles				
Yr. Mo.	N	Max.	Min.	Mean	S.D.	10th	25th	50th	75th	90th	N	Max.	Min.	Mean	S.D.	10th	25th	50th	75th	90
0 - 1	62	183	109	153	17.4	128	141	154	165	173	69	216	108	155	18.9	133	142	152	165	1
0 - 2	50	182	121	148	15.8	127	136	147	164	169	63	211	114	152	18.2	134	140	152	163	1
0 - 3	50	185	109	142	15.3	124	133	142	151	164	69	216	104	145	20.4	120	132	144	157	1
0 - 6	91	184	110	140	14.4	126	130	138	149	159	94	189	115	143	14.6	125	132	142	151	1
0 - 9	81	188	89	136	13.8	120	129	136	145	153	74	190	105	138	15.8	121	126	135	147	1
1 - 0	77	199	93	133	14.5	114	126	134	142	148	66	191	104	133	14.8	116	122	130	141	1
1 - 6	47	167	96	123	15.0	105	112	122	130	143	61	200	92	123	16.8	104	115	121	130	1
2 - 0	55	155	85	115	13.6	99	106	113	122	133	70	188	86	117	17.6	98	107	115	125	1
2 - 6	64	158	85	111	13.2	95	102	110	118	125	72	158	78	109	13.8	93	98	106	116	1
3 - 0	64	150	75	105	13.1	87	98	103	112	122	69	146	86	109	13.8	92	98	106	116	1
3 - 6	51	138	76	104	12.8	88	95	102	112	122	40	146	85	106	14.2	89	96	103	116	1
4 - 0	38	118	71	98	12.9	79	91	99	108	115	47	119	80	97	10.0	83	89	97	104	1
4 - 6	37	120	73	97	10.8	83	92	97	104	111	33	128	76	96	11.8	84	88	93	102	1
5 - 0	37	125	64	96	13.4	80	87	97	106	114	40	119	72	94	11.8	78	85	96	103	1
5 - 6	37	132	65	91	13.8	74	81	90	100	108	32	134	67	94	14.4	76	84	93	103	1
6 - 0	33	116	60	88	13.4	72	78	86	98	109	32	131	68	93	13.9	76	85	92	102	1
6 - 6	27	121	68	88	13.1	71	80	88	95	106	28	110	75	89	10.1	77	80	88	96	1
7 - 0	38	110	54	86	12.6	72	77	84	93	106	27	116	61	88	13.6	70	80	86	97	1
7 - 6	39	116	60	85	12.3	69	76	85	93	105	24	132	70	86	13.6	72	74	84	92	1
8 - 0	25	100	63	82	9.4	69	76	82	87	95	32	129	67	86	14.7	70	74	84	93	1
8 - 6	28	104	64	82	9.7	69	75	81	88	94	19	121	68	82	14.4	70	72	80	87	1
9 - 0	29	102	57	77	10.8	63	68	78	85	89	32	122	61	83	12.4	67	74	82	89	
9 - 6	18	93	62	78	8.0	66	73	77	84	87	14	103	63	83	12.6	65	72	87	92	
10 - 0	19	97	58	77	11.5	63	70	76	84	94	19	97	62	79	9.3	69	74	77	86	
10 - 6	25	96	59	75	10.4	63	67	75	84	88	15	108	59	76	12.5	63	68	73	82	
11 - 0	20	90	51	72	10.6	55	67	72	78	86	16	100	56	78	12.7	60	70	76	91	
11 - 6	18	91	62	75	9.1	66	68	72	82	88	14	119	60	78	18.2	62	64	72	92	1
12 - 0	22	89	53	71	9.4	56	65	73	77	81	16	99	54	79	11.7	61	72	81	87	
[illegible]	[illegible]	81	56	71	5.8	64	68	72	75	78	26	99	55	77	10.2	62	70	76	83	
13 - 0	18	101	58	76	10.8	64	70	74	82	89	22	88	52	71	8.4	63	65	72	78	
13 - 6	18	88	56	72	6.9	64	68	72	75	78	22	93	60	73	10.4	61	64	72	81	
14 - 0	27	98	49	70	10.8	59	62	68	76	86	23	92	53	73	11.7	59	64	72	83	
14 - 6	25	105	55	74	12.0	62	65	72	80	89	18	85	49	69	9.0	55	63	69	75	
15 - 0	22	92	51	70	11.2	55	60	68	78	87	34	94	52	72	11.2	59	63	71	79	
15 - 6	27	95	51	67	10.8	53	59	66	74	81	10	93	53	77	11.9	65	70	77	87	
16 - 0	26	91	49	63	10.6	51	54	62	70	74	39	93	50	68	10.1	54	60	67	73	
16 - 6	13	86	45	66	12.0	50	62	66	73	83	1	-	-	-	-	-	-	-	-	
17 - 0	31	96	44	67	13.2	49	57	67	76	85	42	94	49	70	10.6	56	63	68	75	
18 - 0	28	86	44	63	10.2	50	55	62	71	76	26	92	50	71	11.8	55	63	72	80	
19 - 0	21	99	50	66	10.8	53	60	66	73	78	31	89	52	69	9.6	57	62	70	75	
20 - 0	29	83	46	64	8.3	53	59	65	70	74	27	94	51	72	11.7	58	64	68	81	
21 - 0	32	85	47	65	9.3	55	58	66	72	79	27	94	48	68	10.5	52	62	68	75	
22 - 0	28	86	47	65	9.4	53	60	64	70	78	23	86	53	68	8.7	57	60	68	74	
23 - 0	24	84	48	64	7.9	53	60	62	70	73	21	91	56	72	8.5	63	67	69	80	
24 - 0	26	93	47	68	11.6	54	59	67	77	82	16	89	54	70	9.8	58	61	70	76	
25 - 0	22	86	52	65	8.8	56	58	64	71	76	15	93	54	70	10.6	59	63	72	76	
26 - 0	20	88	52	67	9.5	56	60	66	72	81	15	87	58	73	7.9	62	69	74	77	
27 - 0	22	79	49	65	8.3	51	62	66	70	76	11	91	56	74	9.0	67	70	74	76	
28 - 0	21	86	50	64	9.3	52	56	63	71	74	12	86	62	71	7.4	63	66	70	74	
29 - 0	14	83	53	64	8.8	54	58	62	70	79	10	88	66	74	6.7	67	69	74	78	
30 - 0	17	83	51	67	8.3	55	63	67	73	78	10	86	61	72	7.5	64	65	71	77	
31 - 0	12	84	51	66	10.4	53	58	63	74	80	9	-	-	-	-	-	-	-	-	
32 - 0	13	78	49	65	7.0	58	62	65	68	74	8	-	-	-	-	-	-	-	-	
33 - 0	15	79	43	65	10.5	48	59	66	73	77	8	-	-	-	-	-	-	-	-	

VITAL SIGNS

TABLE C-5

Pulse Rate/Minute during Physical Examination

Age	Male										Female									
						Percentiles										Percentiles				
Yr. Mo.	N	Max.	Min.	Mean	S.D.	10th	25th	50th	75th	90th	N	Max.	Min.	Mean	S.D.	10th	25th	50th	75th	90th
0 - 1	41	200	90	137	20.9	113	121	132	153	164	47	200	100	139	20.2	111	119	138	149	158
0 - 2	36	180	100	140	17.8	117	123	138	154	161	41	168	100	136	19.7	107	118	135	155	160
0 - 3	44	180	100	135	17.0	112	121	135	145	157	46	168	100	139	16.9	116	128	139	155	159
0 - 6	67	172	100	133	18.0	110	118	133	147	159	80	200	95	137	19.5	112	123	136	149	163
0 - 9	54	168	100	128	15.6	109	116	127	137	147	50	180	90	128	18.4	108	119	125	137	155
1 - 0	47	182	90	129	18.9	104	120	130	140	155	50	200	100	127	17.5	106	113	121	131	143
1 - 6	44	180	92	120	18.6	97	105	119	129	144	47	180	90	124	19.6	102	109	122	132	154
2 - 0	49	150	88	115	12.9	96	107	119	123	130	47	168	90	116	16.6	96	105	114	128	136
2 - 6	38	132	90	113	10.8	99	105	113	122	127	55	144	86	112	14.0	98	102	110	120	131
3 - 0	58	128	72	107	13.0	90	97	106	117	123	65	150	86	109	14.3	89	99	108	118	124
3 - 6	56	134	76	106	13.5	90	97	103	118	124	51	144	82	106	13.9	87	96	103	116	124
4 - 0	56	140	84	102	11.5	90	95	99	109	120	67	132	80	102	11.0	87	95	101	109	117
4 - 6	60	132	76	100	11.3	87	92	99	105	115	69	136	72	102	12.9	86	93	99	109	121
5 - 0	51	128	76	96	11.5	82	85	94	105	111	59	132	80	102	11.9	88	95	99	110	118
5 - 6	58	120	68	96	12.5	80	87	97	103	115	56	128	76	96	11.9	83	88	95	102	114
6 - 0	55	130	64	94	12.4	80	86	92	103	110	64	118	68	92	10.2	81	85	91	99	106
6 - 6	51	120	74	92	10.8	79	85	92	98	106	58	124	72	94	11.1	82	87	91	99	108
7 - 0	57	112	60	87	10.1	74	81	88	94	100	62	136	72	92	11.9	79	83	91	99	105
7 - 6	56	116	64	87	11.6	72	79	85	93	103	65	136	64	91	13.0	77	82	90	98	106
8 - 0	55	108	60	85	10.6	71	80	83	93	99	52	130	68	89	12.8	75	78	87	95	105
8 - 6	57	120	60	84	11.9	67	78	82	90	97	56	120	68	88	12.0	74	80	86	93	106
9 - 0	62	104	56	81	9.9	71	76	79	87	94	55	116	60	86	12.3	71	76	85	96	102
9 - 6	63	116	60	80	11.1	66	73	79	85	96	47	106	58	86	10.2	74	80	86	93	100
10 - 0	66	108	60	81	9.6	68	75	81	84	94	64	120	60	84	11.5	69	76	83	89	99
10 - 6	67	96	60	77	9.0	65	72	77	83	88	51	116	60	83	11.7	69	76	83	87	101
11 - 0	73	108	56	77	10.4	62	72	77	84	90	50	110	60	82	10.9	68	73	79	89	97
11 - 6	74	100	58	77	10.1	63	70	77	84	91	50	108	68	81	8.1	70	74	78	84	90
12 - 0	68	100	60	77	9.1	64	69	76	82	89	44	104	60	80	9.7	68	72	79	88	94
12 - 6	70	96	54	75	8.6	65	70	75	82	88	48	120	56	80	11.1	66	75	81	86	93
13 - 0	73	100	54	77	10.5	65	69	75	85	91	51	120	64	82	12.4	70	74	79	88	101
13 - 6	65	100	46	76	9.6	64	70	75	82	88	37	100	60	77	9.0	65	70	76	81	89
14 - 0	75	96	56	75	9.7	61	65	74	80	87	39	108	60	80	9.2	68	73	80	84	89
14 - 6	67	108	58	76	11.3	63	67	76	84	91	27	96	56	79	9.6	65	71	79	84	89
15 - 0	68	110	52	74	10.8	64	67	74	80	86	35	98	58	77	9.7	64	71	76	83	91
15 - 6	59	100	52	72	10.1	59	64	72	75	81	15	98	56	75	9.9	65	68	74	79	88
16 - 0	67	112	48	72	12.1	57	65	71	77	85	35	104	54	76	9.6	63	70	76	82	86
16 - 6	46	112	48	72	10.4	61	66	72	77	83	8	-	-	-	-	-	-	-	-	-
17 - 0	53	104	52	71	11.2	57	62	71	77	84	30	102	54	76	10.6	65	68	76	83	90
17 - 6	31	132	54	74	14.7	60	65	72	79	85	3	-	-	-	-	-	-	-	-	-
18 - 0	35	100	48	74	10.3	61	69	74	81	84	23	96	54	77	12.1	59	69	77	86	93
19 - 0	32	104	52	71	10.1	58	66	71	76	80	23	96	54	75	10.8	63	66	74	85	90
20 - 0	33	88	53	72	9.3	56	68	72	79	82	22	88	60	76	7.2	64	72	78	81	84
21 - 0	34	92	50	73	9.4	63	68	73	79	88	18	98	54	74	12.0	60	66	71	82	90
22 - 0	30	90	52	69	9.5	60	64	69	78	82	24	100	56	76	10.8	62	69	73	84	90
23 - 0	27	96	52	70	9.6	58	62	70	75	82	15	98	60	78	10.0	66	72	77	84	92
24 - 0	32	110	56	75	10.6	62	67	72	81	86	10	84	56	75	8.4	67	71	77	80	83
25 - 0	26	88	52	76	8.0	65	74	77	80	84	15	96	62	78	8.5	67	75	78	83	91
26 - 0	27	100	52	72	12.4	56	64	71	76	96	16	104	62	80	10.5	65	72	82	86	93
27 - 0	24	80	50	69	9.3	52	62	68	76	79	11	88	68	77	7.0	69	70	77	82	84
28 - 0	24	130	54	73	15.3	59	65	71	76	87	7	-	-	-	-	-	-	-	-	-
29 - 0	17	108	54	71	12.1	60	64	68	77	80	5	-	-	-	-	-	-	-	-	-
30 - 0	21	92	56	69	9.7	60	62	69	77	81	7	-	-	-	-	-	-	-	-	-
31 - 0	19	92	52	70	11.2	55	63	69	77	86	7	-	-	-	-	-	-	-	-	-
32 - 0	19	96	56	72	10.1	59	64	70	77	84	9	-	-	-	-	-	-	-	-	-
33 - 0	16	92	56	69	9.7	60	63	66	73	84	3	-	-	-	-	-	-	-	-	-
34 - 0	15	84	60	72	6.8	62	69	71	77	81										

Section D

NUTRITIONAL INTAKE

VIRGINIA A. BEAL

NUTRITIONAL INTAKE

Methods

NUTRITIONAL studies were added to the Child Research Council program November 1, 1946. One nutritionist (V. Beal) has been in charge of these studies since their inception. A total of six assistant nutritionists participated in data collection and analysis between 1953 and 1967; all were trained in history-taking and evaluation by V. Beal. Techniques have therefore remained as constant as possible over the 20-year span.

The nutrition history(1) was designed to provide continuous data on kind, amount and frequency of foods consumed during a period of one, three or six months. It was adapted from the method developed in the Growth Study of the Harvard School of Public Health(2). The questions were carefully formulated to give a maximum of information with a minimum of misunderstanding and without suggesting responses. During the interview each response was compared to the corresponding response on the preceding history and an effort made to date any change in the intake of a food. In addition, four records of 24-hour intake (one obtained by recall during the interview, and three recorded and mailed by the mother or older subject) were used as a cross-check on the history. Histories on infants since 1948 have been augmented by a tally sheet on which the mother recorded the number of jars or cans of strained or junior foods consumed during the interval between histories.

Histories were obtained during prearranged home visits. Each interview took approximately one hour. Presence in the home permitted measurement of serving size as well as checking on food brands, recipes, dairy order cards and shopping lists. Families were not asked to weigh or measure all foods; such a procedure would be patently unrealistic over a period of years. However, most mothers or older subjects intermittently made such measurements voluntarily because of their concern about their own accuracy or on request of the nutritionist when there was doubt about the cross-check. Because of the common difficulty in estimation of size of meat servings, scales weighing by half-ounces to eight ounces were loaned to families at intervals.

For the young child, the mother was usually the major informant, with supplementary information from relatives and sitters. Information about meals and between-meal feedings was obtained from public and private schools and preschools and from the child himself. Repeated contact with and questioning of each child facilitated determination of the age when he was competent to give his own history. Transfer from parent to subject as major informant was successfully made at a mean age of 12.5 years for girls (range 9.75 to 14.25 years) and 13.25 years for boys (range 11.25 to 15.25 years).

Calculation of diets for nutrient content was done by hand from 1946 to 1961 and by computer program from 1961 to 1966. Food values were compiled into a single table in 1946, with revisions in 1958 and 1961. With each revision several histories were calculated by both old and new tables to ensure that no consistent errors were introduced. Sources of food values for this table included published food value tables, dairy product analyses from the Milk Sanitation Division of the Denver Department of Health and from dairy companies and data from food manufacturers. When food values were not available from reliable sources, calculations were made from stated contents of containers. Some recipes and prepackaged foods were prepared, weighed and measured for comparison with published tables. The use of a single table of food values for all calculations kept food value errors as constant as possible.

Calculations included the following nutrients: calories, carbohydrate, fat, protein (total, animal, milk, meat and fish, egg, gelatine and plant), calcium (total and milk), phosphorus, iron (total and baby cereal), vitamin A (total, animal and plant), ascorbic acid, thiamine, riboflavin and niacin. Vitamin D from natural food sources was calculated only after 1961; no correction of previous calculations was made since food intake of this vitamin was small in contrast to intake from irradiated products and supplements. All calculations were made for average daily nutrient intake during one, three or six months. Foods consumed with less than daily frequency were appropriately prorated, as were changes in amount or frequency during the time interval.

The number of decimal places used in the calculations was identical to those in Tables D-1 through D-24, with the exception of carbohydrate, fat and protein (Tables D-3 through D-8) for which one decimal place was used in calculation but rounded to the nearest whole number for the summary of average daily intake. The rounding of values for calories and vitamins A and D for statistical summaries will be explained in that section.

Derived values obtained were: percent of calories from carbohydrate, fat and protein; ratio of calcium to phosphorus; percent of vitamin A from plant sources; and thiamine as mg per 1000 calories.

Differentiation was made between foods and supplements as sources of nutrients. The only nutrients from fortification of foods included in the dietary figures were iron, thiamine, riboflavin and niacin in enriched flour products and vitamin A in margarine. All other nutrients added to foods were considered as supplements. As part of each nutrition history information was obtained on the brand, dose and actual frequency of intake of vitamin or mineral supplements. Because of frequent changes in content, the average daily intake of nutrients from these sources was calculated by hand throughout the 20 years of this program.

For the calculation of nutrient intake per kilogram of body weight and per centimeter of height, the value used for weight and height was the average of those measurements of each child at the beginning and at the end of the time interval covered by the history. When the date of the nutrition history deviated from the date of measurement of the subject, weight and height were interpolated to the date of the nutrition history.

Selection of Subjects and Schedule of Histories

Nutritional intake data are based on a total of 5,205 histories on 122 subjects (59 male and 63 female) divided into three groups by age of birth and timing of histories:

1. Ninety-six subjects (52 male and 44 female) born since 1946 were included in the nutrition study from birth. Histories were taken at monthly intervals during the first 6 months of life. For children born between 1946 and 1951 histories in the last half of the first year were taken only at 9 and at 12 months; the need for more precise data resulted in extension of the monthly schedule to 12 months of age for subjects born since 1951. After the first year of life histories were taken every three months, even after the maximum physical growth spurt in adolescence when less frequent scheduling was adopted for other phases of the Child Research Council program. Since the validity of a nutrition history is partially dependent upon memory, the shorter time interval was retained except when subjects attended college out of the state. The age to which these 96 subjects have been studied is as follows:

	Number of Subjects		
Age at last history	Male	Female	Total
1/3 to 2 years	6	2	8
2+ to 5 years	11	11	22
5+ to 10 years	10	10	20
10+ to 15 years	15	11	26
15+ to 20 years	9	10	19
20+ years	1	-	1
Total	52	44	96

2. All children born between 1944 and 1946 were included in the nutrition study in November, 1946. With these 8 subjects (1 male and 7 female) nutrition histories were started at ages ranging from 9 to 27 months. All histories were taken at 3-month intervals.

3. In 1947, 18 subjects (6 male and 12 female), born prior to 1944, were added to the nutrition study at the request of other staff members because of interesting physical or biochemical findings which might have a nutritional component. Their ages

ranged from 4 to 13 years at the start of nutrition follow-up. Histories were taken only twice yearly for this group.

For groups 2 and 3, the mean length of nutrition study was 14 years for males and 12 years for females, with the following distribution:

	Number of Subjects		
Total years of study	Male	Female	Total
3/4 to 5 years	-	4	4
5+ to 10 years	1	3	4
10+ to 15 years	2	4	6
15+ to 20 years	4	6	10
20+ years	-	2	2
Total	7	19	26

Nutritional intake data from all three groups were used in the statistical summaries. The records of these 122 subjects are complete for the time intervals indicated above with the exception of a total of 34 missed histories for 3-month periods and 4 missed histories for 6-month periods, nearly always due to extended absence of the subjects from Denver. There were 36 additional periods of absence when the succeeding history was considered sufficiently valid for the missing time period to permit dietary calculation for the interim age.

The mothers of two children withdrew from the nutrition study and one mother of three children was dropped when divorce and full-time employment made reliable data impossible; their children continued with other phases of the study. One mother of four children gave unreliable data and was shown by psychological tests to have a memory defect; nutritional data for that family were discarded. Two subjects were unable to give valid dietary data at ages when their mothers' information was no longer complete; they were dropped from nutrition follow-up during adolescence.

The interview for a nutrition history was timed usually within a few days of the birthday or corresponding day of the appropriate month and close to the date of the physical examination. However, for convenience of mothers with more than one child in the nutrition study, some concessions were permitted after the preschool period so that nutritional data on two or more children could be obtained at a single interview.

In addition to nutritional data on 122 subjects, nutrient intake was evaluated during 95 pregnancies of 54 mothers and during the lactation periods of 64 mothers. These data are not included in this volume and will be published separately. Since no attempt was made to determine either quantity or nutrient content of breast milk consumed, data on nutritional intake of breast-fed infants during the period of such feeding(3) were excluded from the statistical summaries.

Validity of Data

No practical means of weighing or measuring food intake or replicating histories over an extended time period is possible without influencing intake. It is believed that the nutrition history method used in this study provides as accurate data as possible within the limits of time and cost of personnel and tolerance of the subjects. The remarkable cooperation of nearly all mothers and older subjects for the nutrition interviews and the standardization of interview techniques were major factors producing confidence in the method. A notation was made on each history form when behavior or events during an interview might affect the validity of the data obtained. Appropriate cross-check techniques were used whenever there was suspicion that a response was exaggerated, minimized or uncertain.

Records of 24-hour intake were a means of cross-check, but had two major drawbacks. Despite willingness to be questioned for an hour about food consumption, both mothers and older subjects disliked recording intake for 3 days. To 8 years of age slightly more than 50 percent of nutrition histories were accompanied by at least three 24-hour intakes from the mother. Thereafter cooperation became progressively poorer despite repeated requests until by 17 years only 20 percent of the subjects supplied a 3-day record, 10 percent supplied records for one or two days and 70 percent of the subjects recorded none. Throughout the years, both mothers and subjects freely expressed their aversion to this part of the program. The other disadvantage of 24-hour intakes was the wide variation observed from one day to another. The difference in caloric intake between the lowest and highest of four one-day records increased with age. The median differences, expressed as percent of average daily caloric intake calculated from the nutrition history, were as follows:

Variation in Caloric Intake in Four Days

	Male		Female	
Age (Years)	Median Difference	Percent of Calorie Intake	Median Difference	Percent of Calorie Intake
0 - 0.5	83	16	100	17
0.5 - 1	155	18	162	20
1 - 2	301	26	289	24
2 - 4	465	30	385	30
4 - 6	478	28	425	29
6 - 8	549	26	542	34
8 - 10	577	23	565	30
10 - 18	659	21	640	30

A notation was made by mother or subject on each 24-hour record of whether it was considered usual or more or less than usual. This frequently disagreed with the relative level of calorie content. Other nutrients, when occasionally calculated, tended to be equally variable. Therefore, even as a cross-check, which was its sole use in this study, the 24-hour intake was of limited value.

Errors in the food values used, whether from published tables or other sources, were unavoidable. Except for the fat and vitamin content of dairy products, no figures were available for analysis of foods sold in Denver. The use of a single table for all calculations was adopted at the start of this study in an effort to keep food value errors as constant as possible.

The permanence of the senior nutritionist and the intensive training of all assistants maintained relative standardization of techniques in history-taking and data analysis. Differences in results due to change in personnel were kept to a minimum.

Statistical Summaries, Tables and Graphs

The data in Tables D-1 through D-24 were selected for the widest representative use. Since the number of cases for each age and sex was constant, these numbers appear in Tables D-1 and D-2; thereafter they are repeated for clarity only for nutrients which have a second N to indicate the number of subjects taking supplements. Supplements of calcium and phosphorus were not included because the largest N at any age was 5.

Because the distribution of total intake of any nutrient tended to be skewed to the right, percentiles were used consistently. However, means and standard deviations were also included for intake of total calories and total protein for comparison with studies in which these statistical values are used. Because derived data tended to be normally distributed, means and standard deviations were used for ratio of calcium to phosphorus and for percent of vitamin A from plant sources. For derived values which showed no significant change during some age periods, arrows have been used where appropriate, as in percent of calories from carbohydrate, fat and protein and in thiamine as mg per 1000 calories. Values for total calories and vitamins A and D have been rounded to the nearest 5 units.

Age ranges were selected primarily on the basis of rapidity of change in intake. Monthly values were used in the first 6 months of life. Although histories were taken at monthly intervals between 6 and 12 months of age after 1951, 3-month averages were used in the tables because the inclusion of all data from 1946 increased the number of cases. Between 1 and 4 years of age the 3-month time interval was maintained because of irregularity of intake of some nutrients during the preschool period(4). After 4 years changes in intake were gradual, so two succeeding 3-month levels of intake were averaged to give a single value for each 6 months, with the mid-point of each interval at the birthday or half-birthday. Data on males were limited to 17 years and on females to 18 years because the number of subjects with nutrition data beyond those ages was too small to be meaningful.

No consistent sex differences were found in percentile levels of total intake of ascorbic acid or vitamins A and D (Tables D-14 through D-18). However, all other nutrients showed sex differences in total intake which became progressively more divergent with age (Figures D-1 through D-5). By 17 years the medians of females tended to be close to the 10th percentiles of males, and the medians of males were usually between the 75th and 90th percentiles of females. Males tended to have a wider range of intakes (Figure D-4). When weight or height was used as a factor in the calculation, sex differences were less pronounced. After 4 years of age, the percentile levels of intake per kilogram of body weight for females were parallel to but lower than those for males (Figures D-1 and D-3).

REFERENCES

1. Beal, V.A.: The nutritional history in longitudinal research. J Amer Diet Ass, 51:426, 1967.
2. Burke, B.S.: The dietary history as a tool in research. J Amer Diet Ass, 23:1041, 1947.
3. Beal, V.A.: Breast- and formula-feeding of infants. J Amer Diet Ass, 55:31, 1969.
4. Beal, V.A.: On the acceptance of solid foods and other food patterns of infants and children. Pediatrics, 20:448, 1957.

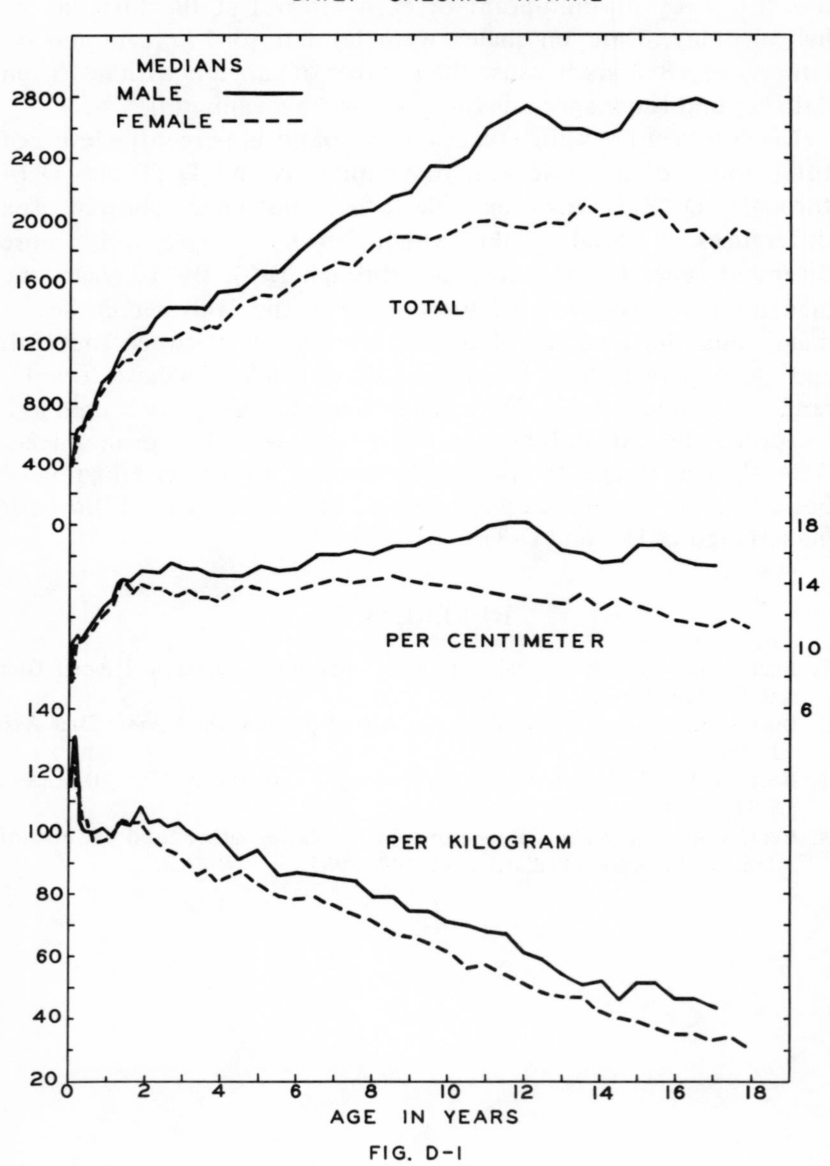
DAILY CALORIE INTAKE
MEDIANS
MALE
FEMALE
2800
2400
2000
1600
1200
800
400
0
TOTAL
18
14
10
6
PER CENTIMETER
140
120
100
80
60
40
20
PER KILOGRAM
0 2 4 6 8 10 12 14 16 18
AGE IN YEARS

FIG. D-1

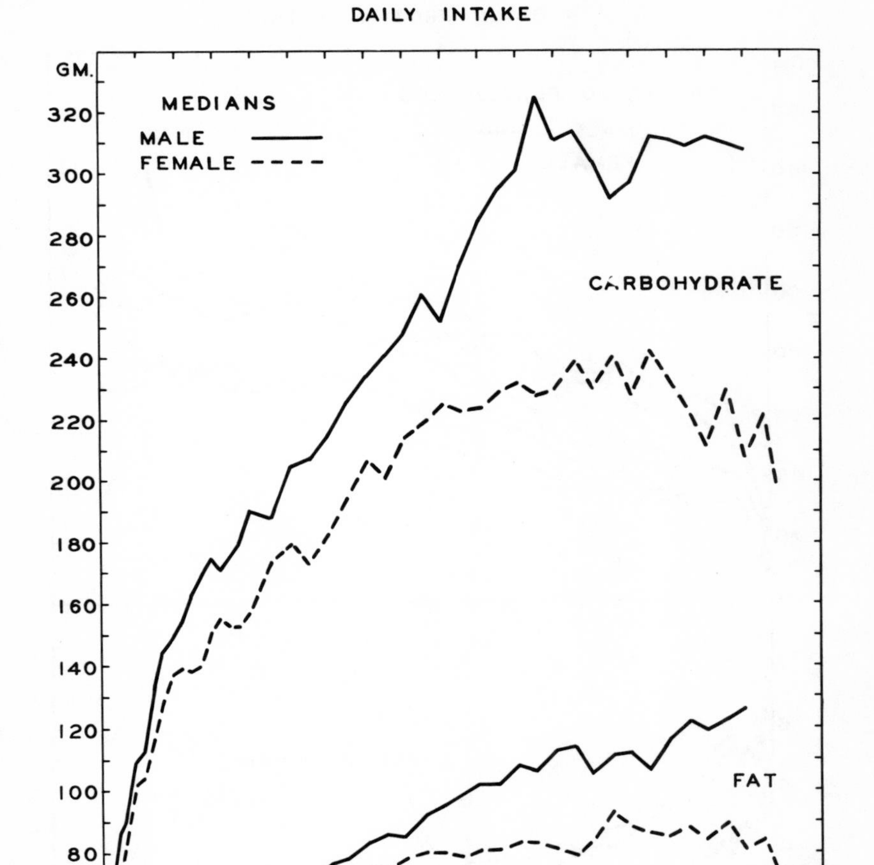
DAILY INTAKE
GM.
MEDIANS
MALE
FEMALE
CARBOHYDRATE
FAT
0
20
40
60
80
100
120
140
160
180
200
220
240
260
280
300
320
0
2
4
6
8
10
12
14
16
18
AGE IN YEARS

FIG. D-2

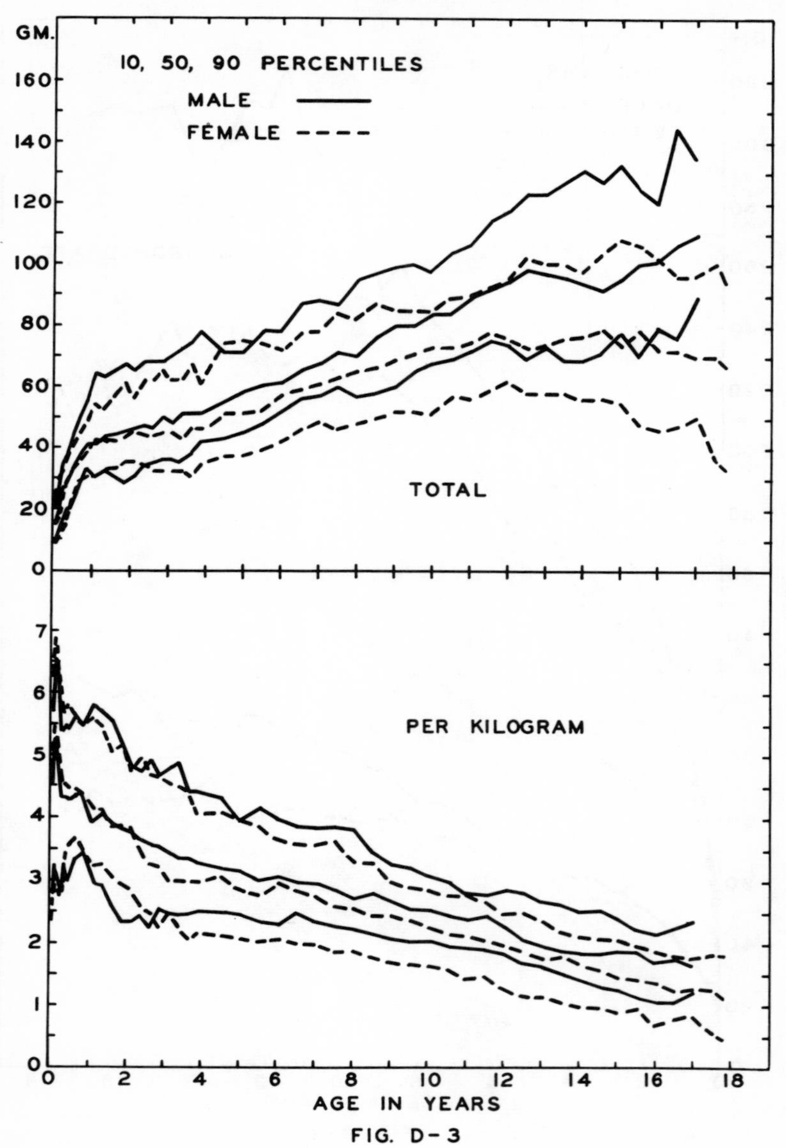

AGE IN YEARS

FIG. D-3

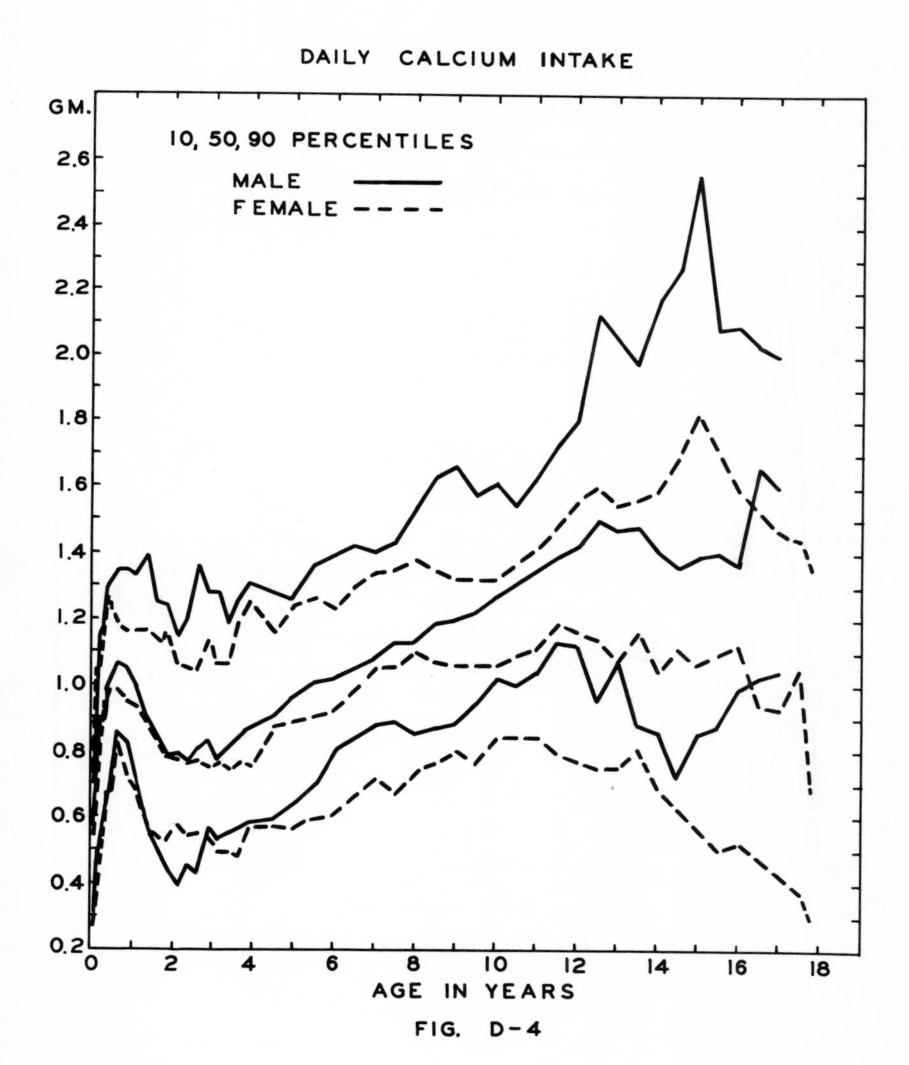
DAILY CALCIUM INTAKE
GM.
10, 50, 90 PERCENTILES
MALE
FEMALE
2.6
2.4
2.2
2.0
1.8
1.6
1.4
1.2
1.0
0.8
0.6
0.4
0.2
0
2
4
6
8
10
12
14
16
18
AGE IN YEARS

FIG. D-4

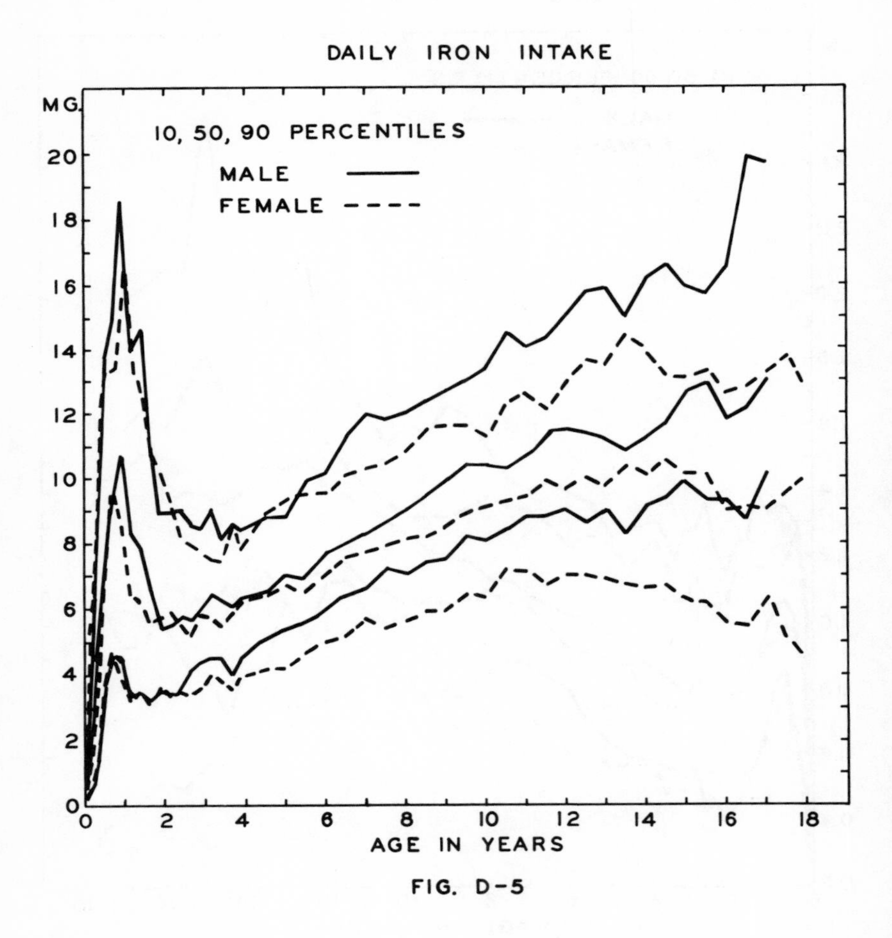
DAILY IRON INTAKE
MG.
10, 50, 90 PERCENTILES
MALE
FEMALE
20
18
16
14
12
10
8
6
4
2
0
0
2
4
6
8
10
12
14
16
18
AGE IN YEARS

FIG. D-5

NUTRITION

TABLE D-1

Daily Calorie Intake - Male

Age Range	N	Total Calories							Calories/kg. Wt.			Calories/cm. Ht.		
				Percentiles					Percentiles			Percentiles		
Yr. Mo.		Mean	S.D.	10th	25th	50th	75th	90th	10th	50th	90th	10th	50th	90th
0-0 to 0-1	33	405	110	275	315	400	480	580	88	115	150	5.7	7.7	10.7
0-1 to 0-2	39	575	86	465	515	565	635	680	108	131	157	8.7	10.3	12.0
0-2 to 0-3	42	630	107	505	545	625	715	795	93	116	139	8.4	10.8	13.3
0-3 to 0-4	44	655	97	550	590	640	715	785	90	103	124	9.1	10.4	12.7
0-4 to 0-5	46	710	124	550	625	675	810	885	88	101	122	8.9	10.5	13.5
0-5 to 0-6	45	760	138	615	670	740	850	960	81	100	122	9.4	11.0	14.3
0-6 to 0-9	46	845	135	710	760	820	895	1020	82	100	123	10.1	11.8	14.5
0-9 to 1-0	49	985	196	795	845	925	1070	1230	81	101	137	10.6	12.5	17.7
1-0 to 1-3	47	1060	277	745	845	990	1240	1430	71	98	138	9.6	13.0	19.2
1-3 to 1-6	46	1165	276	850	935	1135	1350	1480	78	103	136	10.6	14.3	18.6
1-6 to 1-9	45	1215	271	855	1000	1220	1425	1565	75	102	136	10.3	14.3	19.0
1-9 to 2-0	44	1260	265	895	1050	1255	1415	1560	73	108	127	10.6	14.9	18.2
2-0 to 2-3	45	1320	298	965	1135	1290	1475	1705	75	103	135	10.8	14.8	19.2
2-3 to 2-6	44	1385	294	1055	1205	1375	1560	1840	81	104	136	11.6	14.8	20.6
2-6 to 2-9	45	1420	312	1050	1150	1435	1625	1850	73	102	129	11.4	15.4	20.0
2-9 to 3-0	43	1480	286	1175	1275	1430	1635	1975	78	103	129	12.1	15.2	20.0
3-0 to 3-3	39	1485	334	1100	1260	1430	1635	1980	72	100	132	11.3	15.1	20.4
3-3 to 3-6	39	1525	336	1180	1275	1430	1755	2050	76	98	132	11.9	15.1	19.8
3-6 to 3-9	40	1535	405	1060	1210	1430	1820	2100	68	98	131	10.7	14.7	20.8
3-9 to 4-0	39	1575	366	1235	1355	1520	1755	2025	74	99	125	12.3	14.6	20.4
4-3 to 4-9	40	1630	347	1270	1345	1540	1875	2110	73	91	120	11.9	14.6	20.3
4-9 to 5-3	38	1700	343	1280	1470	1655	1900	2090	70	94	116	12.0	15.2	19.5
5-3 to 5-9	38	1755	370	1355	1480	1655	1970	2270	69	86	122	12.1	15.0	20.3
5-9 to 6-3	37	1870	378	1505	1645	1780	2035	2395	68	87	117	12.8	15.1	20.5
6-3 to 6-9	36	1940	393	1535	1650	1880	2100	2535	65	86	116	12.6	16.0	21.4
6-9 to 7-3	35	2035	449	1575	1695	1980	2340	2670	63	85	114	12.7	16.0	22.3
7-3 to 7-9	32	2105	432	1600	1745	2045	2420	2720	61	84	114	12.8	16.3	22.2
7-9 to 8-3	34	2150	447	1670	1800	2055	2445	2860	61	79	109	13.0	16.1	22.6
8-3 to 8-9	32	2230	480	1660	1820	2145	2550	2885	59	79	102	12.5	16.6	22.1
8-9 to 9-3	31	2255	501	1640	1850	2175	2570	2975	56	74	98	12.2	16.6	22.4
9-3 to 9-9	32	2345	448	1795	1990	2345	2635	2985	54	74	95	12.6	17.1	22.2
9-9 to 10-3	31	2420	530	1790	1985	2330	2745	3145	54	71	98	12.9	16.8	22.4
10-3 to 10-9	29	2470	491	1915	2045	2400	2805	3210	53	70	94	13.2	17.1	22.4
10-9 to 11-3	28	2560	456	1915	2275	2590	2860	3100	53	68	86	13.0	17.9	21.9
11-3 to 11-9	29	2630	477	1975	2225	2660	3025	3175	51	67	84	13.3	18.1	22.2
11-9 to 12-3	29	2720	570	2035	2275	2730	2985	3550	49	61	89	13.0	18.1	23.0
12-3 to 12-9	28	2715	604	1960	2275	2675	3075	3560	44	59	86	12.4	17.3	23.0
12-9 to 13-3	27	2665	614	1980	2175	2580	3025	3585	42	54	81	12.8	16.2	22.4
13-3 to 13-9	25	2640	594	1935	2140	2575	2970	3425	40	51	79	12.4	16.1	21.3
13-9 to 14-3	23	2660	663	1955	2155	2530	2885	3715	38	52	74	11.7	15.5	22.0
14-3 to 14-9	20	2640	660	1830	2285	2585	2975	3485	35	46	72	11.1	15.6	22.1
14-9 to 15-3	15	2715	591	1955	2290	2760	3085	3450	31	51	66	11.4	16.6	21.1
15-3 to 15-9	15	2740	679	1865	2215	2755	3365	3525	29	51	66	10.7	16.6	21.3
15-9 to 16-3	16	2720	630	1925	2225	2755	3135	3360	28	46	65	11.2	15.7	20.5
16-3 to 16-9	13	2795	696	2060	2410	2785	3080	3300	28	46	64	11.4	15.4	20.2
16-9 to 17-3	10	2830	627	2205	2440	2745	3110	3990	31	44	60	12.3	15.3	22.5

NUTRITION

TABLE D-2

Daily Calorie Intake - Female

Age Range Yr. Mo.	N	Total Calories							Calories/kg. Wt.			Calories/cm. Ht.		
				Percentiles					Percentiles			Percentiles		
		Mean	S.D.	10th	25th	50th	75th	90th	10th	50th	90th	10th	50th	90th
0-0 to 0-1	23	385	86	290	310	375	440	510	84	115	144	5.8	7.7	9.7
0-1 to 0-2	30	530	105	415	445	510	580	700	100	131	160	7.6	9.6	13.0
0-2 to 0-3	32	565	90	455	510	580	645	675	98	115	133	8.0	10.1	11.4
0-3 to 0-4	34	620	84	515	575	615	665	730	97	111	130	8.8	10.5	12.1
0-4 to 0-5	37	665	85	540	615	675	725	775	89	104	120	8.8	10.7	12.5
0-5 to 0-6	38	715	93	610	635	690	770	840	89	104	127	9.6	10.8	12.7
0-6 to 0-9	41	770	122	620	690	760	825	915	76	97	122	9.2	11.1	14.3
0-9 to 1-0	44	885	149	705	755	890	950	1125	80	97	129	9.8	12.0	15.8
1-0 to 1-3	45	985	216	720	820	980	1095	1245	79	98	136	9.9	12.7	17.2
1-3 to 1-6	45	1080	212	810	880	1075	1250	1355	79	104	139	10.4	14.2	17.7
1-6 to 1-9	44	1140	214	915	970	1080	1290	1430	79	103	135	11.0	13.4	17.7
1-9 to 2-0	45	1195	215	945	1015	1165	1330	1485	78	103	134	11.1	14.0	17.7
2-0 to 2-3	47	1230	248	945	1075	1200	1330	1545	78	99	135	11.0	13.8	17.8
2-3 to 2-6	48	1235	232	945	1070	1210	1375	1515	75	96	131	10.8	13.8	17.3
2-6 to 2-9	46	1245	261	970	1095	1210	1345	1585	74	94	124	10.6	13.4	17.5
2-9 to 3-0	45	1300	296	990	1125	1250	1460	1765	72	93	124	10.6	13.3	19.0
3-0 to 3-3	44	1315	271	955	1125	1290	1475	1640	68	90	126	10.5	13.7	18.0
3-3 to 3-6	44	1325	257	1010	1105	1280	1465	1705	68	86	120	10.5	13.2	17.8
3-6 to 3-9	45	1340	290	960	1175	1290	1525	1720	62	87	119	9.4	13.2	17.8
3-9 to 4-0	43	1370	276	1070	1175	1285	1590	1740	65	84	117	10.5	12.9	17.6
4-3 to 4-9	42	1490	300	1090	1295	1445	1715	1915	63	87	116	10.6	13.8	18.4
4-9 to 5-3	41	1515	330	1130	1290	1505	1735	1980	58	83	107	10.6	13.7	18.3
5-3 to 5-9	41	1555	328	1155	1325	1505	1740	2090	59	79	108	10.6	13.3	18.5
5-9 to 6-3	40	1625	321	1180	1405	1605	1830	2070	55	78	106	10.4	13.7	18.3
6-3 to 6-9	41	1720	374	1290	1470	1660	1965	2255	59	79	108	11.0	14.0	19.3
6-9 to 7-3	42	1780	382	1380	1500	1710	2005	2360	57	76	102	11.3	14.4	19.6
7-3 to 7-9	41	1785	381	1350	1495	1700	2060	2280	51	73	97	10.8	14.1	18.7
7-9 to 8-3	41	1835	382	1360	1515	1830	2070	2365	51	71	95	10.7	14.3	18.8
8-3 to 8-9	39	1870	386	1360	1545	1885	2170	2375	48	67	90	10.3	14.6	18.1
8-9 to 9-3	41	1875	382	1305	1595	1880	2130	2335	44	66	86	9.8	14.2	18.2
9-3 to 9-9	37	1895	361	1385	1645	1870	2145	2350	43	64	83	10.2	14.0	17.5
9-9 to 10-3	35	1950	381	1435	1720	1900	2165	2455	42	61	80	10.4	13.9	18.0
10-3 to 10-9	35	1995	409	1470	1690	1975	2190	2545	41	56	81	10.7	13.7	18.0
10-9 to 11-3	35	2000	460	1445	1640	1990	2250	2560	34	57	78	9.8	13.5	18.4
11-3 to 11-9	33	2025	418	1530	1755	1955	2305	2575	34	54	75	10.1	13.3	18.1
11-9 to 12-3	30	2020	459	1455	1650	1950	2270	2610	31	51	71	9.6	13.0	17.9
12-3 to 12-9	30	2085	533	1465	1700	1985	2475	2945	29	48	71	9.6	12.9	19.1
12-9 to 13-3	30	2105	545	1435	1695	1980	2650	2865	27	47	67	9.1	12.8	18.3
13-3 to 13-9	26	2150	596	1430	1665	2100	2640	2945	26	47	66	8.7	13.4	18.7
13-9 to 14-3	26	2050	575	1405	1595	2025	2365	2815	24	42	57	8.4	12.4	17.4
14-3 to 14-9	25	2145	612	1375	1635	2045	2600	3025	25	40	63	8.5	13.1	18.4
14-9 to 15-3	24	2080	631	1310	1600	2000	2465	3055	22	39	60	7.7	12.6	18.2
15-3 to 15-9	21	2115	663	1230	1640	2060	2560	3025	22	37	58	7.4	12.2	17.7
15-9 to 16-3	18	2030	682	1100	1520	1915	2535	3050	19	35	55	7.4	11.6	17.6
16-3 to 16-9	18	1980	647	1145	1460	1925	2455	2905	20	35	52	6.9	11.5	16.8
16-9 to 17-3	18	1930	614	1185	1455	1820	2485	2825	20	33	48	7.3	11.2	15.8
17-3 to 17-9	16	1890	749	985	1270	1935	2475	2855	14	34	51	6.3	11.7	16.5
17-9 to 18-0	14	1745	737	810	1090	1850	2395	2645	12	31	47	4.9	11.3	15.4

NUTRITION

TABLE D-3

Daily Carbohydrate Intake - Male

Age Range	Gm. Total					Percent of Cals.			Gm./kg. Wt.			Gm./cm. Ht.		
	Percentiles						Range		Percentiles			Percentiles		
Yr. Mo.	10th	25th	50th	75th	90th	Med.	Min.	Max.	10th	50th	90th	10th	50th	90th
0-0 to 0-1	25	32	39	51	59	41	28	63	8.1	12.2	15.6	0.49	0.78	1.09
0-1 to 0-2	44	51	60	69	75	43	28	54	9.9	13.7	18.5	0.85	1.07	1.35
0-2 to 0-3	49	55	66	78	93	44	28	56	9.1	12.5	16.5	0.84	1.15	1.59
0-3 to 0-4	55	62	69	84	99	45	29	58	9.2	11.7	14.9	0.91	1.10	1.54
0-4 to 0-5	58	68	78	90	104	46	31	78	9.0	11.7	15.8	0.93	1.21	1.66
0-5 to 0-6	68	77	87	99	117	46	32	78	9.0	11.5	15.6	1.00	1.33	1.77
0-6 to 0-9	72	81	91	103	130	45	33	74	8.5	11.4	14.3	1.03	1.36	1.87
0-9 to 1-0	85	96	109	133	151	46	34	74	8.8	11.7	15.9	1.14	1.49	1.99
1-0 to 1-3	87	98	113	145	174	45	39	58	8.3	11.2	16.4	1.13	1.49	2.38
1-3 to 1-6	98	107	133	176	194	47	38	63	8.5	12.4	16.9	1.23	1.66	2.39
1-6 to 1-9	102	116	145	173	194	46	40	64	8.8	12.3	16.9	1.21	1.74	2.35
1-9 to 2-0	109	125	149	175	201	47	39	65	8.7	12.5	16.6	1.30	1.74	2.40
2-0 to 2-3	115	132	154	182	233	48	40	61	8.8	12.3	17.7	1.33	1.77	2.70
2-3 to 2-6	123	140	163	192	235	48.5	39	64	9.0	12.2	16.9	1.37	1.81	2.48
2-6 to 2-9	124	141	169	212	230		38	63	8.8	12.6	17.1	1.31	1.86	2.51
2-9 to 3-0	136	151	175	211	225		38	57	9.2	12.5	15.8	1.40	1.84	2.40
3-0 to 3-3	129	154	171	205	230		37	58	8.3	12.2	15.8	1.32	1.76	2.43
3-3 to 3-6	137	154	175	213	249		36	59	9.0	12.0	15.6	1.40	1.81	2.52
3-6 to 3-9	126	145	180	219	262		35	59	8.0	12.6	15.9	1.28	1.83	2.58
3-9 to 4-0	140	166	190	215	269		38	63	9.0	11.9	15.6	1.41	1.81	2.58
4-3 to 4-9	148	168	188	230	266		39	57	8.6	11.3	15.0	1.42	1.78	2.51
4-9 to 5-3	158	170	205	232	282		40	60	8.4	11.1	15.1	1.44	1.86	2.59
5-3 to 5-9	153	179	207	235	287		37	56	8.0	10.5	15.2	1.43	1.83	2.56
5-9 to 6-3	172	190	215	252	310		36	57	7.7	10.6	14.7	1.47	1.85	2.66
6-3 to 6-9	164	197	226	262	319		33	57	7.4	10.5	14.5	1.38	1.86	2.65
6-9 to 7-3	165	197	234	290	338		36	58	7.1	10.0	14.7	1.34	1.91	2.78
7-3 to 7-9	190	207	241	302	342		34	58	7.2	9.9	14.4	1.52	1.94	2.80
7-9 to 8-3	189	214	248	300	361		38	56	6.9	9.6	13.1	1.47	1.94	2.91
8-3 to 8-9	201	223	261	309	354		37	58	6.9	9.8	13.2	1.47	2.00	2.75
8-9 to 9-3	191	217	252	326	372		37	60	6.3	8.8	12.7	1.43	1.86	2.82
9-3 to 9-9	216	238	271	332	387		38	58	6.3	9.2	12.6	1.54	2.01	2.90
9-9 to 10-3	196	233	285	346	407		38	57	5.8	9.1	12.4	1.43	2.03	2.98
10-3 to 10-9	219	247	295	344	410		39	57	6.1	8.4	11.6	1.56	2.10	2.86
10-9 to 11-3	236	258	311	352	406		39	59	5.9	8.1	11.3	1.62	2.17	2.78
11-3 to 11-9	234	264	325	375	406		38	61	5.6	8.1	10.6	1.54	2.13	2.88
11-9 to 12-3	243	272	311	384	441		39	60	5.4	7.6	11.1	1.56	2.12	2.95
12-3 to 12-9	229	271	314	390	447		40	58	5.0	7.2	11.3	1.46	2.02	2.89
12-9 to 13-3	235	266	304	365	432	48.5	40	59	4.8	6.5	10.6	1.50	1.95	2.72
13-3 to 13-9	229	246	292	349	405	46	37	59	4.3	6.3	10.3	1.39	1.88	2.61
13-9 to 14-3	216	253	297	344	437		36	56	4.1	6.1	8.6	1.29	1.83	2.59
14-3 to 14-9	203	252	312	365	414		37	56	3.5	5.9	8.8	1.21	1.86	2.51
14-9 to 15-3	220	256	311	370	415		38	56	3.6	5.6	8.1	1.28	1.88	2.44
15-3 to 15-9	208	255	309	374	419		38	58	3.4	5.7	7.6	1.19	1.82	2.54
15-9 to 16-3	213	251	312	347	434		39	56	2.8	5.4	7.6	1.20	1.81	2.57
16-3 to 16-9	228	260	310	366	421		37	58	3.4	4.9	7.6	1.29	1.72	2.48
16-9 to 17-3	227	253	308	365	433	46	37	51	3.0	4.9	6.7	1.26	1.72	2.46

NUTRITION

TABLE D-4

Daily Carbohydrate Intake - Female

Age Range	Gm. Total					Percent of Cals.			Gm./kg. Wt.			Gm./cm. Ht.		
	Percentiles						Range		Percentiles			Percentiles		
Yr. Mo.	10th	25th	50th	75th	90th	Med.	Min.	Max.	10th	50th	90th	10th	50th	90th
0-0 to 0-1	25	33	37	50	57	42	28	52	8.8	11.5	15.4	0.59	0.77	1.10
0-1 to 0-2	37	43	50	64	78	41	28	64	9.9	13.3	18.6	0.66	0.95	1.48
0-2 to 0-3	40	52	59	71	86	43	28	60	8.2	12.5	15.7	0.69	1.03	1.47
0-3 to 0-4	47	56	66	78	93	44	27	59	8.5	11.9	15.4	0.80	1.10	1.60
0-4 to 0-5	54	58	69	82	92	42	30	58	8.4	10.7	15.4	0.90	1.09	1.49
0-5 to 0-6	56	63	75	90	98	43	30	60	8.0	10.9	14.8	0.87	1.16	1.61
0-6 to 0-9	64	72	84	94	112	44	35	65	8.1	10.8	15.2	0.95	1.21	1.62
0-9 to 1-0	76	84	102	117	128	46	29	61	7.8	11.4	15.2	1.04	1.40	1.84
1-0 to 1-3	76	85	104	124	140	45	30	52	7.9	10.9	15.2	1.03	1.37	1.92
1-3 to 1-6	86	97	117	140	162	45	33	56	8.5	11.0	16.0	1.12	1.47	2.14
1-6 to 1-9	91	101	129	158	178	46	35	60	8.1	11.8	16.7	1.15	1.60	2.22
1-9 to 2-0	104	116	137	158	186	45	34	64	8.8	11.6	16.3	1.24	1.66	2.20
2-0 to 2-3	98	112	139	162	181	46	33	55	7.8	11.1	16.0	1.11	1.59	2.11
2-3 to 2-6	107	117	138	159	183	46	36	54	8.0	11.9	15.2	1.17	1.56	2.09
2-6 to 2-9	108	128	140	160	201	48	35	61	7.9	10.7	15.6	1.23	1.53	2.21
2-9 to 3-0	117	127	151	183	217		32	65	7.9	11.1	15.2	1.15	1.57	2.22
3-0 to 3-3	108	131	155	178	206		34	53	7.6	10.8	15.6	1.15	1.62	2.22
3-3 to 3-6	118	135	153	177	222		31	61	7.3	10.6	15.5	1.24	1.60	2.31
3-6 to 3-9	107	138	153	190	213		28	64	6.9	10.5	14.5	1.11	1.56	2.19
3-9 to 4-0	116	136	157	200	221		36	57	7.1	10.1	14.5	1.14	1.56	2.23
4-3 to 4-9	130	151	173	208	233		32	57	7.1	10.4	14.2	1.24	1.62	2.27
4-9 to 5-3	126	151	179	209	242		32	57	6.9	9.9	13.0	1.19	1.63	2.22
5-3 to 5-9	137	155	173	213	245		34	57	6.9	9.5	12.8	1.22	1.59	2.21
5-9 to 6-3	146	166	183	226	261		36	57	6.7	9.5	12.7	1.24	1.62	2.19
6-3 to 6-9	149	170	194	241	282		38	57	6.7	9.4	13.2	1.34	1.66	2.38
6-9 to 7-3	155	178	206	240	291		38	57	6.7	9.1	12.2	1.32	1.70	2.36
7-3 to 7-9	156	172	201	245	278		37	54	6.1	8.5	11.7	1.25	1.59	2.24
7-9 to 8-3	162	179	214	252	285		37	56	6.2	8.3	11.2	1.29	1.65	2.24
8-3 to 8-9	149	184	219	255	292		35	54	5.7	7.9	10.6	1.15	1.66	2.20
8-9 to 9-3	145	182	225	257	288		36	56	5.0	7.7	10.4	1.13	1.71	2.19
9-3 to 9-9	159	191	223	264	292	↓	36	57	5.1	7.6	10.3	1.23	1.64	2.23
9-9 to 10-3	166	195	224	272	314	48	34	57	4.9	7.2	10.1	1.23	1.62	2.27
10-3 to 10-9	174	202	229	274	336	47	36	57	4.7	6.6	10.5	1.23	1.61	2.36
10-9 to 11-3	162	189	232	280	346		34	57	4.1	6.5	10.3	1.13	1.58	2.41
11-3 to 11-9	172	205	228	266	331		36	58	4.0	6.0	9.3	1.14	1.56	2.28
11-9 to 12-3	155	197	230	267	351		36	59	3.3	5.5	9.4	1.09	1.50	2.42
12-3 to 12-9	163	207	239	296	364	↓	37	59	3.5	5.7	8.6	1.08	1.55	2.35
12-9 to 13-3	147	196	230	300	359	47	31	56	3.0	5.4	8.2	0.95	1.51	2.23
13-3 to 13-9	160	198	240	304	359	46.5	34	55	2.9	5.4	7.4	0.98	1.51	2.17
13-9 to 14-3	144	186	228	275	347		34	58	2.8	4.7	6.9	0.93	1.42	2.15
14-3 to 14-9	160	187	242	303	365		35	55	2.8	4.7	7.0	0.95	1.46	2.12
14-9 to 15-3	144	190	233	293	351		33	59	2.6	4.4	6.7	0.84	1.46	2.13
15-3 to 15-9	145	180	224	312	384		30	57	2.2	4.4	7.3	0.88	1.39	2.18
15-9 to 16-3	132	166	212	304	385		39	55	2.4	4.0	7.1	0.85	1.32	2.24
16-3 to 16-9	131	175	229	289	354		38	54	2.4	4.1	6.2	0.85	1.34	2.05
16-9 to 17-3	137	160	208	280	332		38	55	2.2	3.7	5.8	0.84	1.23	1.92
17-3 to 17-9	122	139	222	287	320	↓	40	51	1.9	3.7	5.7	0.73	1.34	1.88
17-9 to 18-0	100	122	199	258	304	46.5	40	54	1.4	3.7	5.1	0.66	1.27	1.81

NUTRITION

TABLE D-5

Daily Fat Intake - Male

Age Range	Gm. Total					Percent of Cals.			Gm./kg. Wt.			Gm./cm. Ht.		
	Percentiles						Range		Percentiles			Percentiles		
Yr. Mo.	10th	25th	50th	75th	90th	Med.	Min.	Max.	10th	50th	90th	10th	50th	90th
0-0 to 0-1	12	16	19	24	29	45	22	52	4.1	5.7	7.6	0.27	0.38	0.53
0-1 to 0-2	22	24	27	29	33	42	35	51	5.1	6.2	7.4	0.39	0.48	0.56
0-2 to 0-3	21	24	28	33	35	40	29	52	3.7	5.2	6.5	0.36	0.48	0.58
0-3 to 0-4	21	24	27	32	35	39	27	50	3.4	4.4	5.8	0.36	0.44	0.56
0-4 to 0-5	19	23	27	34	41	37.5	1	51	3.1	4.2	5.5	0.32	0.44	0.58
0-5 to 0-6	22	26	31	36	42		2	50	2.7	4.3	5.4	0.31	0.47	0.58
0-6 to 0-9	23	30	35	38	46		9	49	2.6	4.1	5.6	0.31	0.50	0.65
0-9 to 1-0	24	33	38	46	56		10	47	2.6	4.2	5.5	0.33	0.52	0.75
1-0 to 1-3	28	33	40	50	70		20	44	2.5	4.0	5.8	0.36	0.53	0.90
1-3 to 1-6	31	37	45	53	65		18	47	2.7	4.1	5.8	0.37	0.57	0.81
1-6 to 1-9	32	40	48	60	68		17	44	2.7	4.2	5.9	0.39	0.58	0.83
1-9 to 2-0	35	45	50	57	69		19	46	2.7	4.3	5.6	0.43	0.58	0.81
2-0 to 2-3	36	45	53	62	70		20	45	2.7	4.5	5.8	0.41	0.62	0.79
2-3 to 2-6	41	47	55	65	75		22	44	2.9	4.3	5.5	0.45	0.61	0.83
2-6 to 2-9	40	48	57	68	77		26	45	2.8	4.2	5.5	0.46	0.60	0.84
2-9 to 3-0	46	51	57	69	81		30	45	3.2	4.2	5.7	0.48	0.62	0.89
3-0 to 3-3	43	52	60	71	89		30	46	2.8	4.4	5.7	0.44	0.63	0.90
3-3 to 3-6	46	51	62	77	89		30	46	3.0	4.2	5.9	0.47	0.62	0.91
3-6 to 3-9	39	53	60	73	95		23	46	2.8	4.2	5.8	0.43	0.61	0.94
3-9 to 4-0	44	53	62	76	93		26	45	2.9	3.8	5.5	0.43	0.60	0.91
4-3 to 4-9	47	55	65	77	89		28	46	2.8	3.9	5.3	0.45	0.63	0.86
4-9 to 5-3	53	60	71	82	93		24	46	2.8	4.0	5.0	0.48	0.64	0.84
5-3 to 5-9	54	61	71	86	99		28	47	2.8	3.7	5.0	0.47	0.64	0.87
5-9 to 6-3	58	67	76	90	105		29	48	2.7	3.9	5.0	0.48	0.66	0.90
6-3 to 6-9	61	70	78	96	109		28	51	2.6	3.7	4.9	0.51	0.65	0.90
6-9 to 7-3	64	72	83	103	113		29	49	2.6	3.7	4.7	0.52	0.69	0.94
7-3 to 7-9	65	76	86	100	117		29	49	2.4	3.5	4.7	0.51	0.69	0.92
7-9 to 8-3	67	74	85	110	118		30	46	2.5	3.4	4.6	0.50	0.65	0.94
8-3 to 8-9	67	74	92	116	126		29	45	2.3	3.4	4.5	0.48	0.68	0.95
8-9 to 9-3	65	73	95	113	129		29	45	2.2	3.3	4.2	0.49	0.71	0.95
9-3 to 9-9	67	80	99	111	125		30	45	2.1	3.1	4.1	0.47	0.73	0.94
9-9 to 10-3	76	83	102	115	130		31	45	2.3	3.0	4.2	0.54	0.71	0.97
10-3 to 10-9	77	86	102	119	128		31	45	2.3	2.8	3.9	0.53	0.72	0.92
10-9 to 11-3	77	85	108	119	133		29	44	1.9	2.7	3.7	0.51	0.73	0.91
11-3 to 11-9	79	88	106	129	141		27	45	2.0	2.7	3.7	0.53	0.70	0.97
11-9 to 12-3	78	90	113	130	160		28	45	2.0	2.6	3.8	0.53	0.76	1.03
12-3 to 12-9	72	88	114	135	150		29	45	1.8	2.5	3.7	0.48	0.76	0.98
12-9 to 13-3	76	85	107	135	160	37.5	29	45	1.6	2.2	3.7	0.48	0.69	0.99
13-3 to 13-9	78	90	111	138	156	39	30	46	1.6	2.2	3.5	0.49	0.69	0.97
13-9 to 14-3	81	89	112	135	173		32	47	1.6	2.2	3.2	0.50	0.68	0.99
14-3 to 14-9	74	90	106	131	163		32	46	1.3	1.9	3.0	0.45	0.64	1.00
14-9 to 15-3	82	94	116	139	157		30	46	1.2	2.1	2.9	0.48	0.68	0.96
15-3 to 15-9	72	87	122	139	172		28	46	1.1	2.0	2.9	0.42	0.70	1.00
15-9 to 16-3	79	93	119	138	156		32	46	1.1	1.9	2.7	0.45	0.68	0.88
16-3 to 16-9	79	105	122	137	151		29	47	1.1	2.1	2.6	0.44	0.70	0.86
16-9 to 17-3	98	105	126	136	154	39	35	46	1.4	2.1	2.8	0.54	0.72	1.07

NUTRITION

TABLE D-6

Daily Fat Intake - Female

Age Range	Gm. Total					Percent of Cals.			Gm./kg. Wt.			Gm./cm. Ht.		
	Percentiles						Range		Percentiles			Percentiles		
Yr. Mo.	10th	25th	50th	75th	90th	Med.	Min.	Max.	10th	50th	90th	10th	50th	90th
0-0 to 0-1	12	15	18	20	24	44	22	52	3.5	5.4	6.8	0.25	0.37	0.49
0-1 to 0-2	18	22	24	27	31	43	23	51	4.6	5.8	7.5	0.32	0.45	0.58
0-2 to 0-3	19	23	25	29	31	41	23	51	4.0	5.3	6.2	0.29	0.45	0.55
0-3 to 0-4	18	24	27	30	33		22	51	3.4	4.9	6.2	0.30	0.47	0.58
0-4 to 0-5	22	25	30	32	38		25	50	3.4	4.7	5.8	0.34	0.47	0.62
0-5 to 0-6	22	27	32	35	39	41	22	50	3.2	4.6	5.6	0.34	0.48	0.61
0-6 to 0-9	14	28	33	37	39	39	11	45	1.6	4.1	5.0	0.20	0.49	0.57
0-9 to 1-0	25	30	36	41	45		14	51	2.9	3.8	5.5	0.36	0.49	0.65
1-0 to 1-3	30	35	41	49	56		22	50	3.1	4.2	6.2	0.39	0.54	0.76
1-3 to 1-6	31	38	46	57	60		26	50	2.9	4.5	6.3	0.39	0.59	0.80
1-6 to 1-9	36	43	48	53	57		28	49	3.2	4.4	5.8	0.44	0.59	0.74
1-9 to 2-0	36	44	51	60	67		24	48	3.0	4.5	6.0	0.43	0.61	0.80
2-0 to 2-3	41	46	52	61	69		27	49	3.3	4.4	6.1	0.47	0.60	0.79
2-3 to 2-6	39	46	53	60	70		29	48	2.9	4.3	5.9	0.43	0.60	0.83
2-6 to 2-9	39	46	54	60	69	39	26	47	2.7	4.2	5.2	0.41	0.59	0.74
2-9 to 3-0	40	46	54	63	76	38	22	46	2.7	4.1	5.8	0.42	0.59	0.86
3-0 to 3-3	40	46	53	64	72		28	48	2.8	4.0	5.4	0.43	0.57	0.75
3-3 to 3-6	42	46	55	62	76		30	48	2.8	3.7	5.2	0.44	0.56	0.76
3-6 to 3-9	36	48	54	63	73		24	51	2.4	3.7	5.1	0.37	0.55	0.77
3-9 to 4-0	43	50	55	65	75		30	47	2.7	3.7	4.9	0.41	0.55	0.74
4-3 to 4-9	43	56	62	73	83		29	48	2.5	3.8	5.0	0.41	0.60	0.81
4-9 to 5-3	47	54	63	73	84		28	48	2.4	3.5	4.6	0.41	0.58	0.78
5-3 to 5-9	44	56	66	77	87		28	47	2.3	3.5	4.6	0.41	0.59	0.79
5-9 to 6-3	49	59	66	80	89		29	49	2.3	3.4	4.6	0.43	0.60	0.78
6-3 to 6-9	50	63	71	81	96		29	45	2.3	3.4	4.8	0.41	0.60	0.83
6-9 to 7-3	53	63	74	84	102		30	45	2.3	3.3	4.5	0.44	0.62	0.85
7-3 to 7-9	53	62	75	90	102		31	45	2.1	3.2	4.3	0.43	0.61	0.81
7-9 to 8-3	54	63	78	94	103		28	45	2.0	3.0	4.1	0.43	0.62	0.82
8-3 to 8-9	57	67	80	93	107		31	45	1.9	3.0	4.1	0.44	0.62	0.80
8-9 to 9-3	56	65	80	90	102		31	46	1.8	2.9	3.7	0.42	0.62	0.77
9-3 to 9-9	55	68	79	93	102		31	48	1.7	2.7	3.6	0.41	0.59	0.74
9-9 to 10-3	58	69	81	92	106		31	46	1.7	2.6	3.5	0.42	0.57	0.80
10-3 to 10-9	61	72	81	94	109		31	43	1.7	2.4	3.4	0.44	0.57	0.77
10-9 to 11-3	57	68	83	97	111		30	45	1.4	2.4	3.4	0.40	0.58	0.77
11-3 to 11-9	57	72	83	98	113		28	47	1.3	2.4	3.2	0.39	0.57	0.77
11-9 to 12-3	57	67	81	103	110		29	47	1.1	2.2	3.0	0.37	0.55	0.78
12-3 to 12-9	57	65	79	103	126		27	46	1.1	2.0	3.0	0.37	0.53	0.82
12-9 to 13-3	59	68	84	111	127	38	27	54	1.1	2.1	3.0	0.36	0.53	0.82
13-3 to 13-9	56	67	93	114	127	38.5	29	46	1.0	2.1	2.8	0.35	0.58	0.80
13-9 to 14-3	57	71	88	101	125		25	45	0.9	1.8	2.7	0.35	0.53	0.77
14-3 to 14-9	54	69	86	110	139		29	48	1.0	1.8	2.9	0.34	0.54	0.84
14-9 to 15-3	45	69	85	105	137		24	50	0.8	1.7	2.8	0.27	0.52	0.81
15-3 to 15-9	52	68	88	117	127		29	51	0.9	1.6	2.5	0.31	0.52	0.75
15-9 to 16-3	45	58	84	108	127		30	45	0.7	1.5	2.4	0.26	0.51	0.76
16-3 to 16-9	46	56	89	106	125		29	46	0.7	1.6	2.4	0.27	0.52	0.74
16-9 to 17-3	47	55	81	112	120		29	46	0.8	1.4	2.1	0.28	0.48	0.69
17-3 to 17-9	38	51	84	120	133		33	46	0.6	1.4	2.4	0.25	0.48	0.75
17-9 to 18-0	31	44	75	111	124	38.5	28	44	0.5	1.3	2.2	0.19	0.45	0.72

NUTRITION

TABLE D-7

Daily Protein Intake - Male

Age Range Yr. Mo.	Gm. Total							% of Calories			Gm./kg. Wt.			Gm./cm. Ht.			Gm. Animal				
	Mean	S.D.	Percentiles 10th	25th	50th	75th	90th	Med.	Range Min.	Max.	Percentiles 10th	50th	90th	Percentiles 10th	50th	90th	Percentiles 10th	25th	50th	75th	90th
0-0 to 0-1	15	4.5	9	12	15	19	20	16	9	20	2.79	4.54	5.69	0.18	0.28	0.40	9	12	15	18	20
0-1 to 0-2	22	5.4	14	18	23	26	28	16	9	20	3.24	5.29	6.55	0.26	0.42	0.50	13	18	22	25	28
0-2 to 0-3	26	6.4	16	21	27	30	34	16	8	27	3.02	4.97	6.18	0.27	0.44	0.53	14	19	25	29	32
0-3 to 0-4	26	6.5	18	23	26	31	36	16	8	26	2.87	4.31	5.37	0.28	0.42	0.57	14	21	25	28	33
0-4 to 0-5	29	6.8	20	26	29	35	38	17	8	25	3.25	4.31	5.49	0.32	0.45	0.60	15	23	27	32	35
0-5 to 0-6	32	7.6	20	29	32	36	43	17	9	25	2.96	4.29	5.40	0.33	0.47	0.64	18	25	28	33	39
0-6 to 0-9	37	7.1	29	31	36	40	49	18	13	24	3.31	4.36	5.73	0.41	0.51	0.70	25	27	32	34	41
0-9 to 1-0	42	7.5	33	36	41	48	53	17	14	22	3.44	4.37	5.45	0.44	0.55	0.75	26	29	33	40	43
1-0 to 1-3	44	12.3	30	34	41	51	64	16	13	23	2.93	3.91	5.80	0.38	0.54	0.80	22	27	33	42	51
1-3 to 1-6	46	12.0	32	37	44	52	63	16	11	21	2.92	4.06	5.68	0.41	0.55	0.79	22	28	33	43	50
1-6 to 1-9	46	12.9	30	37	44	56	65	15	10	21	2.55	3.90	5.54	0.35	0.52	0.81	21	28	35	43	50
1-9 to 2-0	46	12.9	28	38	45	54	67	15	9	19	2.35	3.87	5.21	0.33	0.53	0.77	21	29	35	43	52
2-0 to 2-3	47	13.6	30	38	46	55	63	14	8	20	2.34	3.78	4.79	0.35	0.53	0.75	20	26	34	44	52
2-3 to 2-6	49	13.6	34	40	47	56	68		10	20	2.44	3.62	4.70	0.37	0.52	0.75	24	29	35	45	52
2-6 to 2-9	50	14.0	35	41	46	59	68		9	18	2.22	3.58	4.94	0.37	0.51	0.75	22	29	36	44	57
2-9 to 3-0	51	12.3	36	42	50	59	68		9	18	2.51	3.55	4.63	0.37	0.53	0.71	25	31	38	45	53
3-0 to 3-3	52	14.1	36	41	48	61	70		10	19	2.43	3.42	4.76	0.36	0.51	0.71	24	29	37	48	59
3-3 to 3-6	52	14.1	35	41	51	58	72		10	19	2.42	3.34	4.86	0.36	0.51	0.72	25	31	36	45	58
3-6 to 3-9	53	14.4	38	44	51	59	74		10	19	2.44	3.34	4.40	0.40	0.50	0.73	26	32	38	44	57
3-9 to 4-0	54	13.7	42	46	51	58	78		10	18	2.50	3.27	4.40	0.40	0.50	0.76	28	31	39	46	62
4-3 to 4-9	56	11.7	43	48	55	63	71		11	17	2.49	3.19	4.30	0.40	0.53	0.69	30	34	41	48	54
4-9 to 5-3	58	11.2	45	49	58	63	71		11	17	2.47	3.14	3.92	0.40	0.53	0.63	33	36	42	47	53
5-3 to 5-9	61	12.9	48	52	60	67	78		11	17	2.35	3.00	4.10	0.41	0.52	0.69	34	39	44	49	59
5-9 to 6-3	63	11.2	52	56	61	68	78		11	16	2.30	3.03	3.96	0.44	0.52	0.67	38	41	45	51	61
6-3 to 6-9	68	11.3	56	60	65	72	87		11	20	2.48	2.98	3.87	0.47	0.54	0.72	40	44	48	54	65
6-9 to 7-3	70	12.5	57	61	67	77	88		11	21	2.32	2.96	3.82	0.47	0.55	0.73	41	44	50	58	67
7-3 to 7-9	73	12.6	60	63	71	80	87		11	19	2.28	2.85	3.85	0.47	0.55	0.73	43	46	52	59	70
7-9 to 8-3	74	14.9	57	62	70	86	95		11	19	2.21	2.70	3.80	0.44	0.54	0.76	41	45	52	64	73
8-3 to 8-9	77	15.2	58	66	76	89	97		11	21	2.12	2.78	3.47	0.43	0.57	0.77	41	48	55	65	77
8-9 to 9-3	80	15.5	60	69	80	90	99		12	22	2.08	2.68	3.25	0.43	0.59	0.75	40	50	58	68	79
9-3 to 9-9	82	13.9	65	72	80	87	100		12	22	2.01	2.55	3.20	0.46	0.58	0.79	45	53	60	68	78
9-9 to 10-3	85	13.6	68	75	84	92	98		12	21	2.03	2.53	3.08	0.48	0.59	0.72	48	55	63	70	77
10-3 to 10-9	86	13.2	69	76	84	97	104		12	18	1.93	2.42	2.97	0.48	0.58	0.75	48	55	64	70	79
10-9 to 11-3	88	13.6	72	79	89	99	106		11	18	1.91	2.39	2.79	0.48	0.60	0.74	47	57	63	75	85
11-3 to 11-9	93	14.7	75	80	92	103	114		11	19	1.90	2.41	2.76	0.50	0.62	0.78	49	60	68	78	87
11-9 to 12-3	95	17.1	74	83	94	107	117		11	17	1.84	2.27	2.83	0.49	0.62	0.78	49	60	72	81	90
12-3 to 12-9	97	19.6	69	83	98	109	123	14	11	21	1.68	2.08	2.80	0.46	0.64	0.78	46	61	74	84	93
12-9 to 13-3	97	20.3	73	80	97	109	123	15	11	18	1.61	1.97	2.68	0.45	0.62	0.77	44	60	74	84	90
13-3 to 13-9	96	20.8	69	82	96	105	127		11	18	1.52	1.87	2.61	0.44	0.61	0.76	44	62	73	83	88
13-9 to 14-3	97	22.6	69	81	94	108	131		11	19	1.39	1.82	2.50	0.42	0.58	0.79	48	59	75	85	97
14-3 to 14-9	97	20.9	71	82	92	109	127		11	19	1.30	1.82	2.51	0.44	0.57	0.78	42	60	74	87	95
14-9 to 15-3	102	20.6	78	86	95	117	133		12	19	1.26	1.87	2.40	0.47	0.57	0.78	37	65	78	89	101
15-3 to 15-9	102	23.3	70	89	100	116	125		11	20	1.13	1.87	2.31	0.42	0.59	0.73	46	70	78	93	97
15-9 to 16-3	101	17.9	79	89	101	113	120		12	19	1.07	1.69	2.15	0.46	0.58	0.70	51	71	77	87	94
16-3 to 16-9	106	25.0	76	92	106	114	145		12	18	1.04	1.75	2.35	0.42	0.61	0.86	57	68	83	90	106
16-9 to 17-3	111	19.8	89	96	110	118	137	15	13	19	1.31	1.66	2.42	0.50	0.63	0.83	64	74	86	95	103

NUTRITION TABLE D-8

Daily Protein Intake - Female

Age Range	Gm. Total							% of Calories			Gm./kg. Wt.			Gm./cm. Ht.			Gm. Animal				
			Percentiles						Range		Percentiles			Percentiles			Percentiles				
Yr. Mo.	Mean	S.D.	10th	25th	50th	75th	90th	Med.	Min.	Max.	10th	50th	90th	10th	50th	90th	10th	25th	50th	75th	90th
0-0 to 0-1	15	5.2	9	11	15	18	22	17	8	31	2.34	4.62	6.24	0.17	0.32	0.41	9	11	15	18	22
0-1 to 0-2	21	6.3	13	16	21	27	29	17	9	21	3.08	5.46	6.87	0.24	0.40	0.53	11	16	21	25	28
0-2 to 0-3	23	6.7	13	18	24	27	30	17	9	22	2.74	4.82	5.77	0.22	0.41	0.52	9	17	23	27	30
0-3 to 0-4	26	7.2	15	22	27	29	32	17	9	26	2.83	4.52	5.97	0.26	0.44	0.53	11	18	24	28	32
0-4 to 0-5	28	6.6	19	25	29	32	37	18	9	21	3.02	4.51	5.69	0.30	0.46	0.59	13	21	26	30	34
0-5 to 0-6	31	6.8	23	27	32	35	40	18	10	22	3.54	4.46	5.80	0.36	0.48	0.61	16	23	27	33	36
0-6 to 0-9	35	5.5	29	31	34	38	43	18	14	31	3.62	4.43	5.68	0.42	0.51	0.63	24	26	30	34	38
0-9 to 1-0	39	6.4	30	34	38	42	48	17	13	26	3.43	4.24	5.49	0.43	0.53	0.68	24	27	32	37	42
1-0 to 1-3	42	8.3	30	36	42	46	54	17	13	29	3.22	4.16	5.54	0.42	0.55	0.71	25	29	34	39	44
1-3 to 1-6	43	7.8	33	37	44	49	53	16	12	22	3.25	4.10	5.46	0.44	0.55	0.68	26	28	34	39	45
1-6 to 1-9	43	9.0	33	37	42	49	57	15	12	21	3.06	3.82	5.07	0.41	0.51	0.70	25	28	33	39	46
1-9 to 2-0	45	9.3	35	39	43	50	61	15	11	21	2.97	3.88	5.12	0.41	0.52	0.69	27	30	33	41	48
2-0 to 2-3	46	9.2	35	39	45	51	56	15	11	21	2.85	3.84	4.76	0.40	0.53	0.64	27	31	36	40	45
2-3 to 2-6	45	10.3	34	38	44	50	62	15	10	20	2.58	3.46	4.91	0.38	0.50	0.71	24	29	35	39	49
2-6 to 2-9	44	10.9	32	37	44	50	62	14	10	21	2.49	3.24	4.66	0.33	0.47	0.65	23	28	33	40	48
2-9 to 3-0	45	12.0	32	37	45	51	65		11	22	2.24	3.23	4.60	0.33	0.47	0.68	21	25	35	41	48
3-0 to 3-3	46	11.2	32	38	45	54	62		10	22	2.42	2.99	4.51	0.33	0.45	0.64	23	28	34	41	48
3-3 to 3-6	46	12.2	32	39	43	51	62		9	21	2.26	2.99	4.48	0.33	0.45	0.66	22	28	33	41	50
3-6 to 3-9	47	13.3	30	39	46	55	67		10	22	2.08	2.97	4.39	0.30	0.47	0.70	20	28	35	42	55
3-9 to 4-0	48	11.8	34	39	46	55	61		11	18	2.13	2.96	4.07	0.34	0.47	0.62	24	29	36	43	49
4-3 to 4-9	52	13.0	37	43	51	59	74		9	20	2.10	3.07	4.07	0.34	0.48	0.69	26	32	38	45	54
4-9 to 5-3	53	13.3	37	44	51	61	75		10	21	2.05	2.83	3.99	0.35	0.47	0.69	25	32	40	45	57
5-3 to 5-9	54	12.4	39	46	52	59	74		10	23	2.00	2.77	3.86	0.35	0.46	0.67	27	34	40	47	59
5-9 to 6-3	57	10.9	42	49	57	63	72		10	23	2.06	2.94	3.61	0.37	0.49	0.63	29	36	44	50	56
6-3 to 6-9	60	12.8	46	51	59	67	77		11	21	1.99	2.81	3.58	0.38	0.50	0.64	32	37	45	52	61
6-9 to 7-3	63	11.9	48	55	61	71	78		11	21	1.98	2.74	3.56	0.40	0.51	0.64	34	41	47	55	62
7-3 to 7-9	64	13.4	46	55	63	71	84		11	21	1.85	2.58	3.61	0.38	0.50	0.67	30	39	48	57	67
7-9 to 8-3	65	12.0	48	56	65	74	83		10	24	1.87	2.55	3.30	0.40	0.50	0.66	34	42	49	59	65
8-3 to 8-9	67	13.3	50	58	66	76	87		10	23	1.77	2.41	3.29	0.39	0.51	0.68	34	43	51	61	68
8-9 to 9-3	68	12.9	52	59	69	76	85		11	24	1.69	2.43	2.99	0.38	0.52	0.63	35	43	52	61	68
9-3 to 9-9	69	12.4	52	60	71	77	85		11	23	1.66	2.36	2.89	0.39	0.52	0.62	33	43	53	60	66
9-9 to 10-3	71	12.0	51	63	73	79	85	14	11	25	1.61	2.27	2.82	0.38	0.52	0.63	36	45	54	61	66
10-3 to 10-9	72	12.4	56	64	73	82	89	15	11	24	1.59	2.12	2.76	0.41	0.51	0.63	35	46	56	62	68
10-9 to 11-3	74	11.8	56	66	75	82	90		12	26	1.30	2.11	2.78	0.39	0.52	0.65	40	48	56	63	70
11-3 to 11-9	76	12.9	59	69	78	86	92		11	24	1.38	2.04	2.64	0.38	0.52	0.64	42	51	60	66	71
11-9 to 12-3	77	13.2	62	67	76	87	95		11	25	1.24	1.96	2.43	0.40	0.52	0.64	43	49	57	69	74
12-3 to 12-9	78	17.5	58	65	73	92	102		11	21	1.13	1.86	2.49	0.38	0.48	0.67	43	49	57	70	78
12-9 to 13-3	78	16.2	58	65	74	93	100		11	23	1.13	1.75	2.33	0.37	0.47	0.64	41	48	56	71	78
13-3 to 13-9	80	16.8	58	67	76	94	100		11	22	1.03	1.79	2.18	0.35	0.48	0.63	41	52	60	70	76
13-9 to 14-3	78	16.1	56	65	77	90	98		11	23	0.97	1.64	2.10	0.34	0.48	0.59	40	50	59	68	76
14-3 to 14-9	79	18.1	56	63	79	93	103		11	20	0.95	1.58	2.08	0.34	0.50	0.63	40	47	60	70	82
14-9 to 15-3	77	20.5	55	61	74	89	108		11	22	0.89	1.45	2.03	0.33	0.45	0.64	37	45	54	72	86
15-3 to 15-9	78	21.1	48	64	79	93	106		11	21	0.92	1.40	1.96	0.31	0.46	0.62	36	44	58	74	81
15-9 to 16-3	75	19.7	46	64	73	88	102		10	21	0.66	1.36	1.86	0.27	0.44	0.59	32	45	55	68	77
16-3 to 16-9	72	19.6	47	58	72	86	96		11	19	0.79	1.24	1.78	0.27	0.42	0.56	33	41	53	62	73
16-9 to 17-3	71	19.0	50	55	70	84	96		11	20	0.82	1.26	1.77	0.30	0.42	0.57	29	42	51	63	76
17-3 to 17-9	70	23.3	37	54	70	86	100		12	22	0.57	1.25	1.82	0.25	0.42	0.59	25	35	53	70	78
17-9 to 18-0	64	24.0	33	41	67	85	94	15	12	23	0.48	1.10	1.76	0.20	0.41	0.55	22	27	47	67	72

NUTRITION

TABLE D-9

Daily Calcium Intake - Male

Age Range	Gm. Total					Mg./kg. Wt.			Mg./cm. Ht.			Ca:P Ratio	
	Percentiles					Percentiles			Percentiles				
Yr. Mo.	10th	25th	50th	75th	90th	10th	50th	90th	10th	50th	90th	Mean	S.D.
0-0 to 0-1	0.31	0.43	0.57	0.65	0.70	96	156	215	6.4	10.8	13.7	1.28	.09
0-1 to 0-2	0.49	0.66	0.81	0.89	0.97	114	180	225	9.5	14.3	17.3	1.26	.11
0-2 to 0-3	0.55	0.71	0.91	1.03	1.15	103	171	210	9.7	15.4	19.3	1.23	.15
0-3 to 0-4	0.62	0.78	0.89	1.02	1.18	105	147	186	8.9	14.5	18.1	1.20	.13
0-4 to 0-5	0.66	0.85	0.98	1.15	1.29	95	143	178	10.8	15.1	19.4	1.18	.13
0-5 to 0-6	0.69	0.86	1.01	1.17	1.31	81	138	174	10.2	15.2	20.1	1.13	.16
0-6 to 0-9	0.86	0.97	1.06	1.14	1.35	100	126	162	12.1	15.0	18.9	1.10	.14
0-9 to 1-0	0.82	0.94	1.05	1.18	1.35	83	112	141	11.1	14.1	18.2	1.05	.10
1-0 to 1-3	0.66	0.79	0.99	1.20	1.33	64	92	129	8.3	12.9	17.4	1.02	.11
1-3 to 1-6	0.58	0.69	0.89	1.10	1.39	52	78	122	7.5	11.4	17.0	0.96	.11
1-6 to 1-9	0.49	0.64	0.84	1.06	1.25	44	69	104	5.9	10.2	14.2	0.93	.11
1-9 to 2-0	0.44	0.64	0.78	0.97	1.24	35	63	98	5.3	9.3	14.6	0.90	.11
2-0 to 2-3	0.39	0.58	0.79	0.99	1.14	31	59	88	5.2	8.9	12.8	0.88	.13
2-3 to 2-6	0.45	0.59	0.76	1.00	1.20	37	56	88	5.1	8.4	13.6	0.87	.12
2-6 to 2-9	0.43	0.61	0.81	1.02	1.36	32	58	90	5.0	8.8	14.4	0.87	.11
2-9 to 3-0	0.56	0.67	0.83	0.95	1.28	39	56	81	5.9	9.0	13.2	0.87	.09
3-0 to 3-3	0.53	0.61	0.77	0.99	1.28	33	54	81	5.3	8.3	13.1	0.86	.11
3-3 to 3-6	0.55	0.68	0.80	1.00	1.18	37	52	73	5.6	8.0	12.2	0.86	.09
3-6 to 3-9	0.56	0.70	0.83	1.04	1.26	34	57	75	5.9	8.5	12.3	0.87	.09
3-9 to 4-0	0.58	0.68	0.86	0.98	1.31	37	51	85	5.9	8.3	13.3	0.87	.09
4-3 to 4-9	0.59	0.71	0.90	1.09	1.28	33	52	70	5.6	8.5	12.0	0.86	.10
4-9 to 5-3	0.64	0.75	0.96	1.11	1.26	34	52	69	6.0	8.8	11.9	0.87	.09
5-3 to 5-9	0.70	0.82	1.01	1.18	1.36	36	51	72	6.2	8.9	12.3	0.87	.09
5-9 to 6-3	0.80	0.91	1.02	1.18	1.39	36	50	68	6.8	8.7	11.9	0.87	.08
6-3 to 6-9	0.84	0.96	1.05	1.20	1.42	36	48	64	6.8	9.0	11.9	0.87	.08
6-9 to 7-3	0.88	0.95	1.08	1.29	1.40	34	46	61	7.0	8.8	11.5	0.85	.08
7-3 to 7-9	0.89	1.00	1.13	1.29	1.43	33	45	58	6.9	9.1	11.4	0.84	.06
7-9 to 8-3	0.85	0.95	1.13	1.38	1.53	31	43	59	6.4	8.8	12.1	0.85	.06
8-3 to 8-9	0.87	1.03	1.19	1.38	1.63	30	43	55	6.6	8.9	12.6	0.84	.06
8-9 to 9-3	0.88	1.08	1.20	1.41	1.66	30	40	54	6.4	8.9	12.3	0.84	.07
9-3 to 9-9	0.94	1.07	1.22	1.42	1.57	29	39	49	6.8	9.0	11.7	0.83	.06
9-9 to 10-3	1.02	1.12	1.27	1.42	1.61	29	37	48	7.2	9.2	11.4	0.83	.06
10-3 to 10-9	1.00	1.16	1.31	1.44	1.54	28	36	47	7.0	9.3	11.2	0.84	.07
10-9 to 11-3	1.04	1.17	1.35	1.47	1.63	28	34	45	7.1	9.2	11.2	0.83	.06
11-3 to 11-9	1.13	1.24	1.39	1.54	1.72	27	35	44	7.6	9.6	11.3	0.84	.07
11-9 to 12-3	1.12	1.29	1.42	1.64	1.80	26	32	46	7.0	9.5	12.0	0.83	.08
12-3 to 12-9	0.95	1.27	1.50	1.83	2.13	23	32	48	6.2	10.0	13.6	0.85	.09
12-9 to 13-3	1.07	1.25	1.47	1.87	2.05	22	31	45	6.5	9.5	13.0	0.85	.08
13-3 to 13-9	0.88	1.30	1.48	1.79	1.98	21	30	43	5.6	9.3	12.8	0.85	.09
13-9 to 14-3	0.86	1.11	1.41	1.66	2.18	18	28	43	4.9	9.0	10.4	0.82	.10
14-3 to 14-9	0.72	1.07	1.36	1.67	2.28	15	24	40	4.5	8.4	13.5	0.81	.11
14-9 to 15-3	0.85	1.14	1.39	1.62	2.56	17	22	43	5.4	7.6	14.6	0.81	.11
15-3 to 15-9	0.87	1.14	1.40	1.65	2.08	15	22	40	4.8	8.1	12.4	0.80	.12
15-9 to 16-3	0.99	1.20	1.37	1.82	2.09	15	21	33	5.9	7.9	12.2	0.82	.11
16-3 to 16-9	1.02	1.19	1.66	1.90	2.03	16	26	32	5.8	9.7	12.4	0.83	.11
16-9 to 17-3	1.04	1.30	1.60	1.84	2.00	16	22	46	5.9	9.0	15.3	0.82	.12

NUTRITION

TABLE D-10

Daily Calcium Intake - Female

Age Range Yr. Mo.	Gm. Total					Mg./kg. Wt.			Mg./cm. Ht.			Ca:P Ratio	
	Percentiles					Percentiles			Percentiles				
	10th	25th	50th	75th	90th	10th	50th	90th	10th	50th	90th	Mean	S.D.
0-0 to 0-1	0.27	0.39	0.54	0.63	0.73	79	167	210	5.3	11.1	14.2	1.26	.04
0-1 to 0-2	0.45	0.58	0.74	0.88	1.04	107	191	233	7.8	13.7	18.6	1.27	.05
0-2 to 0-3	0.45	0.67	0.82	0.93	1.05	94	166	196	7.5	14.4	18.0	1.27	.16
0-3 to 0-4	0.56	0.76	0.94	1.01	1.13	103	157	195	9.4	15.4	18.2	1.24	.15
0-4 to 0-5	0.67	0.79	0.96	1.06	1.26	106	149	186	10.6	15.3	19.9	1.20	.15
0-5 to 0-6	0.67	0.87	0.98	1.13	1.23	108	146	180	11.3	15.4	18.6	1.15	.14
0-6 to 0-9	0.82	0.88	0.98	1.05	1.18	104	126	149	12.0	14.5	17.8	1.08	.09
0-9 to 1-0	0.73	0.86	0.94	1.08	1.16	83	109	131	10.5	13.3	16.1	1.03	.10
1-0 to 1-3	0.68	0.80	0.93	1.05	1.16	71	93	118	9.1	12.5	15.5	1.00	.10
1-3 to 1-6	0.58	0.73	0.87	1.01	1.16	53	84	110	7.5	11.4	14.4	0.94	.11
1-6 to 1-9	0.54	0.69	0.83	0.99	1.13	52	74	110	6.9	10.3	14.0	0.94	.12
1-9 to 2-0	0.53	0.67	0.78	0.92	1.15	49	66	100	6.7	9.4	13.7	0.91	.12
2-0 to 2-3	0.57	0.66	0.77	0.95	1.06	45	63	92	6.5	9.0	12.4	0.90	.13
2-3 to 2-6	0.54	0.63	0.76	0.93	1.05	40	59	88	6.1	8.6	12.0	0.91	.14
2-6 to 2-9	0.55	0.66	0.77	0.89	1.04	40	59	79	5.9	8.3	11.2	0.90	.10
2-9 to 3-0	0.54	0.63	0.75	0.89	1.13	35	54	78	5.8	7.9	11.4	0.88	.12
3-0 to 3-3	0.49	0.66	0.76	0.88	1.06	34	51	77	5.4	7.9	11.2	0.88	.09
3-3 to 3-6	0.49	0.64	0.74	0.89	1.06	36	49	76	5.1	7.6	11.0	0.88	.10
3-6 to 3-9	0.48	0.63	0.76	0.92	1.19	34	49	81	5.0	7.7	12.5	0.89	.09
3-9 to 4-0	0.56	0.63	0.75	0.93	1.25	32	49	79	5.0	7.6	12.4	0.89	.11
4-3 to 4-9	0.57	0.73	0.87	1.04	1.16	32	50	68	5.4	8.2	11.1	0.88	.09
4-9 to 5-3	0.56	0.71	0.89	1.08	1.24	30	48	68	5.5	8.0	11.5	0.88	.11
5-3 to 5-9	0.59	0.73	0.90	1.06	1.26	29	46	67	5.4	8.1	11.2	0.88	.11
5-9 to 6-3	0.60	0.73	0.92	1.09	1.23	28	45	62	5.2	8.1	11.1	0.86	.11
6-3 to 6-9	0.66	0.84	0.98	1.14	1.30	30	44	61	5.4	8.3	11.1	0.87	.09
6-9 to 7-3	0.71	0.87	1.05	1.17	1.34	30	44	60	6.2	8.5	10.9	0.87	.09
7-3 to 7-9	0.67	0.83	1.05	1.25	1.35	27	42	58	5.4	8.5	10.9	0.86	.10
7-9 to 8-3	0.73	0.86	1.10	1.27	1.38	27	40	55	5.9	8.5	10.8	0.87	.10
8-3 to 8-9	0.76	0.91	1.07	1.23	1.35	27	37	52	6.2	8.1	10.4	0.86	.08
8-9 to 9-3	0.80	0.93	1.06	1.18	1.32	26	36	47	6.1	7.9	9.9	0.84	.09
9-3 to 9-9	0.76	0.95	1.06	1.18	1.32	24	34	44	5.7	7.8	9.8	0.84	.08
9-9 to 10-3	0.83	0.93	1.06	1.17	1.32	23	31	42	6.0	7.7	9.6	0.83	.08
10-3 to 10-9	0.84	0.95	1.09	1.23	1.37	23	30	42	6.3	7.6	9.6	0.83	.08
10-9 to 11-3	0.84	0.93	1.11	1.26	1.41	21	30	43	5.6	7.6	9.8	0.83	.09
11-3 to 11-9	0.79	0.96	1.18	1.32	1.48	19	30	43	5.4	7.9	10.4	0.83	.09
11-9 to 12-3	0.77	1.00	1.16	1.35	1.55	17	28	39	4.8	7.7	10.5	0.83	.10
12-3 to 12-9	0.75	0.91	1.14	1.37	1.60	16	26	35	4.5	7.2	10.2	0.82	.09
12-9 to 13-3	0.75	0.89	1.07	1.40	1.54	15	23	34	4.6	6.9	9.5	0.82	.09
13-3 to 13-9	0.80	0.91	1.16	1.45	1.56	15	25	33	5.1	7.5	9.5	0.83	.09
13-9 to 14-3	0.69	0.91	1.04	1.36	1.59	13	21	32	4.1	6.7	9.6	0.81	.10
14-3 to 14-9	0.62	0.80	1.11	1.41	1.69	12	20	33	4.2	7.0	10.2	0.80	.12
14-9 to 15-3	0.56	0.74	1.06	1.34	1.82	10	19	32	3.5	6.7	10.2	0.78	.13
15-3 to 15-9	0.50	0.67	1.09	1.38	1.70	9	19	30	3.0	6.7	9.9	0.79	.15
15-9 to 16-3	0.52	0.72	1.12	1.42	1.59	9	19	30	3.0	6.5	9.6	0.82	.13
16-3 to 16-9	0.48	0.65	0.94	1.28	1.53	7	16	28	2.8	6.0	9.1	0.78	.15
16-9 to 17-3	0.43	0.60	0.93	1.30	1.46	7	16	27	2.6	5.5	8.6	0.74	.17
17-3 to 17-9	0.37	0.60	1.04	1.33	1.44	6	15	26	2.1	6.1	8.5	0.76	.17
17-9 to 18-0	0.30	0.40	0.68	1.28	1.35	4	11	24	1.9	4.2	8.0	0.71	.12

NUTRITION

TABLE D-11

Daily Phosphorus Intake

Age Range	Male						Female					
	Gm. Total			Mg./kg. Wt.			Gm. Total			Mg./kg. Wt.		
	Percentiles			Percentiles			Percentiles			Percentiles		
Yr. Mo.	10th	50th	90th	10th	50th	90th	10th	50th	90th	10th	50th	90th
0-0 to 0-1	0.27	0.44	0.55	71	124	155	0.23	0.43	0.59	65	138	172
0-1 to 0-2	0.40	0.64	0.78	88	146	179	0.37	0.59	0.80	83	149	185
0-2 to 0-3	0.43	0.76	0.92	83	142	170	0.35	0.67	0.85	72	133	159
0-3 to 0-4	0.53	0.75	0.97	81	121	149	0.43	0.75	0.89	79	129	165
0-4 to 0-5	0.55	0.83	1.08	87	122	151	0.51	0.82	1.00	91	129	151
0-5 to 0-6	0.51	0.87	1.18	67	120	152	0.59	0.87	1.06	84	126	150
0-6 to 0-9	0.76	0.95	1.25	84	115	142	0.77	0.90	1.10	98	117	139
0-9 to 1-0	0.83	0.97	1.29	80	108	130	0.76	0.90	1.10	83	104	128
1-0 to 1-3	0.65	0.93	1.33	67	91	122	0.71	0.90	1.17	71	93	117
1-3 to 1-6	0.65	0.94	1.33	59	84	120	0.66	0.90	1.14	67	88	113
1-6 to 1-9	0.55	0.93	1.30	48	79	108	0.66	0.88	1.19	61	79	106
1-9 to 2-0	0.50	0.90	1.29	43	77	101	0.66	0.87	1.18	56	75	101
2-0 to 2-3	0.54	0.86	1.23	42	70	91	0.67	0.88	1.07	54	73	90
2-3 to 2-6	0.62	0.86	1.33	44	68	94	0.66	0.84	1.16	47	66	86
2-6 to 2-9	0.55	0.90	1.33	41	67	95	0.62	0.83	1.15	46	63	86
2-9 to 3-0	0.69	0.94	1.30	47	65	90	0.62	0.89	1.20	42	64	83
3-0 to 3-3	0.63	0.91	1.38	44	65	91	0.57	0.86	1.11	44	58	85
3-3 to 3-6	0.70	0.93	1.35	44	63	84	0.58	0.84	1.19	40	57	84
3-6 to 3-9	0.71	0.98	1.41	43	64	87	0.52	0.88	1.27	35	57	84
3-9 to 4-0	0.72	0.95	1.47	45	59	86	0.63	0.87	1.25	38	57	79
4-3 to 4-9	0.78	1.03	1.43	43	59	80	0.68	1.00	1.30	38	56	76
4-9 to 5-3	0.81	1.11	1.34	44	60	76	0.67	0.99	1.36	39	52	73
5-3 to 5-9	0.88	1.14	1.47	43	57	79	0.71	1.00	1.37	36	52	70
5-9 to 6-3	0.96	1.18	1.51	42	56	76	0.75	1.06	1.36	36	52	69
6-3 to 6-9	1.06	1.22	1.56	44	55	72	0.82	1.11	1.46	36	51	67
6-9 to 7-3	1.07	1.26	1.64	42	54	70	0.87	1.18	1.46	37	51	66
7-3 to 7-9	1.06	1.34	1.56	41	53	70	0.81	1.21	1.52	33	50	65
7-9 to 8-3	1.03	1.31	1.76	38	49	69	0.92	1.23	1.55	33	48	62
8-3 to 8-9	1.08	1.40	1.81	38	51	65	0.96	1.21	1.60	32	44	61
8-9 to 9-3	1.06	1.45	1.90	36	48	60	0.99	1.24	1.57	30	43	56
9-3 to 9-9	1.16	1.45	1.85	35	46	58	0.94	1.29	1.51	29	42	53
9-9 to 10-3	1.23	1.51	1.87	37	45	55	1.01	1.32	1.55	27	40	51
10-3 to 10-9	1.24	1.56	1.91	36	44	54	1.06	1.31	1.57	27	38	50
10-9 to 11-3	1.32	1.61	1.90	35	42	50	1.02	1.32	1.61	25	37	48
11-3 to 11-9	1.32	1.67	2.06	34	41	50	1.06	1.41	1.72	24	35	47
11-9 to 12-3	1.32	1.75	2.17	32	40	51	1.06	1.42	1.78	21	34	45
12-3 to 12-9	1.21	1.82	2.36	30	38	52	1.00	1.33	1.89	21	32	44
12-9 to 13-3	1.31	1.73	2.26	28	34	50	0.98	1.35	1.81	19	30	41
13-3 to 13-9	1.20	1.76	2.36	25	34	50	1.00	1.41	1.79	18	31	39
13-9 to 14-3	1.16	1.72	2.60	24	32	49	0.98	1.36	1.83	16	27	39
14-3 to 14-9	1.17	1.69	2.45	21	30	47	0.93	1.37	1.95	15	26	39
14-9 to 15-3	1.27	1.70	2.49	21	31	44	0.90	1.26	1.98	14	24	38
15-3 to 15-9	1.19	1.74	2.33	20	31	43	0.79	1.32	1.79	13	23	32
15-9 to 16-3	1.38	1.79	2.22	19	29	37	0.72	1.31	1.77	12	23	32
16-3 to 16-9	1.43	1.88	2.60	19	30	40	0.70	1.17	1.75	12	20	32
16-9 to 17-3	1.43	1.87	2.48	23	26	49	0.76	1.17	1.73	12	20	31
17-3 to 17-9	-	-	-	-	-	-	0.61	1.21	1.79	9	20	31
17-9 to 18-0	-	-	-	-	-	-	0.48	1.08	1.71	7	18	31

NUTRITION

TABLE D-12

Daily Iron Intake - Male

Age Range Yr. Mo.	Diet N	Mg. Percentiles 10th	25th	50th	75th	90th	Mg./kg. Wt. Percentiles 10th	50th	90th	Supplement N	Mg. Med.	Range Min.	Max.
0-0 to 0-1	33	0.2	0.3	0.4	0.7	0.9	0.04	0.12	0.27	4		2.3	6.5
0-1 to 0-2	39	0.5	0.8	1.3	3.2	4.0	0.14	0.32	0.98	7		0.5	21.2
0-2 to 0-3	42	0.7	1.2	2.8	5.0	6.9	0.15	0.52	1.33	3		0.9	21.2
0-3 to 0-4	44	1.3	2.2	4.4	5.8	8.4	0.20	0.70	1.51	4		0.9	6.0
0-4 to 0-5	46	2.1	3.7	5.8	7.6	10.6	0.34	0.85	1.45	3		0.6	8.7
0-5 to 0-6	45	3.2	4.9	7.0	9.6	13.6	0.41	0.96	1.81	2		2.5	3.3
0-6 to 0-9	46	4.4	6.3	8.9	12.0	14.7	0.50	1.12	1.83	4		0.8	10.8
0-9 to 1-0	49	4.6	7.5	10.7	13.4	18.5	0.46	1.15	1.78	4		0.2	13.9
1-0 to 1-3	47	3.4	5.6	8.3	12.2	13.9	0.33	0.83	1.48	5		0.2	6.8
1-3 to 1-6	46	3.4	5.3	7.9	10.9	14.6	0.35	0.69	1.34	7		0.1	9.3
1-6 to 1-9	45	3.2	4.2	6.5	8.4	10.9	0.27	0.54	1.03	5		0.8	4.6
1-9 to 2-0	44	3.5	4.3	5.4	7.0	8.9	0.28	0.47	0.69	4		0.1	6.2
2-0 to 2-3	45	3.4	4.3	5.5	7.2	8.9	0.29	0.44	0.75	6		0.1	19.2
2-3 to 2-6	44	3.5	4.4	5.7	6.9	9.0	0.29	0.44	0.63	12	0.8	0.1	6.9
2-6 to 2-9	45	4.1	4.6	5.6	7.5	8.5	0.30	0.43	0.59	8		0.2	5.1
2-9 to 3-0	43	4.4	5.1	6.0	7.3	8.4	0.30	0.42	0.61	5		0.1	5.6
3-0 to 3-3	39	4.5	5.3	6.4	7.5	9.0	0.31	0.44	0.61	10	1.0	0.1	6.2
3-3 to 3-6	39	4.5	5.1	6.2	7.2	8.2	0.29	0.42	0.60	11	0.7	0.1	6.3
3-6 to 3-9	40	4.0	4.9	6.0	7.3	8.6	0.27	0.39	0.56	9		0.5	23.8
3-9 to 4-0	39	4.5	5.2	6.3	7.2	8.4	0.30	0.40	0.50	12	1.7	0.1	23.8
4-3 to 4-9	40	5.0	5.8	6.5	7.8	8.8	0.30	0.37	0.53	13	0.8	0.1	6.7
4-9 to 5-3	38	5.3	6.0	7.0	8.1	8.8	0.30	0.38	0.50	10	2.0	0.1	22.9
5-3 to 5-9	38	5.5	6.1	6.9	8.5	9.9	0.28	0.36	0.53	16	1.0	0.2	10.0
5-9 to 6-3	37	5.8	6.7	7.7	9.0	10.1	0.28	0.38	0.49	11	0.8	0.1	5.5
6-3 to 6-9	36	6.3	7.0	8.0	9.1	11.3	0.28	0.36	0.51	15	1.7	0.1	33.0
6-9 to 7-3	35	6.6	7.3	8.3	9.6	12.0	0.29	0.35	0.50	10	2.2	0.1	33.0
7-3 to 7-9	32	7.2	7.9	8.7	10.0	11.8	0.27	0.35	0.49	12	1.2	0.1	4.8
7-9 to 8-3	34	7.0	7.7	9.0	10.6	12.0	0.27	0.34	0.47	11	1.8	0.2	14.0
8-3 to 8-9	32	7.4	8.2	9.5	10.8	12.4	0.27	0.34	0.44	9		0.1	3.2
8-9 to 9-3	31	7.5	8.5	9.9	11.4	12.7	0.25	0.33	0.43	10	0.9	0.1	13.3
9-3 to 9-9	32	8.2	9.2	10.4	11.7	13.0	0.24	0.32	0.42	10	0.6	0.2	28.0
9-9 to 10-3	31	8.1	8.8	10.4	11.5	13.4	0.25	0.31	0.41	11	1.8	0.1	28.0
10-3 to 10-9	29	8.4	8.9	10.3	12.1	14.5	0.23	0.29	0.40	10	1.0	0.1	16.8
10-9 to 11-3	28	8.8	9.5	10.7	12.3	14.0	0.24	0.29	0.36	11	0.7	0.1	14.6
11-3 to 11-9	29	8.8	9.7	11.4	12.8	14.3	0.23	0.29	0.35	9		0.2	114.0
11-9 to 12-3	29	9.0	10.2	11.5	13.1	15.1	0.22	0.27	0.37	11	5.4	0.1	114.0
12-3 to 12-9	28	8.6	10.0	11.4	13.0	15.8	0.19	0.26	0.36	13	4.6	0.1	83.6
12-9 to 13-3	27	9.0	9.8	11.2	12.7	15.9	0.17	0.24	0.36	10	6.1	0.1	83.6
13-3 to 13-9	25	8.3	9.3	10.8	13.2	15.0	0.16	0.23	0.35	7		0.1	42.8
13-9 to 14-3	23	9.1	9.9	11.2	13.0	16.2	0.16	0.23	0.34	6		0.1	6.2
14-3 to 14-9	20	9.4	10.6	11.7	13.6	16.6	0.16	0.22	0.35	5		0.1	3.6
14-9 to 15-3	15	9.9	10.4	12.6	13.9	15.9	0.15	0.22	0.32	5		0.2	3.5
15-3 to 15-9	15	9.3	10.6	12.9	14.2	15.7	0.15	0.22	0.31	6		0.2	3.9
15-9 to 16-3	16	9.3	10.4	11.8	13.7	16.5	0.13	0.20	0.31	6		0.1	6.3
16-3 to 16-9	13	8.7	10.2	12.1	16.3	19.8	0.13	0.20	0.35	4		0.2	4.8
16-9 to 17-3	10	10.1	11.2	13.0	14.4	19.7	0.13	0.21	0.33	1		0.1	

NUTRITION

TABLE D-13

Daily Iron Intake - Female

Age Range Yr. Mo.	Diet										Supplement			
		Mg.					Mg./kg. Wt.				Mg.			
		Percentiles					Percentiles					Range		
	N	10th	25th	50th	75th	90th	10th	50th	90th	N	Med.	Min.	Max.
0-0 to 0-1	23	0.3	0.4	0.5	0.8	1.3	0.07	0.14	0.38	5		1.5	4.5
0-1 to 0-2	30	0.5	0.8	1.3	2.0	5.3	0.12	0.31	0.99	4		0.1	3.1
0-2 to 0-3	32	0.8	1.3	2.3	4.4	6.3	0.17	0.47	1.16	2		3.3	6.2
0-3 to 0-4	34	1.2	2.1	3.6	6.1	7.9	0.20	0.63	1.57	3		3.3	10.5
0-4 to 0-5	37	2.6	3.6	5.5	8.0	12.2	0.38	0.77	2.15	8		1.3	29.8
0-5 to 0-6	38	3.4	4.4	6.3	9.6	13.0	0.50	0.94	2.08	6		0.7	59.6
0-6 to 0-9	41	4.7	5.9	9.4	12.2	13.3	0.58	1.20	1.81	7		0.1	19.9
0-9 to 1-0	44	4.4	6.1	8.7	13.8	16.4	0.53	0.97	1.79	5		0.5	59.6
1-0 to 1-3	45	3.2	4.4	6.4	11.0	13.2	0.35	0.67	1.42	3		0.4	59.6
1-3 to 1-6	45	3.5	4.7	6.3	8.5	11.9	0.35	0.56	1.07	6		0.6	39.9
1-6 to 1-9	44	3.1	4.2	5.6	7.3	10.7	0.29	0.54	0.89	9		0.1	188.0
1-9 to 2-0	45	3.6	4.3	5.7	7.3	10.1	0.32	0.51	0.89	7		0.1	119.2
2-0 to 2-3	47	3.4	4.5	5.9	7.3	9.1	0.32	0.48	0.76	10	19.9	0.1	357.0
2-3 to 2-6	48	3.5	4.3	5.5	7.0	8.2	0.26	0.45	0.63	8		0.1	265.0
2-6 to 2-9	46	3.4	4.2	5.2	6.5	8.0	0.28	0.40	0.62	8		0.1	4.9
2-9 to 3-0	45	3.6	4.6	5.8	6.8	7.8	0.26	0.40	0.63	8		0.1	163.5
3-0 to 3-3	44	4.0	4.8	5.7	6.6	7.5	0.28	0.41	0.56	10	1.7	0.1	5.5
3-3 to 3-6	44	3.8	4.5	5.5	6.5	7.4	0.28	0.37	0.54	9		0.1	7.3
3-6 to 3-9	45	3.6	4.8	5.8	7.1	8.4	0.25	0.39	0.56	10	0.8	0.1	5.7
3-9 to 4-0	43	3.9	4.7	6.1	6.9	7.8	0.26	0.38	0.50	10	3.5	0.2	59.5
4-3 to 4-9	42	4.2	5.3	6.4	7.5	8.9	0.24	0.38	0.50	10	3.1	0.1	79.4
4-9 to 5-3	41	4.2	5.3	6.7	7.9	9.3	0.24	0.36	0.50	10	1.1	0.1	10.0
5-3 to 5-9	41	4.7	5.5	6.5	7.7	9.5	0.24	0.34	0.49	13	2.1	0.2	31.6
5-9 to 6-3	40	5.0	5.7	7.0	8.3	9.5	0.24	0.35	0.48	12	2.2	0.1	29.8
6-3 to 6-9	41	5.2	6.0	7.5	8.5	10.1	0.24	0.34	0.48	10	1.3	0.1	25.2
6-9 to 7-3	42	5.7	6.5	7.7	8.8	10.3	0.24	0.34	0.46	12	0.6	0.1	5.5
7-3 to 7-9	41	5.4	6.3	7.9	9.4	10.4	0.21	0.31	0.46	13	1.8	0.1	25.9
7-9 to 8-3	41	5.6	6.8	8.1	9.4	10.8	0.22	0.31	0.44	16	2.6	0.1	64.3
8-3 to 8-9	39	5.9	7.1	8.2	9.6	11.5	0.21	0.30	0.44	18	3.3	0.1	64.3
8-9 to 9-3	41	5.9	7.4	8.5	10.3	11.6	0.21	0.30	0.42	14	1.6	0.1	47.0
9-3 to 9-9	37	6.4	7.5	8.9	10.2	11.6	0.21	0.30	0.38	11	0.8	0.1	7.1
9-9 to 10-3	35	6.3	8.1	9.1	10.3	11.3	0.20	0.29	0.38	10	1.8	0.1	20.5
10-3 to 10-9	35	7.1	7.9	9.3	10.6	12.2	0.19	0.27	0.36	8		0.1	6.7
10-9 to 11-3	35	7.1	8.2	9.4	10.8	12.6	0.17	0.28	0.38	10	3.7	0.1	64.7
11-3 to 11-9	33	6.7	7.9	9.9	11.3	12.1	0.16	0.26	0.34	12	1.8	0.1	41.5
11-9 to 12-3	30	7.0	8.5	9.6	11.6	12.9	0.16	0.24	0.34	9		0.1	13.3
12-3 to 12-9	30	7.0	8.0	10.0	12.4	13.6	0.14	0.22	0.34	9		0.1	25.3
12-9 to 13-3	30	6.9	8.3	9.7	12.0	13.5	0.14	0.21	0.32	7		0.1	25.0
13-3 to 13-9	26	6.7	8.2	10.3	12.0	14.4	0.12	0.21	0.31	8		0.1	39.8
13-9 to 14-3	26	6.6	8.1	10.1	11.6	13.9	0.11	0.20	0.30	7		0.1	13.8
14-3 to 14-9	25	6.7	8.2	10.5	12.0	13.2	0.10	0.20	0.27	9		0.1	12.9
14-9 to 15-3	24	6.3	7.8	10.1	11.7	13.1	0.11	0.18	0.26	8		0.1	50.6
15-3 to 15-9	21	6.2	7.6	10.1	12.0	13.3	0.10	0.19	0.24	5		0.1	23.4
15-9 to 16-3	18	5.6	7.3	9.0	11.6	12.6	0.09	0.17	0.23	6		0.3	51.1
16-3 to 16-9	18	5.5	7.3	9.1	11.6	12.8	0.09	0.17	0.23	6		0.3	35.0
16-9 to 17-3	18	6.3	7.2	9.0	11.9	13.2	0.10	0.17	0.23	3		0.3	19.4
17-3 to 17-9	16	5.1	6.7	9.5	11.2	13.7	0.08	0.17	0.23	2		0.1	0.3
17-9 to 18-0	14	4.6	5.7	9.9	11.8	12.9	0.07	0.16	0.22	2		0.1	0.1

NUTRITION TABLE D-14

Daily Vitamin A Intake - Male

Age Range	Diet								Supplement			
		International Units					Percent from Plant Sources			International Units		
		Percentiles									Range	
Yr. Mo.	N	10th	25th	50th	75th	90th	Mean	S.D.	N	Med.	Min.	Max.
0-0 to 0-1	33	120	525	825	1065	1175	3		23	1220	335	3,620
0-1 to 0-2	39	205	845	1205	1495	1710	6		38	2520	535	11,430
0-2 to 0-3	42	435	1035	1515	1990	2735	24		41	3335	1100	14,715
0-3 to 0-4	44	1055	1585	2195	2760	3220	41	29	44	2980	150	11,720
0-4 to 0-5	46	1030	2020	2960	3935	4530	52	26	45	2710	575	13,000
0-5 to 0-6	45	1575	2365	3545	4405	5430	56	20	44	3000	825	13,000
0-6 to 0-9	46	2865	3350	4515	5645	7460	59	17	45	2780	695	13,000
0-9 to 1-0	49	3235	4165	5530	7205	8825	62	18	45	2595	465	13,000
1-0 to 1-3	47	2580	3345	4590	6825	9100	56	20	40	2725	155	13,000
1-3 to 1-6	46	1815	2735	4090	5800	8465	51	21	40	2340	210	13,000
1-6 to 1-9	45	1540	2050	3110	4570	7815	44	19	38	2630	185	13,000
1-9 to 2-0	44	1645	2100	2720	4280	5505	43	17	32	2700	100	5,875
2-0 to 2-3	45	1405	2150	2960	4245	5510	43	19	33	2155	55	7,205
2-3 to 2-6	44	1720	2080	2825	3800	5060	41	17	33	2485	40	6,010
2-6 to 2-9	45	1630	2035	2850	4410	6250	41	15	32	2480	75	13,200
2-9 to 3-0	43	1875	2290	3250	4340	5510	42	16	26	1630	90	6,250
3-0 to 3-3	39	1725	2355	3315	4485	5905	42	16	21	2675	110	6,370
3-3 to 3-6	39	1955	2560	3340	4160	5065	42	14	27	1745	50	6,500
3-6 to 3-9	40	1625	2270	3340	4640	5680	41	14	26	2895	95	6,560
3-9 to 4-0	39	1825	2635	3325	4675	5640	47	13	25	2445	65	6,270
4-3 to 4-9	40	1860	2660	3735	4665	5850	46	15	28	2440	40	12,500
4-9 to 5-3	38	2210	3080	3820	4910	5585	45	14	28	2320	30	12,500
5-3 to 5-9	38	2400	3275	4045	5170	6045	46	12	26	1920	10	12,500
5-9 to 6-3	37	2490	3220	4385	5475	6550	46	12	23	1675	15	11,850
6-3 to 6-9	36	2820	3335	4500	5425	6855	47	14	22	1485	35	11,850
6-9 to 7-3	35	2805	3425	4735	6020	7240	50	15	18	885	30	5,000
7-3 to 7-9	32	2970	3520	4760	5905	7360	49	16	17	2065	20	4,915
7-9 to 8-3	34	3145	3870	4870	6610	7765	50	14	18	1615	45	5,000
8-3 to 8-9	32	3415	4070	5030	6070	8380	51	16	15	2200	25	5,590
8-9 to 9-3	31	3250	3980	4940	5865	7470	51	15	15	1730	55	7,050
9-3 to 9-9	32	3320	4140	5240	6300	7650	51	15	15	1240	85	7,500
9-9 to 10-3	31	3390	4025	5080	6140	7850	52	13	18	1200	20	7,500
10-3 to 10-9	29	3665	4370	5285	6240	7760	52	13	19	1235	25	6,600
10-9 to 11-3	28	3235	3925	5575	6740	7700	52	14	13	940	25	5,000
11-3 to 11-9	29	3420	4485	5955	7185	9090	55	15	16	1255	30	6,585
11-9 to 12-3	29	3525	4410	5860	7620	9145	52	16	12	1275	60	5,000
12-3 to 12-9	28	3360	4195	5925	7425	8515	52	17	16	1335	25	7,995
12-9 to 13-3	27	3110	3785	5420	7055	8645	48	19	15	1125	30	7,400
13-3 to 13-9	25	3335	3985	5005	6950	8270	46	17	14	1085	30	7,400
13-9 to 14-3	23	3660	4220	5165	7050	9035	48	15	8	-	25	6,615
14-3 to 14-9	20	3505	4515	5485	6875	9260	53	17	9	-	640	5,000
14-9 to 15-3	15	3475	4090	5180	6765	8610	49	17	10	1575	110	5,000
15-3 to 15-9	15	2795	3670	5070	6750	8485	49	18	8	-	95	6,410
15-9 to 16-3	16	3095	3920	5160	6555	9220	50	17	7	-	15	6,410
16-3 to 16-9	13	3315	4220	4975	6960	9470	46	17	5	-	525	10,330
16-9 to 17-3	10	4220	4870	5575	7810	8955	47	18	4	-	355	10,330

NUTRITION

TABLE D-15

Daily Vitamin A Intake - Female

Age Range Yr. Mo.	Diet N	Diet International Units Percentiles 10th	25th	50th	75th	90th	Percent from Plant Sources Mean	S.D.	Supplement N	Supplement International Units Med.	Range Min.	Max.
0-0 to 0-1	23	65	175	740	895	1045	0		16	2145	75	10,420
0-1 to 0-2	30	160	725	1155	1315	1535	7		30	3750	240	10,770
0-2 to 0-3	32	210	980	1300	1525	1990	22		32	4060	770	14,865
0-3 to 0-4	34	1205	1550	1860	2595	3420	37	36	34	2950	545	12,580
0-4 to 0-5	37	1285	1690	2965	3830	5235	46	28	37	3745	215	12,500
0-5 to 0-6	38	1825	2410	3020	4110	5965	53	22	37	3525	215	10,400
0-6 to 0-9	41	3065	3520	4515	5895	7035	60	16	41	3910	40	10,500
0-9 to 1-0	44	2880	3770	5030	6970	8895	62	15	43	3665	95	12,915
1-0 to 1-3	45	1705	2415	4580	6400	8065	49	17	41	3345	430	12,500
1-3 to 1-6	45	1775	2365	4225	5810	7610	46	16	40	3140	450	13,900
1-6 to 1-9	44	1810	2270	3370	5095	6735	43	15	38	3460	210	13,900
1-9 to 2-0	45	1605	2325	3450	4575	6390	44	16	41	3015	240	17,500
2-0 to 2-3	47	1560	2250	3405	4775	6425	40	16	37	3035	240	7,650
2-3 to 2-6	48	1620	2165	3300	4380	6050	40	17	40	3380	110	13,400
2-6 to 2-9	46	1665	2365	3150	4000	5600	44	17	37	2815	60	12,500
2-9 to 3-0	45	1570	2155	3300	4350	5270	44	17	34	2970	55	8,000
3-0 to 3-3	44	1870	2600	3510	4305	4940	45	16	33	2435	190	7,885
3-3 to 3-6	44	1660	2325	3725	4605	5520	46	16	30	2965	120	14,350
3-6 to 3-9	45	1820	2505	3530	4755	6235	49	15	30	3095	140	16,250
3-9 to 4-0	43	1905	2715	3655	4630	5970	50	15	33	2155	140	11,250
4-3 to 4-9	42	2075	3070	4040	5105	5845	49	15	35	2540	30	18,855
4-9 to 5-3	41	2055	2910	4165	5315	6370	49	14	29	2725	35	7,350
5-3 to 5-9	41	1955	3165	4095	5285	7335	51	15	28	2430	10	7,150
5-9 to 6-3	40	2035	3110	4385	5865	7595	50	16	30	1885	25	10,800
6-3 to 6-9	41	2865	3635	4350	5710	7320	50	14	28	1840	20	10,000
6-9 to 7-3	42	2710	3925	4885	6390	8410	52	13	30	1755	30	8,125
7-3 to 7-9	41	2795	3690	4885	5950	7660	52	14	26	2685	30	9,375
7-9 to 8-3	41	2995	3860	5215	6455	8075	52	16	26	2080	25	11,450
8-3 to 8-9	39	2830	4125	5220	7265	8230	52	14	27	2355	20	11,450
8-9 to 9-3	41	2900	4105	5460	6975	8830	53	15	27	1370	10	6,250
9-3 to 9-9	37	2540	4265	5480	6550	8240	53	15	25	2080	40	9,800
9-9 to 10-3	35	3240	4185	5065	5975	7590	53	14	18	1600	30	7,150
10-3 to 10-9	35	3445	4355	5505	6580	7690	54	13	16	1645	20	7,150
10-9 to 11-3	35	3300	4400	5590	6725	7945	55	14	19	1500	80	6,650
11-3 to 11-9	33	3310	4175	5510	6855	8415	53	13	17	1515	15	8,550
11-9 to 12-3	30	3290	3960	5265	6695	7990	54	15	15	1745	10	6,360
12-3 to 12-9	30	3050	3705	4895	6520	7955	51	13	15	1045	25	5,000
12-9 to 13-3	30	3175	3955	5100	6810	7830	53	13	14	1360	10	5,550
13-3 to 13-9	26	3165	4120	5305	7135	8290	55	13	11	845	70	5,000
13-9 to 14-3	26	3010	3980	4875	6630	7940	58	13	13	980	10	5,000
14-3 to 14-9	25	3050	4195	5095	6140	7795	57	14	12	1340	100	8,375
14-9 to 15-3	24	3080	3845	5155	6720	8425	55	16	10	1325	10	21,700
15-3 to 15-9	21	3110	3945	4965	6665	9300	57	17	5	-	35	6,250
15-9 to 16-3	18	2745	3800	5180	7060	8040	57	19	7	-	45	6,020
16-3 to 16-9	18	3060	3060	5135	7665	8600	60	18	8	-	45	33,000
16-9 to 17-3	18	2925	3640	4995	7310	8900	62	17	10	1740	30	33,000
17-3 to 17-9	16	2190	4140	5630	7450	8990	69	15	7	-	45	51,655
17-9 to 18-0	14	3085	4615	5365	6575	7215	67	17	7	-	265	4,505

NUTRITION

TABLE D-16

Daily Vitamin D Intake

Age Range Yr. Mo.	Male							Female						
	Total N	N with Suppl.	International Units Percentiles 10th	25th	50th	75th	90th	Total N	N with Suppl.	International Units Percentiles 10th	25th	50th	75th	90th
0-0 to 0-1	33	33	175	220	290	370	475	23	23	125	185	245	440	765
0-1 to 0-2	39	39	385	555	690	825	1145	30	30	320	485	630	1180	1300
0-2 to 0-3	42	42	440	590	825	1215	1405	32	32	310	505	770	1085	1330
0-3 to 0-4	44	44	365	540	765	1145	1430	34	34	315	480	755	1220	1405
0-4 to 0-5	46	45	405	485	715	1145	1340	37	37	330	535	790	1115	1330
0-5 to 0-6	45	44	395	505	795	1190	1370	38	38	275	455	770	1100	1330
0-6 to 0-9	46	45	370	475	710	975	1335	41	41	130	495	905	1145	1315
0-9 to 0-1	49	47	260	420	670	930	1105	44	43	250	405	780	1135	1510
1-0 to 1-3	47	44	225	355	550	795	1080	45	42	235	385	725	1060	1410
1-3 to 1-6	46	42	140	350	540	685	945	45	41	270	440	665	965	1245
1-6 to 1-9	45	41	205	305	505	730	965	44	41	145	310	585	945	1200
1-9 to 2-0	44	39	130	210	380	715	975	45	43	175	365	660	910	1145
2-0 to 2-3	45	39	125	250	415	680	925	47	41	120	325	620	880	1015
2-3 to 2-6	44	38	125	195	385	690	860	48	46	115	295	560	870	1100
2-6 to 2-9	45	38	105	190	370	690	890	46	42	90	215	500	745	1030
2-9 to 3-0	43	35	65	140	260	610	785	45	40	65	170	465	730	920
3-0 to 3-3	39	32	75	140	255	565	800	44	40	70	180	455	620	970
3-3 to 3-6	39	34	65	145	285	580	915	44	37	75	160	370	660	930
3-6 to 3-9	40	34	75	190	405	620	915	45	39	90	205	395	650	950
3-9 to 4-0	39	34	65	145	265	585	840	43	41	60	135	375	650	1080
4-3 to 4-9	40	36	105	195	315	670	930	42	38	80	180	435	750	1050
4-9 to 5-3	38	34	85	180	320	700	940	41	35	70	155	470	780	1045
5-3 to 5-9	38	35	75	180	285	525	970	41	38	50	115	380	605	780
5-9 to 6-3	37	33	85	180	280	480	775	40	38	70	160	345	565	860
6-3 to 6-9	36	32	75	190	305	470	755	41	39	55	130	290	470	735
6-9 to 7-3	35	26	60	130	245	360	590	42	39	65	140	290	565	810
7-3 to 7-9	32	26	85	175	330	590	760	41	36	65	155	335	655	965
7-9 to 8-3	34	27	50	135	285	400	650	41	34	75	200	310	540	785
8-3 to 8-9	32	26	85	195	295	425	665	39	34	70	155	305	530	835
8-9 to 9-3	31	25	90	140	240	400	660	41	37	40	95	275	405	675
9-3 to 9-9	32	26	85	150	275	370	590	37	32	45	120	310	485	770
9-9 to 10-3	31	26	70	120	280	425	745	35	28	35	75	245	405	665
10-3 to 10-9	29	24	90	155	310	440	880	35	27	25	60	235	380	620
10-9 to 11-3	28	24	65	135	280	405	740	35	30	35	75	190	405	610
11-3 to 11-9	29	25	70	115	325	425	860	33	26	40	75	215	490	830
11-9 to 12-3	29	25	45	90	305	425	590	30	24	35	70	225	430	780
12-3 to 12-9	28	24	75	135	300	480	750	30	25	40	80	145	320	560
12-9 to 13-3	27	21	85	145	285	435	825	30	25	35	70	125	345	610
13-3 to 13-9	25	21	85	175	355	460	830	26	22	35	70	125	260	580
13-9 to 14-3	23	20	110	180	270	500	680	26	22	25	55	95	270	530
14-3 to 14-9	20	16	150	230	350	455	610	25	20	35	75	140	295	680
14-9 to 15-3	15	14	60	175	330	455	520	24	21	40	75	135	305	710
15-3 to 15-9	15	14	70	235	330	430	595	21	16	40	80	145	305	1030
15-9 to 16-3	16	15	95	155	290	405	515	18	15	35	75	135	375	925
16-3 to 16-9	13	12	85	150	300	565	715	18	15	55	95	155	290	535
16-9 to 17-3	10	9						18	15	75	120	205	325	455
17-3 to 17-9	-	-	-	-	-	-	-	16	13	45	90	170	285	440
17-9 to 18-0	-	-	-	-	-	-	-	14	13	40	75	175	345	445

NUTRITION

TABLE D-17

Daily Ascorbic Acid Intake - Male

Age Range Yr. Mo.	Diet N	Mg. Percentiles 10th	25th	50th	75th	90th	Mg./kg. Wt. Percentiles 10th	50th	90th	Supplement N	Mg. Med.	Range Min.	Max.
0-0 to 0-1	33	<1	<1	<1	<1	<1	0.01	0.04	0.07	21	17	3	75
0-1 to 0-2	39	<1	<1	1	1	8	0.03	0.17	1.42	35	27	4	84
0-2 to 0-3	42	<1	1	2	3	12	0.07	0.33	1.42	38	29	11	88
0-3 to 0-4	44	1	1	3	6	24	0.08	0.39	3.59	41	28	2	93
0-4 to 0-5	46	2	3	6	18	26	0.24	0.67	3.96	42	30	6	88
0-5 to 0-6	45	2	4	6	21	33	0.27	0.84	4.49	41	32	8	95
0-6 to 0-9	46	3	6	15	29	39	0.35	2.09	4.67	40	28	8	75
0-9 to 1-0	49	7	11	22	37	62	0.70	2.16	6.27	40	28	1	69
1-0 to 1-3	47	9	15	33	50	82	0.98	3.19	6.98	33	29	2	63
1-3 to 1-6	46	14	28	44	61	84	1.56	4.07	6.92	34	24	2	56
1-6 to 1-9	45	17	30	48	68	86	1.55	3.85	7.17	29	30	2	56
1-9 to 2-0	44	22	32	47	70	86	1.82	4.23	7.58	24	24	2	61
2-0 to 2-3	45	23	34	54	69	80	1.89	4.08	6.67	29	26	1	65
2-3 to 2-6	44	19	30	46	72	89	1.48	3.55	6.68	28	26	1	135
2-6 to 2-9	45	21	33	51	70	99	1.61	3.85	6.76	25	33	2	135
2-9 to 3-0	43	20	32	58	78	93	1.36	3.75	6.77	21	21	1	75
3-0 to 3-3	39	20	29	50	78	89	1.41	3.34	6.35	21	20	1	77
3-3 to 3-6	39	27	37	55	76	87	1.64	3.59	6.00	25	24	1	75
3-6 to 3-9	40	22	35	54	75	90	1.71	3.58	6.20	24	33	2	135
3-9 to 4-0	39	29	36	48	66	83	1.89	3.11	5.06	24	28	1	92
4-3 to 4-9	40	25	38	59	77	93	1.41	3.38	5.52	26	25	1	214
4-9 to 5-3	38	29	40	55	75	97	1.51	3.04	5.12	24	18	1	73
5-3 to 5-9	38	26	38	64	84	102	1.29	3.36	5.28	26	19	1	72
5-9 to 6-3	37	28	37	56	81	101	1.29	2.65	5.10	22	24	1	75
6-3 to 6-9	36	30	41	56	77	100	1.32	2.62	4.54	23	21	1	140
6-9 to 7-3	35	35	44	60	90	111	1.41	2.78	4.66	20	11	1	70
7-3 to 7-9	32	34	47	67	89	108	1.43	2.69	4.35	20	27	1	132
7-9 to 8-3	34	32	44	65	92	117	1.13	2.54	4.46	20	17	1	90
8-3 to 8-9	32	38	50	69	91	116	1.26	2.54	4.18	18	19	1	100
8-9 to 9-3	31	31	43	68	98	128	1.06	2.42	4.35	17	12	1	125
9-3 to 9-9	32	40	49	72	93	107	1.21	2.34	3.77	17	9	1	75
9-9 to 10-3	31	34	45	75	94	111	1.09	2.29	3.21	16	15	1	75
10-3 to 10-9	29	39	52	72	92	118	1.12	2.01	3.50	18	14	1	82
10-9 to 11-3	28	30	49	70	97	112	0.87	1.94	3.28	15	16	1	84
11-3 to 11-9	29	32	44	70	104	131	0.90	1.79	3.72	18	11	1	150
11-9 to 12-3	29	37	46	76	113	128	0.85	1.84	3.41	16	12	1	150
12-3 to 12-9	28	36	44	70	108	132	0.81	1.69	3.40	16	20	1	115
12-9 to 13-3	27	26	49	77	104	132	0.55	1.57	3.23	16	17	1	287
13-3 to 13-9	25	33	50	71	105	138	0.69	1.52	2.99	15	29	1	331
13-9 to 14-3	23	36	52	70	107	129	0.64	1.47	2.80	12	39	1	719
14-3 to 14-9	20	30	45	78	107	143	0.55	1.47	3.25	11	35	1	353
14-9 to 15-3	15	28	39	59	100	140	0.43	1.19	2.86	9	-	1	361
15-3 to 15-9	15	24	36	62	113	143	0.35	1.14	2.61	9	-	2	361
15-9 to 16-3	16	25	40	68	98	131	0.32	1.08	2.66	9	-	1	391
16-3 to 16-9	13	20	45	73	106	142	0.31	1.29	2.37	8	-	1	390
16-9 to 17-3	10	24	40	78	108	142	0.37	1.12	2.99	6	-	2	250

NUTRITION

TABLE D-18

Daily Ascorbic Acid Intake - Female

	Diet									Supplement			
		Mg.					Mg./kg. Wt.				Mg.		
Age Range		Percentiles					Percentiles					Range	
Yr. Mo.	N	10th	25th	50th	75th	90th	10th	50th	90th	N	Med.	Min.	Max.
0-0 to 0-1	23	<1	<1	<1	<1	<1	<0.01	<0.01	<0.01	14	22	1	86
0-1 to 0-2	30	<1	<1	1	1	5	0.04	0.21	1.26	28	25	4	82
0-2 to 0-3	32	<1	1	2	3	17	0.09	0.44	3.86	30	30	1	80
0-3 to 0-4	34	1	2	4	6	20	0.13	0.64	3.58	31	29	9	82
0-4 to 0-5	37	1	2	4	9	20	0.14	0.68	2.81	35	30	3	84
0-5 to 0-6	38	1	2	6	15	30	0.16	0.82	4.37	35	30	4	68
0-6 to 0-9	41	3	5	10	22	33	0.33	1.38	4.52	36	30	1	70
0-9 to 1-0	44	4	9	20	40	60	0.42	2.30	6.16	37	29	1	109
1-0 to 1-3	45	6	14	29	44	58	0.73	3.07	6.53	32	29	2	112
1-3 to 1-6	45	12	24	37	52	68	1.21	3.78	6.49	33	30	3	50
1-6 to 1-9	44	17	27	40	66	83	1.59	3.76	7.96	30	33	3	71
1-9 to 2-0	45	13	26	47	67	79	1.18	3.87	6.69	33	30	2	100
2-0 to 2-3	47	15	30	44	69	88	1.24	3.67	7.12	31	36	2	70
2-3 to 2-6	48	14	29	46	66	79	1.07	3.74	6.49	30	37	2	58
2-6 to 2-9	46	14	29	51	69	86	1.13	4.11	6.27	28	28	3	80
2-9 to 3-0	45	23	32	50	70	92	1.75	3.48	6.84	26	26	1	75
3-0 to 3-3	44	24	40	57	70	80	1.70	4.16	6.15	25	28	4	54
3-3 to 3-6	44	24	39	53	70	83	1.74	3.72	5.70	22	30	1	60
3-6 to 3-9	45	29	45	67	83	98	2.09	4.31	6.70	22	19	1	60
3-9 to 4-0	43	28	39	52	74	99	1.88	3.52	6.14	24	23	1	75
4-3 to 4-9	42	24	39	60	79	98	1.45	3.52	5.74	30	22	1	135
4-9 to 5-3	41	29	46	59	78	99	1.51	3.28	5.48	27	28	1	77
5-3 to 5-9	41	28	44	63	78	103	1.51	3.20	5.53	25	14	1	71
5-9 to 6-3	40	32	45	62	82	109	1.51	3.17	5.48	26	20	1	81
6-3 to 6-9	41	31	44	65	85	102	1.38	3.28	5.15	22	20	1	75
6-9 to 7-3	42	36	54	67	87	113	1.55	2.97	4.90	25	23	1	199
7-3 to 7-9	41	34	52	67	85	110	1.24	2.79	4.71	22	26	1	75
7-9 to 8-3	41	32	53	70	97	112	1.22	2.79	4.59	23	20	1	75
8-3 to 8-9	39	35	49	70	102	127	1.09	2.69	4.69	25	19	1	78
8-9 to 9-3	41	29	51	69	99	127	0.98	2.42	4.74	24	13	1	108
9-3 to 9-9	37	30	52	77	103	119	0.94	2.71	4.06	26	20	1	84
9-9 to 10-3	35	40	54	70	97	122	1.18	2.31	3.69	19	14	1	75
10-3 to 10-9	35	41	56	79	94	122	1.17	2.23	3.47	16	16	1	87
10-9 to 11-3	35	44	58	77	100	122	1.08	2.17	3.81	19	14	1	124
11-3 to 11-9	33	41	57	78	100	131	0.98	2.14	3.24	22	15	1	163
11-9 to 12-3	30	39	54	75	111	145	0.87	1.92	3.31	16	15	1	100
12-3 to 12-9	30	40	57	81	112	155	0.95	1.91	3.62	16	10	1	100
12-9 to 13-3	30	39	65	86	111	145	0.85	1.81	3.39	14	15	1	100
13-3 to 13-9	26	46	62	92	120	153	0.92	1.90	3.42	10	9	1	50
13-9 to 14-3	26	44	69	82	120	147	0.77	1.68	3.27	10	10	1	50
14-3 to 14-9	25	37	56	79	109	143	0.69	1.46	2.59	10	7	1	63
14-9 to 15-3	24	37	53	81	116	147	0.59	1.40	2.83	11	10	1	128
15-3 to 15-9	21	32	49	83	110	151	0.53	1.38	2.74	6		1	52
15-9 to 16-3	18	27	46	66	94	162	0.50	1.19	2.91	8		1	50
16-3 to 16-9	18	43	59	81	110	164	0.72	1.41	2.83	9		1	50
16-9 to 17-3	18	39	57	78	114	161	0.59	1.45	2.84	10	9	1	53
17-3 to 17-9	16	52	65	101	119	170	0.87	1.66	2.88	8		1	219
17-9 to 18-0	14	47	64	78	92	131	0.67	1.35	2.19	8		1	38

NUTRITION

TABLE D-19

Daily Thiamine Intake - Male

Age Range Yr. Mo.	Diet												Supplement			
	N	Mg.					Mcg./kg. Wt.			Mg./1000 Cals.			N	Mg.		
		Percentiles					Percentiles			Percentiles					Range	
		10th	25th	50th	75th	90th	10th	50th	90th	10th	50th	90th		Med.	Min.	Max.
0-0 to 0-1	33	0.08	0.10	0.13	0.16	0.22	25	36	65	0.25	0.31	0.44	11	0.20	0.07	0.59
0-1 to 0-2	39	0.14	0.17	0.21	0.31	0.38	33	49	90	0.27	0.36	0.68	17	0.42	0.02	1.30
0-2 to 0-3	42	0.18	0.21	0.26	0.39	0.56	35	48	103	0.28	0.42	0.78	12	0.50	0.02	1.34
0-3 to 0-4	44	0.20	0.24	0.31	0.45	0.57	32	53	105	0.31	0.49	0.91	14	0.44	0.01	1.32
0-4 to 0-5	46	0.26	0.31	0.41	0.56	0.75	40	60	113	0.39	0.59	1.06	13	0.49	0.22	1.00
0-5 to 0-6	45	0.30	0.37	0.49	0.63	0.87	39	70	110	0.43	0.63	1.07	14	0.44	0.20	1.00
0-6 to 0-9	46	0.40	0.51	0.62	0.77	0.91	46	77	108	0.52	0.72	1.16	14	0.47	0.12	1.00
0-9 to 1-0	49	0.51	0.62	0.73	0.89	1.14	53	78	115	0.54	0.75	1.11	18	0.53	0.02	1.47
1-0 to 1-3	47	0.41	0.54	0.74	0.88	1.01	38	70	103	0.44	0.64	1.01	18	0.55	0.06	2.01
1-3 to 1-6	46	0.44	0.58	0.74	0.93	1.03	41	66	101	0.46	0.61	0.91	22	0.46	0.01	3.00
1-6 to 1-9	45	0.44	0.54	0.64	0.81	0.95	34	52	85	0.45	0.54	0.67	20	0.64	0.06	2.25
1-9 to 2-0	44	0.43	0.50	0.60	0.79	0.89	32	49	77	0.41	0.48	0.63	17	0.58	0.04	2.00
2-0 to 2-3	45	0.47	0.55	0.62	0.79	0.91	34	48	71	0.42	0.49	0.61	22	0.62	0.01	1.24
2-3 to 2-6	44	0.45	0.55	0.67	0.81	0.93	33	50	73	0.41	0.47	0.59	23	0.59	0.02	1.51
2-6 to 2-9	45	0.46	0.56	0.67	0.83	0.93	34	50	64	0.41	0.49	0.60	22	0.58	0.01	1.50
2-9 to 3-0	43	0.51	0.59	0.67	0.81	0.96	35	49	63	0.40	0.47	0.56	16	0.51	0.02	1.50
3-0 to 3-3	39	0.50	0.60	0.72	0.84	1.01	34	48	64	0.42	0.49	0.56	16	0.53	0.01	1.50
3-3 to 3-6	39	0.55	0.61	0.71	0.87	0.99	33	48	66	0.41	0.48	0.58	22	0.42	0.01	2.08
3-6 to 3-9	40	0.53	0.62	0.72	0.87	1.04	31	49	62	0.41	0.48	0.58	18	0.85	0.04	2.73
3-9 to 4-0	39	0.52	0.59	0.70	0.88	0.97	33	45	61	0.39	0.46	0.55	16	0.89	0.03	3.25
4-3 to 4-9	40	0.55	0.64	0.75	0.94	1.07	32	44	62	0.43	0.49	0.58	18	0.97	0.21	2.80
4-9 to 5-3	38	0.60	0.69	0.81	0.93	1.04	30	44	58	↓	↓	↓	19	0.73	0.01	4.20
5-3 to 5-9	38	0.62	0.70	0.81	1.00	1.13	32	41	59	↓	↓	↓	22	0.63	0.01	2.50
5-9 to 6-3	37	0.68	0.73	0.83	1.02	1.17	31	40	55	↓	↓	↓	16	0.74	0.03	2.14
6-3 to 6-9	36	0.75	0.81	0.92	1.07	1.21	31	41	55	↓	↓	↓	20	0.64	0.01	3.00
6-9 to 7-3	35	0.75	0.82	0.96	1.14	1.28	31	40	55	↓	↓	↓	15	0.59	0.02	2.50
7-3 to 7-9	32	0.82	0.87	0.98	1.14	1.34	31	40	54	↓	↓	↓	15	1.02	0.01	2.31
7-9 to 8-3	34	0.79	0.86	0.99	1.19	1.40	29	37	55	↓	↓	↓	14	0.79	0.02	2.50
8-3 to 8-9	32	0.84	0.91	1.08	1.30	1.45	28	39	52	↓	↓	↓	12	1.10	0.01	2.77
8-9 to 9-3	31	0.81	0.91	1.16	1.32	1.52	27	37	50	↓	↓	↓	14	0.54	0.01	2.78
9-3 to 9-9	32	0.89	0.97	1.16	1.34	1.45	26	36	47	↓	↓	↓	10	0.43	0.02	8.00
9-9 to 10-3	31	0.90	0.96	1.15	1.31	1.53	26	33	46	↓	↓	↓	11	0.83	0.01	8.00
10-3 to 10-9	29	0.91	0.99	1.13	1.34	1.55	24	32	42	↓	↓	↓	12	0.78	0.01	3.73
10-9 to 11-3	28	0.92	0.98	1.20	1.32	1.58	24	31	40	↓	↓	↓	11	0.28	0.04	3.00
11-3 to 11-9	29	0.97	1.04	1.26	1.42	1.56	23	31	40	↓	↓	↓	12	0.33	0.05	3.00
11-9 to 12-3	29	0.98	1.11	1.27	1.50	1.74	22	30	42	↓	↓	↓	9	-	0.01	2.52
12-3 to 12-9	28	0.91	1.11	1.27	1.51	1.75	20	27	40	↓	↓	↓	11	0.34	0.01	3.21
12-9 to 13-3	27	0.95	1.03	1.26	1.45	1.74	19	26	38	↓	↓	↓	11	0.72	0.01	13.87
13-3 to 13-9	25	0.93	1.02	1.20	1.46	1.86	18	25	38	↓	↓	↓	10	1.54	0.01	15.32
13-9 to 14-3	23	0.95	1.05	1.21	1.43	1.90	17	24	37	↓	↓	↓	7	-	0.04	15.12
14-3 to 14-9	20	0.97	1.07	1.20	1.47	1.75	16	22	36	↓	↓	↓	7	-	0.02	15.04
14-9 to 15-3	15	1.01	1.08	1.38	1.63	1.81	15	23	36	↓	↓	↓	8	-	0.04	15.07
15-3 to 15-9	15	0.98	1.10	1.36	1.60	1.83	14	23	33	↓	↓	↓	7	-	0.01	15.05
15-9 to 16-3	16	0.98	1.14	1.29	1.55	1.84	13	21	33	↓	↓	↓	6	-	0.01	15.07
16-3 to 16-9	13	1.06	1.14	1.32	1.74	1.93	15	21	36	↓	↓	↓	4	-	0.05	15.00
16-9 to 17-3	10	1.15	1.26	1.40	1.66	2.00	15	22	31	0.43	0.49	0.58	3	-	0.14	3.18

NUTRITION

TABLE D-20

Daily Thiamine Intake - Female

Age Range	Diet												Supplement		
		Mg.					Mcg./kg. Wt.			Mg./1000 Cals.				Mg.		
		Percentiles					Percentiles			Percentiles					Range	
Yr. Mo.	N	10th	25th	50th	75th	90th	10th	50th	90th	10th	50th	90th	N	Med.	Min.	Max.
0-0 to 0-1	23	0.08	0.09	0.12	0.16	0.27	27	37	79	0.26	0.33	0.87	5	-	0.11	0.40
0-1 to 0-2	30	0.13	0.15	0.19	0.27	0.47	31	47	104	0.23	0.39	0.76	11	0.35	0.13	1.00
0-2 to 0-3	32	0.17	0.20	0.24	0.31	0.56	30	48	117	0.30	0.45	1.01	12	0.54	0.11	1.18
0-3 to 0-4	34	0.20	0.25	0.30	0.48	0.65	31	57	119	0.30	0.49	1.10	12	0.52	0.10	1.62
0-4 to 0-5	37	0.26	0.34	0.42	0.56	0.84	38	64	144	0.37	0.62	1.21	13	0.46	0.04	1.74
0-5 to 0-6	38	0.31	0.36	0.44	0.63	0.85	45	69	122	0.46	0.66	1.07	14	0.61	0.10	1.62
0-6 to 0-9	41	0.40	0.47	0.56	0.73	0.85	51	73	118	0.56	0.72	1.14	14	0.75	0.03	1.58
0-9 to 1-0	44	0.46	0.51	0.62	0.76	0.86	47	74	100	0.50	0.69	1.00	19	0.62	0.05	1.58
1-0 to 1-3	45	0.42	0.46	0.62	0.72	0.84	43	63	89	0.48	0.59	0.86	17	0.63	0.04	1.42
1-3 to 1-6	45	0.45	0.52	0.61	0.72	0.78	43	62	77	0.45	0.58	0.72	21	0.64	0.04	1.18
1-6 to 1-9	44	0.47	0.52	0.58	0.71	0.80	40	54	75	0.44	0.52	0.68	20	0.89	0.01	3.75
1-9 to 2-0	45	0.47	0.52	0.59	0.71	0.81	39	53	70	0.42	0.51	0.63	21	0.92	0.05	3.75
2-0 to 2-3	47	0.48	0.53	0.64	0.74	0.81	39	51	71	0.43	0.51	0.66	21	0.75	0.05	1.72
2-3 to 2-6	48	0.46	0.52	0.63	0.75	0.82	35	49	69	0.40	0.51	0.63	21	0.67	0.07	1.50
2-6 to 2-9	46	0.44	0.52	0.60	0.74	0.84	32	45	64	0.41	0.50	0.62	19	0.51	0.04	2.23
2-9 to 3-0	45	0.42	0.54	0.64	0.73	0.81	30	46	61	0.39	0.49	0.57	19	0.63	0.04	2.50
3-0 to 3-3	44	0.47	0.55	0.67	0.74	0.84	33	45	61	0.41	0.49	0.61	21	0.62	0.07	2.50
3-3 to 3-6	44	0.46	0.55	0.64	0.72	0.82	30	43	59	0.40	0.49	0.57	15	0.64	0.02	2.50
3-6 to 3-9	45	0.41	0.54	0.69	0.79	0.88	28	44	58	0.41	0.49	0.61	19	0.49	0.01	5.05
3-9 to 4-0	43	0.44	0.56	0.68	0.76	0.90	28	41	56	0.41	0.47	0.61	21	0.70	0.03	7.71
4-3 to 4-9	42	0.48	0.65	0.76	0.84	0.93	28	42	54	0.41	0.49	0.58	22	0.83	0.01	5.50
4-9 to 5-3	41	0.54	0.62	0.76	0.86	0.96	28	40	54	↓	↓	↓	22	0.97	0.01	3.67
5-3 to 5-9	41	0.54	0.66	0.78	0.87	1.01	27	38	52	↓	↓	↓	21	0.87	0.01	3.57
5-9 to 6-3	40	0.60	0.68	0.78	0.86	1.00	27	38	50	↓	↓	↓	25	0.52	0.01	3.23
6-3 to 6-9	41	0.65	0.72	0.80	0.95	1.05	27	38	50	↓	↓	↓	21	0.80	0.01	2.50
6-9 to 7-3	42	0.63	0.71	0.85	0.97	1.15	26	36	51	↓	↓	↓	23	0.92	0.01	3.00
7-3 to 7-9	41	0.61	0.71	0.88	1.01	1.12	24	35	47	↓	↓	↓	21	0.80	0.02	3.00
7-9 to 8-3	41	0.67	0.76	0.90	1.03	1.14	24	34	44	↓	↓	↓	25	0.81	0.01	3.00
8-3 to 8-9	39	0.67	0.79	0.92	1.08	1.19	22	32	46	↓	↓	↓	22	0.82	0.05	3.00
8-9 to 9-3	41	0.69	0.78	0.89	1.06	1.21	21	31	42	↓	↓	↓	23	0.49	0.01	2.89
9-3 to 9-9	37	0.71	0.82	0.92	1.03	1.20	21	30	38	↓	↓	↓	20	1.14	0.01	2.93
9-9 to 10-3	35	0.71	0.85	0.96	1.08	1.22	20	29	38	↓	↓	↓	14	0.74	0.02	3.39
10-3 to 10-9	35	0.74	0.87	0.99	1.15	1.24	20	28	38	↓	↓	↓	13	0.95	0.01	3.40
10-9 to 11-3	35	0.75	0.86	1.01	1.12	1.27	18	28	39	↓	↓	↓	15	0.89	0.01	2.85
11-3 to 11-9	33	0.76	0.89	1.05	1.16	1.32	17	27	36	↓	↓	↓	12	1.40	0.05	3.00
11-9 to 12-3	30	0.77	0.89	1.03	1.17	1.29	16	25	34	↓	↓	↓	11	1.11	0.03	2.50
12-3 to 12-9	30	0.71	0.88	1.03	1.25	1.47	14	24	33	↓	↓	↓	10	0.48	0.03	3.94
12-9 to 13-3	30	0.70	0.84	1.03	1.23	1.35	14	22	32	↓	↓	↓	12	0.36	0.01	4.00
13-3 to 13-9	26	0.73	0.82	1.02	1.29	1.40	13	22	30	↓	↓	↓	9	-	0.04	4.00
13-9 to 14-3	26	0.70	0.78	1.04	1.23	1.40	12	21	28	↓	↓	↓	9	-	0.01	4.00
14-3 to 14-9	25	0.66	0.80	1.08	1.19	1.41	11	19	27	↓	↓	↓	10	0.61	0.01	4.00
14-9 to 15-3	24	0.65	0.79	0.96	1.20	1.35	10	17	26	↓	↓	↓	9	-	0.01	7.72
15-3 to 15-9	21	0.59	0.75	0.96	1.18	1.42	10	17	26	↓	↓	↓	5	-	0.01	5.00
15-9 to 16-3	18	0.59	0.77	0.90	1.21	1.38	9	16	24	↓	↓	↓	6	-	0.01	4.33
16-3 to 16-9	18	0.54	0.70	0.93	1.25	1.36	9	16	25	↓	↓	↓	6	-	0.02	2.50
16-9 to 17-3	18	0.59	0.67	0.88	1.22	1.40	9	16	23	↓	↓	↓	8	-	0.04	5.00
17-3 to 17-9	16	0.50	0.65	0.99	1.13	1.40	8	16	24	↓	↓	↓	5	-	0.02	5.00
17-9 to 18-0	14	0.40	0.52	0.87	1.11	1.28	5	15	22	0.41	0.49	0.58	6	-	0.01	3.35

NUTRITION

TABLE D-21

Daily Riboflavin Intake - Male

Age Range Yr. Mo.	Diet											Supplement			
	N	Mg.					Mcg./kg. Wt.					N	Mg.		
		Percentiles					Percentiles							Range	
		10th	25th	50th	75th	90th	10th	25th	50th	75th	90th		Med.	Min.	Max.
0-0 to 0-1	33	0.49	0.63	0.81	0.95	1.02	156	185	225	255	303	9	-	0.01	0.47
0-1 to 0-2	39	0.74	1.00	1.18	1.31	1.47	177	222	261	305	341	13	0.26	0.04	0.80
0-2 to 0-3	42	0.81	1.08	1.33	1.50	1.63	153	194	244	274	307	11	0.42	0.10	0.80
0-3 to 0-4	44	0.89	1.14	1.33	1.52	1.75	151	180	215	247	277	13	0.34	0.01	0.80
0-4 to 0-5	46	1.01	1.24	1.45	1.75	1.91	155	181	212	248	271	12	0.41	0.09	0.60
0-5 to 0-6	45	1.09	1.35	1.57	1.77	1.99	152	182	216	238	277	13	0.41	0.07	0.53
0-6 to 0-9	46	1.39	1.53	1.70	1.91	2.14	162	183	206	244	259	13	0.37	0.27	1.59
0-9 to 1-0	49	1.41	1.63	1.82	2.03	2.29	142	168	190	215	238	18	0.44	0.01	1.66
1-0 to 1-3	47	1.15	1.37	1.66	2.04	2.30	104	135	164	190	213	18	0.39	0.07	1.67
1-3 to 1-6	46	1.05	1.35	1.60	1.98	2.33	87	121	145	174	209	20	0.29	0.02	3.00
1-6 to 1-9	45	0.92	1.17	1.47	1.71	2.12	80	97	124	145	169	20	0.44	0.05	2.25
1-9 to 2-0	44	0.83	1.16	1.37	1.61	2.13	69	89	115	138	172	17	0.40	0.02	2.00
2-0 to 2-3	45	0.79	1.09	1.35	1.67	1.98	66	87	108	130	150	20	0.52	0.01	1.29
2-3 to 2-6	44	0.95	1.13	1.35	1.67	2.06	68	85	104	127	159	19	0.49	0.02	1.91
2-6 to 2-9	45	0.85	1.16	1.43	1.82	2.27	61	83	102	122	165	21	0.64	0.01	1.42
2-9 to 3-0	43	1.03	1.19	1.41	1.69	2.11	73	86	99	121	148	13	0.49	0.05	1.20
3-0 to 3-3	39	0.94	1.14	1.42	1.81	2.35	65	77	96	123	145	14	0.47	0.03	1.23
3-3 to 3-6	39	0.99	1.19	1.45	1.73	2.24	65	77	94	117	133	20	0.42	0.01	2.08
3-6 to 3-9	40	1.06	1.21	1.47	1.83	2.20	66	80	95	119	138	17	0.92	0.05	2.54
3-9 to 4-0	39	1.10	1.22	1.47	1.80	2.27	68	77	90	111	147	16	0.99	0.02	3.25
4-3 to 4-9	40	1.09	1.28	1.56	1.92	2.17	63	75	90	110	125	17	1.12	0.21	2.10
4-9 to 5-3	38	1.17	1.40	1.68	1.91	2.07	63	75	91	106	117	17	0.89	0.01	2.79
5-3 to 5-9	38	1.27	1.45	1.78	2.01	2.30	63	74	91	102	122	19	0.79	0.02	2.50
5-9 to 6-3	37	1.45	1.65	1.82	2.07	2.32	64	75	88	103	112	15	0.82	0.03	2.29
6-3 to 6-9	36	1.56	1.72	1.88	2.13	2.44	66	75	85	98	113	18	0.61	0.06	3.00
6-9 to 7-3	35	1.58	1.70	1.88	2.17	2.44	64	71	82	94	107	15	0.43	0.01	2.50
7-3 to 7-9	32	1.55	1.79	1.99	2.26	2.45	60	70	81	92	105	15	0.93	0.01	2.39
7-9 to 8-3	34	1.54	1.72	2.01	2.42	2.64	57	66	78	93	104	14	0.75	0.02	2.50
8-3 to 8-9	32	1.59	1.85	2.05	2.46	2.82	56	65	78	90	98	13	0.89	0.02	2.77
8-9 to 9-3	31	1.54	1.93	2.13	2.55	2.88	54	62	73	86	94	14	0.54	0.01	2.78
9-3 to 9-9	32	1.72	1.96	2.17	2.56	2.79	51	60	70	80	90	11	0.34	0.02	4.50
9-9 to 10-3	31	1.84	2.06	2.25	2.54	2.80	54	60	68	75	83	12	0.76	0.01	4.50
10-3 to 10-9	29	1.80	2.03	2.33	2.56	2.70	52	59	66	72	78	11	0.78	0.01	3.10
10-9 to 11-3	28	1.79	2.07	2.33	2.57	2.90	49	56	63	70	76	9	-	0.01	3.00
11-3 to 11-9	29	2.02	2.24	2.48	2.74	3.08	49	55	63	71	78	12	0.47	0.07	3.00
11-9 to 12-3	29	1.96	2.25	2.51	2.90	3.21	47	52	58	71	78	10	0.52	0.01	2.50
12-3 to 12-9	28	1.75	2.18	2.68	3.16	3.59	42	48	59	73	82	9	-	0.02	2.85
12-9 to 13-3	27	1.87	2.22	2.59	3.20	3.61	40	46	55	69	78	10	0.78	0.02	9.08
13-3 to 13-9	25	1.63	2.28	2.56	3.09	3.63	38	44	52	68	77	10	1.01	0.01	10.00
13-9 to 14-3	23	1.59	2.08	2.56	3.05	3.66	34	40	49	61	76	6	-	0.10	10.00
14-3 to 14-9	20	1.51	1.92	2.51	3.06	3.84	30	34	47	58	70	7	-	0.02	10.00
14-9 to 15-3	15	1.75	2.18	2.44	3.19	4.22	30	34	46	63	73	8	-	0.04	10.00
15-3 to 15-9	15	1.58	2.21	2.66	3.13	3.64	27	34	43	60	70	6	-	0.08	10.00
15-9 to 16-3	16	1.84	2.22	2.63	3.25	3.58	27	34	42	53	59	5	-	0.01	10.00
16-3 to 16-9	13	1.91	2.37	2.91	3.37	3.90	26	35	46	55	62	4	-	0.17	10.00
16-9 to 17-3	10	2.18	2.42	2.92	3.42	4.22	34	36	43	54	76	4	-	0.01	2.85

NUTRITION

TABLE D-22

Daily Riboflavin Intake - Female

Age Range Yr. Mo.	Diet											Supplement			
		Mg.					Mcg./kg. Wt.						Mg.		
		Percentiles					Percentiles							Range	
	N	10th	25th	50th	75th	90th	10th	25th	50th	75th	90th	N	Med.	Min.	Max.
0-0 to 0-1	23	0.53	0.65	0.79	0.87	1.09	143	191	227	270	294	4	-	0.05	0.60
0-1 to 0-2	30	0.75	0.88	1.09	1.20	1.41	163	219	272	294	336	10	0.19	0.04	0.80
0-2 to 0-3	32	0.60	0.95	1.19	1.36	1.52	139	203	237	265	305	11	0.55	0.05	1.23
0-3 to 0-4	34	0.76	1.07	1.35	1.47	1.62	128	202	237	263	283	11	0.32	0.05	1.85
0-4 to 0-5	37	0.99	1.25	1.44	1.67	1.86	163	193	226	261	284	12	0.27	0.06	2.19
0-5 to 0-6	38	1.03	1.33	1.48	1.70	1.92	142	188	219	246	292	14	0.36	0.05	2.27
0-6 to 0-9	41	1.33	1.46	1.61	1.75	2.00	162	189	207	218	256	14	0.40	0.03	2.17
0-9 to 1-0	44	1.29	1.42	1.54	1.78	2.05	139	159	171	209	233	19	0.44	0.04	2.16
1-0 to 1-3	45	1.10	1.38	1.61	1.80	1.96	121	139	160	183	207	17	0.55	0.09	1.92
1-3 to 1-6	45	1.08	1.28	1.48	1.70	1.88	106	125	145	169	190	21	0.43	0.05	1.42
1-6 to 1-9	44	1.04	1.26	1.44	1.63	2.02	99	110	125	155	192	20	0.73	0.01	1.80
1-9 to 2-0	45	1.08	1.21	1.36	1.64	2.04	93	106	120	144	181	21	0.73	0.02	3.00
2-0 to 2-3	47	1.09	1.25	1.41	1.64	1.81	86	100	117	130	151	21	0.71	0.04	2.10
2-3 to 2-6	48	0.98	1.16	1.35	1.57	1.86	72	95	108	126	150	21	0.59	0.05	1.50
2-6 to 2-9	46	0.93	1.16	1.37	1.59	1.81	72	87	104	119	144	19	0.39	0.04	2.40
2-9 to 3-0	45	0.97	1.11	1.36	1.57	1.86	64	84	100	113	137	18	0.65	0.03	2.50
3-0 to 3-3	44	0.87	1.14	1.35	1.54	1.88	61	77	91	111	140	22	0.51	0.01	2.50
3-3 to 3-6	44	0.90	1.07	1.34	1.66	1.90	62	71	88	110	134	15	0.45	0.01	2.50
3-6 to 3-9	45	0.79	1.14	1.37	1.60	2.08	55	73	91	105	131	18	0.38	0.01	2.50
3-9 to 4-0	43	0.88	1.14	1.37	1.68	2.07	55	74	88	106	130	20	0.42	0.02	3.00
4-3 to 4-9	42	1.04	1.25	1.53	1.84	2.03	57	74	89	107	121	22	0.87	0.01	5.50
4-9 to 5-3	41	0.98	1.23	1.61	1.87	2.19	55	70	86	102	118	20	1.06	0.01	3.13
5-3 to 5-9	41	0.99	1.34	1.60	1.88	2.20	54	67	85	99	115	20	0.93	0.02	3.57
5-9 to 6-3	40	1.11	1.37	1.61	1.92	2.22	55	65	82	98	110	25	0.50	0.01	3.23
6-3 to 6-9	41	1.22	1.47	1.76	2.02	2.24	59	67	80	96	108	21	0.70	0.01	3.00
6-9 to 7-3	42	1.28	1.57	1.84	2.12	2.33	56	64	79	91	105	22	0.94	0.02	3.00
7-3 to 7-9	41	1.23	1.60	1.84	2.13	2.42	49	62	75	86	104	21	0.94	0.08	3.00
7-9 to 8-3	41	1.35	1.61	1.93	2.19	2.44	49	61	74	85	98	24	0.93	0.01	3.00
8-3 to 8-9	39	1.43	1.68	1.89	2.18	2.56	48	59	70	82	96	22	0.88	0.07	3.00
8-9 to 9-3	41	1.48	1.67	1.87	2.15	2.46	45	54	67	78	88	22	0.62	0.01	3.00
9-3 to 9-9	37	1.40	1.67	1.92	2.17	2.36	44	51	63	74	81	20	0.98	0.02	2.93
9-9 to 10-3	35	1.52	1.72	1.98	2.14	2.34	42	51	60	69	76	14	0.80	0.02	3.57
10-3 to 10-9	35	1.54	1.76	1.99	2.23	2.48	42	48	56	67	81	12	0.83	0.01	3.40
10-9 to 11-3	35	1.55	1.73	1.99	2.29	2.52	37	47	55	65	76	15	0.87	0.09	2.68
11-3 to 11-9	33	1.54	1.82	2.15	2.42	2.59	34	46	54	65	75	11	1.17	0.03	2.86
11-9 to 12-3	30	1.52	1.74	2.14	2.41	2.74	33	42	50	63	70	12	0.84	0.01	2.50
12-3 to 12-9	30	1.53	1.76	2.01	2.49	2.79	32	36	47	57	66	11	0.42	0.03	1.97
12-9 to 13-3	30	1.45	1.76	2.01	2.44	2.77	31	36	44	55	62	12	0.39	0.01	3.00
13-3 to 13-9	26	1.46	1.77	2.14	2.52	2.70	27	34	46	54	58	9	-	0.02	2.36
13-9 to 14-3	26	1.43	1.67	1.99	2.38	2.64	25	32	40	49	57	9	-	0.02	2.00
14-3 to 14-9	25	1.29	1.58	1.94	2.47	2.96	23	28	38	49	57	10	0.38	0.01	2.50
14-9 to 15-3	24	1.29	1.54	1.90	2.40	3.25	20	27	35	48	58	8	-	0.04	5.57
15-3 to 15-9	21	1.12	1.47	1.98	2.53	3.05	17	25	37	47	58	5	-	0.01	3.00
15-9 to 16-3	18	1.07	1.56	1.94	2.46	2.76	17	27	34	45	52	6	-	0.01	2.91
16-3 to 16-9	18	1.05	1.38	1.71	2.30	2.57	18	24	29	42	49	6	-	0.02	2.50
16-9 to 17-3	18	1.04	1.33	1.70	2.34	2.60	16	23	29	41	46	8	-	0.03	3.00
17-3 to 17-9	16	0.79	1.24	1.79	2.30	2.67	13	21	29	40	46	5	-	0.01	3.00
17-9 to 18-0	14	0.63	1.01	1.65	2.21	2.47	10	15	26	37	43	6	-	0.01	2.18

NUTRITION

TABLE D-23

Daily Niacin Intake - Male

Age Range	Diet												Supplement			
		Mg.					Mg./kg. Wt.							Mg.		
		Percentiles					Percentiles								Range	
Yr. Mo.	N	10th	25th	50th	75th	90th	10th	25th	50th	75th	90th	N	Med.	Min.	Max.
0-0 to 0-1	33	0.3	0.4	0.5	0.6	0.6	0.09	0.10	0.13	0.16	0.19	10	0.6	0.3	3.7
0-1 to 0-2	39	0.5	0.7	0.9	1.3	1.8	0.11	0.14	0.19	0.30	0.41	16	2.6	0.3	12.0
0-2 to 0-3	42	0.6	0.8	1.1	1.8	2.9	0.12	0.15	0.21	0.35	0.54	12	3.2	0.6	9.4
0-3 to 0-4	44	0.8	1.1	1.5	2.0	2.9	0.13	0.17	0.24	0.31	0.49	14	2.6	0.2	12.0
0-4 to 0-5	46	1.0	1.5	2.0	2.9	4.2	0.15	0.22	0.31	0.43	0.61	13	4.0	0.4	12.0
0-5 to 0-6	45	1.4	1.9	2.7	3.4	4.7	0.18	0.24	0.35	0.49	0.67	14	3.5	0.5	5.0
0-6 to 0-9	46	2.1	2.8	3.5	4.8	6.0	0.25	0.33	0.43	0.60	0.71	14	4.5	0.3	7.9
0-9 to 1-0	49	3.1	3.7	4.6	6.2	8.1	0.32	0.38	0.49	0.66	0.81	18	3.7	0.3	16.0
1-0 to 1-3	47	2.9	3.6	4.8	6.6	7.9	0.29	0.35	0.49	0.60	0.77	18	3.2	0.6	13.4
1-3 to 1-6	46	3.5	4.5	5.9	7.9	8.6	0.31	0.41	0.53	0.68	0.80	21	3.1	0.1	20.0
1-6 to 1-9	45	3.2	3.9	5.6	7.5	8.8	0.28	0.36	0.47	0.63	0.76	20	4.3	0.4	15.0
1-9 to 2-0	44	3.2	4.7	5.8	7.5	9.4	0.28	0.38	0.50	0.64	0.74	18	4.6	0.1	11.3
2-0 to 2-3	45	4.1	4.8	6.4	7.9	9.1	0.30	0.39	0.52	0.64	0.74	20	4.3	0.1	16.0
2-3 to 2-6	44	4.5	5.1	6.5	8.2	9.6	0.33	0.40	0.49	0.62	0.78	19	4.8	0.2	11.3
2-6 to 2-9	45	4.6	5.3	6.7	8.1	9.7	0.34	0.41	0.49	0.58	0.64	21	4.4	0.1	10.0
2-9 to 3-0	43	4.8	5.8	7.3	8.5	9.9	0.36	0.41	0.49	0.57	0.66	14	4.1	0.1	10.0
3-0 to 3-3	39	4.9	5.7	7.1	9.0	11.0	0.34	0.40	0.49	0.58	0.74	13	4.3	C.2	10.0
3-3 to 3-6	39	5.0	5.7	7.6	9.3	10.6	0.34	0.41	0.47	0.62	0.74	21	2.8	0.1	16.6
3-6 to 3-9	40	4.8	5.7	7.1	8.9	11.4	0.33	0.37	0.46	0.58	0.69	17	5.2	0.3	18.3
3-9 to 4-0	39	5.3	6.2	7.5	8.5	11.1	0.34	0.40	0.47	0.55	0.63	16	5.2	0.2	20.1
4-3 to 4-9	40	5.9	6.8	7.9	9.0	11.3	0.36	0.40	0.45	0.55	0.68	17	6.4	1.7	17.0
4-9 to 5-3	38	6.6	7.3	8.5	10.0	11.8	0.35	0.39	0.47	0.57	0.68	17	5.4	0.4	21.7
5-3 to 5-9	38	7.0	7.7	8.7	10.0	12.2	0.35	0.39	0.45	0.54	0.64	20	4.4	0.2	15.2
5-9 to 6-3	37	7.4	8.5	9.7	10.7	12.3	0.34	0.38	0.47	0.54	0.60	16	4.9	0.1	15.6
6-3 to 6-9	36	8.1	8.7	9.8	11.5	13.6	0.34	0.39	0.45	0.54	0.62	18	4.7	0.7	20.0
6-9 to 7-3	35	8.1	9.1	10.4	12.8	15.1	0.35	0.39	0.46	0.54	0.61	14	3.8	0.2	20.0
7-3 to 7-9	32	8.9	9.9	11.0	12.6	14.4	0.34	0.38	0.45	0.51	0.58	15	7.3	0.1	16.1
7-9 to 8-3	34	9.0	9.7	10.7	13.4	15.6	0.35	0.38	0.42	0.48	0.58	13	7.0	0.8	20.0
8-3 to 8-9	32	9.0	10.5	11.8	13.4	15.3	0.33	0.37	0.43	0.49	0.54	11	9.4	0.2	23.2
8-9 to 9-3	31	9.5	10.8	12.4	13.6	15.1	0.32	0.36	0.41	0.45	0.50	12	4.9	0.2	23.1
9-3 to 9-9	32	10.4	11.3	12.7	14.5	15.8	0.31	0.34	0.41	0.45	0.52	10	3.2	0.2	30.0
9-9 to 10-3	31	11.0	11.6	13.1	14.6	16.1	0.31	0.35	0.39	0.45	0.51	10	4.6	0.1	30.0
10-3 to 10-9	29	10.4	11.3	13.0	14.8	16.7	0.29	0.32	0.37	0.43	0.47	12	5.1	0.2	24.5
10-9 to 11-3	28	11.2	12.1	13.7	15.3	17.0	0.29	0.32	0.36	0.42	0.46	8	-	0.1	20.0
11-3 to 11-9	29	11.1	12.7	14.2	16.0	17.5	0.28	0.31	0.36	0.40	0.44	11	3.4	0.5	20.0
11-9 to 12-3	29	11.2	12.7	14.6	16.5	19.3	0.28	0.30	0.34	0.39	0.48	8	-	0.3	20.0
12-3 to 12-9	28	10.6	12.9	14.4	16.2	19.2	0.25	0.28	0.32	0.38	0.42	9	-	0.1	29.7
12-9 to 13-3	27	10.9	12.2	14.5	16.7	18.7	0.23	0.25	0.29	0.37	0.48	11	6.9	0.1	45.4
13-3 to 13-9	25	10.3	11.7	14.4	17.4	19.9	0.20	0.24	0.28	0.39	0.46	9	-	0.1	50.0
13-9 to 14-3	23	10.8	12.7	14.8	17.0	21.9	0.20	0.24	0.29	0.38	0.45	6	-	0.8	50.0
14-3 to 14-9	20	11.5	12.8	14.8	17.8	20.1	0.19	0.24	0.28	0.36	0.42	6	-	2.6	50.0
14-9 to 15-3	15	11.0	13.3	15.9	18.5	22.3	0.18	0.21	0.29	0.38	0.42	8	-	0.3	50.0
15-3 to 15-9	15	11.3	13.6	16.0	18.2	23.4	0.17	0.21	0.27	0.34	0.41	6	-	0.2	50.0
15-9 to 16-3	16	11.7	13.6	15.3	17.6	25.4	0.15	0.21	0.26	0.30	0.39	4	-	0.8	50.0
16-3 to 16-9	13	10.9	12.6	15.8	20.2	23.3	0.15	0.19	0.26	0.35	0.41	4	-	1.2	50.0
16-9 to 17-3	10	13.2	14.2	16.3	19.5	26.2	0.17	0.21	0.27	0.33	0.38	3	-	1.4	28.5

NUTRITION

TABLE D-24

Daily Niacin Intake - Female

Age Range	Diet											Supplement			
		Mg.					Mg./kg. Wt.						Mg.		
		Percentiles					Percentiles							Range	
Yr. Mo.	N	10th	25th	50th	75th	90th	10th	25th	50th	75th	90th	N	Med.	Min.	Max.
0-0 to 0-1	23	0.3	0.4	0.5	0.6	1.5	0.09	0.11	0.14	0.16	0.37	5	-	0.6	2.8
0-1 to 0-2	30	0.5	0.6	0.7	1.0	2.0	0.12	0.14	0.19	0.27	0.42	11	1.9	0.8	5.0
0-2 to 0-3	32	0.6	0.8	1.0	1.1	2.2	0.12	0.15	0.20	0.27	0.45	12	4.3	0.9	10.5
0-3 to 0-4	34	0.6	0.9	1.4	2.0	3.1	0.13	0.16	0.24	0.34	0.51	12	3.3	0.8	14.7
0-4 to 0-5	37	1.2	1.5	2.0	2.9	4.0	0.17	0.22	0.31	0.43	0.64	13	3.0	0.1	15.6
0-5 to 0-6	38	1.1	1.5	2.1	3.3	4.6	0.19	0.24	0.32	0.44	0.70	14	4.4	1.4	16.2
0-6 to 0-9	41	1.9	2.4	3.1	4.2	5.4	0.25	0.31	0.41	0.56	0.78	14	4.9	0.2	15.8
0-9 to 1-0	44	2.8	3.3	4.1	5.0	6.3	0.27	0.36	0.46	0.56	0.74	18	4.1	0.3	15.8
1-0 to 1-3	45	2.7	3.6	4.3	5.5	6.6	0.29	0.35	0.43	0.56	0.72	17	4.2	0.4	14.2
1-3 to 1-6	45	3.4	4.0	4.9	5.7	6.9	0.34	0.39	0.49	0.57	0.65	20	4.1	0.8	11.8
1-6 to 1-9	44	3.4	4.0	4.9	5.8	7.5	0.30	0.36	0.46	0.55	0.66	19	4.9	0.1	13.4
1-9 to 2-0	45	3.7	4.6	5.4	6.5	8.0	0.32	0.39	0.47	0.58	0.70	20	4.8	0.3	30.0
2-0 to 2-3	47	3.5	4.6	6.0	7.1	8.5	0.29	0.38	0.47	0.60	0.69	21	5.1	0.3	21.0
2-3 to 2-6	48	3.3	4.6	5.9	7.2	8.1	0.25	0.37	0.46	0.60	0.68	20	4.0	0.4	10.0
2-6 to 2-9	46	3.5	4.4	5.7	7.2	8.6	0.27	0.33	0.42	0.56	0.65	17	4.7	0.2	13.8
2-9 to 3-0	45	3.4	4.6	6.0	7.3	8.7	0.26	0.33	0.44	0.54	0.68	18	4.6	0.3	20.0
3-0 to 3-3	44	4.3	5.1	6.3	7.4	10.0	0.30	0.35	0.43	0.54	0.71	21	3.6	0.7	20.0
3-3 to 3-6	44	4.1	5.0	6.1	7.3	10.1	0.30	0.35	0.41	0.51	0.68	15	4.5	0.2	20.0
3-6 to 3-9	45	4.1	5.1	6.4	8.6	9.3	0.28	0.34	0.41	0.57	0.65	17	3.2	0.2	20.0
3-9 to 4-0	43	3.9	5.1	6.9	7.9	9.0	0.27	0.34	0.42	0.51	0.59	19	3.7	0.2	20.0
4-3 to 4-9	42	4.8	5.8	7.3	8.9	11.1	0.28	0.34	0.42	0.52	0.64	22	5.5	0.1	27.5
4-9 to 5-3	41	4.6	6.0	7.6	9.2	11.3	0.26	0.34	0.43	0.50	0.61	20	7.6	0.1	36.2
5-3 to 5-9	41	5.0	6.2	7.6	8.8	11.1	0.27	0.32	0.39	0.46	0.55	19	6.8	0.2	20.0
5-9 to 6-3	40	5.8	6.7	8.1	9.7	11.1	0.28	0.33	0.41	0.47	0.55	25	3.8	0.1	21.5
6-3 to 6-9	41	6.3	7.5	8.6	10.0	11.7	0.30	0.34	0.40	0.48	0.56	20	6.4	0.1	20.0
6-9 to 7-3	42	6.8	8.1	9.2	10.3	11.7	0.29	0.35	0.40	0.45	0.52	20	6.7	0.5	20.0
7-3 to 7-9	41	6.5	7.8	9.3	10.9	11.9	0.27	0.32	0.37	0.44	0.52	20	7.2	0.4	20.0
7-9 to 8-3	41	6.9	8.2	9.5	10.8	12.5	0.26	0.31	0.37	0.41	0.47	24	6.7	0.1	20.0
8-3 to 8-9	39	7.1	8.4	9.8	11.5	13.6	0.25	0.30	0.36	0.43	0.52	22	6.0	0.1	20.0
8-9 to 9-3	41	7.3	8.6	10.3	12.3	13.8	0.26	0.29	0.36	0.43	0.47	22	4.4	0.1	20.0
9-3 to 9-9	37	7.9	9.1	10.8	12.1	13.7	0.26	0.30	0.35	0.41	0.46	20	8.2	0.1	24.4
9-9 to 10-3	35	7.6	9.4	10.9	12.3	13.8	0.24	0.29	0.35	0.39	0.43	14	6.5	0.1	25.1
10-3 to 10-9	35	8.0	9.3	11.1	12.8	14.4	0.24	0.28	0.31	0.37	0.41	12	6.8	0.1	25.1
10-9 to 11-3	35	8.1	9.8	11.8	13.1	14.5	0.22	0.28	0.33	0.37	0.44	15	6.8	0.6	24.8
11-3 to 11-9	33	8.3	10.3	11.9	13.2	14.6	0.21	0.27	0.31	0.36	0.40	12	10.1	0.2	21.4
11-9 to 12-3	30	8.7	10.0	11.6	13.6	15.5	0.20	0.25	0.29	0.34	0.42	12	7.1	0.2	20.0
12-3 to 12-9	30	8.3	9.7	12.2	14.1	16.1	0.17	0.22	0.28	0.33	0.40	10	2.6	0.2	24.6
12-9 to 13-3	30	9.0	10.2	11.8	14.0	16.0	0.17	0.21	0.27	0.31	0.37	10	3.6	0.2	25.0
13-3 to 13-9	26	8.0	9.6	12.6	14.4	16.0	0.15	0.18	0.27	0.31	0.35	9	-	0.2	25.0
13-9 to 14-3	26	7.6	10.0	12.4	14.4	15.9	0.14	0.20	0.26	0.29	0.33	9	-	0.1	25.0
14-3 to 14-9	25	8.4	10.2	12.4	13.9	14.9	0.13	0.20	0.25	0.28	0.31	10	2.6	0.1	25.0
14-9 to 15-3	24	7.5	10.1	12.0	14.3	15.7	0.12	0.18	0.23	0.27	0.30	8	-	0.2	32.1
15-3 to 15-9	21	6.8	9.3	12.7	14.8	16.5	0.11	0.18	0.23	0.27	0.30	5	-	0.1	25.0
15-9 to 16-3	18	6.1	10.2	12.4	14.2	15.6	0.09	0.18	0.22	0.26	0.28	6	-	0.1	24.1
16-3 to 16-9	18	6.2	8.3	11.9	14.4	15.5	0.09	0.16	0.21	0.26	0.27	6	-	0.5	25.0
16-9 to 17-3	18	6.2	8.6	12.1	14.8	16.1	0.11	0.14	0.22	0.26	0.28	8	-	0.3	25.0
17-3 to 17-9	16	5.3	8.9	11.8	14.6	16.5	0.09	0.15	0.21	0.25	0.30	5	-	0.2	25.0
17-9 to 18-0	14	4.9	7.3	11.0	14.6	15.5	0.08	0.11	0.19	0.24	0.28	6	-	0.1	18.0

Section E

ANTHROPOMETRY AND RELATED DATA

ANTHROPOMETRY

SKINFOLD THICKNESS MEASUREMENTS

CHARLOTTE HANSMAN

ANTHROPOMETRY AND RELATED DATA

THE heading, anthropometry and related data, covers not only the anthropometric data, per se, and skinfold thickness measurements but also that part of the radiologic data concerned with maturation of the skeleton and the measurements made on cephalograms. All of these data were first recorded on measurement sheets and tabulation cards, then punched on IBM cards and verified. This information was programmed from the cards to magnetic tape. The printed output was proofread against the original records. When the data were as clean as possible, a statistical summary, parts of which are presented here, was computed (see Introduction, p. 18).

Only certain aspects of this material have been chosen for this publication. Since the ages of appearance and fusion of the ossification centers of the skeleton were published in 1962(1), and the percentile standards for growth of interorbital distance and skull thickness were published in 1966(2), these have been omitted. A small block of data, circumpuberal growth, was compiled from a combination of physical measurements and examinations and radiologic data and is being analyzed and prepared for separate publication at the present time.

The estimation of skeletal maturation from roentgenograms of the left hand and wrist is discussed with the other radiologic data.

ANTHROPOMETRY

Introduction, Method and Materials

The first anthropometric measurements were done on members of the Child Research Council series January 7, 1933 and the final measurements included here on December 31, 1966. These measurements, patterned after Rudolph Martin in his *Lehrbuch der Anthropologie*(3), ranged from a maximum number of 86 in the early days of the study to a minimum of 11. By January, 1954, under the guidance of Dr. Edith Boyd, 31 dimensions were chosen as representative of the segments of the human body. These dimensions grouped according to the instruments with which they were measured are as follows:

Over-all dimensions

1. Weight
2. Height (Length)
3. Sitting height (Crown-rump length)

Circumferences taken with a steel tape fitting the skin but without compression

1. Hand
2. Bistyloid
3. Minimum forearm
4. Maximum forearm
5. Biceps
6. Fronto-occipital
7. Xiphisternal
8. Iliac
9. Foot
10. Ankle
11. Calf
12. Knee

Widths, depths and lengths measured with straight steel caliper, straight wooden caliper or bow caliper pressed firmly against underlying bone

1. Xiphisternal width and depth
2. Iliac width
3. Biacromial width
4. Foot length
5. Stylo-medius length
6. Medius length
7. Head width
8. Fronto-occipital length
9. Hand width
10. Bistyloid width
11. Elbow width

12. Foot width
13. Ankle width
14. Knee width (without compressing the tissue)

Five derived ratios were also included and are

1. Weight-height ratio
2. Biacromial-iliac ratio
3. Xiphisternal-iliac ratio
4. Thoracic index
5. Cephalic index

The unit of measurement for all but weight was the centimeter, and all measurements were read to the nearest millimeter. Weights were converted from pounds and ounces to kilograms for the permanent record.

The first neonatal measurements were done in January, 1942. In general subjects were measured supine to 2 years of age and in the erect position for subsequent years. Babies were seen each month during the first year. Thereafter, the interval between examinations was increased to 6 months. Babies were weighed and measured without clothing, older individuals with shorts or panties and teenage girls and young women with panties and a gown. One half pound was subtracted for the weight of the gown. The records for subjects who were born prematurely have been omitted from the compilation of standards. If a young woman was known to be pregnant at the time of examination that particular set of measurements was also omitted. There are 8502 sets of original measurements on 236 subjects and 1372 sets of interpolated measurements. (See below for explanation of interpolated measurements.)

Heights and weights only were measured with the physical examinations done 3 and 9 months after the child's birthday. These are recorded on tape and are available to anyone desiring them. Weight-height ratios are also included. Summary statistics have not been computed on these data. There are 4841 of these measurements from 1 year 3 months to 19 years 3 months.

Presentation of Data

Eighteen measurements from the group of 31 were chosen for

this publication as being, perhaps, the most valuable in the study of physical growth. The number of individuals, the range, 10th, 25th, 50th, 75th and 90th percentiles, means and standard deviations are presented according to age for height (length); weight; sitting height (crown-rump length); fronto-occipital circumference; xiphisternal circumference, width and depth; iliac circumference and width; and biacromial width. In all instances "age" is stated age ± 15 days. The statistical summary is available for the complete set of measurements and for the derived ratios. It was felt that number of individuals, 10th, 50th and 90th percentiles were adequate for the circumferences of the extremities (hand, bistyloid, maximum forearm, biceps, foot, ankle, calf and knee). These values are given in Tables E-1 through E-24.

All measurements were converted to a percent of height (dimension/height x 100) and summarized in the same manner. The number of individuals, 10th, 50th and 90th percentiles for these "relative" measurements of sitting height (crown-rump length); fronto-occipital circumference; xiphisternal circumference, width and depth; iliac circumference and width; and biacromial width are in Tables E-25 through E-28. Complete summary statistics are available for all of the relative measurements.

Increments in height (length) and weight have been derived from the individual data and summarized statistically. This was done from birth to 6 months by month then to 9 months, 1 year, 1 year 6 months and 2 years for length and weight. Increments in erect height begin at 2 years. Both height and weight increments then continue by 6-month intervals to 18 years; then by yearly intervals to 25 years. Number of individuals, median and range according to age are presented in Tables E-29 and E-30. Increments of other dimensions have not been derived.

Reliability of Measurements

1. *Experimental error:* The accuracy of the anthropometric measurements depended on a number of factors. All instruments were kept clean and calibration was checked as indicated. Each

new examiner became familiar with the instruments before measuring for the permanent record. From 1946 to 1957 measuring was done by E. Boyd and from 1957 to 1966 by C. Hansman. A trained assistant substituted when necessary.

Measuring error was found to depend not only on the dimension being evaluated but also on the age, sex and general physique of the subject. The margin of error is much less if the measurement is taken across bony end points than if it is done over soft tissue. However, in individuals with a thick layer of fat the bony landmarks are difficult to palpate.

Trunk measurements present another problem. Since the bones of a thin six-year-old are readily visible under the overlying tissue, landmarks such as iliac crest are easily located. Respiration became the primary concern in children of this physique. The children were distracted so that breathing was not exaggerated and the measurement read in mid-quiet respiration. As fat and muscle layers increased the iliac circumference, particularly, became hard to measure.

The acromion was often difficult to locate in the well-padded individual. Adolescent boys "squared" their shoulders to broaden them and thereby defeated their purpose because it was found that biocromial width was greater if the arms were allowed to hang loosely at the sides. This relaxed position was extremely difficult to duplicate from one examination to the next. The heavily muscled shoulder girdle of the young adult male also entered into the determination of height by preventing the head from touching the measuring board, making it difficult to maintain the tragion-orbitale plane at right angles to the long axis of the body.

In children under 3 years the posture in which they could stand was accepted. From 3 to 6 years they usually stood well but did not always comprehend the direction to stretch. From 6 to 9 years children automatically stood straight to be measured and from 9 to puberty would stretch to their maximum, especially boys. During puberty the response was highly variable and many of the tall girls would not stretch to their maximum. The same sources of error applied to sitting height as did to standing height plus the degree of contraction of the gluteal muscles.

Cooperation of the individual is important in obtaining reliable data. The tiny infant squirms and a slightly older baby does not wish to be held in any position long enough for the instruments to be read. Under these circumstances the order in which the measuring was accomplished was left to the baby with the parts he disliked most done last. This meant that the extremity measurements were usually first, followed by head and trunk. The baby was weighed while the anthropometer was made ready for the determination of length and crown-rump length. This measurement was never attempted by the anthropometrist alone. An assistant, often the child's mother, held his head in place against the headboard while the anthropometrist stretched one leg, positioned the footboard against the sole of the foot and read the instrument. The other leg was always left free to kick so the baby would not feel as restrained as when both were held down. As the period of negativism in the child's life disappeared, the measurements became much more reliable.

The magnitude of the experimental error was determined by the dimension, whether of compressible soft tissue or bone, fatness or thinness of the subject and the age and behavior of the subject. The error allowed for the bony measurements where the landmarks were palpable was 2 mm. This figure also applied to height and sitting height. The soft-tissue measurements and the trunk measurements in non-fat individuals were allowed 5 mm. During the first 18 months the full centimeter allowed on all dimensions sometimes stretched to 2 cm for a struggling baby. The 1 cm error also applied to the soft-tissue and trunk measurements for fat individuals with 5 mm for the bony measurements not easily palpated as in thin people.

2. *Tests of accuracy:* Since anthropometric measurements were rarely done in duplicate other means of checking accuracy were resorted to. Height and weight were also determined as part of the study of metabolism by different examiners and at ages offset from the anthropometry. For the metabolism tests the subject was picked up at home as soon as he was out of bed in the morning and before breakfast. Following the test, for which the individual was lying, his height and weight were obtained. These two sets of completely independent measurements were correlated to provide a check on the accuracy of the anthropometric data. The

measurements done at the time of the metabolism test were first adjusted for age differences. The increments in cm/6 mo. or kg/6 mo. were then determined to eliminate the differences in the measurements due to the time of day at which they were done. These increments were twice smoothed arithmetically by a three-point moving average.

Correlation coefficients between the metabolism figures and the anthropometric figures were computed for both unsmoothed and smoothed increments of both height and weight for each individual. Twenty-five girls and young women and 43 boys and young men made up the group that was tested in this way.

The correlation coefficients for the unsmoothed increments from these two sets of data for female heights were all above 0.70 and when the increments were smoothed none of the 25 fell below 0.95. Similar correlation coefficients for 43 male heights were all above 0.65 except for 2 of the unsmoothed increments while smoothing brought all but one to above 0.90.

The weights of the members of this group were tested in the same way, but, as expected, were not quite so highly correlated. The correlation coefficients computed from the unsmoothed female weight increments between the two sets of measurements were all above 0.55 except for 3 and smoothing brought them all to above 0.75. Again the correlation coefficients for male weight increments were a little lower with all but 1 above 0.50 for unsmoothed data and all above 0.60 for smoothed values.

As another comparison the anthropometric heights of eight-year-old children were correlated with heights interpolated to 8 years from the metabolic data. There were 64 boys and 62 girls in this group. The correlation coefficients for both height and weight for both sexes were of the order of 0.98 for this selected group.

3. *Determination and correction of errors in measuring:* As the anthropometric measurements were done they were dictated to a recorder who compared the new value with previous values as she wrote them down. If the new value seemed to be "out-of-line," the examiner was asked to repeat the measurement without knowing in which direction the error lay. Errors in positioning the instruments or reading the scales were thus easily corrected.

In addition all measurements were plotted on millimeter paper against age. Any unusual deviations from the expected curve could then be spotted. Deciding if these deviations were true errors became the next step. When an unexpected change in the direction of the curve occurred, and this change exceeded the measuring error, the value in question was checked in various ways before it was replaced by a new one.

a. Who did the measuring? The initials of the examiner were recorded with each set of measurements. If the error was made by a new examiner, this was taken into consideration by increasing the margin of error. Occasionally an examiner was found to make a consistent error in a particular dimension. These were corrected if possible or if not they were omitted.

b. At what time was the measuring done? Time of day has a profound effect on height. Any individual was taller on arising in the morning than he was on retiring at night. This difference averages about 2 cm from morning to night with about one-half of this drop occurring in the first hour after arising. An individual who retires at 2:00 A.M. and is up again at 6:00 A.M. will be shorter on arising than if he had retired at 10:00 P.M. and arose at 6:00 A.M. For this reason, the time the measurements were taken was recorded with each set. In examining the curves of total height and sitting height for errors, time of day was always taken into consideration. Apparent mistakes in these figures for total height were explained almost without fail by the time of day, e.g., a short, late afternoon measurement between two taller morning ones.

c. How old was the subject? Since babies were difficult to measure, the procedure was done each month during the first year and as a result only the grossest errors were corrected. All errors were corrected at other ages as indicated.

d. Which sex was the subject? From the time a girl's hips began to widen in early adolescence, this dimension became increasingly more difficult to determine. The rounded feminine figure presents problems not encountered with the angular masculine one. However, the sexes were equally difficult to measure as both added excess weight.

e. What was being measured? Soft tissue and trunk dimensions reflect changes in weight per unit of height. If the questioned rise or fall in a curve was a true one there would be a corresponding rise or fall in the curve for weight-height ratio. The curves for these dimensions were, therefore, compared to the weight-height ratio curve and the interpolated correction substituted only when the deviant measurement could not be explained by changes in weight for height.

In summary, errors in measuring were corrected at all ages depending on the size of the experimental error, the examiner, the dimension, sex and changes in weight-height ratio. All corrections were made by interpolation between the preceding and the succeeding measurements.

4. *Interpolated measurements:* Unfortunately it was not always possible to examine the subjects within plus or minus 2 weeks of the desired age. In order to compile useful percentile standards, figures for yearly and half-yearly age groups were desirable. For example, if a child was seen at 5 years 3 weeks of age those measurements were recorded and an additional set of measurements for a "missed visit" were interpolated to 5 years to conform to the age limits of 5 years ± 15 days. The substitution of the interpolated measurements for the "missed visits" was accepted after certain criteria had been met. During the first 6 months of life the child is growing at a rapid but gradually decelerating rate. No measurements were interpolated during this period. For a number of years babies were seen monthly for the first 6 months then at 9 months and 1 year. Since growth has slowed at this time, interpolated measurements for all dimensions for 7 and 8 months and 10 and 11 months were accepted. Almost straight-line growth characterizes the childhood years so measurements for all dimensions could be interpolated from 1 year to the onset of the adolescent growth spurt in height. During the period of circumpuberal growth in height no interpolations were done from the age of onset of this rapid growth to the age when growth in height was complete. After the individual had attained his adult height, measurements interpolated to the desired age were again resumed. However, the interval between examinations was not allowed to exceed three years and only those dimensions which remained stable throughout adult life

were handled this way. From the present group height, sitting height, head circumference, width and length remain stable. Adult weight was so variable that any dimension such as knee, biceps or hips which would reflect this variation was not interpolated. Of course, weight, itself, was never interpolated for adults which accounts for the discrepancy between N's for heights and weights from 19 to 25 years.

Discussion

The medians and ranges of certain dimensions of the members of the Child Research Council series are plotted in Figures E-1 through E-5. Heights (lengths) and weights are seen in Figure E-1. From birth to 2 years the boys in this population are larger on the average than girls. The sexes are nearly equal in size during the childhood years. The difference in timing of the adolescent growth spurt then becomes very apparent with the girls being larger than boys for a short period of time following which young men are both taller and heavier and remain so. The change in stature with position is brought out at 2 years when the children are first measured in the erect position.

Sitting height (crown-rump length) and sitting height as a percent of height (relative sitting height) are plotted in Figure E-2. The same sex differences as described for height are demonstrated in sitting height. When the median trunk lengths of the individuals in this study are compared to their total statures there is very little difference between sexes prior to the adolescent years. From age 11 years to 25 years the female trunk makes up a larger proportion of her height than is seen in the male who conversely has longer legs.

Xiphisternal circumference and width are illustrated in Figure E-3. At birth the 50th percentile is the same for boys and girls for both dimensions. Thereafter boys are larger and remain so throughout the growth period and into adult life. The difference between the medians of the supine and erect measurements at age 2 years is very small.

Two other trunk measurements, biacromial and iliac widths, are in Figure E-4. From birth boys' shoulders are slightly broader on the average than girls' except for a short period of time during the adolescent years when girls' shoulders become somewhat broader. After this the broader masculine build appears. A greater difference than has been demonstrated previously between the larger erect and the smaller supine medians is seen here.

During the first 2 years of life boys, on the average, have broader hips than girls. From 2 to 6½ years they are almost identical after which girls' hips become broader as they mature. However, as young men attain full growth their hips are absolutely wider than the more slightly built young women. Differences in measurements between erect and supine positions are again apparent with erect measurements greater.

Biacromial-iliac and xiphisternal-iliac ratios serve as a means of describing body build and are included in Figure E-5 although the corresponding tables are not in this publication. During the first 2 years of life there seems to be a tendency on the part of the girls to have broader shoulders in relation to their hips than do boys. During early childhood there is little difference but after about the age of 6 years the masculine build of broad shoulders and narrow hips becomes apparent. For the first 2 years of life there is little sex difference when chest and hip widths are compared. When the erect position is assumed the ratio is greater for boys and is approximately equal to 1 through the childhood and early adolescent years. The less than 1 ratio seen in girls is another indication of the broader hips which characterize the feminine build.

Figure E-6 shows the rates of growth in height (length) and weight with the median increments adjusted to 6-month intervals. Boys grow more during the first 6 months than girls. The same is noted in regard to weight but the difference is a great deal less. The sexes are nearly identical in growth from this age to the girls' adolescence when for a short period girls are growing more rapidly than boys in both height and weight. The increments level off as adulthood is reached.

SKINFOLD THICKNESS MEASUREMENTS

Introduction, Method and Materials

In October, 1955 a group of 10 skinfold thickness

measurements were added to the physical dimensions measured on Child Research Council subjects. The instrument employed for these measurements was a vernier caliper designed by Dr. Josef Brozek and the method of measuring was described by him in 1956(4).

The 10 sites chosen for measurement were maximum forearm, biceps, triceps, subscapular, mid-axilla, pectoral, lateral iliac, umbilical, calf and medial thigh. The unit of measurement was the millimeter and the measurements were read to 1 decimal place.

Most children accepted the skinfold measurements well by the fourth birthday. If the child was very anxious, they were delayed for 6 months. At no time were any skinfold measurements corrected or interpolated if missed. There are 2029 sets of the 10 skinfold thickness measurements on 198 subjects.

Presentation of Data

Triceps and subscapular skinfold thickness measurements which are felt by many investigators to be the most representative of overall subcutaneous tissue were chosen for this publication. The number of subjects according to age at 6-month intervals from 4 to 18 years, and the 10th, 50th and 90th percentiles are presented in Table E-31.

Tests for Accuracy of Measuring

The Lange caliper became available the end of October, 1966. For the remainder of that year each skinfold thickness was done twice, once with the Lange and once with the vernier caliper. The resulting figures were plotted on millimeter paper revealing that with the exception of one child out of 23 neither caliper measured consistently greater nor less than the other.

The accuracy of measurement of the subcutaneous fat layer was investigated by computing the technical error (see Introduction, p. 18) between these two sets of data. With the sexes combined the skinfold measurement over the biceps showed the smallest technical error, 0.84 mm, while the largest was that in the umbilical area, 2.07 mm. With the sexes separated the smallest for the male was the biceps, 0.35 mm, and the greatest in this group was thigh, 1.62 mm. In the female group the smallest was subscapular, 0.98 mm, and the largest was umbilical, 2.97 mm.

An arbitrary figure of 8 mm was chosen to separate the group into "thinner" and "fatter" subjects. The smallest technical error for the individuals whose average fat layer was less than 8 mm was similar to that of the male group and for the group averaging over 8 mm it was similar to that of the female group except the lowest error was biceps rather than subscapular.

The above figures confirm the clinical impression that skinfold thickness measurements are more easily and more accurately done when this layer of tissue is thin rather than when it is thick.

Definitions and a more detailed account of the tests for accuracy plus the 25th and 75th percentiles, ranges, means and standard deviations for both absolute and relative (percent of height) skinfold thicknesses are available.

Discussion

Three sites for measurements of skinfold thickness are illustrated. Figure E-7 presents the 10th, 50th and 90th percentiles of skinfold thickness at the triceps, subscapular and thigh areas.

The fatter boys and girls during the pubertal years seem to deposit about the same amount of fat in the triceps area but at all other ages whether the child is fat or thin the girls have a thicker layer than boys. This sex difference is much less pronounced in the subscapular area; however, during the prepubertal years, the heavier girls carry a considerably thicker layer than the heavier boys.

Sex difference is demonstrated perhaps even better in the thigh area with the boys who fall at the 90th percentile having the heavier layer during the adolescent years only.

REFERENCES

1. Hansman, C.F.: Appearance and fusion of ossification centers in the human skeleton. Am J Roentgen, 88:476, 1962.
2. Hansman, C.F.: Growth of interorbital distance and skull thickness as observed in roentgenographic measurements. Radiology, 86:87, 1966.

3. Martin, R.: Lehrbuch der Anthropologie. 2nd ed., Jena, Gustav Fischer, 1928, 3 vols.
4. Brozek, J.: Physique and nutritional status of adult men. Hum Biol, 28:124 (May), 1956.

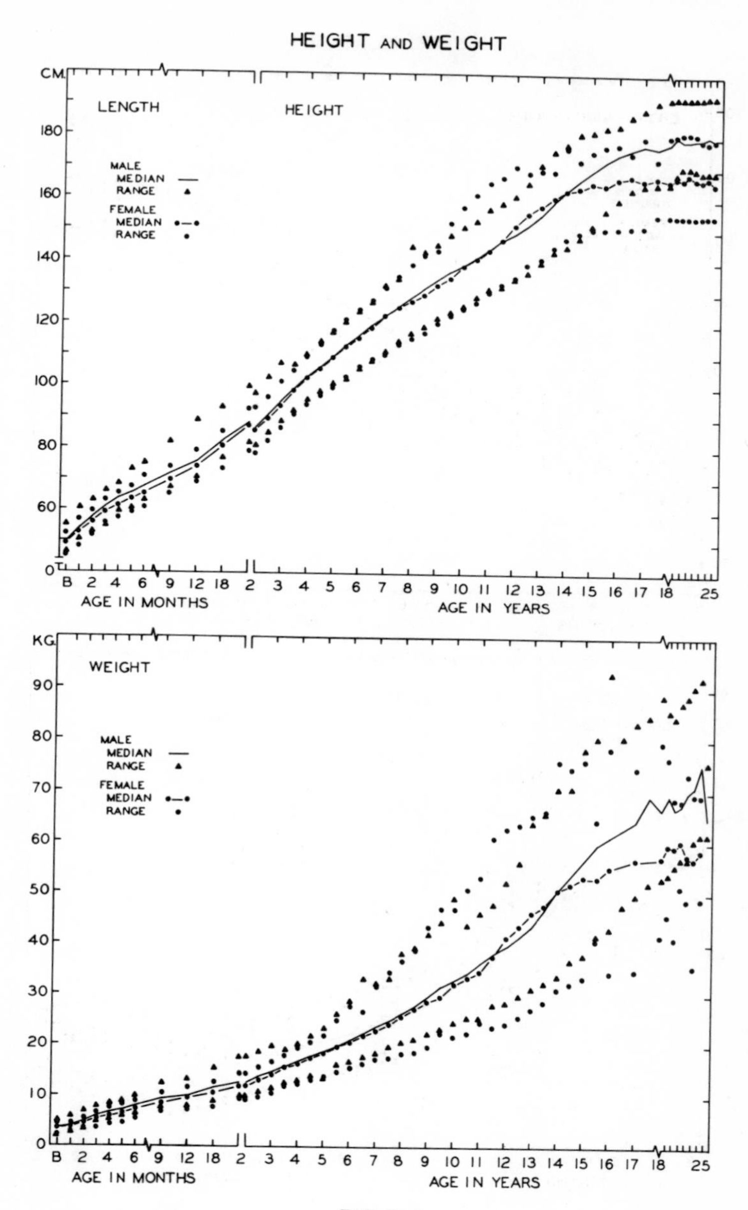
HEIGHT AND WEIGHT
CM
LENGTH
HEIGHT
MALE
MEDIAN
RANGE
FEMALE
MEDIAN
RANGE
180
160
140
120
100
80
60
0
B 2 4 6 9 12 18 2 3 4 5 6 7 8 9 10 11 12 13 14 15 16 17 18 25
AGE IN MONTHS
AGE IN YEARS
KG
WEIGHT
MALE
MEDIAN
RANGE
FEMALE
MEDIAN
RANGE
90
80
70
60
50
40
30
20
10
0
B 2 4 6 9 12 18 2 3 4 5 6 7 8 9 10 11 12 13 14 15 16 17 18 25
AGE IN MONTHS
AGE IN YEARS

FIG. E-1

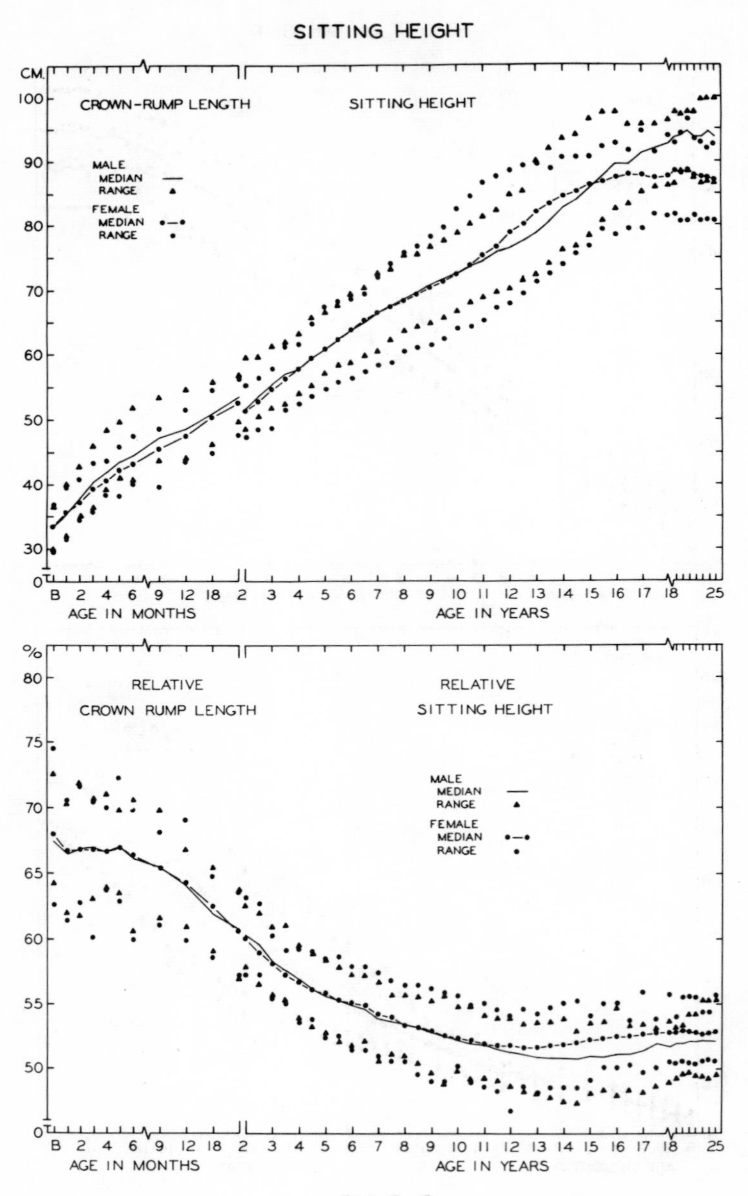
SITTING HEIGHT
CM.
CROWN-RUMP LENGTH
SITTING HEIGHT
MALE
MEDIAN
RANGE
FEMALE
MEDIAN
RANGE
AGE IN MONTHS
AGE IN YEARS
%
RELATIVE
CROWN RUMP LENGTH
RELATIVE
SITTING HEIGHT
MALE
MEDIAN
RANGE
FEMALE
MEDIAN
RANGE
AGE IN MONTHS
AGE IN YEARS

FIG. E-2

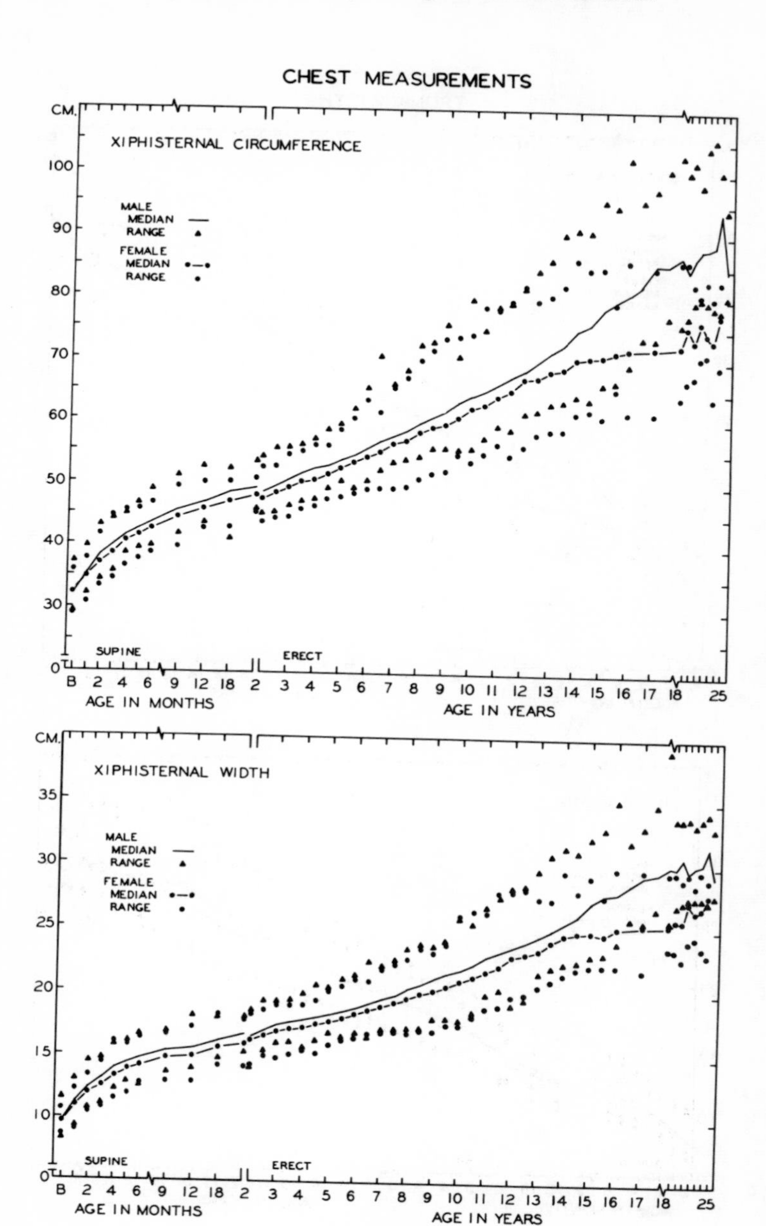
CHEST MEASUREMENTS
XIPHISTERNAL CIRCUMFERENCE
CM.
MALE
MEDIAN
RANGE
FEMALE
MEDIAN
RANGE
SUPINE
ERECT
AGE IN MONTHS
AGE IN YEARS
XIPHISTERNAL WIDTH

FIG. E-3

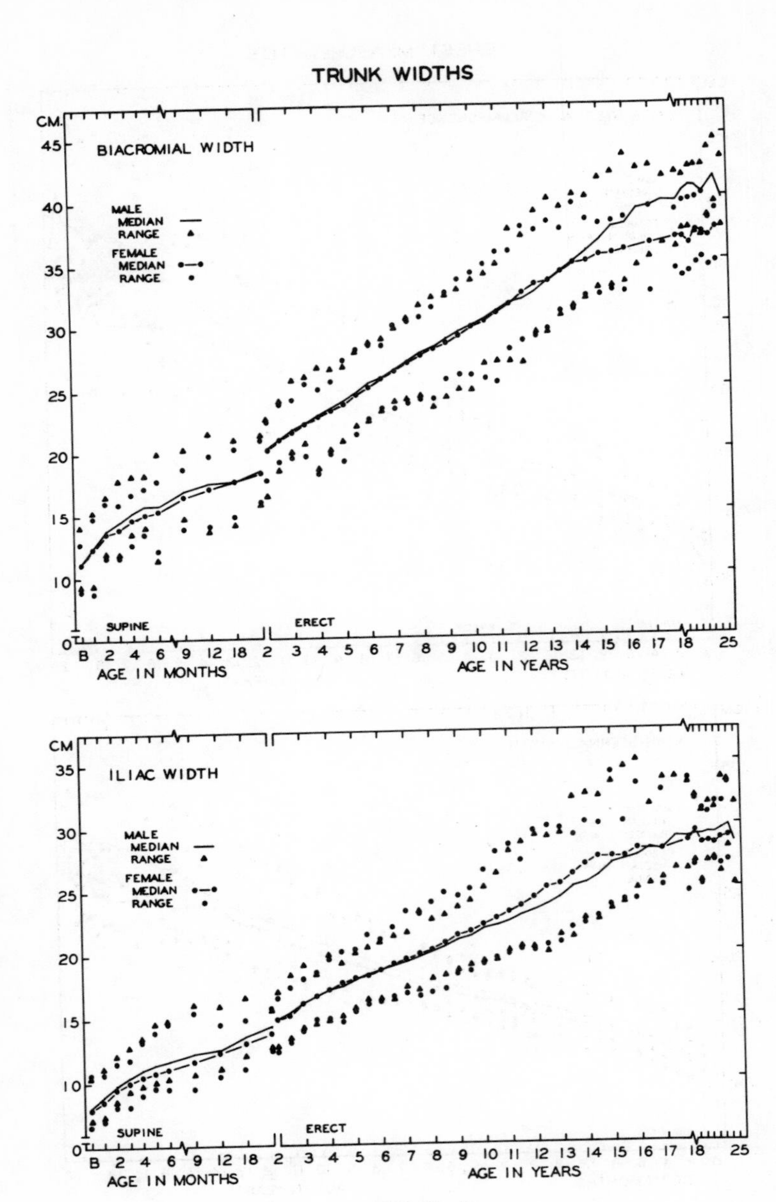
TRUNK WIDTHS
BIACROMIAL WIDTH
CM.
MALE
MEDIAN
RANGE
FEMALE
MEDIAN
RANGE
SUPINE
ERECT
AGE IN MONTHS
AGE IN YEARS
ILIAC WIDTH
CM
MALE
MEDIAN
RANGE
FEMALE
MEDIAN
RANGE
SUPINE
ERECT
AGE IN MONTHS
AGE IN YEARS

FIG. E-4

BODY PROPORTIONS

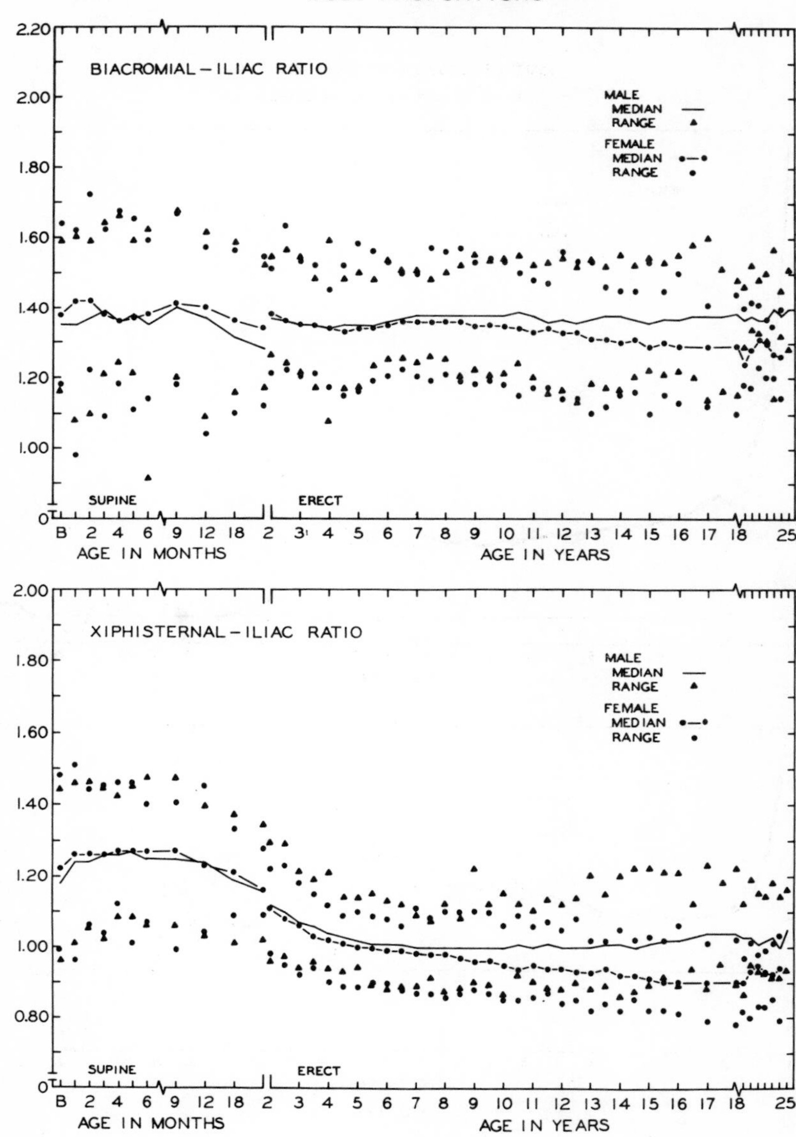

FIG. E-5

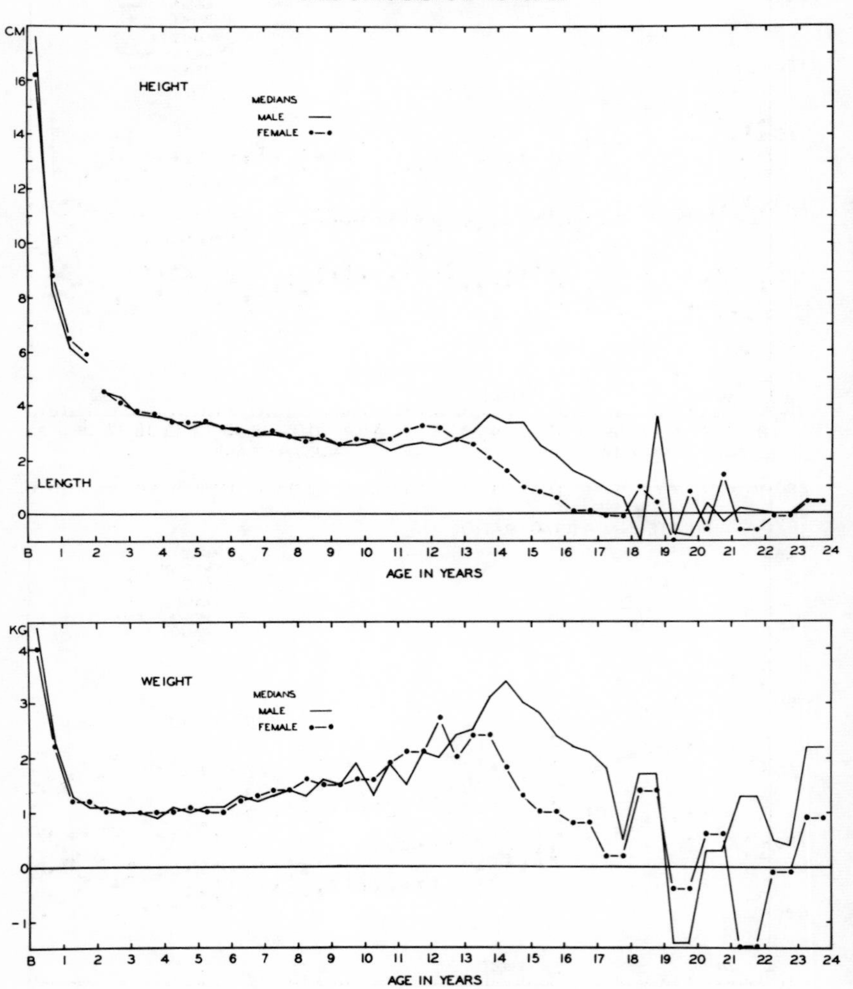
RATE OF GROWTH PER SIX MONTHS
BASED ON INCREMENTS OF INDIVIDUALS
CM
HEIGHT
MEDIANS
MALE
FEMALE
LENGTH
AGE IN YEARS
KG
WEIGHT
MEDIANS
MALE
FEMALE
AGE IN YEARS

FIG. E-6

SKINFOLD THICKNESS MEASUREMENTS

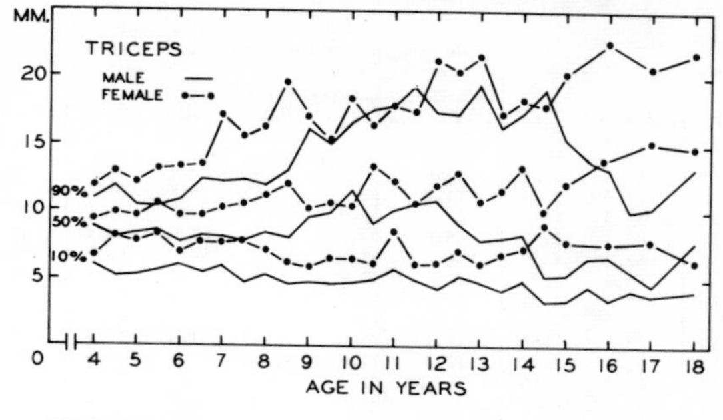

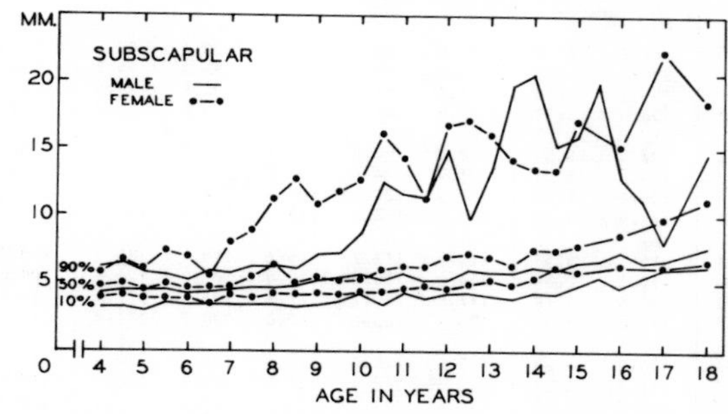

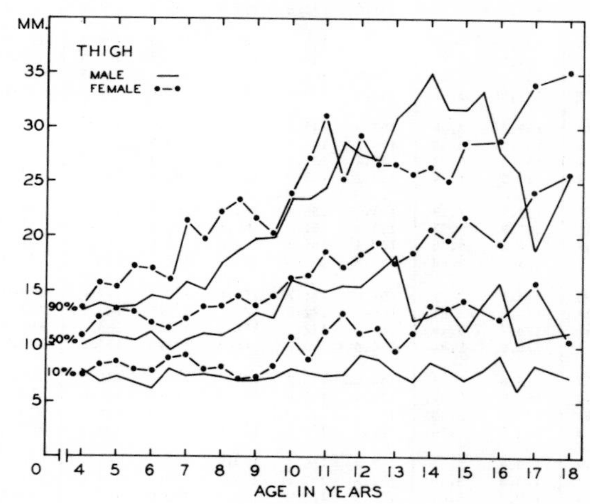

FIG. E-7

ANTHROPOMETRY

TABLE E-1

Male

Height in Centimeters

Age Yr. Mo.	N	Mean	S.D.	Percentiles 10th	25th	50th	75th	90th	Range Min.	Max.
Length										
Birth	49	49.6	2.25	47.0	48.0	49.6	51.3	53.0	45.9	55.0
0 - 1	62	53.9	2.24	51.2	52.2	53.5	55.6	57.0	50.0	60.1
0 - 2	53	57.5	2.40	54.7	55.6	57.1	59.7	60.9	52.6	62.6
0 - 3	59	60.7	2.32	58.0	59.2	60.4	61.6	64.6	55.5	65.9
0 - 4	49	63.3	1.98	60.8	61.9	63.1	64.5	66.0	59.3	68.0
0 - 5	51	65.4	2.32	62.7	63.9	65.1	66.8	68.4	60.0	72.7
0 - 6	70	67.5	2.31	64.5	65.9	67.2	69.2	70.4	62.6	75.0
0 - 9	53	72.1	2.66	68.7	70.4	71.9	73.4	75.2	67.2	81.9
1 - 0	72	75.8	2.76	72.3	74.0	75.5	77.3	78.6	70.1	88.5
1 - 6	75	82.2	2.78	78.2	80.5	82.3	83.9	85.3	76.4	92.9
2 - 0	69	87.9	2.84	84.2	86.7	88.0	89.5	90.6	81.6	99.5
Erect										
2 - 0	53	86.2	2.97	82.6	84.3	86.3	88.1	89.4	80.6	97.6
2 - 6	60	90.8	3.00	86.7	88.8	90.7	92.3	94.3	84.6	102.6
3 - 0	59	95.2	3.24	91.0	93.7	95.2	96.8	98.5	88.5	107.4
3 - 6	57	98.6	3.03	94.6	96.9	98.6	100.8	101.9	91.9	106.5
4 - 0	74	102.3	2.88	98.5	100.5	102.7	104.4	105.6	95.4	109.7
4 - 6	93	106.2	3.07	101.9	104.4	106.2	108.3	110.0	97.2	114.0
5 - 0	87	109.5	3.29	104.9	107.4	109.5	111.7	113.5	100.5	117.5
5 - 6	91	112.9	3.29	108.7	110.8	113.0	114.9	117.2	102.4	120.9
6 - 0	91	116.2	3.53	111.7	113.7	116.2	118.4	121.0	105.7	124.2
6 - 6	92	119.5	3.64	114.8	116.8	119.8	121.8	124.4	108.6	127.2
7 - 0	92	122.6	3.76	117.6	120.1	122.7	125.1	127.3	110.9	132.3
7 - 6	88	125.6	3.90	120.3	123.0	125.6	128.2	131.0	114.2	134.8
8 - 0	92	128.8	4.28	123.2	126.0	128.8	131.5	134.3	117.1	144.4
8 - 6	90	131.2	4.29	125.5	128.4	131.5	134.3	136.6	119.4	142.2
9 - 0	92	134.0	4.41	128.6	131.3	134.1	137.4	139.9	121.4	145.2
9 - 6	88	136.7	4.52	131.0	133.8	136.9	140.0	142.4	123.3	148.2
10 - 0	85	139.0	4.62	133.6	135.9	139.0	142.3	144.9	125.9	150.9
10 - 6	80	141.6	4.77	136.1	138.3	141.4	145.3	147.4	128.4	152.8
11 - 0	76	144.2	4.84	138.9	141.3	144.0	147.4	150.5	130.3	157.1
11 - 6	78	146.8	5.01	140.9	143.6	147.0	150.0	153.3	132.1	158.5
12 - 0	70	149.2	5.46	143.3	145.6	149.1	152.6	156.5	134.9	160.8
12 - 6	73	151.8	5.68	145.2	147.7	151.9	155.9	158.8	136.5	165.4
13 - 0	71	155.6	6.23	147.4	151.4	155.0	159.5	163.7	139.8	170.8
13 - 6	69	159.3	7.24	150.2	153.9	159.4	163.8	169.1	143.0	175.5
14 - 0	67	163.2	7.13	153.1	156.8	163.5	167.5	173.0	144.9	177.4
14 - 6	61	165.8	6.97	157.8	161.2	166.4	170.0	174.2	147.9	180.9
15 - 0	55	168.8	6.76	160.1	164.1	169.6	173.9	176.9	151.9	181.7
15 - 6	52	171.7	6.45	162.8	167.5	172.3	176.6	180.1	156.4	182.9
16 - 0	50	174.3	5.57	167.0	171.2	174.6	178.1	182.0	160.0	183.5
16 - 6	37	175.6	5.81	166.7	172.0	176.2	179.6	182.8	163.6	186.7
17 - 0	42	176.7	6.14	167.7	172.5	177.8	181.4	183.7	164.5	189.0
17 - 6	23	176.6	6.44	168.5	171.2	176.8	181.0	185.6	165.0	191.2
18 - 0	33	178.6	5.97	169.6	175.7	178.3	182.2	186.0	165.8	192.1
19 - 0	25	180.0	6.42	170.1	176.0	180.9	184.6	187.4	168.6	192.6
20 - 0	31	179.9	5.48	172.4	176.5	179.4	184.0	186.4	170.1	192.4
21 - 0	35	180.1	5.26	172.8	177.1	179.4	183.7	186.9	170.2	192.5
22 - 0	39	179.8	5.45	172.8	176.1	179.7	183.2	188.2	170.0	192.6
23 - 0	37	179.8	5.69	171.8	175.4	179.7	183.4	188.6	168.6	192.6
24 - 0	34	180.3	6.03	171.9	175.5	180.7	185.0	187.7	169.0	193.2
25 - 0	30	179.8	6.33	171.5	173.7	179.7	184.2	187.8	169.1	193.3

ANTHROPOMETRY

TABLE E-2

Female

Height in Centimeters

Age Yr. Mo.	N	Mean	S.D.	Percentiles 10th	25th	50th	75th	90th	Range Min.	Max.
Length										
Birth	56	49.0	1.71	46.4	48.2	49.1	50.5	51.2	45.5	52.2
0 - 1	69	52.6	1.91	50.1	51.6	52.8	53.8	55.0	48.0	56.7
0 - 2	62	56.0	1.69	53.6	55.1	56.0	57.2	58.1	51.8	59.7
0 - 3	67	59.3	1.72	57.1	58.1	59.2	60.4	61.5	55.3	63.2
0 - 4	59	61.3	1.85	58.7	60.0	61.3	62.5	63.6	57.2	65.7
0 - 5	57	63.5	1.71	61.4	62.5	63.4	64.4	65.9	59.2	67.5
0 - 6	63	65.4	2.15	62.7	64.0	65.3	66.6	68.9	60.5	71.1
0 - 9	61	69.8	2.12	67.1	68.2	69.9	71.4	72.7	65.1	74.0
1 - 0	75	74.0	2.32	71.1	72.3	74.1	75.7	77.3	68.8	79.1
1 - 6	74	80.4	2.83	76.5	78.1	80.7	82.6	84.2	73.5	85.2
2 - 0	68	86.8	2.92	82.6	84.2	87.3	89.1	90.4	79.2	92.5
Erect										
2 - 0	58	85.1	3.07	80.9	83.0	85.5	87.2	88.8	78.6	93.1
2 - 6	71	89.2	3.20	84.6	87.0	89.7	91.8	93.3	82.3	96.5
3 - 0	71	93.8	3.39	89.0	91.2	93.8	96.4	98.2	86.5	101.6
3 - 6	68	97.8	3.54	93.2	94.9	98.1	100.6	102.5	90.9	105.0
4 - 0	78	101.8	3.72	96.6	98.9	102.3	104.6	106.6	94.0	109.3
4 - 6	91	105.5	3.98	100.0	102.4	105.9	108.6	110.3	97.1	113.6
5 - 0	90	108.9	4.15	103.0	105.6	109.4	111.9	114.4	99.8	118.0
5 - 6	90	112.3	4.30	106.2	108.6	112.5	115.8	118.2	103.2	121.5
6 - 0	95	115.6	4.48	109.6	111.6	116.0	118.9	121.6	106.5	124.6
6 - 6	95	118.7	4.62	112.6	114.7	118.9	122.3	124.9	109.2	127.8
7 - 0	90	121.7	4.91	115.1	117.4	122.4	125.6	128.4	110.2	132.0
7 - 6	92	124.8	5.07	118.2	120.1	125.4	128.5	131.1	113.7	135.5
8 - 0	90	127.7	5.16	121.0	123.5	128.0	131.6	133.9	115.5	138.9
8 - 6	90	130.1	5.30	123.4	125.6	129.8	134.0	137.1	117.5	142.0
9 - 0	80	132.6	5.49	125.9	127.9	132.5	137.4	139.5	120.2	143.7
9 - 6	75	135.5	6.08	128.1	130.3	135.1	140.3	143.3	122.8	152.3
10 - 0	76	138.6	6.37	130.7	133.3	138.7	143.3	146.2	124.9	157.7
10 - 6	73	141.4	6.71	133.2	136.2	140.8	146.3	149.8	127.7	161.6
11 - 0	70	144.6	7.25	134.9	138.8	143.8	150.3	153.8	130.2	165.5
11 - 6	67	148.3	7.59	137.9	143.5	147.4	154.0	158.1	133.1	167.2
12 - 0	69	152.2	7.96	140.5	146.5	152.0	158.1	162.5	135.6	170.4
12 - 6	64	154.7	7.34	143.5	150.2	155.2	160.3	164.1	139.6	168.6
13 - 0	68	157.8	7.28	147.2	152.6	158.0	164.0	166.6	141.2	169.7
13 - 6	53	159.6	6.63	150.4	153.9	160.7	165.1	167.6	144.9	169.5
14 - 0	61	162.3	6.35	153.6	157.1	163.1	166.8	170.3	147.8	176.7
14 - 6	43	163.3	6.09	154.4	158.2	163.9	168.1	170.9	149.5	172.6
15 - 0	52	165.2	5.87	156.6	160.6	165.8	169.7	172.1	150.6	175.5
15 - 6	23	165.3	6.67	158.8	160.3	164.6	171.2	174.3	150.7	177.2
16 - 0	57	165.7	6.14	157.4	160.9	167.0	170.1	172.8	151.1	177.9
16 - 6	12	165.9	7.35	154.2	160.9	168.0	171.5	172.6	151.4	175.1
17 - 0	47	166.4	6.52	157.2	162.4	166.6	171.1	174.1	151.8	180.1
17 - 6	18	166.0	5.17	158.6	161.2	167.3	169.9	171.6	155.4	173.2
18 - 0	35	166.5	5.94	159.1	162.4	166.2	170.6	174.9	155.3	180.6
19 - 0	35	167.2	6.16	158.6	162.4	167.6	170.9	175.3	155.3	181.1
20 - 0	36	166.8	6.04	159.2	162.2	167.3	171.5	174.6	155.1	181.6
21 - 0	35	167.1	6.29	159.6	162.1	168.0	170.8	175.1	154.9	181.8
22 - 0	33	166.8	6.05	160.2	162.1	166.7	171.1	174.3	154.8	181.3
23 - 0	31	166.3	5.62	158.9	161.5	166.4	169.7	173.1	154.7	179.4
24 - 0	26	166.2	5.88	158.3	160.9	167.2	170.6	174.2	154.7	178.5
25 - 0	26	165.7	5.83	158.5	161.2	165.5	169.9	171.8	154.7	179.6

ANTHROPOMETRY

TABLE E-3

Male

Weight in Kilograms

Age	N	Mean	S.D.	Percentiles					Range	
Yr. Mo.				10th	25th	50th	75th	90th	Min.	Max.
Birth	50	3.2	0.49	2.6	2.8	3.3	3.6	3.8	2.1	4.5
0 - 1	62	4.0	0.55	3.4	3.6	3.9	4.4	4.8	2.8	5.4
0 - 2	53	5.0	0.70	4.3	4.5	4.9	5.4	6.0	3.6	6.7
0 - 3	59	5.9	0.73	5.1	5.3	5.8	6.3	7.0	4.8	7.7
0 - 4	49	6.6	0.78	5.7	6.0	6.6	7.1	7.7	5.3	8.6
0 - 5	51	7.2	0.83	6.2	6.5	7.2	7.7	8.3	5.9	9.4
0 - 6	70	7.8	0.88	6.8	7.2	7.7	8.5	8.9	6.1	10.0
0 - 9	54	9.1	1.08	7.7	8.2	9.2	9.8	10.4	7.4	12.4
1 - 0	73	10.0	1.12	8.6	9.2	10.0	10.6	11.4	7.7	13.0
1 - 6	82	11.4	1.15	10.0	10.5	11.3	12.1	12.9	8.6	15.1
2 - 0	88	12.5	1.26	10.9	11.6	12.4	13.2	14.2	9.4	17.3
2 - 6	91	13.6	1.32	12.1	12.8	13.6	14.3	15.4	10.6	18.3
3 - 0	92	14.6	1.40	12.8	13.7	14.5	15.5	16.4	11.2	19.5
3 - 6	91	15.5	1.40	13.7	14.5	15.6	16.5	17.5	12.2	18.5
4 - 0	91	16.4	1.48	14.3	15.4	16.5	17.5	18.4	12.4	19.8
4 - 6	93	17.6	1.53	15.6	16.7	17.6	18.5	19.6	13.6	21.2
5 - 0	87	18.7	1.71	16.6	17.3	18.6	19.7	21.2	13.6	23.0
5 - 6	91	19.8	1.84	17.6	18.6	19.7	20.8	22.2	16.0	26.0
6 - 0	91	21.0	2.15	18.3	19.5	20.8	22.2	23.6	16.6	28.5
6 - 6	92	22.4	2.41	19.5	20.8	22.2	23.7	25.0	17.5	32.9
7 - 0	92	23.7	2.56	20.4	21.8	23.7	24.9	26.9	18.2	31.9
7 - 6	88	25.1	2.76	21.8	23.0	24.9	27.0	28.6	19.6	32.9
8 - 0	92	26.8	3.31	23.0	24.3	26.3	28.7	30.7	20.2	37.8
8 - 6	90	28.0	3.52	23.9	25.5	27.6	30.2	32.6	21.0	38.9
9 - 0	92	29.7	3.75	25.5	27.1	29.5	32.4	34.8	22.2	41.3
9 - 6	88	31.3	3.92	26.1	28.4	31.4	33.7	36.6	22.9	43.8
10 - 0	85	33.1	4.54	27.5	29.4	32.8	36.2	38.9	24.3	48.9
10 - 6	80	34.3	4.46	28.7	30.7	34.0	38.1	40.7	25.1	43.4
11 - 0	76	36.4	4.83	30.1	32.3	36.0	40.4	43.1	25.1	45.8
11 - 6	78	38.0	5.23	31.0	33.8	37.6	42.1	45.7	27.7	47.6
12 - 0	70	39.9	5.94	32.2	34.9	39.3	44.2	48.9	28.1	52.0
12 - 6	72	41.9	6.25	34.0	37.1	41.3	46.2	51.7	29.8	55.9
13 - 0	71	44.6	7.38	35.2	38.7	43.5	49.5	55.7	30.8	63.6
13 - 6	69	47.7	8.09	37.0	41.4	47.0	53.7	58.9	32.4	65.4
14 - 0	67	50.9	8.16	40.0	44.4	51.0	56.8	62.1	33.3	70.4
14 - 6	61	53.0	8.45	41.6	45.9	53.6	58.8	64.5	36.4	70.5
15 - 0	55	56.5	8.61	45.8	50.4	56.6	61.6	68.0	37.4	78.1
15 - 6	52	59.1	8.40	47.8	53.4	59.9	64.8	69.5	41.4	80.4
16 - 0	49	61.8	8.98	52.5	55.8	61.2	67.2	71.6	42.6	93.0
16 - 6	37	63.1	7.76	53.6	57.5	62.9	67.6	75.1	47.6	80.2
17 - 0	41	65.5	8.90	52.4	60.2	64.4	73.0	77.5	49.7	83.2
17 - 6	23	68.0	9.34	55.5	59.7	69.2	74.0	82.1	51.9	84.6
18 - 0	32	68.1	8.98	56.6	61.7	66.2	75.3	79.6	52.7	88.8
19 - 0	16	68.9	9.44	56.2	61.6	69.6	77.1	80.5	53.6	85.6
20 - 0	14	69.7	9.47	58.4	60.5	66.8	77.1	82.4	55.1	84.4
21 - 0	12	68.6	9.03	60.0	61.8	67.4	75.0	80.5	56.7	87.2
22 - 0	11	69.8	9.69	60.0	62.6	70.0	76.8	82.1	56.6	88.9
23 - 0	12	73.1	10.33	61.5	63.4	71.0	78.6	88.9	60.3	90.7
24 - 0	10	76.4	11.24	63.3	65.6	75.4	87.5	90.6	61.8	92.1
25 - 0	12	66.6	4.77	62.2	63.2	64.9	68.4	74.6	61.4	75.4

ANTHROPOMETRY

TABLE E-4

Female

Weight in Kilograms

Age Yr. Mo.	N	Mean	S.D.	Percentiles 10th	25th	50th	75th	90th	Range Min.	Max.
Birth	54	3.2	0.44	2.6	2.9	3.2	3.5	3.9	2.2	4.1
0 - 1	69	3.7	0.44	3.1	3.5	3.7	4.0	4.3	2.6	4.6
0 - 2	62	4.6	0.41	4.1	4.3	4.6	4.8	5.1	3.1	5.6
0 - 3	67	5.4	0.52	4.8	5.0	5.3	5.7	6.1	3.7	6.6
0 - 4	59	6.0	0.56	5.4	5.6	6.0	6.4	6.8	4.3	7.5
0 - 5	57	6.6	0.66	5.8	6.3	6.6	7.0	7.5	4.5	8.2
0 - 6	63	7.2	0.75	6.2	6.8	7.2	7.7	8.2	5.3	8.8
0 - 9	61	8.4	0.83	7.3	7.9	8.5	8.8	9.6	6.7	10.3
1 - 0	78	9.4	0.99	8.0	8.7	9.4	10.1	10.7	7.3	11.6
1 - 6	88	10.6	1.15	9.0	9.7	10.6	11.4	12.1	7.8	12.8
2 - 0	90	11.9	1.24	10.0	11.1	11.9	12.7	13.5	9.2	14.3
2 - 6	95	12.8	1.26	11.0	12.0	13.0	13.7	14.5	9.8	15.2
3 - 0	93	13.9	1.41	11.9	12.8	14.0	14.9	15.7	10.4	16.9
3 - 6	90	15.0	1.49	12.8	13.6	15.2	16.1	16.8	11.9	17.8
4 - 0	92	16.0	1.64	13.7	14.6	16.3	17.3	18.1	12.2	19.0
4 - 6	91	17.1	1.83	14.6	15.6	17.3	18.6	19.5	13.0	20.4
5 - 0	90	18.2	1.94	15.3	16.5	18.5	19.7	20.6	13.8	21.7
5 - 6	90	19.3	2.24	16.3	17.4	19.8	21.1	22.1	14.6	24.8
6 - 0	95	20.5	2.49	17.1	18.3	20.5	22.3	23.5	15.3	27.3
6 - 6	95	21.6	2.51	17.9	19.7	21.9	23.7	24.9	16.2	26.5
7 - 0	90	23.0	3.10	19.0	20.7	22.7	25.0	26.9	17.0	31.2
7 - 6	92	24.5	3.49	20.0	22.0	24.0	26.7	28.9	17.4	34.2
8 - 0	90	26.0	3.78	21.0	23.3	25.6	28.2	31.4	18.0	36.5
8 - 6	90	27.4	4.17	21.8	24.2	27.0	29.8	33.3	18.7	38.8
9 - 0	80	28.8	4.70	23.1	25.3	28.7	31.2	35.8	19.5	43.3
9 - 6	75	30.4	5.09	23.9	26.3	29.8	33.6	37.5	22.2	47.0
10 - 0	76	32.2	5.62	25.6	27.9	32.0	35.6	40.4	21.4	46.8
10 - 6	73	34.0	6.64	26.2	29.0	33.3	37.8	44.2	22.2	50.8
11 - 0	70	36.0	7.04	27.8	30.6	34.6	40.8	46.5	24.2	53.0
11 - 6	67	38.6	7.80	29.2	32.9	37.5	43.4	48.4	23.5	60.9
12 - 0	69	41.9	8.52	31.7	36.1	41.1	47.7	53.3	24.0	62.9
12 - 6	64	43.5	7.82	33.4	38.0	43.5	48.8	53.6	25.6	63.5
13 - 0	67	45.5	8.11	34.5	38.8	46.2	51.3	54.9	27.1	65.1
13 - 6	52	47.1	7.58	37.2	42.2	47.7	52.0	56.5	28.6	66.1
14 - 0	61	50.9	7.89	41.0	45.0	50.9	56.0	61.3	31.1	76.0
14 - 6	42	51.6	7.64	41.7	46.7	51.9	56.2	60.7	32.1	74.8
15 - 0	52	53.3	7.70	44.6	49.0	53.1	57.4	64.2	33.2	76.2
15 - 6	22	52.6	6.46	43.1	47.1	53.0	57.6	60.6	40.5	64.4
16 - 0	57	55.5	8.34	45.4	50.1	55.0	60.0	65.9	34.2	78.5
17 - 0	43	56.3	7.81	47.0	50.7	56.7	60.7	65.5	34.9	74.7
18 - 0	25	57.9	8.12	48.2	52.2	57.2	62.2	69.2	41.5	79.7
19 - 0	19	60.2	6.92	51.7	56.9	59.9	65.0	66.7	45.9	76.4
20 - 0	15	57.9	7.47	48.0	51.8	59.1	63.6	66.6	41.2	68.7
21 - 0	13	60.8	5.08	55.2	57.5	60.3	64.6	67.4	51.3	68.5
22 - 0	10	59.3	8.26	50.0	54.3	57.0	64.9	72.4	48.8	73.6
23 - 0	11	55.7	9.61	42.8	50.4	56.8	63.1	65.9	35.7	69.4
24 - 0	10	60.6	6.41	53.0	57.3	58.6	66.2	68.3	48.9	69.3

ANTHROPOMETRY TABLE E-5

Male Sitting Height in Centimeters

Age Yr. Mo.	N	Mean	S.D.	Percentiles 10th	25th	50th	75th	90th	Range Min.	Max.
Crown-rump length										
Birth	48	33.6	1.83	31.0	32.3	33.5	35.2	36.1	29.9	36.5
0 - 1	56	35.7	1.72	33.4	34.7	35.4	36.6	38.4	31.9	39.9
0 - 2	51	38.4	1.87	36.0	37.3	38.0	39.7	41.3	35.0	42.7
0 - 3	59	40.6	1.97	38.1	39.2	40.4	41.7	43.2	36.2	45.9
0 - 4	49	42.3	1.73	40.3	41.1	42.0	43.2	44.6	39.1	48.3
0 - 5	51	43.7	1.72	41.6	42.3	43.6	44.8	45.9	40.9	49.6
0 - 6	64	44.7	1.92	42.7	43.3	44.5	45.9	47.0	40.4	51.8
0 - 9	53	47.2	1.67	45.5	46.1	47.1	48.1	49.1	43.5	53.2
1 - 0	67	48.6	1.83	46.5	47.4	48.4	49.7	50.9	43.8	54.4
1 - 6	59	50.9	1.73	48.9	49.9	50.9	52.1	52.8	46.1	55.4
2 - 0	41	53.4	1.67	51.2	52.4	53.5	54.4	55.8	49.7	56.4
Erect										
2 - 0	51	51.9	1.93	49.7	50.5	51.8	52.9	53.8	48.4	59.4
2 - 6	58	54.0	1.75	51.8	52.8	53.7	55.2	56.1	50.2	59.5
3 - 0	59	55.4	1.87	52.9	54.0	55.3	56.5	57.3	51.7	61.0
3 - 6	57	56.7	1.89	54.2	55.6	57.0	57.9	59.1	52.4	61.9
4 - 0	73	58.0	1.86	55.6	56.7	57.8	59.1	60.4	54.0	63.0
4 - 6	90	59.6	1.82	57.2	58.4	59.5	60.8	61.9	55.1	65.7
5 - 0	86	61.0	1.98	58.5	59.5	60.8	62.3	63.5	57.0	66.4
5 - 6	91	62.4	1.84	59.9	61.2	62.4	63.7	64.7	58.2	67.6
6 - 0	91	63.7	2.00	61.0	62.6	63.7	64.9	66.0	58.7	69.3
6 - 6	92	65.0	1.94	62.7	64.0	65.0	66.0	67.1	59.8	70.2
7 - 0	92	66.2	2.03	63.7	64.9	66.2	67.4	68.5	60.2	72.5
7 - 6	88	67.4	2.07	64.7	66.1	67.4	68.5	70.1	62.2	73.0
8 - 0	91	68.7	2.27	65.9	67.2	68.7	70.2	71.4	63.5	75.3
8 - 6	90	69.6	2.32	66.4	68.1	69.7	71.2	72.5	64.1	75.5
9 - 0	92	70.7	2.34	67.6	69.3	70.8	72.2	73.6	64.7	76.5
9 - 6	88	71.7	2.30	68.8	70.2	71.8	72.7	74.8	65.7	77.4
10 - 0	85	72.6	2.36	69.5	71.1	72.5	74.2	75.6	66.6	78.5
10 - 6	78	73.7	2.41	70.4	71.9	73.7	75.2	76.8	68.2	80.0
11 - 0	76	74.6	2.41	71.6	72.9	74.5	76.2	77.8	68.8	81.1
11 - 6	78	75.6	2.56	72.3	73.7	75.8	77.1	79.1	69.5	82.0
12 - 0	70	76.4	2.73	73.2	74.5	76.4	78.0	79.2	70.0	84.8
12 - 6	72	77.5	2.72	73.9	75.6	77.5	79.2	80.6	71.3	85.1
13 - 0	71	79.2	3.42	74.9	76.8	78.8	80.7	83.3	72.1	89.9
13 - 6	69	81.0	4.02	76.3	78.3	80.4	82.9	86.6	74.0	91.9
14 - 0	66	82.7	4.03	77.6	79.4	82.7	85.4	87.8	76.0	93.3
14 - 6	61	83.9	4.01	78.9	80.6	83.8	86.6	89.2	76.4	93.9
15 - 0	55	85.8	3.88	80.8	83.0	85.6	88.9	90.8	78.2	96.4
15 - 6	52	87.4	3.76	82.7	84.5	87.3	90.4	92.0	80.6	97.3
16 - 0	49	89.2	3.45	84.6	86.4	89.5	91.5	93.0	82.4	97.4
16 - 6	37	89.5	2.98	85.5	87.4	89.5	91.8	93.6	83.1	95.7
17 - 0	42	90.6	2.64	86.8	88.3	91.1	92.6	93.8	85.0	95.7
17 - 6	24	91.4	3.13	87.0	89.0	91.9	94.1	95.1	85.8	95.6
18 - 0	33	92.0	2.61	88.4	90.5	92.6	93.9	95.0	86.0	96.1
19 - 0	25	93.0	3.12	88.6	90.1	93.7	95.4	96.3	86.2	97.5
20 - 0	31	93.2	2.58	89.2	90.6	93.9	95.4	96.1	88.2	97.0
21 - 0	35	93.6	2.75	88.9	91.3	94.6	95.8	96.4	88.3	97.5
22 - 0	39	93.3	2.76	88.4	91.4	93.8	95.2	96.4	87.6	97.6
23 - 0	37	93.5	3.05	88.8	91.3	93.8	95.8	97.0	86.6	99.5
24 - 0	34	93.7	3.02	89.0	91.6	94.2	95.6	97.2	86.7	99.5
25 - 0	30	93.3	3.30	88.5	90.9	93.6	95.8	97.0	86.5	99.6

ANTHROPOMETRY

TABLE E-6

Female

Sitting Height in Centimeters

Age Yr. Mo.	N	Mean	S.D.	Percentiles 10th	25th	50th	75th	90th	Range Min.	Max.
Crown-rump length										
Birth	55	33.3	1.64	31.0	32.0	33.3	34.5	35.2	29.4	36.5
0 - 1	63	35.2	1.70	32.9	34.2	35.5	36.3	37.0	31.2	39.5
0 - 2	61	37.4	1.45	35.4	36.4	37.2	38.5	39.6	34.5	40.8
0 - 3	67	39.5	1.58	37.1	38.6	39.4	40.5	41.5	35.7	43.2
0 - 4	59	40.8	1.45	38.9	39.6	40.7	41.6	42.9	38.2	43.7
0 - 5	57	42.3	1.62	40.2	41.4	42.3	43.7	44.5	38.1	45.8
0 - 6	58	43.4	1.73	41.3	42.3	43.2	44.6	45.6	40.0	47.3
0 - 9	59	45.6	1.66	43.7	44.5	45.6	47.1	47.8	39.8	48.5
1 - 0	65	47.4	1.85	44.9	45.8	47.4	48.9	49.7	43.6	51.5
1 - 6	58	50.0	2.07	47.0	48.4	50.4	51.7	52.4	44.9	54.5
2 - 0	43	52.8	1.87	50.3	51.6	52.8	54.2	55.2	47.7	56.2
Erect										
2 - 0	56	51.1	1.90	48.4	49.6	51.2	52.6	53.4	47.1	55.1
2 - 6	71	52.7	1.86	50.4	51.4	52.7	54.2	55.1	48.3	56.4
3 - 0	71	54.4	2.02	51.8	53.0	54.6	55.8	56.8	48.8	57.9
3 - 6	68	56.0	2.05	53.1	54.7	56.1	57.3	58.3	51.5	61.1
4 - 0	77	57.7	2.05	54.6	56.2	57.8	59.2	60.1	52.4	61.7
4 - 6	89	59.4	2.15	56.3	58.2	59.6	60.8	61.7	53.7	64.9
5 - 0	89	60.8	2.36	57.3	59.3	60.9	62.5	63.4	54.9	67.2
5 - 6	90	62.1	2.45	58.6	60.5	62.3	63.9	65.2	55.9	68.1
6 - 0	95	63.5	2.48	60.3	61.7	63.8	65.3	66.5	56.2	68.7
6 - 6	95	64.8	2.54	61.3	63.1	65.2	66.5	67.7	57.4	69.4
7 - 0	90	66.0	2.70	62.1	64.2	66.4	68.0	69.1	58.3	72.0
7 - 6	92	67.2	2.66	63.7	65.5	67.5	68.9	70.2	58.7	74.0
8 - 0	90	68.3	2.77	64.6	66.2	68.4	70.3	71.4	60.5	75.5
8 - 6	90	69.2	2.85	65.5	67.5	69.2	71.3	72.4	61.0	76.8
9 - 0	80	70.2	2.97	66.0	68.4	70.4	72.5	73.8	61.3	78.1
9 - 6	75	71.2	3.01	67.6	69.0	71.1	73.4	75.0	62.4	79.6
10 - 0	76	72.6	3.04	69.4	70.4	72.4	74.8	76.3	64.0	82.5
10 - 6	73	73.8	3.43	69.3	71.3	73.8	76.0	77.7	64.1	84.6
11 - 0	70	75.1	3.79	70.3	72.5	75.2	77.4	79.4	65.1	86.8
11 - 6	67	76.7	3.92	71.5	74.0	76.6	78.9	81.1	67.1	87.8
12 - 0	69	78.5	4.25	72.7	75.4	78.9	81.5	83.6	67.9	88.5
12 - 6	64	80.0	4.22	73.6	77.3	80.2	83.2	85.1	69.4	89.1
13 - 0	68	81.3	4.34	74.7	78.4	82.1	84.8	86.8	71.2	89.3
13 - 6	53	82.6	4.04	76.5	79.9	83.3	85.6	87.8	72.5	88.9
14 - 0	61	84.1	3.61	79.1	81.8	84.6	86.6	88.5	74.0	90.5
14 - 6	43	84.8	3.85	79.1	82.4	85.3	87.7	89.5	75.6	90.6
15 - 0	52	86.0	3.35	81.1	84.0	86.4	88.6	89.8	76.8	90.7
15 - 6	23	86.4	3.68	80.8	83.6	86.8	89.6	90.7	79.3	92.1
16 - 0	57	87.0	3.27	82.2	85.0	87.4	89.5	90.8	78.4	92.7
16 - 6	12	86.9	4.30	80.1	81.8	87.9	90.4	91.1	79.4	91.6
17 - 0	47	87.6	3.48	82.9	85.0	87.9	90.2	91.8	79.4	94.7
17 - 6	18	87.3	2.77	83.5	85.7	87.1	90.0	90.8	81.8	91.2
18 - 0	35	87.8	3.11	83.4	85.5	87.7	90.4	91.3	81.1	94.0
19 - 0	35	87.9	2.87	84.1	85.5	88.6	90.3	91.4	81.7	92.8
20 - 0	36	88.0	3.16	83.5	86.3	88.1	90.6	91.3	80.5	94.1
21 - 0	35	88.2	3.40	83.4	85.7	88.3	90.7	91.4	80.6	96.4
22 - 0	32	88.0	3.00	83.9	86.2	87.7	90.4	91.5	81.3	93.5
23 - 0	30	87.6	3.13	84.3	85.7	87.6	90.1	91.4	80.6	92.9
24 - 0	26	87.5	3.27	82.5	85.4	87.2	90.4	91.3	80.7	91.9
25 - 0	26	87.3	3.21	82.6	85.6	87.0	90.3	91.3	80.7	92.6

TABLE E-7

ANTHROPOMETRY

Male

Fronto-occipital Circumference in Centimeters

Age Yr. Mo.	N	Mean	S.D.	Percentiles 10th	25th	50th	75th	90th	Range Min.	Max.
Birth	50	34.3	1.26	32.8	33.2	34.3	35.2	36.0	31.8	36.7
0 - 1	62	37.0	1.16	35.4	36.2	36.9	38.0	38.6	34.4	39.8
0 - 2	52	38.9	1.18	37.4	38.0	38.8	39.8	40.4	36.2	41.7
0 - 3	59	40.3	1.17	38.7	39.4	40.4	41.1	41.9	38.0	43.4
0 - 4	49	41.6	1.17	40.1	40.7	41.4	42.5	43.1	39.5	44.4
0 - 5	51	42.5	1.22	40.8	41.8	42.4	43.4	44.1	40.0	45.3
0 - 6	70	43.6	1.20	41.9	42.8	43.5	44.3	45.0	41.0	46.5
0 - 9	54	45.5	1.13	43.9	44.8	45.3	46.3	47.1	43.4	48.0
1 - 0	73	46.6	1.18	45.0	45.7	46.6	47.2	48.1	44.2	49.8
1 - 6	82	48.2	1.17	46.8	47.4	48.2	49.0	49.7	44.4	50.8
2 - 0	88	49.2	1.19	47.6	48.2	49.1	49.9	50.7	46.5	52.6
2 - 6	91	49.8	1.16	48.3	48.9	49.7	50.5	51.2	47.2	53.2
3 - 0	92	50.3	1.15	48.8	49.5	50.2	50.8	51.9	47.8	53.2
3 - 6	91	50.7	1.14	49.2	49.8	50.5	51.4	52.1	48.5	53.8
4 - 0	91	51.0	1.14	49.5	50.1	50.8	51.6	52.2	48.8	54.5
4 - 6	93	51.3	1.19	49.7	50.4	51.2	52.0	52.7	48.5	54.5
5 - 0	87	51.6	1.22	50.0	50.7	51.4	52.3	53.1	49.0	55.1
5 - 6	91	51.9	1.20	50.4	51.1	51.8	52.7	53.4	48.2	55.1
6 - 0	91	52.6	1.22	50.6	51.2	51.9	52.8	53.6	48.1	55.5
6 - 6	92	52.3	1.24	50.8	51.4	52.2	53.1	54.0	48.2	55.5
7 - 0	92	52.4	1.20	51.1	51.6	52.3	53.2	54.0	48.2	55.6
7 - 6	87	52.6	1.22	51.4	51.8	52.5	53.4	54.3	48.3	55.9
8 - 0	91	52.8	1.20	51.4	52.0	52.8	53.6	54.4	48.6	55.9
8 - 6	87	52.9	1.18	51.6	52.2	52.8	53.8	54.4	48.4	55.9
9 - 0	88	53.2	1.22	51.9	52.3	53.1	54.0	54.8	48.8	56.4
9 - 6	83	53.3	1.24	51.8	52.5	53.2	54.1	54.9	48.4	56.7
10 - 0	82	53.5	1.25	52.1	52.7	53.5	54.3	55.2	48.5	56.7
10 - 6	78	53.7	1.30	52.2	52.8	53.6	54.5	55.4	48.7	56.8
11 - 0	72	53.8	1.35	52.3	53.0	53.8	54.5	55.3	48.6	57.0
11 - 6	74	53.9	1.26	52.4	53.1	53.8	54.6	55.5	48.8	57.0
12 - 0	69	54.1	1.36	52.7	53.3	54.0	54.8	56.1	49.2	57.1
12 - 6	68	54.2	1.23	52.8	53.4	54.2	54.9	55.7	49.5	57.5
13 - 0	66	54.4	1.23	52.8	53.6	54.4	55.1	55.9	49.6	57.4
13 - 6	63	54.8	1.31	53.1	54.0	54.8	55.5	56.3	49.3	57.9
14 - 0	61	54.9	1.26	53.4	54.2	54.9	55.7	56.5	49.7	57.6
14 - 6	59	55.0	1.22	53.5	54.3	55.1	55.8	56.4	50.1	57.6
15 - 0	50	55.3	1.36	53.6	54.4	55.3	56.1	57.2	50.3	57.7
15 - 6	46	55.6	1.42	53.7	54.8	55.6	56.7	57.2	50.3	58.3
16 - 0	47	56.0	1.44	54.3	55.2	56.1	56.9	57.6	50.3	59.5
16 - 6	36	56.0	1.54	54.2	55.2	56.0	56.9	57.7	50.4	60.1
17 - 0	41	56.3	1.47	54.7	55.6	56.2	57.4	58.2	50.7	58.6
17 - 6	24	56.4	1.59	55.0	55.7	56.6	57.5	58.3	51.1	58.8
18 - 0	33	56.4	1.40	54.7	55.7	56.5	57.1	57.8	51.4	59.4
19 - 0	25	56.7	1.50	55.0	55.8	56.9	57.5	58.6	52.3	59.9
20 - 0	31	57.0	1.54	55.3	56.0	57.0	57.9	58.8	52.0	59.9
21 - 0	35	57.2	1.48	55.7	56.1	57.1	58.3	59.1	52.7	59.9
22 - 0	39	57.3	1.43	55.8	56.6	57.4	58.3	59.2	52.8	60.0
23 - 0	37	57.3	1.40	55.7	56.5	57.2	58.0	59.4	53.1	60.2
24 - 0	33	57.4	1.50	55.7	56.4	57.5	58.7	59.4	53.0	60.2
25 - 0	30	57.4	1.60	55.6	56.3	57.4	58.6	59.7	53.0	60.2

ANTHROPOMETRY

TABLE E-8

Female

Fronto-occipital Circumference in Centimeters

Age Yr. Mo.	N	Mean	S.D.	Percentiles 10th	25th	50th	75th	90th	Range Min.	Max.
Birth	55	33.8	1.23	32.1	33.1	33.8	34.5	35.3	30.6	36.1
0 - 1	69	36.2	1.33	34.4	35.4	36.3	37.0	37.8	31.0	38.5
0 - 2	62	38.1	1.11	36.6	37.5	38.0	38.9	39.4	35.2	40.6
0 - 3	67	39.5	1.08	38.1	38.8	39.6	40.4	40.8	36.4	42.0
0 - 4	58	40.5	1.12	39.3	39.9	40.6	41.4	41.8	36.7	42.6
0 - 5	57	41.6	1.12	40.0	40.8	41.5	42.3	42.9	38.3	44.0
0 - 6	63	42.4	1.21	40.9	41.7	42.4	43.3	44.0	39.1	45.0
0 - 9	61	44.3	1.21	42.5	43.6	44.1	45.3	45.8	41.3	47.0
1 - 0	76	45.6	1.31	43.9	44.8	45.4	46.5	47.4	42.3	48.7
1 - 6	86	47.0	1.46	45.1	46.0	47.0	47.9	48.8	42.3	50.4
2 - 0	90	48.1	1.41	46.4	47.1	48.1	49.0	49.8	44.2	51.4
2 - 6	95	48.7	1.39	47.0	47.8	48.6	49.7	50.5	44.7	52.1
3 - 0	93	49.2	1.44	47.4	48.4	49.3	50.2	51.1	44.4	53.1
3 - 6	90	49.7	1.52	47.8	48.6	49.6	50.8	51.6	44.5	53.3
4 - 0	92	50.2	1.52	48.2	49.1	50.2	51.2	52.0	45.7	53.6
4 - 6	91	50.4	1.49	48.6	49.4	50.5	51.5	52.3	46.5	53.8
5 - 0	90	50.7	1.45	48.8	49.7	50.8	51.8	52.6	46.6	54.0
5 - 6	90	51.0	1.46	49.1	49.9	51.0	52.0	52.8	46.9	54.4
6 - 0	95	51.2	1.46	49.2	50.2	51.2	52.2	53.0	47.0	54.6
6 - 6	95	51.4	1.47	49.5	50.4	51.6	52.4	53.3	47.1	54.7
7 - 0	90	51.6	1.43	49.8	50.7	51.8	52.5	53.5	47.5	54.8
7 - 6	88	51.8	1.48	49.9	50.8	51.6	52.8	53.5	47.8	55.0
8 - 0	85	52.1	1.38	50.2	51.1	52.0	53.1	54.0	48.7	55.5
8 - 6	85	52.2	1.35	50.3	51.3	52.3	53.1	53.9	49.0	55.5
9 - 0	79	52.3	1.38	50.1	51.2	52.4	53.3	54.0	49.0	55.5
9 - 6	72	52.6	1.45	50.3	51.5	52.6	53.5	54.4	49.2	55.8
10 - 0	72	52.8	1.46	50.9	51.8	52.9	54.0	54.7	49.2	56.3
10 - 6	73	53.0	1.45	50.9	52.0	53.0	54.0	54.8	50.0	56.2
11 - 0	67	53.0	1.40	51.1	52.1	53.2	54.1	54.8	50.4	56.1
11 - 6	67	53.3	1.60	51.2	52.2	53.2	54.6	55.4	50.1	57.0
12 - 0	67	53.7	1.61	51.6	52.4	53.7	54.8	55.9	50.6	57.7
12 - 6	63	53.8	1.54	51.8	52.6	53.7	54.8	55.8	50.5	57.4
13 - 0	66	53.9	1.50	52.2	52.8	53.9	54.9	56.2	50.6	57.5
13 - 6	47	54.0	1.56	52.1	52.8	53.9	55.0	56.2	50.9	57.9
14 - 0	53	54.2	1.63	52.3	53.0	54.2	55.4	56.6	50.8	58.1
14 - 6	41	54.5	1.54	52.7	53.3	54.3	55.7	56.5	51.9	58.1
15 - 0	50	54.4	1.59	52.4	53.0	54.3	55.5	56.7	50.6	57.4
15 - 6	23	54.9	1.31	53.1	53.8	55.1	55.8	56.5	52.5	57.0
16 - 0	55	54.6	1.70	52.4	53.3	54.5	56.0	57.0	50.6	58.1
16 - 6	12	55.0	2.05	52.7	53.1	55.7	56.4	56.8	50.5	57.6
17 - 0	47	54.8	1.69	52.3	53.6	54.9	55.8	56.9	50.4	58.9
17 - 6	18	55.1	1.66	52.9	54.6	55.4	56.0	56.7	50.4	57.7
18 - 0	35	54.8	1.79	52.5	53.4	55.0	55.7	56.8	50.4	59.7
19 - 0	35	55.0	1.77	52.8	54.3	55.1	56.1	57.0	50.4	60.3
20 - 0	35	55.0	1.77	52.9	53.8	54.9	56.1	57.0	50.7	59.8
21 - 0	34	55.3	1.75	53.0	53.9	55.3	56.2	58.0	51.2	58.6
22 - 0	32	55.1	1.74	52.8	53.6	54.9	56.2	57.6	51.6	58.4
23 - 0	30	55.1	1.76	52.7	53.5	55.0	56.3	57.8	51.9	58.4
24 - 0	26	55.0	1.84	52.8	53.7	54.8	56.5	57.8	51.8	58.4
25 - 0	26	55.1	1.81	52.8	53.9	54.9	56.2	57.8	51.8	58.4

ANTHROPOMETRY TABLE E-9

Male — Xiphisternal Circumference in Centimeters

Age Yr. Mo.	N	Mean	S.D.	Percentiles 10th	25th	50th	75th	90th	Range Min.	Max.
Supine										
Birth	49	32.2	1.97	29.6	30.5	32.1	33.4	35.0	29.0	37.0
0 - 1	61	35.3	1.75	32.9	34.0	35.4	36.4	37.3	32.0	39.6
0 - 2	53	38.1	1.90	35.4	37.0	38.2	39.5	40.5	34.2	43.0
0 - 3	57	39.8	1.73	37.5	38.4	39.7	41.0	41.9	35.5	44.0
0 - 4	49	41.4	1.66	38.8	40.3	41.4	42.8	43.5	38.3	44.8
0 - 5	51	42.5	1.85	39.8	41.0	42.5	43.8	44.8	39.0	46.7
0 - 6	70	43.5	1.80	41.4	42.2	43.4	44.8	45.8	39.5	48.9
0 - 9	52	45.7	1.95	43.3	44.3	45.6	46.8	48.0	41.6	51.0
1 - 0	64	46.9	1.87	44.4	45.6	46.8	48.1	49.4	43.5	52.4
1 - 6	46	48.5	2.18	46.2	47.3	48.5	49.8	51.3	41.0	52.2
2 - 0	33	49.3	1.68	47.4	48.4	49.1	50.2	51.6	45.8	53.2
Erect										
2 - 0	52	48.9	2.67	45.7	47.4	48.6	50.6	51.7	45.0	54.0
2 - 6	60	50.0	2.18	47.5	48.2	49.6	51.5	53.4	45.3	55.4
3 - 0	57	50.8	2.06	48.2	49.4	50.7	52.2	53.7	46.2	55.5
3 - 6	55	51.6	2.16	49.0	50.1	51.6	53.1	55.0	47.0	56.0
4 - 0	72	52.2	2.13	49.4	50.8	52.3	53.7	54.9	47.5	57.0
4 - 6	91	52.9	2.06	50.3	51.4	52.8	54.3	55.8	49.1	58.4
5 - 0	87	53.9	1.87	51.5	52.6	53.8	55.2	56.4	50.2	59.5
5 - 6	91	54.7	2.08	52.1	53.3	54.4	56.0	56.8	49.3	61.9
6 - 0	90	55.8	2.30	52.8	54.1	55.7	57.3	58.7	50.3	65.5
6 - 6	91	56.9	2.59	53.7	55.2	56.9	58.5	59.8	52.0	70.5
7 - 0	92	57.8	2.50	54.5	56.0	57.5	59.6	61.3	53.2	66.0
7 - 6	85	58.9	2.75	55.2	56.9	58.5	61.0	62.2	53.7	68.2
8 - 0	91	60.0	3.04	56.2	58.0	59.8	62.1	63.7	54.2	72.3
8 - 6	89	61.0	3.19	57.4	58.4	60.8	62.8	65.0	55.3	72.8
9 - 0	89	62.3	3.42	58.2	59.6	61.8	64.6	66.8	55.4	75.5
9 - 6	87	63.3	3.34	59.0	60.6	63.3	66.0	67.7	55.4	70.3
10 - 0	82	64.7	4.09	60.4	61.7	64.3	67.4	69.8	55.5	79.8
10 - 6	79	65.5	3.77	61.1	62.4	65.2	67.6	71.1	57.2	74.9
11 - 0	76	66.7	4.22	61.5	63.2	66.3	69.7	72.2	59.0	78.4
11 - 6	77	67.7	4.42	62.3	64.5	67.5	70.6	73.1	58.5	79.6
12 - 0	69	69.2	4.73	63.8	65.8	68.5	72.3	75.4	61.3	81.9
12 - 6	73	70.4	4.92	64.7	66.8	69.9	73.3	77.1	61.8	84.4
13 - 0	68	72.4	5.32	66.1	68.2	71.4	76.4	79.8	63.0	86.0
13 - 6	69	73.6	5.86	66.4	68.9	72.7	77.9	82.1	63.2	90.1
14 - 0	67	75.6	5.88	68.3	70.8	75.0	79.9	83.9	64.2	90.9
14 - 6	61	76.6	5.90	69.8	71.9	75.9	80.6	84.8	63.8	91.3
15 - 0	55	79.0	5.76	71.7	74.8	78.4	83.1	87.6	66.2	95.3
15 - 6	49	80.1	5.68	73.2	76.1	79.8	84.8	87.4	66.7	94.8
16 - 0	49	81.9	6.33	74.2	77.5	81.0	86.2	90.2	69.3	102.3
16 - 6	36	82.7	5.45	76.0	78.5	82.3	86.8	88.7	73.5	95.6
17 - 0	41	84.6	6.59	75.8	79.1	85.6	90.1	93.4	73.3	97.5
17 - 6	23	86.4	6.99	78.4	80.8	85.6	90.4	95.8	77.0	100.8
18 - 0	32	87.1	6.49	79.3	82.1	86.9	92.0	96.3	75.8	102.8
19 - 0	17	86.8	6.48	79.1	81.9	84.6	90.7	97.2	77.1	100.3
20 - 0	15	87.5	7.02	80.4	81.7	86.8	92.4	96.3	79.6	101.9
21 - 0	12	87.2	4.82	81.5	83.0	88.0	90.0	91.9	80.5	97.2
22 - 0	12	88.4	7.01	80.6	82.0	88.2	93.1	94.2	79.6	104.1
23 - 0	13	90.3	8.54	80.4	84.4	88.7	96.6	101.8	78.7	105.3
24 - 0	11	91.0	7.35	79.4	84.2	94.0	96.4	99.0	78.2	100.2
25 - 0	12	85.9	3.97	81.3	82.5	84.6	88.2	89.7	80.5	94.0

ANTHROPOMETRY TABLE E-10

Female Xiphisternal Circumference in Centimeters

Age Yr. Mo.	N	Mean	S.D.	Percentiles 10th	25th	50th	75th	90th	Range Min.	Max.
Supine										
Birth	55	32.3	1.53	30.1	31.3	32.3	33.5	34.2	28.9	35.8
0 - 1	67	34.5	1.59	32.1	33.3	34.9	35.5	36.5	30.8	37.6
0 - 2	61	36.9	1.38	35.4	36.1	36.9	37.8	38.4	33.2	41.5
0 - 3	65	38.7	1.67	36.8	37.6	38.5	39.6	40.4	34.5	44.5
0 - 4	57	40.2	1.74	38.3	39.0	40.2	41.1	41.9	36.5	45.3
0 - 5	56	41.3	1.65	38.9	40.3	41.3	42.3	43.6	37.6	45.7
0 - 6	61	42.6	1.87	40.5	41.4	42.2	43.8	45.1	37.3	46.7
0 - 9	58	44.4	1.88	42.5	43.2	44.3	45.3	47.0	39.6	49.2
1 - 0	63	45.7	1.78	43.3	44.4	45.7	46.8	48.3	42.6	50.0
1 - 6	46	47.1	1.76	44.6	46.0	47.0	48.5	49.4	42.8	50.0
2 - 0	27	48.0	1.51	46.1	46.7	48.0	49.4	50.0	45.1	50.7
Erect										
2 - 0	53	47.7	1.90	45.3	46.3	47.7	48.9	50.2	43.8	52.5
2 - 6	69	48.5	1.74	46.0	47.4	48.5	49.4	50.5	44.2	52.6
3 - 0	67	49.2	1.89	46.4	48.0	49.2	50.4	51.5	44.6	54.6
3 - 6	67	50.2	1.74	48.0	49.0	50.1	51.5	52.3	45.8	55.0
4 - 0	77	50.9	1.70	48.7	49.7	50.7	52.0	53.0	46.4	56.0
4 - 6	87	51.8	1.94	49.3	50.5	51.6	53.1	54.4	47.5	56.0
5 - 0	88	52.5	2.17	49.6	50.8	52.4	54.0	55.6	48.0	58.5
5 - 6	90	53.4	2.26	50.4	51.7	53.4	54.9	56.4	48.5	60.4
6 - 0	95	54.3	2.41	51.0	52.5	54.1	56.0	57.4	49.1	63.6
6 - 6	95	55.0	2.35	52.1	53.3	55.0	56.6	58.2	49.4	61.2
7 - 0	90	56.2	2.94	52.5	53.9	56.2	58.2	60.1	49.4	65.6
7 - 6	92	57.3	3.12	53.8	55.2	56.8	59.2	61.5	49.7	67.1
8 - 0	90	58.6	3.34	54.5	55.9	58.1	60.8	63.2	50.9	70.0
8 - 6	88	59.5	3.66	55.0	56.6	59.0	62.2	64.5	51.6	71.7
9 - 0	80	60.3	3.91	56.5	57.5	59.6	62.6	65.8	52.0	73.3
9 - 6	75	61.5	3.83	57.2	58.4	60.8	64.0	66.8	54.8	73.6
10 - 0	76	62.8	4.28	58.0	59.5	62.2	65.5	69.4	53.5	74.0
10 - 6	73	63.8	4.98	58.2	60.0	62.9	67.0	70.9	54.9	78.7
11 - 0	70	65.0	5.34	59.0	61.3	64.1	68.0	73.7	56.3	78.1
11 - 6	67	66.1	4.90	60.6	62.5	65.2	68.8	73.9	54.6	79.5
12 - 0	69	67.4	5.39	61.6	63.9	67.1	69.5	75.4	56.0	82.1
12 - 6	64	67.7	4.77	61.8	64.4	67.3	70.7	75.4	58.0	79.5
13 - 0	67	68.9	4.78	63.2	65.6	68.4	72.1	75.5	58.7	80.3
13 - 6	51	69.6	4.48	64.3	66.7	68.8	72.1	76.6	58.8	82.1
14 - 0	61	71.3	4.91	66.4	67.8	70.2	74.3	78.6	61.4	86.2
14 - 6	42	71.1	4.34	66.1	68.6	70.7	73.2	77.4	62.0	84.6
15 - 0	52	71.6	4.60	66.1	68.3	70.9	74.1	78.3	60.9	84.9
15 - 6	22	71.2	3.20	67.1	68.9	71.4	73.1	74.3	65.5	79.2
16 - 0	57	73.0	5.04	66.7	69.5	72.0	76.4	80.2	61.5	86.0
17 - 0	44	73.3	5.35	67.8	69.6	72.1	77.0	81.7	61.5	85.0
18 - 0	25	74.0	5.00	69.2	70.3	72.5	76.8	81.1	64.4	86.0
19 - 0	19	75.7	4.82	70.6	72.1	75.6	79.2	81.3	67.0	86.0
20 - 0	15	74.0	4.52	68.5	69.8	73.2	78.1	79.2	67.8	82.3
21 - 0	13	76.2	3.15	72.0	73.4	76.3	79.1	79.8	70.7	80.9
22 - 0	10	75.7	3.77	71.5	72.1	74.7	78.8	80.6	71.1	83.0
23 - 0	11	74.4	4.74	70.6	72.4	73.5	78.6	79.5	64.0	80.1
24 - 0	10	76.9	4.36	70.6	75.1	77.5	79.6	82.3	69.2	83.0

ANTHROPOMETRY TABLE E-11

Male Xiphisternal Width in Centimeters

Age Yr. Mo.	N	Mean	S.D.	Percentiles 10th	25th	50th	75th	90th	Range Min.	Max.
Supine										
Birth	49	9.7	0.73	8.8	9.2	9.6	10.0	10.5	8.3	11.5
0 - 1	62	11.2	0.78	10.2	10.6	11.3	11.8	12.2	9.1	12.9
0 - 2	52	12.4	0.80	11.4	11.9	12.4	13.0	13.5	10.6	14.4
0 - 3	58	13.1	0.82	12.0	12.5	13.2	13.7	14.2	11.0	14.5
0 - 4	49	13.9	0.77	12.7	13.4	14.0	14.3	14.6	12.3	15.8
0 - 5	51	14.4	0.77	13.4	13.9	14.4	15.0	15.4	12.9	16.1
0 - 6	70	14.7	0.79	13.5	14.2	14.7	15.2	15.5	12.6	16.5
0 - 9	50	15.4	0.73	14.4	14.8	15.4	15.8	16.4	13.6	16.7
1 - 0	64	15.6	0.81	14.5	15.2	15.6	16.0	16.6	13.9	18.1
1 - 6	45	16.2	0.73	15.2	15.7	16.2	16.7	17.1	14.8	18.0
2 - 0	33	16.7	0.66	15.8	16.2	16.7	17.1	17.6	15.2	17.9
Erect										
2 - 0	53	16.6	0.89	15.6	16.0	16.6	17.3	17.9	14.2	18.6
2 - 6	60	17.1	0.83	16.1	16.5	17.0	17.6	18.1	15.4	19.3
3 - 0	58	17.5	0.71	16.6	17.0	17.4	17.9	18.4	16.0	19.2
3 - 6	57	17.7	0.77	16.7	17.2	17.7	18.3	18.8	16.1	19.4
4 - 0	74	17.8	0.84	16.7	17.3	17.8	18.5	18.9	15.4	19.8
4 - 6	93	18.0	0.90	16.8	17.4	18.0	18.5	19.2	16.2	20.5
5 - 0	87	18.3	0.89	17.1	17.6	18.3	19.0	19.5	16.8	20.2
5 - 6	91	18.6	0.95	17.4	17.9	18.5	19.2	19.9	16.5	21.1
6 - 0	91	18.9	1.00	17.5	18.2	18.8	19.6	20.2	16.8	21.3
6 - 6	92	19.2	1.04	17.9	18.5	19.2	19.9	20.5	16.5	22.4
7 - 0	92	19.6	1.06	18.2	18.9	19.5	20.2	21.1	16.9	22.0
7 - 6	88	19.9	1.10	18.6	19.1	19.8	20.6	21.4	17.0	22.5
8 - 0	92	20.3	1.22	18.8	19.4	20.3	21.2	21.9	17.2	23.4
8 - 6	90	20.6	1.24	19.0	19.7	20.6	21.4	22.1	17.2	23.7
9 - 0	92	21.2	1.32	19.4	20.3	21.0	22.3	23.0	18.0	23.7
9 - 6	88	21.5	1.38	19.8	20.4	21.5	22.7	23.2	18.0	23.9
10 - 0	85	22.0	1.51	20.0	20.7	21.8	23.1	23.9	17.8	25.8
10 - 6	80	22.3	1.42	20.6	21.3	22.2	23.4	24.1	18.5	25.4
11 - 0	76	22.9	1.62	20.7	21.6	22.8	24.1	24.9	19.8	26.7
11 - 6	78	23.3	1.64	21.0	22.1	23.2	24.7	25.3	20.2	27.5
12 - 0	70	23.7	1.88	21.2	22.3	23.6	25.0	26.1	19.0	28.0
12 - 6	73	24.0	1.81	21.5	22.7	24.0	25.2	26.4	19.5	28.4
13 - 0	71	24.8	1.94	22.3	23.2	24.5	26.1	27.6	21.5	29.6
13 - 6	69	25.2	2.05	22.7	23.6	25.1	26.8	27.8	22.0	30.8
14 - 0	67	25.8	2.09	23.0	24.2	25.6	27.4	28.4	22.3	31.4
14 - 6	61	26.4	1.97	24.2	24.7	26.2	27.9	29.0	22.4	31.1
15 - 0	55	27.2	1.99	24.7	25.9	27.2	28.3	29.9	23.0	32.2
15 - 6	52	27.9	1.96	25.6	26.7	27.8	29.4	30.6	23.1	32.8
16 - 0	50	28.2	2.22	25.5	26.5	27.9	29.8	30.9	24.0	35.1
16 - 6	37	28.8	1.51	26.9	27.6	28.7	29.8	30.9	25.8	31.9
17 - 0	42	29.3	1.98	26.7	27.9	29.3	30.9	31.9	25.5	33.1
17 - 6	23	29.9	2.38	27.5	28.2	29.5	32.1	33.1	26.6	34.8
18 - 0	32	30.2	2.74	27.1	28.2	30.1	31.5	33.7	25.7	39.3
19 - 0	16	29.9	2.23	27.3	27.9	30.0	31.0	33.3	26.9	33.7
20 - 0	15	30.4	2.02	27.7	28.4	30.8	31.8	32.7	27.2	33.7
21 - 0	12	29.9	1.80	27.9	28.8	29.7	31.3	31.8	27.5	33.8
22 - 0	13	29.8	1.66	27.9	28.3	30.1	30.9	31.5	27.5	33.3
23 - 0	14	30.6	2.31	27.9	28.4	30.3	33.2	33.5	27.5	33.7
24 - 0	11	30.8	2.31	27.6	28.4	31.6	32.4	32.8	27.2	34.2
25 - 0	12	29.9	1.71	28.2	28.5	29.3	31.3	32.3	27.7	32.9

ANTHROPOMETRY TABLE E-12

Female Xiphisternal Width in Centimeters

Age Yr. Mo.	N	Mean	S.D.	Percentiles 10th	25th	50th	75th	90th	Range Min.	Max.
Supine										
Birth	55	9.7	0.56	8.9	9.3	9.7	10.1	10.5	8.6	10.7
0 - 1	69	10.8	0.73	9.9	10.3	10.9	11.4	11.8	9.0	12.2
0 - 2	62	11.9	0.66	11.1	11.4	11.9	12.3	12.6	10.4	13.3
0 - 3	66	12.6	0.74	11.7	12.1	12.5	13.2	13.6	10.8	14.4
0 - 4	58	13.4	0.79	12.5	12.8	13.3	13.9	14.4	11.5	16.0
0 - 5	56	13.9	0.76	13.0	13.3	13.9	14.4	14.9	11.9	15.8
0 - 6	63	14.2	0.77	13.2	13.6	14.2	14.8	15.2	12.7	16.4
0 - 9	58	14.8	0.86	13.6	14.1	14.8	15.4	15.8	12.9	16.7
1 - 0	59	15.1	0.84	14.1	14.5	14.9	15.6	16.3	12.9	17.2
1 - 6	42	15.7	0.86	14.5	15.1	15.6	16.1	16.8	14.2	18.2
2 - 0	28	16.0	0.86	15.1	15.5	16.0	16.5	17.0	14.1	17.7
Erect										
2 - 0	59	16.3	0.83	15.2	15.6	16.2	16.7	17.3	14.3	18.3
2 - 6	70	16.6	0.77	15.5	16.0	16.6	17.0	17.5	15.0	18.6
3 - 0	71	16.9	0.84	15.8	16.4	16.9	17.3	18.0	14.8	19.0
3 - 6	68	17.1	0.75	16.3	16.7	17.1	17.7	18.1	15.1	19.0
4 - 0	77	17.4	0.81	16.5	16.8	17.2	18.0	18.5	15.4	19.0
4 - 6	90	17.5	0.78	16.6	17.0	17.5	18.0	18.5	15.2	19.4
5 - 0	90	17.8	0.91	16.7	17.1	17.7	18.3	19.0	15.9	20.0
5 - 6	90	18.1	0.92	17.0	17.5	18.0	18.6	19.5	16.2	20.5
6 - 0	95	18.4	0.87	17.4	17.8	18.3	18.9	19.6	16.5	21.0
6 - 6	95	18.7	0.93	17.4	18.0	18.6	19.3	19.8	16.8	20.9
7 - 0	90	19.0	0.97	17.8	18.4	19.0	19.5	20.2	16.9	21.8
7 - 6	92	19.4	1.04	18.2	18.7	19.2	20.0	20.6	17.0	22.3
8 - 0	90	19.7	1.20	18.2	18.8	19.6	20.4	21.2	16.9	22.7
8 - 6	90	20.0	1.27	18.5	19.1	20.0	20.8	21.7	17.0	23.5
9 - 0	80	20.4	1.25	18.9	19.6	20.1	21.2	22.3	17.0	23.2
9 - 6	75	20.8	1.29	19.2	20.0	20.6	21.6	22.8	17.6	23.8
10 - 0	76	21.2	1.58	19.2	20.1	21.0	22.2	23.2	17.5	26.0
10 - 6	73	21.6	1.74	19.6	20.4	21.3	22.5	23.9	18.2	26.4
11 - 0	70	22.1	1.82	19.8	20.9	21.8	23.4	24.6	18.8	26.3
11 - 6	67	22.4	1.81	20.2	21.1	22.1	23.6	24.8	19.0	27.9
12 - 0	69	23.1	1.98	20.9	21.8	22.8	24.3	26.1	19.8	27.9
12 - 6	64	23.4	1.79	21.0	22.4	23.1	24.6	26.0	19.9	28.1
13 - 0	68	23.8	1.68	21.6	22.7	23.5	25.0	26.2	20.6	27.4
13 - 6	53	24.2	1.49	22.4	23.3	24.1	25.1	26.5	21.1	27.3
14 - 0	61	24.9	1.71	22.8	23.5	24.6	25.9	27.3	21.5	29.5
14 - 6	42	25.0	1.46	23.2	23.8	24.8	25.7	27.2	22.0	28.0
15 - 0	51	25.0	1.44	23.3	24.0	24.8	25.8	27.1	22.2	29.2
15 - 6	22	24.7	1.39	22.8	24.1	24.7	25.6	26.7	22.2	27.6
16 - 0	57	25.6	1.80	23.3	24.4	25.2	27.0	28.2	22.2	29.8
17 - 0	43	25.7	1.88	23.2	24.5	25.4	27.1	28.5	21.8	29.7
18 - 0	25	26.0	1.67	24.3	24.8	25.4	27.0	29.0	23.6	29.5
19 - 0	19	26.2	1.70	24.3	24.9	25.8	27.3	28.7	23.5	29.6
20 - 0	15	25.9	1.70	23.7	24.9	25.7	27.0	28.1	22.8	29.0
21 - 0	13	27.0	1.60	24.9	25.9	27.2	27.9	28.9	24.2	29.5
22 - 0	10	26.7	1.38	25.3	25.5	26.6	27.7	28.4	24.5	28.6
23 - 0	11	26.7	1.92	24.0	25.4	26.8	27.7	29.0	23.7	29.7
24 - 0	10	27.0	1.92	24.9	25.8	27.8	28.5	28.8	23.1	29.0

ANTHROPOMETRY — TABLE E-13

Male — Xiphisternal Depth in Centimeters

Age Yr. Mo.	N	Mean	S.D.	Percentiles 10th	25th	50th	75th	90th	Range Min.	Max.
Supine										
Birth	48	8.8	0.65	8.0	8.3	8.7	9.3	9.6	7.2	10.5
0 - 1	62	9.4	0.60	8.6	9.0	9.4	9.8	10.2	8.3	11.1
0 - 2	51	9.7	0.55	9.0	9.3	9.6	10.0	10.6	8.6	10.8
0 - 3	57	9.9	0.54	9.2	9.5	9.8	10.3	10.6	8.5	11.0
0 - 4	49	9.9	0.51	9.2	9.4	9.9	10.2	10.6	9.0	11.0
0 - 5	51	10.3	0.62	9.5	9.8	10.2	10.6	11.1	8.9	11.8
0 - 6	69	10.6	0.74	9.6	10.1	10.5	11.1	11.6	9.3	12.5
0 - 9	51	11.2	0.72	10.3	10.6	11.2	11.7	12.2	9.7	12.9
1 - 0	63	11.6	0.78	10.6	11.0	11.6	12.2	12.6	9.7	13.3
1 - 6	46	12.2	0.58	11.5	11.8	12.3	12.6	12.9	10.8	13.4
2 - 0	31	12.2	0.51	11.6	11.7	12.3	12.5	12.9	11.5	13.6
Erect										
2 - 0	53	11.8	0.93	10.6	11.2	11.7	12.5	13.1	10.0	13.8
2 - 6	59	12.2	0.90	11.0	11.5	12.1	12.6	13.3	10.2	14.2
3 - 0	58	12.4	0.72	11.5	11.9	12.4	12.8	13.4	10.8	14.1
3 - 6	57	12.6	0.68	11.8	12.1	12.6	13.0	13.6	11.3	14.0
4 - 0	73	12.9	0.80	11.8	12.4	12.9	13.4	14.1	11.3	14.9
4 - 6	90	13.0	0.81	11.9	12.3	12.9	13.6	14.1	11.6	14.6
5 - 0	87	13.2	0.77	12.1	12.6	13.1	13.8	14.2	11.3	15.1
5 - 6	91	13.4	0.85	12.2	12.8	13.4	14.0	14.5	11.4	16.0
6 - 0	91	13.6	0.91	12.6	13.0	13.6	14.3	14.9	11.1	16.2
6 - 6	92	13.9	1.00	12.6	13.3	13.9	14.6	15.0	11.1	17.8
7 - 0	92	14.2	1.11	12.6	13.4	14.2	14.9	15.6	11.4	17.5
7 - 6	88	14.4	1.13	12.9	13.7	14.4	15.2	15.9	11.5	18.1
8 - 0	91	14.6	1.09	13.2	13.9	14.7	15.3	15.9	11.5	18.7
8 - 6	90	14.8	1.23	13.1	13.9	14.8	15.7	16.3	11.6	18.7
9 - 0	92	15.1	1.24	13.5	14.2	15.2	16.0	16.5	11.9	18.4
9 - 6	88	15.4	1.26	13.8	14.5	15.5	16.4	16.9	11.9	18.0
10 - 0	85	15.6	1.36	13.9	14.6	15.6	16.6	17.4	12.1	20.3
10 - 6	80	15.9	1.36	14.2	14.8	15.9	16.8	17.8	12.5	18.8
11 - 0	76	16.1	1.44	14.2	15.2	16.0	17.3	18.0	12.3	19.5
11 - 6	78	16.4	1.52	14.4	15.4	16.5	17.5	18.6	12.8	19.9
12 - 0	70	16.8	1.55	14.6	15.8	16.7	18.0	18.9	13.5	20.3
12 - 6	73	17.0	1.58	14.9	15.8	17.0	18.2	19.1	13.0	20.7
13 - 0	71	17.4	1.71	15.3	16.1	17.3	18.4	19.8	13.7	21.5
13 - 6	69	17.9	1.83	15.7	16.6	17.8	19.0	20.6	13.7	22.1
14 - 0	66	18.3	1.74	16.1	17.0	18.3	19.4	20.5	14.0	22.3
14 - 6	61	18.6	1.94	16.3	17.1	18.8	20.0	21.6	14.2	22.3
15 - 0	55	19.1	1.87	16.4	17.8	19.2	20.4	21.5	14.4	22.4
15 - 6	52	19.5	1.78	17.3	18.4	19.5	20.9	21.7	15.1	23.0
16 - 0	50	19.8	1.88	17.4	18.6	19.8	21.2	22.0	15.3	25.2
16 - 6	37	20.2	1.84	18.0	19.3	20.0	21.4	22.5	16.1	24.0
17 - 0	42	20.3	2.06	17.6	18.8	19.9	22.2	22.9	16.1	24.8
17 - 6	23	20.9	2.18	18.0	19.2	20.6	22.4	24.1	17.4	25.0
18 - 0	32	21.1	2.04	18.0	19.9	21.0	22.5	23.7	17.1	25.6
19 - 0	16	21.1	2.01	18.6	19.7	20.9	22.5	24.0	17.4	25.2
20 - 0	15	20.8	2.15	18.5	19.4	20.4	22.6	23.2	17.9	25.7
21 - 0	12	20.5	1.78	18.7	19.1	20.7	21.2	21.9	18.0	24.7
22 - 0	12	21.3	2.57	18.1	18.9	20.6	23.2	24.7	17.2	25.7
23 - 0	13	21.5	2.68	18.4	20.0	20.7	23.7	25.4	17.4	26.0
24 - 0	11	22.1	2.30	19.4	20.1	21.8	23.3	23.8	19.0	27.0
25 - 0	12	20.5	1.38	19.3	19.8	20.9	21.4	21.9	17.1	22.5

ANTHROPOMETRY

TABLE E-14

Female

Xiphisternal Depth in Centimeters

Age Yr. Mo.	N	Mean	S.D.	Percentiles 10th	25th	50th	75th	90th	Range Min.	Max.
Supine										
Birth	56	8.6	0.59	7.9	8.2	8.5	9.0	9.3	6.8	10.1
0 - 1	69	9.2	0.58	8.4	8.7	9.1	9.5	9.9	7.5	10.5
0 - 2	62	9.5	0.48	8.9	9.2	9.4	9.8	10.0	8.5	11.0
0 - 3	66	9.7	0.54	9.1	9.4	9.6	10.0	10.4	8.5	11.5
0 - 4	58	10.0	0.51	9.4	9.6	9.9	10.3	10.7	8.7	11.0
0 - 5	56	10.2	0.56	9.4	9.8	10.2	10.5	10.9	8.9	11.4
0 - 6	63	10.5	0.64	9.5	10.0	10.4	10.9	11.2	9.0	12.0
0 - 9	57	10.9	0.60	10.0	10.4	11.0	11.3	11.6	9.7	12.2
1 - 0	58	11.4	0.57	10.7	11.0	11.4	11.7	12.1	9.8	12.9
1 - 6	38	11.7	0.72	11.0	11.2	11.6	12.0	12.7	10.0	13.4
2 - 0	26	11.7	0.65	10.7	11.4	11.7	12.1	12.6	10.2	13.0
Erect										
2 - 0	55	11.6	0.80	10.6	11.1	11.6	12.1	12.6	9.6	14.1
2 - 6	70	11.6	0.78	10.7	11.1	11.5	12.1	12.7	9.7	13.7
3 - 0	71	12.0	0.74	11.0	11.5	12.0	12.5	12.9	9.6	13.2
3 - 6	68	12.4	0.75	11.5	11.9	12.4	12.8	13.5	10.3	14.0
4 - 0	76	12.6	0.77	11.6	12.0	12.5	13.1	13.6	10.4	14.5
4 - 6	91	12.7	0.74	11.8	12.2	12.7	13.2	13.7	10.6	14.5
5 - 0	90	12.9	0.75	12.0	12.5	12.8	13.4	14.0	11.0	14.6
5 - 6	90	13.1	0.76	12.2	12.6	13.0	13.6	14.3	11.4	15.0
6 - 0	95	13.3	0.78	12.2	12.6	13.2	13.9	14.4	11.8	15.4
6 - 6	95	13.5	0.84	12.4	13.0	13.5	14.0	14.5	11.7	15.9
7 - 0	90	13.7	0.90	12.6	13.0	13.7	14.4	14.9	11.6	16.4
7 - 6	92	14.0	1.01	12.7	13.2	13.9	14.6	15.1	11.9	17.3
8 - 0	90	14.3	1.13	12.7	13.5	14.2	15.0	15.6	12.0	17.5
8 - 6	90	14.4	1.08	13.1	13.7	14.4	15.1	16.0	12.0	17.4
9 - 0	80	14.7	1.18	13.4	14.0	14.4	15.4	16.2	12.0	18.3
9 - 6	75	15.0	1.15	13.5	14.1	14.8	15.6	16.4	12.7	18.2
10 - 0	75	15.3	1.45	13.7	14.3	15.2	16.0	17.5	12.0	19.7
10 - 6	73	15.6	1.53	13.7	14.5	15.5	16.4	17.6	12.4	20.5
11 - 0	70	16.0	1.66	14.0	14.8	15.7	16.9	18.5	12.2	20.3
11 - 6	67	16.4	1.50	14.6	15.2	16.4	17.5	18.2	12.1	20.6
12 - 0	69	16.7	1.82	14.5	15.3	16.5	17.6	18.9	12.1	22.5
12 - 6	64	16.7	1.56	14.8	15.5	16.7	17.8	18.5	13.0	21.0
13 - 0	68	16.9	1.62	15.1	15.9	16.7	17.9	18.9	13.1	21.7
13 - 6	53	17.3	1.47	15.6	16.2	17.2	18.2	18.9	13.4	21.4
14 - 0	61	17.5	1.62	15.6	16.3	17.2	18.3	19.6	14.0	21.5
14 - 6	42	17.7	1.71	15.7	16.5	17.6	18.7	20.1	13.6	22.5
15 - 0	52	17.9	1.73	15.7	16.8	17.8	18.8	20.2	14.5	23.2
15 - 6	22	17.8	1.18	16.5	16.9	17.6	18.6	19.5	15.6	20.0
16 - 0	57	18.1	1.74	16.1	16.9	17.8	19.2	20.5	14.8	23.1
17 - 0	44	18.0	1.47	16.3	17.0	17.8	18.9	20.3	14.5	21.9
18 - 0	25	18.6	1.71	16.8	17.2	18.6	19.4	20.8	16.1	23.1
19 - 0	19	19.1	1.56	17.2	18.1	19.0	20.5	21.4	16.4	22.2
20 - 0	15	18.6	1.31	17.1	17.5	18.4	19.8	20.2	16.8	21.1
21 - 0	13	18.9	1.19	17.5	17.8	19.2	19.8	20.1	17.1	20.9
22 - 0	11	19.0	1.10	17.8	17.9	19.0	19.6	20.5	17.7	20.7
23 - 0	10	18.7	1.30	17.4	18.1	18.6	19.5	20.2	16.1	20.6
24 - 0	10	19.5	1.28	18.0	18.7	19.8	20.2	20.8	16.7	21.2

ANTHROPOMETRY TABLE E-15

Male Iliac Circumference in Centimeters

Age Yr. Mo.	N	Mean	S.D.	Percentiles 10th	25th	50th	75th	90th	Range Min.	Max.
Supine										
Birth	49	26.6	2.24	23.6	24.9	26.6	28.0	29.0	22.2	33.4
0 - 1	62	30.3	2.14	27.7	28.6	29.9	32.0	33.2	26.6	35.8
0 - 2	53	33.6	2.86	30.1	31.6	33.5	35.2	37.5	28.0	40.0
0 - 3	59	36.2	2.79	33.1	34.2	35.9	38.0	40.4	32.0	42.9
0 - 4	49	37.9	2.84	34.5	35.6	37.7	40.0	41.2	33.0	45.0
0 - 5	51	38.9	3.01	35.0	36.3	38.8	41.2	42.5	33.4	46.7
0 - 6	70	40.0	3.00	36.2	37.8	39.7	42.2	43.8	34.1	49.0
0 - 9	53	42.2	3.13	38.4	39.8	42.7	44.4	46.2	35.5	49.6
1 - 0	63	42.6	2.97	38.3	40.5	42.9	44.5	45.4	35.4	52.1
1 - 6	49	43.5	2.96	39.4	41.5	43.6	45.7	47.1	36.9	50.8
2 - 0	34	44.0	2.27	41.2	42.4	43.9	45.7	46.6	39.0	49.5
Erect										
2 - 0	53	47.0	2.96	43.4	44.9	47.3	49.0	50.4	40.0	54.5
2 - 6	60	48.5	2.76	44.6	46.6	48.7	50.3	51.5	42.0	55.0
3 - 0	58	49.4	2.62	46.1	47.0	49.6	51.2	52.7	42.5	54.4
3 - 6	57	50.3	2.61	46.7	47.9	50.1	52.0	53.9	45.0	55.1
4 - 0	74	51.2	2.84	47.2	49.2	51.6	53.5	54.7	43.1	56.0
4 - 6	91	51.7	2.46	48.6	49.9	51.5	53.4	54.9	44.5	56.8
5 - 0	86	52.9	2.66	49.4	51.0	52.6	54.6	56.8	44.2	59.3
5 - 6	90	53.9	2.75	50.3	51.6	53.9	55.3	57.5	47.0	63.0
6 - 0	91	54.7	2.84	51.1	52.8	54.3	56.4	58.4	50.0	65.1
6 - 6	92	55.8	3.38	52.1	53.4	55.3	57.7	59.9	50.1	72.3
7 - 0	92	56.4	3.31	52.7	53.9	56.0	58.1	61.2	48.8	68.0
7 - 6	88	57.5	3.41	54.0	55.2	57.0	59.3	61.7	48.1	68.0
8 - 0	92	58.8	3.75	54.6	56.5	58.0	60.2	63.4	52.3	72.3
8 - 6	90	59.6	4.06	55.0	56.6	58.7	61.9	64.8	52.9	72.7
9 - 0	92	60.9	4.47	56.1	57.5	60.3	63.0	66.6	53.8	77.0
9 - 6	88	62.1	4.62	56.8	58.5	61.2	64.8	69.0	54.7	76.7
10 - 0	85	63.4	5.28	58.0	59.2	62.4	66.3	71.1	54.8	81.6
10 - 6	80	64.0	5.37	57.8	59.8	63.5	67.8	71.1	55.7	82.6
11 - 0	75	65.5	5.62	59.0	61.1	64.3	69.3	74.9	55.7	82.8
11 - 6	77	66.4	5.86	59.6	61.9	65.6	69.7	73.8	57.5	87.6
12 - 0	69	67.2	6.59	59.8	62.3	66.0	71.5	75.2	58.0	92.1
12 - 6	73	68.0	6.39	60.1	63.0	67.2	71.6	75.5	58.0	94.8
13 - 0	70	70.0	6.71	62.5	64.5	69.5	73.7	79.0	59.5	89.5
13 - 6	68	71.4	7.05	63.2	65.9	70.8	75.8	79.7	60.0	97.1
14 - 0	66	72.8	6.69	65.6	68.5	72.3	76.6	80.3	61.9	94.3
14 - 6	61	73.4	6.50	66.5	68.6	72.4	77.0	80.8	63.0	93.3
15 - 0	54	75.5	6.80	67.8	70.5	74.5	78.2	85.0	64.0	97.3
15 - 6	52	76.6	6.53	69.3	71.6	76.2	80.1	84.2	65.6	96.8
16 - 0	49	77.5	7.34	70.1	72.6	75.8	80.6	85.1	67.9	104.5
16 - 6	37	78.7	6.98	71.2	73.5	77.6	80.4	88.2	67.2	100.5
17 - 0	42	79.3	5.94	72.5	75.8	78.8	82.5	86.3	69.4	99.5
17 - 6	23	80.9	7.70	74.5	76.4	79.1	82.1	93.4	71.0	104.4
18 - 0	32	80.3	7.59	72.6	74.8	79.2	82.1	88.2	71.2	107.4
19 - 0	16	80.2	5.46	74.4	76.1	79.7	84.8	86.5	69.6	91.3
20 - 0	15	79.7	3.81	73.9	78.3	79.5	81.9	84.1	72.8	87.4
21 - 0	12	79.6	3.64	75.1	76.7	79.6	82.0	84.9	73.7	85.6
22 - 0	11	82.4	6.26	75.3	78.0	82.4	85.4	87.2	74.1	96.1
23 - 0	13	83.7	8.52	76.0	78.4	82.3	84.4	90.3	74.6	108.0
24 - 0	10	84.0	5.39	78.3	80.5	82.4	87.9	92.3	76.6	94.0
25 - 0	12	79.9	4.78	74.5	77.6	79.2	82.6	85.8	70.8	87.7

ANTHROPOMETRY

TABLE E-16

Female

Iliac Circumference in Centimeters

Age Yr. Mo.	N	Mean	S.D.	Percentiles 10th	25th	50th	75th	90th	Range Min.	Max.
Supine										
Birth	56	26.8	2.17	24.4	25.2	26.4	28.4	29.8	22.5	31.9
0 - 1	68	29.9	2.58	26.6	28.6	30.0	31.2	32.6	24.3	39.2
0 - 2	62	32.8	2.12	30.1	31.5	32.8	34.2	35.6	26.4	36.8
0 - 3	67	34.8	2.52	31.9	33.1	35.1	36.4	38.1	27.9	41.0
0 - 4	59	36.6	2.38	33.6	34.9	36.7	38.5	39.7	30.9	42.2
0 - 5	56	38.1	2.68	34.0	36.5	38.2	40.2	41.5	31.9	44.0
0 - 6	62	39.4	2.86	35.5	37.4	39.6	41.0	43.0	30.6	45.4
0 - 9	59	41.2	2.87	37.6	39.4	41.5	43.5	44.9	33.7	46.8
1 - 0	64	42.0	2.78	38.8	40.0	41.7	43.7	46.0	36.3	48.6
1 - 6	45	43.2	2.71	39.9	41.3	43.0	44.9	46.9	36.7	50.1
2 - 0	29	43.0	2.49	39.4	41.4	43.0	44.9	46.1	37.8	48.8
Erect										
2 - 0	56	46.7	3.02	42.6	44.8	46.8	48.9	49.9	40.7	54.2
2 - 6	70	48.0	2.64	44.3	46.1	48.3	49.5	50.9	41.0	55.3
3 - 0	70	49.0	2.65	45.9	47.3	49.1	50.6	52.7	42.3	55.3
3 - 6	68	50.2	2.47	46.8	48.4	50.1	51.8	53.6	44.0	56.0
4 - 0	78	51.0	2.52	47.8	49.2	50.8	52.8	54.3	44.6	57.2
4 - 6	90	51.8	2.69	48.6	50.0	51.7	54.0	55.4	44.4	58.3
5 - 0	89	52.7	2.80	48.5	50.9	52.7	54.7	56.7	45.9	59.0
5 - 6	90	53.8	3.18	49.3	51.6	53.9	56.1	58.0	47.4	61.5
6 - 0	95	54.7	3.52	49.9	52.4	54.7	57.4	59.3	48.0	63.3
6 - 6	95	55.5	3.56	50.7	52.8	55.2	58.1	60.1	48.5	64.6
7 - 0	90	57.1	4.29	52.2	54.0	56.4	59.7	62.8	49.1	70.1
7 - 6	92	58.1	4.52	52.8	54.7	57.4	60.7	64.4	50.0	73.0
8 - 0	90	59.2	4.81	53.6	55.9	58.6	62.0	65.7	50.2	74.3
8 - 6	90	60.2	5.12	53.9	56.6	59.5	63.1	67.1	50.3	76.2
9 - 0	80	61.2	5.42	54.8	57.0	60.1	65.1	68.4	53.0	75.0
9 - 6	75	62.8	5.68	56.3	58.6	61.7	66.1	71.0	53.2	79.6
10 - 0	76	63.9	6.55	56.9	59.2	62.3	67.4	73.2	53.5	82.0
10 - 6	73	65.3	6.91	57.8	59.7	63.8	69.5	75.0	54.2	85.0
11 - 0	69	66.8	7.19	58.6	61.2	64.7	71.5	77.8	54.0	86.1
11 - 6	67	68.1	6.98	60.6	62.6	66.5	72.6	78.0	56.6	91.8
12 - 0	69	70.2	7.37	61.5	64.9	69.1	74.2	81.3	56.7	91.8
12 - 6	64	71.0	6.71	62.1	65.9	70.2	75.8	80.7	58.0	85.8
13 - 0	68	72.1	6.55	64.6	67.7	71.4	76.6	80.7	57.8	88.6
13 - 6	52	72.8	6.24	65.7	68.8	71.7	77.1	81.4	59.2	91.1
14 - 0	60	75.9	6.40	68.7	71.6	74.9	80.1	84.0	61.6	97.0
14 - 6	42	76.2	6.40	69.2	72.2	75.6	80.7	84.7	62.3	96.2
15 - 0	52	77.6	6.29	70.6	73.3	77.4	81.0	84.8	67.0	98.6
15 - 6	22	76.2	4.60	70.5	72.0	76.1	78.9	82.4	68.7	86.2
16 - 0	56	79.3	6.47	72.2	74.3	78.0	84.2	87.3	71.0	97.3
17 - 0	43	79.4	6.12	72.4	74.4	78.8	82.9	88.7	71.0	94.5
18 - 0	25	80.2	5.79	73.0	75.9	80.0	82.7	86.9	71.0	94.6
19 - 0	19	81.4	4.54	73.9	79.9	82.1	84.1	86.2	72.9	89.3
20 - 0	15	79.2	4.73	73.0	74.8	79.5	82.4	85.6	71.8	88.0
21 - 0	13	81.3	3.32	77.5	78.7	81.9	83.7	85.9	76.2	87.3
22 - 0	10	81.2	5.35	76.6	77.6	80.3	84.8	87.6	73.0	91.2
23 - 0	11	79.2	7.19	70.2	75.4	78.4	85.0	87.9	65.2	89.2
24 - 0	10	82.9	7.69	75.7	78.6	80.6	87.4	93.0	73.2	97.9

ANTHROPOMETRY

TABLE E-17

Male

Iliac Width in Centimeters

Age Yr. Mo.	N	Mean	S.D.	Percentiles 10th	25th	50th	75th	90th	Range Min.	Max.
Supine										
Birth	49	8.2	0.70	7.4	7.8	8.2	8.6	9.0	7.0	10.4
0 - 1	62	9.0	0.67	8.3	8.7	9.0	9.4	9.9	7.3	11.2
0 - 2	53	9.9	0.69	9.1	9.5	9.8	10.4	10.8	8.5	12.1
0 - 3	59	10.4	0.68	9.6	10.0	10.4	10.9	11.3	9.3	12.7
0 - 4	49	11.0	0.77	10.1	10.5	11.0	11.4	11.9	9.7	13.4
0 - 5	51	11.4	0.80	10.5	10.9	11.4	11.8	12.2	9.9	14.5
0 - 6	70	11.7	0.80	10.5	11.1	11.6	12.1	12.4	10.2	14.6
0 - 9	53	12.3	1.04	11.2	11.8	12.3	12.7	13.4	10.5	16.1
1 - 0	67	12.7	0.95	11.6	12.0	12.5	13.2	14.0	10.9	15.9
1 - 6	49	13.6	0.96	12.5	12.8	13.6	14.1	14.6	12.0	16.5
2 - 0	33	14.3	0.85	13.2	13.6	14.3	15.1	15.4	12.5	15.7
Erect										
2 - 0	53	14.9	0.94	13.6	14.3	14.8	15.5	16.0	12.6	16.9
2 - 6	60	15.5	1.02	14.3	14.8	15.4	16.0	17.0	13.3	18.3
3 - 0	59	16.2	1.06	15.0	15.4	16.1	16.8	17.6	14.0	19.0
3 - 6	57	16.7	0.91	15.4	16.2	16.7	17.3	17.8	14.5	18.4
4 - 0	74	17.0	0.90	16.0	16.5	17.0	17.6	18.2	14.9	19.7
4 - 6	92	17.4	0.86	16.1	16.8	17.3	17.9	18.5	15.0	19.2
5 - 0	87	17.8	0.96	16.6	17.1	17.9	18.5	19.0	15.5	20.0
5 - 6	91	18.3	0.98	16.9	17.6	18.2	19.0	19.7	16.3	20.4
6 - 0	91	18.7	0.98	17.4	18.0	18.6	19.5	20.0	16.3	20.8
6 - 6	92	19.0	0.96	17.8	18.3	19.0	19.7	20.5	16.5	21.3
7 - 0	92	19.5	1.00	18.1	18.9	19.3	20.2	20.8	17.2	21.6
7 - 6	88	19.8	1.04	18.5	19.1	19.7	20.6	21.1	16.9	23.2
8 - 0	92	20.2	1.00	18.9	19.4	20.2	21.0	21.6	17.8	22.6
8 - 6	90	20.5	1.09	19.1	19.7	20.5	21.4	22.0	18.1	22.9
9 - 0	92	21.1	1.16	19.5	20.2	21.0	21.8	22.6	18.5	23.5
9 - 6	88	21.5	1.20	19.9	20.6	21.3	22.3	23.1	18.8	24.0
10 - 0	85	21.9	1.36	20.0	20.8	21.8	22.9	23.6	19.0	25.0
10 - 6	80	22.2	1.51	20.4	21.1	22.0	23.3	24.2	19.5	26.1
11 - 0	76	22.8	1.64	21.0	21.5	22.4	24.0	24.9	20.0	27.8
11 - 6	77	23.3	1.70	21.2	22.0	22.9	24.3	25.6	20.1	28.6
12 - 0	69	23.5	1.93	21.1	22.1	23.2	25.0	26.5	20.1	29.2
12 - 6	73	23.9	1.94	21.8	22.4	23.7	25.2	26.6	19.8	29.0
13 - 0	70	24.6	1.91	22.5	23.2	24.3	25.8	27.7	21.2	29.3
13 - 6	68	25.1	2.15	22.4	23.3	25.1	26.4	27.6	21.0	32.1
14 - 0	66	25.5	1.94	23.3	24.1	25.4	26.9	27.9	22.5	32.4
14 - 6	61	26.1	1.98	23.7	24.6	25.9	27.3	28.7	22.4	32.2
15 - 0	55	27.0	2.08	24.3	25.7	26.9	28.2	29.7	23.2	33.3
15 - 6	52	27.5	2.00	25.2	25.9	27.4	28.8	29.8	23.8	34.5
16 - 0	49	27.8	1.84	25.6	26.4	27.5	29.0	29.7	24.8	35.0
16 - 6	37	28.1	1.70	25.9	26.7	28.1	29.5	30.1	25.1	31.5
17 - 0	41	28.3	1.73	26.4	27.1	27.9	29.3	30.3	25.6	33.5
17 - 6	23	28.9	1.96	26.6	27.2	28.8	30.0	31.2	26.3	33.6
18 - 0	31	28.9	1.68	26.8	27.8	28.9	29.8	31.1	26.3	33.2
19 - 0	16	29.3	1.38	27.3	28.4	29.2	30.5	30.9	26.9	32.0
20 - 0	15	29.0	1.61	26.7	28.0	29.1	30.0	30.7	25.3	31.0
21 - 0	12	29.2	1.29	27.5	28.3	29.4	29.7	30.6	26.9	31.6
22 - 0	12	29.1	1.23	27.2	28.2	29.2	29.9	30.6	27.0	31.1
23 - 0	13	29.7	1.89	27.7	28.6	29.6	30.8	31.8	26.0	33.5
24 - 0	11	30.2	1.53	28.3	29.3	29.8	31.2	31.7	28.0	33.3
25 - 0	12	28.8	1.82	27.1	27.7	28.6	30.2	31.1	25.1	31.5

ANTHROPOMETRY

TABLE E-18

Female

Iliac Width in Centimeters

Age Yr. Mo.	N	Mean	S.D.	Percentiles 10th	25th	50th	75th	90th	Range Min.	Max.
Supine										
Birth	55	8.0	0.77	7.0	7.4	7.9	8.2	8.8	6.6	10.6
0 - 1	69	8.6	0.58	7.8	8.2	8.6	8.9	9.2	7.0	10.6
0 - 2	62	9.5	0.71	8.7	9.0	9.5	9.8	10.5	8.1	11.5
0 - 3	67	10.0	0.68	9.2	9.6	10.0	10.3	10.9	8.1	11.8
0 - 4	59	10.5	0.72	9.6	10.1	10.5	11.0	11.4	9.0	13.1
0 - 5	57	10.9	0.87	10.0	10.3	10.7	11.2	12.0	9.5	13.9
0 - 6	63	11.2	0.76	10.4	10.7	11.0	11.6	12.1	9.5	14.5
0 - 9	59	11.8	1.02	10.7	11.2	11.6	12.2	13.0	9.5	15.4
1 - 0	66	12.3	0.87	11.0	11.6	12.2	12.8	13.4	10.5	14.5
1 - 6	42	13.0	0.95	11.7	12.2	13.0	13.7	14.5	11.0	14.8
2 - 0	27	13.8	0.85	12.6	13.3	13.7	14.6	15.0	12.4	15.7
Erect										
2 - 0	59	14.7	0.85	13.7	14.2	14.8	15.2	15.7	12.3	16.5
2 - 6	69	15.2	0.92	13.9	14.7	15.2	15.9	16.4	13.1	17.3
3 - 0	71	16.0	0.94	14.6	15.2	16.1	16.8	17.2	13.9	18.0
3 - 6	68	16.6	0.87	15.4	15.9	16.6	17.2	17.7	14.7	18.5
4 - 0	77	17.0	0.95	15.8	16.3	17.1	17.7	18.3	14.8	19.5
4 - 6	90	17.4	1.01	16.2	16.7	17.6	18.1	18.4	14.5	20.1
5 - 0	90	17.8	1.09	16.4	16.9	18.0	18.6	19.2	15.4	20.3
5 - 6	90	18.2	1.16	16.6	17.3	18.2	19.0	19.8	15.9	21.4
6 - 0	95	18.6	1.13	17.1	17.7	18.7	19.4	20.0	16.1	21.0
6 - 6	94	19.0	1.12	17.5	18.1	19.1	19.8	20.4	16.5	22.0
7 - 0	89	19.5	1.32	17.8	18.7	19.5	20.2	21.1	16.7	23.3
7 - 6	91	19.9	1.31	18.4	19.0	19.9	20.8	21.7	16.5	23.0
8 - 0	90	20.3	1.39	18.2	19.4	20.3	21.2	22.2	16.8	23.9
8 - 6	90	20.7	1.44	18.9	19.7	20.7	21.6	22.6	17.0	24.7
9 - 0	80	21.2	1.42	19.3	20.3	21.3	22.1	23.4	18.2	24.4
9 - 6	75	21.7	1.41	19.9	20.7	21.6	22.6	23.5	18.4	25.0
10 - 0	76	22.2	1.56	20.2	21.0	22.0	23.3	24.2	19.0	26.9
10 - 6	73	22.7	1.84	20.4	21.4	22.6	23.7	25.7	19.5	27.9
11 - 0	70	23.3	1.85	21.1	22.0	23.2	24.6	25.8	19.8	28.4
11 - 6	67	23.8	1.69	21.6	22.4	23.6	24.9	26.4	20.1	27.2
12 - 0	69	24.5	2.02	22.0	23.1	24.3	25.8	27.2	20.1	29.5
12 - 6	64	25.0	1.96	22.4	23.6	25.0	26.1	27.7	20.5	29.9
13 - 0	67	25.4	1.97	22.9	24.2	25.3	26.4	28.0	20.7	29.7
13 - 6	53	25.9	1.78	23.3	24.8	26.0	27.4	28.2	21.8	29.2
14 - 0	61	26.8	1.70	24.4	25.8	26.8	28.1	29.0	22.1	30.2
14 - 6	42	27.0	1.70	24.9	25.7	27.4	28.2	29.0	22.7	30.0
15 - 0	51	27.5	1.83	25.6	26.4	27.4	28.4	30.0	23.5	34.1
15 - 6	22	27.4	1.53	25.3	26.3	27.4	28.2	29.4	23.9	30.2
16 - 0	56	27.8	1.58	26.0	26.7	28.0	28.9	29.9	24.0	33.2
17 - 0	44	28.2	1.66	26.3	27.1	28.0	29.0	30.0	25.0	32.7
18 - 0	25	28.8	2.22	26.0	27.5	28.6	29.8	32.2	24.6	33.6
19 - 0	19	29.0	1.39	27.1	28.0	29.0	30.0	30.8	26.6	31.8
20 - 0	15	28.4	1.79	25.5	27.3	28.4	29.6	30.6	25.0	31.1
21 - 0	13	28.5	1.57	26.7	27.3	28.5	29.6	30.4	25.5	30.8
22 - 0	10	28.9	1.60	27.2	27.6	28.4	30.0	30.8	27.0	31.7
23 - 0	11	28.6	1.59	26.9	27.3	28.8	29.5	30.6	26.6	31.7
24 - 0	10	29.1	1.80	27.6	27.9	28.9	29.8	30.7	27.0	33.2

ANTHROPOMETRY

TABLE E-19

Male

Biacromial Width in Centimeters

Age Yr. Mo.	N	Mean	S.D.	Percentiles 10th	25th	50th	75th	90th	Range Min.	Max.
Supine										
Birth	49	11.2	1.06	9.9	10.4	11.2	11.9	12.7	9.2	14.0
0 - 1	54	12.4	1.31	10.6	11.4	12.4	13.2	14.0	9.4	15.2
0 - 2	45	13.8	1.09	12.5	13.0	13.8	14.6	15.0	11.9	16.6
0 - 3	56	14.5	1.12	13.1	13.8	14.5	15.1	16.0	11.7	17.8
0 - 4	42	15.3	0.97	14.3	14.6	15.2	15.9	16.3	13.4	18.2
0 - 5	45	15.8	0.92	14.5	15.2	15.8	16.4	17.0	13.9	18.2
0 - 6	69	15.7	1.50	13.9	14.9	15.7	16.7	17.2	11.2	19.9
0 - 9	51	17.1	1.31	15.3	16.2	17.0	18.1	18.5	14.6	20.2
1 - 0	64	17.6	1.44	15.6	16.6	17.7	18.7	19.4	13.6	21.4
1 - 6	50	18.0	1.55	16.1	17.0	17.7	18.7	20.3	14.1	20.9
2 - 0	31	18.6	1.20	17.1	17.7	18.6	19.3	19.9	15.8	21.3
Erect										
2 - 0	53	20.4	1.14	19.0	19.8	20.4	21.3	22.1	16.5	22.6
2 - 6	60	21.2	1.13	20.0	20.4	21.1	21.8	22.9	18.5	24.0
3 - 0	59	22.0	1.04	20.7	21.3	21.8	22.6	23.6	19.9	24.7
3 - 6	57	22.5	1.01	21.4	21.7	22.4	23.1	23.9	20.6	25.0
4 - 0	73	22.8	1.43	20.8	22.2	23.0	23.6	24.7	18.6	25.7
4 - 6	89	23.4	1.39	21.2	22.4	23.5	24.3	25.1	20.1	26.6
5 - 0	87	24.0	1.40	21.9	23.3	24.1	24.9	25.6	20.8	26.8
5 - 6	91	24.8	1.37	22.9	23.8	24.8	25.8	26.6	21.9	28.0
6 - 0	91	25.4	1.32	23.8	24.6	25.5	26.4	27.2	22.4	28.5
6 - 6	92	26.0	1.24	24.4	25.2	25.9	26.7	27.9	23.2	28.9
7 - 0	92	26.7	1.29	25.1	25.8	26.7	27.6	28.5	23.9	29.8
7 - 6	88	27.4	1.30	26.0	26.3	27.2	28.3	29.1	24.0	30.5
8 - 0	92	28.0	1.38	26.3	26.9	27.9	28.9	30.1	24.3	31.6
8 - 6	90	28.3	1.46	26.5	27.4	28.4	29.3	30.2	23.4	32.2
9 - 0	92	29.0	1.52	27.2	28.1	29.0	30.1	31.0	24.2	32.4
9 - 6	88	29.5	1.56	27.9	28.6	29.5	30.6	31.6	24.8	32.7
10 - 0	85	30.1	1.66	28.1	29.2	29.9	31.3	32.2	24.8	33.5
10 - 6	80	30.7	1.64	28.6	29.8	30.4	32.0	33.0	26.9	34.0
11 - 0	76	31.2	1.71	28.9	30.2	31.1	32.6	33.5	27.1	34.8
11 - 6	78	31.7	1.91	29.3	30.4	31.8	32.9	34.1	27.1	37.5
12 - 0	70	32.1	2.02	29.6	31.0	32.0	33.5	34.9	26.9	36.9
12 - 6	73	32.6	1.87	30.3	31.2	32.6	33.7	35.2	29.3	38.9
13 - 0	71	33.5	2.04	31.0	32.0	33.4	34.7	36.0	29.3	40.0
13 - 6	69	34.3	2.03	31.5	32.8	34.3	35.6	37.2	30.6	39.2
14 - 0	67	35.0	2.07	32.3	33.4	35.0	36.8	37.9	31.3	40.2
14 - 6	61	35.8	2.02	32.9	34.2	35.8	37.0	38.8	32.1	40.0
15 - 0	55	36.7	2.23	33.5	35.0	36.6	38.1	39.6	32.7	41.6
15 - 6	52	37.5	2.06	34.6	36.4	37.8	39.0	40.0	32.8	41.9
16 - 0	50	38.0	2.08	35.4	36.4	37.8	39.6	40.3	33.2	43.3
16 - 6	37	38.9	1.76	36.7	37.6	39.2	40.0	41.5	34.5	42.2
17 - 0	40	39.1	1.71	36.4	37.9	39.3	40.3	41.0	35.2	42.4
17 - 6	23	39.4	1.46	37.4	38.2	39.7	40.6	40.9	36.3	41.6
18 - 0	32	39.4	1.45	37.2	38.3	39.6	40.6	41.0	35.9	41.8
19 - 0	16	40.0	1.41	37.6	39.0	40.4	41.3	41.5	37.3	41.6
20 - 0	14	40.5	1.55	38.5	39.1	40.8	41.7	42.0	37.4	42.3
21 - 0	12	40.4	1.79	38.2	39.2	40.8	41.9	42.2	37.0	42.4
22 - 0	11	40.2	1.54	39.1	39.5	40.3	41.1	42.1	36.8	42.4
23 - 0	13	41.0	1.95	38.6	39.2	40.9	42.9	43.4	38.3	43.8
24 - 0	11	41.6	1.45	39.7	40.8	41.6	42.3	42.9	39.4	44.5
25 - 0	12	40.2	1.80	37.8	38.6	39.7	41.4	42.7	37.5	43.0

ANTHROPOMETRY

TABLE E-20

Female

Biacromial Width in Centimeters

Age Yr. Mo.	N	Mean	S.D.	Percentiles 10th	25th	50th	75th	90th	Range Min.	Max.
Supine										
Birth	53	11.1	0.81	10.0	10.7	11.1	11.7	12.2	9.0	12.7
0 - 1	58	12.2	1.19	10.7	11.6	12.3	13.0	13.6	8.8	14.7
0 - 2	50	13.5	1.05	12.0	12.8	13.6	14.2	14.9	11.6	16.0
0 - 3	66	13.8	0.87	12.8	13.2	13.8	14.4	14.9	11.6	15.9
0 - 4	46	14.6	0.95	13.2	14.0	14.6	15.3	15.9	12.6	16.7
0 - 5	45	15.2	0.97	14.2	14.5	15.0	16.0	16.6	13.4	17.2
0 - 6	60	15.3	1.10	14.0	14.6	15.2	16.2	16.8	12.1	17.8
0 - 9	55	16.5	1.04	15.2	15.9	16.5	17.0	18.0	13.8	18.7
1 - 0	64	17.1	1.25	15.4	16.4	17.2	18.0	18.7	14.0	19.7
1 - 6	40	17.8	1.38	15.9	17.0	17.7	18.6	19.8	14.8	20.2
2 - 0	29	18.5	1.21	17.0	17.7	18.4	19.3	19.9	16.0	20.9
Erect										
2 - 0	58	20.2	1.00	18.9	19.7	20.2	20.8	21.5	17.8	22.4
2 - 6	70	21.0	1.00	19.6	20.2	20.9	21.7	22.2	19.2	23.8
3 - 0	70	21.5	1.10	20.0	20.6	21.5	22.4	23.0	19.5	24.1
3 - 6	68	22.3	1.17	20.8	21.5	22.2	23.3	23.8	19.6	25.4
4 - 0	76	22.8	1.32	21.3	22.0	22.8	23.9	24.6	18.2	25.0
4 - 6	89	23.3	1.29	21.7	22.3	23.2	24.4	24.9	19.8	25.6
5 - 0	90	23.8	1.42	22.0	22.8	23.7	24.9	25.8	19.2	27.3
5 - 6	90	24.5	1.34	22.8	23.4	24.5	25.5	26.4	21.3	28.1
6 - 0	95	25.2	1.30	23.5	24.2	25.2	26.1	26.9	22.5	28.4
6 - 6	94	25.9	1.28	24.1	24.9	25.8	26.9	27.7	23.3	28.4
7 - 0	90	26.5	1.41	24.7	25.4	26.4	27.6	28.3	23.3	30.0
7 - 6	92	27.1	1.51	25.1	26.0	27.0	28.2	29.1	23.8	30.3
8 - 0	90	27.6	1.55	25.6	26.5	27.6	28.8	29.7	24.1	30.6
8 - 6	90	28.2	1.56	26.0	27.1	28.0	29.3	30.2	24.1	31.4
9 - 0	80	28.7	1.59	26.7	27.5	28.5	30.0	31.1	25.7	32.5
9 - 6	74	29.3	1.73	27.0	28.0	29.0	30.3	31.9	26.0	33.6
10 - 0	76	29.9	1.73	27.7	28.6	29.8	30.9	32.5	26.0	34.1
10 - 6	73	30.3	1.84	28.1	29.0	30.2	31.2	32.9	25.7	34.8
11 - 0	70	31.0	1.97	28.7	29.4	30.9	32.3	33.5	25.4	35.7
11 - 6	66	31.7	1.76	29.7	30.3	31.6	32.8	34.0	28.1	35.8
12 - 0	69	32.5	2.07	29.8	30.7	32.4	34.0	35.5	28.6	37.7
12 - 6	64	33.1	1.92	30.7	31.7	33.2	34.5	35.6	28.9	37.4
13 - 0	67	33.5	1.79	31.3	32.0	33.4	34.9	35.8	29.5	38.1
13 - 6	53	34.1	1.64	32.0	32.9	34.0	35.5	36.2	30.9	37.5
14 - 0	61	34.9	1.78	32.5	33.8	34.8	36.2	37.4	31.0	39.5
14 - 6	42	35.1	1.56	33.1	33.9	35.0	36.2	37.3	32.1	38.2
15 - 0	51	35.4	1.47	33.1	34.6	35.5	36.4	37.5	32.2	37.9
15 - 6	22	35.4	1.78	32.9	33.8	35.6	37.1	37.5	32.5	38.1
16 - 0	57	35.8	1.52	33.5	35.0	35.8	37.1	37.7	32.4	38.3
17 - 0	44	36.1	1.75	33.0	34.9	36.4	37.5	38.1	32.4	39.2
18 - 0	25	36.7	1.24	35.2	35.5	36.7	37.7	38.4	34.2	38.9
19 - 0	19	36.7	1.58	34.5	35.7	36.7	37.6	39.0	33.6	39.6
20 - 0	15	36.3	1.80	34.1	34.4	36.3	36.9	39.3	33.9	39.7
21 - 0	12	37.5	1.56	34.9	37.2	37.7	38.2	39.5	34.6	39.8
22 - 0	10	37.4	1.58	35.6	36.0	37.1	38.5	39.2	35.1	40.2
23 - 0	11	36.6	1.17	34.8	35.8	36.9	37.3	37.8	34.4	38.2
24 - 0	10	37.1	1.43	35.1	35.4	37.4	37.8	38.7	34.7	38.9

ANTHROPOMETRY — TABLE E-21

Male — Upper Extremity Circumferences in Centimeters

Age	Hand				Bistyloid				Maximum Forearm				Biceps			
		Percentiles				Percentiles				Percentiles				Percentiles		
Yr. Mo.	N	10th	50th	90th	N	10th	50th	90th	N	10th	50th	90th	N	10th	50th	90th
Birth	40	7.8	8.6	9.5	40	7.2	8.0	8.8	40	9.0	10.2	11.2	42	8.6	10.2	11.0
0 - 1	47	8.3	9.0	9.8	39	7.3	8.1	9.1	48	9.7	10.6	11.9	51	9.3	10.7	12.0
0 - 2	42	9.0	9.7	10.4	39	8.3	9.0	10.3	42	10.8	11.8	13.3	45	10.6	11.6	13.4
0 - 3	45	9.2	9.8	10.4	39	8.4	9.3	10.5	45	11.3	12.5	14.0	49	11.3	12.4	14.1
0 - 4	39	9.6	10.3	10.8	39	9.0	9.8	10.7	39	12.1	13.2	14.9	42	11.7	13.0	14.9
0 - 5	40	10.0	10.5	11.4	38	9.3	10.1	11.6	40	12.7	13.9	15.3	42	12.4	13.6	15.5
0 - 6	54	10.0	10.8	11.6	37	9.6	10.4	11.6	54	12.8	14.1	15.9	58	12.6	14.1	16.0
0 - 9	44	10.6	11.4	12.4	40	9.8	11.0	12.2	44	13.6	15.0	16.5	49	13.2	15.0	16.7
1 - 0	59	10.7	11.6	12.6	42	10.0	11.3	12.4	59	14.0	15.2	16.4	63	13.8	15.4	17.2
1 - 6	63	11.0	11.8	12.8	37	10.1	11.3	12.5	63	14.0	15.5	16.8	67	14.1	15.8	17.7
2 - 0	67	11.2	12.0	13.0	40	10.1	11.2	12.6	68	14.2	15.6	16.9	80	14.3	15.8	17.6
2 - 6	71	11.3	12.3	13.3	40	10.2	11.6	12.3	71	14.5	15.8	17.0	87	14.6	16.2	17.3
3 - 0	73	11.5	12.6	13.6	40	10.3	11.5	12.6	73	14.8	16.1	17.2	91	14.9	16.2	17.5
3 - 6	69	11.8	12.7	13.7	37	10.5	11.6	12.6	69	14.8	16.0	17.3	87	15.1	16.2	17.6
4 - 0	68	12.2	13.0	14.1	38	10.6	11.8	12.6	68	15.0	16.3	17.4	86	14.9	16.2	17.7
4 - 6	68	12.4	13.3	14.3	36	10.8	11.8	12.7	68	15.4	16.6	17.8	87	15.1	16.3	17.8
5 - 0	62	12.5	13.6	14.8	32	11.1	11.9	13.0	62	15.5	16.7	18.0	83	15.4	16.6	18.0
5 - 6	65	12.8	13.9	15.1	31	11.3	12.2	13.1	65	15.6	17.0	18.4	88	15.5	16.8	18.2
6 - 0	64	13.2	14.2	15.3	34	11.3	12.4	13.3	64	15.7	17.1	18.2	87	15.6	17.1	18.6
6 - 6	66	13.5	14.5	15.6	35	11.7	12.4	13.5	66	16.1	17.4	18.6	88	16.0	17.2	19.0
7 - 0	65	13.8	14.9	15.9	34	11.8	12.6	13.7	65	16.4	17.7	19.4	89	16.0	17.4	19.6
7 - 6	59	13.9	15.1	16.3	35	11.7	12.7	13.9	60	16.6	18.2	19.7	83	16.4	17.8	19.8
8 - 0	64	14.1	15.4	16.8	36	12.0	13.0	14.1	63	16.6	18.4	20.0	84	16.7	18.1	20.3
8 - 6	60	14.4	15.7	16.9	33	11.9	13.0	14.5	59	17.1	18.7	20.2	80	17.0	18.3	21.1
9 - 0	59	14.8	16.2	17.1	35	12.4	13.5	14.8	58	17.1	19.2	21.0	80	17.2	18.8	21.6
9 - 6	54	15.2	16.5	17.4	33	12.6	13.6	14.6	53	17.5	19.4	21.1	77	17.6	19.2	21.9
10 - 0	51	15.4	16.8	17.8	35	12.9	13.9	15.0	51	17.8	19.8	21.5	80	17.8	19.8	23.0
10 - 6	49	15.7	16.8	18.0	37	13.0	13.9	15.0	49	17.8	19.6	21.8	73	17.7	20.0	23.2
11 - 0	47	15.8	17.3	18.4	36	13.2	14.2	15.6	47	18.2	20.0	22.8	71	18.1	20.4	24.0
11 - 6	47	16.3	17.5	18.6	38	13.3	14.4	15.7	47	18.5	20.4	22.8	74	18.5	20.9	24.2
12 - 0	44	16.2	17.6	19.0	36	13.7	14.8	16.3	44	18.7	20.8	23.5	66	18.9	21.1	25.3
12 - 6	45	16.5	18.0	19.4	37	13.7	15.0	16.4	45	19.2	21.1	24.1	69	19.3	21.8	25.3
13 - 0	42	16.8	18.4	20.0	38	13.6	15.3	16.8	42	19.4	21.4	24.7	65	19.6	22.3	26.3
13 - 6	41	17.2	18.9	20.8	36	14.0	15.7	17.0	41	19.4	22.3	24.7	63	19.9	22.8	26.3
14 - 0	39	17.6	19.4	20.9	34	14.4	16.0	17.0	39	20.5	22.2	24.9	62	20.6	23.5	26.4
14 - 6	40	18.0	19.6	21.1	35	14.5	16.4	17.4	40	20.6	23.0	25.8	60	20.6	23.4	26.6
15 - 0	32	18.6	20.1	21.4	27	15.1	16.6	17.6	31	21.7	23.5	26.1	53	21.6	24.2	27.5
15 - 6	29	19.3	20.4	21.7	29	15.3	16.7	17.4	30	22.2	24.0	26.7	47	22.4	24.5	27.6
16 - 0	26	19.0	20.6	21.6	25	15.8	16.9	17.7	26	22.6	23.9	26.5	46	22.8	25.3	28.3
16 - 6	22	20.0	20.8	21.8	22	16.4	17.0	17.6	22	23.4	24.7	27.0	35	23.2	25.4	29.2
17 - 0	22	19.2	21.0	22.0	23	15.8	17.2	18.0	23	24.0	25.2	27.3	40	23.6	26.1	29.4
17 - 6	19	19.3	20.9	22.4	18	15.6	17.1	17.8	19	24.2	26.2	28.0	22	24.3	27.0	30.0
18 - 0	22	19.6	21.0	21.9	22	15.6	17.1	17.9	22	23.8	25.8	27.8	30	24.0	26.8	29.8
19 - 0	19	20.0	20.8	22.1	20	16.2	17.2	18.0	14	24.1	25.7	28.2	19	24.6	27.1	30.3
20 - 0	22	20.0	21.0	22.0	23	16.3	17.1	18.0	12	24.4	27.0	28.2	17	24.1	27.6	29.9
21 - 0	25	20.2	21.1	22.0	28	16.5	17.3	18.0	10	24.5	26.7	27.8	14	24.9	27.2	30.7
22 - 0	27	20.2	21.3	22.2	31	16.4	17.2	18.1	15	24.1	26.2	28.6	11	23.5	27.9	30.3
23 - 0	25	20.2	21.2	22.2	30	16.2	17.3	18.0	15	24.6	26.1	29.4	13	23.9	27.8	31.6
24 - 0	22	20.1	21.3	22.3	28	16.2	17.0	17.9	14	24.7	26.9	30.1	11	25.3	27.9	31.6
25 - 0	22	19.9	21.1	22.5	26	16.1	17.3	18.1	14	24.6	25.8	27.6	11	24.1	26.5	29.4

ANTHROPOMETRY TABLE E-22

Female Upper Extremity Circumferences in Centimeters

Age	Hand				Bistyloid				Maximum Forearm				Biceps			
		Percentiles				Percentiles				Percentiles				Percentiles		
Yr. Mo.	N	10th	50th	90th	N	10th	50th	90th	N	10th	50th	90th	N	10th	50th	90th
Birth	34	7.6	8.3	9.2	34	7.3	7.9	8.7	35	9.5	10.3	11.4	43	9.0	10.5	11.7
0 - 1	44	7.9	8.7	9.4	35	7.5	8.2	8.7	44	9.1	10.6	11.4	51	9.2	10.3	11.5
0 - 2	39	8.4	9.1	10.0	36	8.1	8.9	9.4	39	10.4	11.6	12.3	48	10.4	11.6	12.6
0 - 3	46	8.6	9.3	10.0	35	8.4	9.3	9.9	46	11.3	12.3	13.2	54	10.7	12.3	13.1
0 - 4	37	9.0	9.7	10.5	35	8.9	9.6	10.3	37	11.8	12.8	13.9	46	12.1	13.0	14.0
0 - 5	35	9.3	10.0	10.7	35	9.1	10.0	11.0	35	12.1	13.5	14.5	44	12.0	13.4	14.5
0 - 6	40	9.4	10.2	11.0	33	9.5	10.3	10.9	40	12.4	13.8	14.9	48	12.3	14.2	15.3
0 - 9	43	9.9	10.7	11.7	35	10.1	10.8	11.7	43	13.4	14.8	15.9	50	13.4	14.8	16.4
1 - 0	52	10.2	11.2	12.1	34	10.3	11.2	12.1	52	13.6	15.1	16.3	60	13.8	15.2	16.6
1 - 6	61	10.6	11.4	12.4	38	10.2	11.1	12.0	62	13.7	15.2	16.4	73	13.8	15.6	16.9
2 - 0	64	10.9	11.8	12.8	40	10.2	11.0	12.1	64	14.3	15.4	16.7	81	14.1	15.6	17.2
2 - 6	69	11.0	12.0	13.0	45	10.1	11.0	12.0	69	14.3	15.5	16.8	88	14.3	15.6	17.3
3 - 0	63	11.5	12.2	13.3	41	10.1	11.2	12.3	63	14.4	15.6	17.1	87	14.5	15.9	17.6
3 - 6	60	11.8	12.4	13.4	38	10.5	11.4	12.2	60	14.6	16.0	17.2	84	14.6	16.0	17.5
4 - 0	63	12.0	12.7	13.9	41	10.8	11.5	12.3	63	14.7	16.2	17.4	87	14.8	16.2	17.7
4 - 6	59	12.3	13.1	14.1	39	10.8	11.6	12.4	59	15.1	16.6	17.5	87	15.2	16.6	18.1
5 - 0	59	12.3	13.2	14.3	38	11.0	11.6	12.4	59	15.1	16.8	17.8	86	15.1	16.7	18.2
5 - 6	59	12.8	13.6	14.6	40	11.0	11.8	12.7	59	15.2	16.9	18.0	85	15.2	17.0	18.6
6 - 0	66	13.0	13.9	15.0	45	11.1	11.9	12.8	66	15.2	17.0	18.3	91	15.5	17.0	18.6
6 - 6	66	13.0	14.1	15.2	44	11.3	12.1	12.9	66	15.4	17.2	18.3	90	15.6	17.3	18.9
7 - 0	62	13.3	14.3	15.3	40	11.5	12.1	13.1	62	15.7	17.3	18.7	88	16.0	17.6	19.5
7 - 6	65	13.4	14.6	15.6	43	11.4	12.3	13.2	65	15.9	17.6	19.4	91	16.0	18.0	20.3
8 - 0	66	14.0	14.8	15.9	43	11.7	12.5	13.5	66	16.3	17.9	19.8	89	16.4	18.4	20.8
8 - 6	61	14.1	15.1	16.2	46	12.0	12.7	13.8	61	16.6	18.2	20.0	84	16.7	18.7	21.3
9 - 0	52	14.4	15.3	16.4	42	11.9	12.9	14.1	51	16.6	18.4	20.6	73	16.7	19.0	22.0
9 - 6	48	14.6	15.6	16.6	42	12.2	13.0	13.9	48	17.2	18.6	20.2	67	17.1	19.4	21.9
10 - 0	49	14.6	15.7	17.1	43	12.4	13.2	14.2	49	17.1	18.8	21.2	71	17.4	19.6	22.9
10 - 6	51	15.1	16.0	17.2	45	12.4	13.4	14.5	51	17.5	19.2	21.4	70	17.5	20.0	23.5
11 - 0	47	15.1	16.3	17.4	43	12.5	13.6	14.7	47	17.9	19.4	21.6	69	18.2	20.3	23.8
11 - 6	45	15.4	16.5	17.6	42	12.7	14.1	14.9	45	18.0	19.6	21.7	64	18.6	20.6	24.3
12 - 0	50	15.8	17.0	18.0	45	13.2	14.2	15.3	50	18.4	20.2	22.5	68	18.8	21.4	25.3
12 - 6	46	16.1	17.3	18.4	41	13.3	14.5	15.4	46	19.1	20.8	22.7	64	19.2	21.8	24.8
13 - 0	48	16.2	17.4	18.7	43	13.5	14.7	15.7	48	19.0	21.1	22.9	66	19.1	21.9	24.9
13 - 6	35	17.0	17.7	19.1	33	14.0	14.7	15.7	35	19.5	21.1	23.4	49	19.4	22.2	24.9
14 - 0	40	17.0	17.9	19.2	39	14.2	15.1	15.9	40	20.0	21.5	23.2	57	20.3	22.8	25.9
14 - 6	31	17.1	17.9	19.2	31	14.2	15.0	15.7	31	20.2	21.9	23.5	40	20.8	23.2	25.2
15 - 0	38	17.2	18.1	19.2	37	14.5	15.1	16.1	38	20.5	22.2	23.9	52	20.8	23.2	25.6
15 - 6	16	17.2	17.9	19.2	16	14.3	14.9	16.5	16	20.8	22.0	23.1	19	20.6	23.2	25.4
16 - 0	37	17.3	18.2	19.2	37	14.6	15.2	16.1	37	20.7	22.4	24.3	55	21.0	23.8	26.9
17 - 0	29	17.1	18.2	19.3	29	14.4	15.2	15.8	27	21.2	22.4	24.2	43	21.6	24.0	26.9
18 - 0	24	17.3	18.4	19.1	25	14.4	15.2	15.8	22	21.0	23.0	24.5	28	21.0	24.3	28.1
19 - 0	22	17.4	18.5	19.1	27	14.3	15.2	16.1	15	20.4	23.4	25.2	20	21.8	25.0	27.8
20 - 0	23	17.0	18.2	19.2	27	14.3	15.1	15.9	15	20.5	22.8	24.2	18	20.7	24.0	26.8
21 - 0	22	17.3	18.4	19.4	25	14.3	15.2	15.9	16	20.2	22.6	24.5	18	20.8	24.3	26.1
22 - 0	19	17.2	18.6	19.4	24	14.5	15.2	15.9	14	20.7	22.5	24.3	16	21.0	24.1	25.5
23 - 0	17	16.6	17.9	19.5	25	14.0	15.0	15.6	11	19.5	22.0	23.4	16	19.3	24.1	25.4
24 - 0	18	16.8	18.3	19.2	21	14.2	15.2	15.8	15	19.5	22.3	24.5	13	22.5	24.2	26.3
25 - 0	19	17.2	18.4	19.7	24	14.2	14.9	15.7	16	19.7	21.8	24.3	14	19.9	23.3	25.1

ANTHROPOMETRY

TABLE E-23

Male

Lower Extremity Circumferences in Centimeters

Age	Foot				Ankle				Calf				Knee			
		Percentiles				Percentiles				Percentiles				Percentiles		
Yr. Mo.	N	10th	50th	90th	N	10th	50th	90th	N	10th	50th	90th	N	10th	50th	90th
Supine																
Birth	40	7.8	8.6	9.3	40	7.8	8.6	9.6	42	9.7	11.0	12.3	40	11.1	12.6	14.3
0 - 1	47	8.8	9.3	10.4	47	8.3	9.2	10.1	51	10.8	11.8	13.4	47	12.5	13.4	15.6
0 - 2	42	9.4	10.3	11.1	42	9.2	10.2	11.2	45	12.0	13.5	15.0	42	13.3	15.4	17.5
0 - 3	45	9.8	10.6	11.6	45	9.8	10.9	12.0	49	12.8	14.6	16.2	45	14.0	16.3	18.5
0 - 4	39	10.4	11.1	12.0	39	10.5	11.4	12.5	42	14.1	15.7	17.2	39	15.8	17.7	19.5
0 - 5	40	10.6	11.5	12.3	40	11.0	11.8	13.2	42	15.0	16.4	17.9	40	16.2	18.5	20.5
0 - 6	54	10.8	11.7	12.7	51	11.2	12.2	13.7	58	15.0	17.0	19.2	54	16.4	18.7	21.0
0 - 9	43	11.5	12.3	13.8	42	11.7	13.0	14.4	47	16.5	18.4	20.0	43	17.6	20.4	23.1
1 - 0	56	11.9	12.9	14.0	52	12.1	13.4	14.7	58	17.1	18.6	20.4	56	18.0	20.4	22.5
1 - 6	40	12.4	13.2	14.4	31	12.8	13.3	14.8	41	17.4	19.0	20.7	40	18.8	20.6	22.6
2 - 0	33	12.8	13.7	14.5	21	13.0	13.5	14.5	33	18.4	19.4	20.8	32	19.2	20.6	22.3
Erect																
2 - 0	36	12.7	14.3	15.5	36	12.7	14.5	15.9	48	18.1	19.9	21.7	36	19.5	22.0	24.0
2 - 6	41	13.3	14.6	16.2	40	12.7	14.6	16.2	57	18.6	20.2	22.0	41	19.9	22.5	24.1
3 - 0	40	14.0	15.3	16.4	40	13.0	14.7	16.3	58	19.2	20.6	22.4	40	20.8	22.9	24.5
3 - 6	37	13.9	15.5	16.7	37	13.2	14.6	16.2	54	19.4	20.8	22.6	38	20.7	23.1	24.7
4 - 0	49	13.8	15.8	17.0	48	13.4	14.8	16.2	69	19.6	21.0	23.0	51	21.4	23.1	24.9
4 - 6	64	14.5	15.7	17.4	62	13.7	14.9	16.1	86	19.9	21.5	23.1	67	21.8	23.6	25.0
5 - 0	61	14.9	16.3	18.0	57	13.8	15.1	16.6	84	20.4	22.1	23.7	62	22.4	24.0	25.4
5 - 6	65	15.2	16.6	18.4	58	14.3	15.5	16.7	88	21.0	22.6	24.3	65	22.4	24.4	26.0
6 - 0	64	15.9	17.1	18.6	59	14.6	15.7	16.9	86	21.2	23.1	24.7	65	23.0	24.6	26.3
6 - 6	66	16.2	17.6	18.9	60	14.9	16.1	17.3	88	21.6	23.7	25.3	66	23.6	25.3	26.9
7 - 0	65	16.5	17.9	19.7	58	15.2	16.4	17.6	89	22.2	24.2	25.9	65	24.1	25.7	28.1
7 - 6	61	16.9	18.3	19.8	59	15.6	16.6	18.2	83	22.4	24.7	26.8	61	24.7	26.3	28.7
8 - 0	64	17.5	18.8	20.4	60	15.2	16.9	18.4	85	22.9	25.3	27.8	64	25.2	27.0	29.5
8 - 6	58	17.6	19.2	20.7	53	15.7	17.3	18.8	81	23.4	25.8	28.2	60	25.4	27.2	30.1
9 - 0	58	18.1	19.8	21.1	51	15.7	17.5	19.2	81	23.8	26.3	29.2	59	25.6	28.3	31.0
9 - 6	53	18.4	20.2	21.4	48	15.9	18.0	19.5	78	24.1	27.0	29.5	54	26.4	28.8	31.3
10 - 0	51	18.5	20.4	22.2	49	16.6	18.3	20.2	80	24.9	27.7	30.2	51	26.7	29.3	32.3
10 - 6	49	18.4	20.9	22.2	48	16.7	18.4	20.3	73	25.6	28.0	30.8	49	27.4	30.0	32.8
11 - 0	47	19.0	21.3	22.9	47	17.2	18.8	20.5	71	26.0	28.8	31.8	47	28.2	30.8	34.2
11 - 6	47	19.6	21.6	23.1	47	17.7	19.2	20.7	75	26.5	29.2	32.4	47	28.5	31.0	34.2
12 - 0	44	19.7	22.0	23.8	44	17.6	19.5	21.2	66	26.3	29.6	33.5	44	29.0	31.8	35.0
12 - 6	45	20.0	22.2	24.4	45	18.0	19.7	21.7	70	27.0	30.3	33.8	45	29.1	31.6	35.9
13 - 0	42	21.0	22.7	24.6	41	18.5	20.4	22.1	65	27.9	31.3	34.3	42	30.0	33.1	36.9
13 - 6	41	21.2	23.4	25.3	41	18.8	20.7	23.1	63	28.3	31.9	35.3	41	31.0	33.9	36.8
14 - 0	39	21.5	23.8	25.6	39	19.5	21.3	23.1	62	29.2	32.8	35.4	39	32.0	35.0	36.7
14 - 6	39	22.0	23.9	26.0	39	19.3	21.5	23.2	61	28.9	32.9	36.7	39	31.9	35.4	37.6
15 - 0	31	22.2	24.4	26.0	32	20.3	21.6	23.5	54	30.2	33.3	37.0	32	32.5	35.5	38.2
15 - 6	30	22.5	24.7	26.1	30	20.4	22.1	23.3	49	30.5	33.8	37.2	30	33.9	36.0	38.7
16 - 0	25	23.4	24.8	26.5	25	20.9	22.3	24.0	46	31.5	34.4	37.3	25	34.6	36.4	38.1
16 - 6	22	23.5	24.7	26.8	22	21.1	21.9	23.7	36	31.8	34.6	37.8	22	34.4	36.5	38.9
17 - 0	23	23.3	24.7	26.7	23	20.7	22.7	24.5	41	32.1	35.6	39.0	23	34.0	36.8	38.7
17 - 6	18	23.1	25.2	26.7	17	20.5	22.9	24.2	23	32.1	36.0	38.3	18	34.0	37.3	39.4
18 - 0	22	23.3	25.3	27.0	22	20.8	22.2	23.9	32	32.5	34.9	38.1	22	34.0	37.2	39.0
19 - 0	20	23.5	25.2	27.6	20	20.8	22.6	24.3	19	32.4	35.4	38.9	12	34.2	36.6	39.3
20 - 0	19	23.7	25.2	26.8	21	20.9	22.4	23.8	16	32.6	35.6	38.6	11	35.2	37.3	40.0
21 - 0	28	23.9	25.2	27.0	26	20.8	22.2	24.1	13	32.0	33.7	38.1	10	35.2	36.4	39.3
22 - 0	26	23.7	25.0	26.5	30	20.6	22.2	23.9	14	32.4	34.6	38.7	13	34.6	36.8	39.5
23 - 0	24	23.7	24.9	26.5	28	20.6	22.3	24.2	14	32.4	34.2	39.2	13	33.6	36.0	39.0
24 - 0	22	23.8	25.1	26.1	26	20.5	22.2	24.1	12	32.9	34.4	40.0	10	35.5	36.8	40.2
25 - 0	24	23.2	24.7	26.5	25	20.2	22.4	23.7	13	32.5	34.2	37.8	12	33.6	35.2	37.8

ANTHROPOMETRY | TABLE E-24

Female | Lower Extremity Circumferences in Centimeters

Age	Foot				Ankle				Calf				Knee			
		Percentiles				Percentiles				Percentiles				Percentiles		
Yr. Mo.	N	10th	50th	90th	N	10th	50th	90th	N	10th	50th	90th	N	10th	50th	90th
Supine																
Birth	34	7.5	8.4	9.0	34	7.9	8.7	9.4	43	9.7	11.0	12.2	34	11.5	12.5	14.0
0 - 1	44	8.0	8.9	9.6	44	8.0	8.9	9.8	52	10.0	11.8	12.7	44	11.7	13.1	14.5
0 - 2	39	8.6	9.6	10.2	39	9.1	9.7	10.7	48	11.9	13.2	14.3	39	13.4	15.0	16.7
0 - 3	46	9.0	10.0	10.5	46	9.7	10.5	11.6	54	13.0	14.3	15.5	46	14.1	15.8	17.8
0 - 4	37	9.9	10.4	11.1	36	10.3	10.9	12.0	46	14.0	15.3	16.3	37	15.2	16.8	18.3
0 - 5	35	10.0	10.7	11.7	35	10.8	11.5	12.4	44	14.6	16.0	17.8	35	16.1	18.1	19.6
0 - 6	40	10.3	11.0	11.9	40	11.0	11.9	12.9	48	14.9	16.7	18.2	40	16.3	18.4	21.2
0 - 9	42	10.8	12.0	12.6	40	11.9	12.8	13.5	50	16.4	18.1	19.7	42	17.8	19.4	22.5
1 - 0	50	11.4	12.2	13.2	48	12.0	12.9	13.8	56	17.2	18.5	20.3	50	17.9	19.8	23.4
1 - 6	39	11.9	12.7	13.7	31	12.3	13.2	14.3	43	17.5	19.0	20.7	38	18.2	20.2	22.8
2 - 0	26	12.1	12.8	13.8	14	12.0	13.2	13.9	27	17.7	19.4	20.7	25	18.6	19.8	21.1
Erect																
2 - 0	39	12.8	13.6	14.6	39	12.7	14.0	15.0	54	18.2	19.9	21.5	39	20.1	21.3	24.[illegible]
2 - 6	44	13.1	14.1	15.1	44	12.8	14.1	15.2	64	18.5	20.0	21.7	43	20.2	21.6	23.7
3 - 0	41	13.7	14.6	15.6	41	13.1	14.6	16.0	65	18.8	20.3	22.2	41	20.8	22.1	24.0
3 - 6	38	14.0	15.1	16.2	38	13.4	14.9	15.9	61	19.6	20.8	22.8	38	21.4	22.4	24.3
4 - 0	50	13.8	15.4	16.4	49	13.4	15.0	16.0	73	19.5	21.3	22.9	50	21.6	22.9	24.7
4 - 6	57	14.1	15.6	17.0	53	13.6	15.1	16.3	87	20.1	22.0	23.5	58	22.0	23.4	25.2
5 - 0	58	14.5	15.9	17.3	56	13.8	15.4	16.3	86	20.5	22.4	24.1	59	22.2	23.7	25.5
5 - 6	59	14.9	16.3	17.8	57	14.2	15.6	16.7	85	20.8	23.0	24.7	59	22.6	24.3	26.3
6 - 0	66	15.1	16.8	18.1	62	14.2	16.0	17.0	91	21.3	23.4	25.4	66	23.0	24.6	27.0
6 - 6	66	15.4	16.9	18.3	60	14.4	16.1	17.4	91	21.6	23.9	25.9	66	23.5	25.0	27.3
7 - 0	62	15.8	17.4	18.6	57	14.8	16.5	17.8	88	22.0	24.1	26.6	62	23.9	25.5	28.1
7 - 6	65	16.4	17.7	19.1	60	15.1	16.7	18.1	91	22.6	24.8	27.4	65	24.1	26.0	28.6
8 - 0	66	16.6	18.0	19.2	62	15.3	17.1	18.4	89	23.1	25.4	27.9	66	24.7	26.8	29.2
8 - 6	61	17.2	18.3	19.8	59	15.5	17.4	18.9	84	23.4	26.1	28.7	61	25.4	27.5	30.3
9 - 0	52	17.4	18.9	20.2	49	15.7	17.7	19.5	73	23.7	26.4	29.5	52	26.2	28.2	31.4
9 - 6	48	17.8	19.1	20.6	46	15.8	17.8	19.4	67	24.0	26.9	29.8	48	26.6	28.6	31.9
10 - 0	49	18.0	19.5	21.1	48	16.1	18.2	19.8	71	24.9	27.3	30.4	49	27.0	29.2	32.7
10 - 6	51	18.3	19.9	21.1	50	16.1	18.5	20.1	70	24.8	28.1	31.4	51	27.2	29.5	33.3
11 - 0	47	18.6	20.4	21.9	47	16.7	18.8	20.6	69	25.5	28.5	32.2	47	27.8	30.3	34.1
11 - 6	45	19.2	20.6	22.1	45	17.1	19.1	20.9	64	26.3	29.0	33.1	45	28.8	31.0	34.2
12 - 0	49	19.5	20.9	22.4	50	17.3	19.8	21.2	68	27.0	30.1	34.4	48	28.9	31.8	35.2
12 - 6	46	19.8	21.6	22.7	46	18.1	20.1	21.4	64	27.4	31.2	33.9	46	29.4	33.0	36.1
13 - 0	47	20.2	21.9	23.2	47	17.9	20.5	21.8	65	28.0	31.2	34.0	46	30.6	33.2	37.4
13 - 6	35	20.7	22.0	23.1	35	19.0	20.7	21.8	49	28.6	32.2	34.7	35	31.3	33.6	36.5
14 - 0	40	21.4	22.2	23.8	40	19.6	21.1	22.2	57	30.0	32.6	35.5	40	32.4	34.8	37.4
14 - 6	30	21.4	22.1	23.7	30	19.0	21.1	22.4	39	29.7	32.7	35.9	30	32.8	35.5	38.2
15 - 0	38	21.6	22.7	23.8	38	19.2	21.4	22.2	52	30.1	33.3	36.1	38	33.1	35.6	38.6
15 - 6	16	21.7	22.8	23.8	16	19.4	21.4	22.6	19	29.0	33.0	35.6	15	32.3	36.6	38.2
16 - 0	37	21.4	22.6	23.5	37	19.6	21.1	22.5	55	30.4	33.6	36.8	37	33.2	36.1	39.0
17 - 0	28	21.3	22.6	24.5	29	19.6	21.4	22.6	43	31.0	34.2	36.8	26	33.3	36.3	40.1
18 - 0	23	21.8	22.7	24.1	23	19.4	21.2	22.4	27	31.4	34.7	36.7	21	32.9	36.4	40.8
19 - 0	25	21.8	22.8	24.1	22	19.7	21.0	22.2	24	32.2	35.4	37.4	15	33.2	36.9	38.9
20 - 0	27	21.7	22.6	24.0	24	18.9	20.5	22.1	20	30.9	34.4	36.7	13	33.1	35.6	39.3
21 - 0	23	21.7	22.5	23.3	21	18.7	20.8	22.5	16	31.1	34.7	36.3	12	32.9	35.5	39.9
22 - 0	19	21.8	22.5	23.2	22	19.4	20.6	22.5	16	31.2	34.8	36.6	12	33.2	37.2	40.9
23 - 0	23	21.5	22.4	23.3	21	18.1	20.6	22.2	15	28.7	34.5	36.0	11	32.3	35.3	36.6
24 - 0	21	21.6	22.5	23.6	21	18.1	21.0	22.2	13	32.0	34.6	36.0	9	-	-	-
25 - 0	19	21.4	22.4	23.7	22	18.0	20.7	22.2	13	31.1	33.6	35.9	8	-	-	-

ANTHROPOMETRY

TABLE E-25

Male

Measurements Relative to Height (Measurement/Height X 100)

Age	Sitting Height				Iliac Circumference				Iliac Width				Biacromial Width			
		Percentiles				Percentiles				Percentiles				Percentiles		
Yr. Mo.	N	10th	50th	90th	N	10th	50th	90th	N	10th	50th	90th	N	10th	50th	90th
Supine		Crown-rump length														
Birth	48	65.11	67.40	70.32	49	49.32	53.36	57.16	49	15.54	16.45	17.57	49	20.30	22.49	24.82
0 - 1	56	63.49	66.52	68.72	62	52.29	55.71	61.00	62	15.70	16.84	17.69	54	19.80	22.90	25.71
0 - 2	51	64.87	66.76	69.08	53	53.74	57.88	63.98	53	15.94	17.29	18.32	45	21.91	23.69	26.38
0 - 3	59	64.37	66.96	69.25	59	55.14	59.41	63.93	59	15.92	17.34	18.29	56	21.92	23.91	26.04
0 - 4	49	65.02	66.69	68.62	49	55.39	60.08	65.50	49	16.08	17.36	18.96	42	22.45	24.14	26.20
0 - 5	51	65.14	66.98	68.48	51	54.64	59.48	64.68	51	15.92	17.49	18.50	45	22.53	24.05	26.18
0 - 6	64	63.82	66.23	68.64	70	54.42	59.02	64.80	70	15.97	17.29	18.66	69	20.57	23.35	25.72
0 - 9	53	63.86	65.43	67.29	53	53.16	58.82	63.12	53	15.58	16.98	18.29	51	21.46	23.75	26.15
1 - 0	67	62.37	64.23	65.84	63	51.04	56.31	60.25	67	15.55	16.73	18.80	64	20.64	23.24	25.67
1 - 6	59	59.97	61.98	64.43	49	48.59	52.87	57.11	49	15.36	16.38	17.73	50	19.68	21.56	24.69
2 - 0	41	57.83	60.84	62.55	34	47.20	49.78	53.61	33	15.24	16.22	17.30	31	19.64	21.05	22.54
Erect																
2 - 0	51	58.58	60.42	61.28	52	50.82	54.83	57.88	52	16.07	17.31	18.41	52	22.49	23.68	25.08
2 - 6	58	57.92	59.56	60.79	60	49.58	53.56	56.83	60	15.98	17.00	18.22	60	22.17	23.41	24.52
3 - 0	59	56.32	58.31	59.61	58	48.66	51.77	55.05	59	15.89	17.08	18.20	59	22.08	23.04	24.34
3 - 6	57	55.92	57.63	58.85	57	47.34	50.81	54.53	57	15.97	16.89	17.98	57	21.78	22.70	24.16
4 - 0	73	55.02	56.79	58.28	74	46.30	50.39	53.42	74	15.61	16.71	17.70	73	20.68	22.49	23.70
4 - 6	90	54.54	56.22	57.61	91	45.81	48.32	51.89	92	15.46	16.35	17.39	89	19.91	22.17	23.51
5 - 0	86	54.32	55.64	57.33	86	45.08	48.49	51.40	87	15.23	16.22	17.41	87	20.14	22.19	23.16
5 - 6	91	53.64	55.29	56.76	90	44.47	47.96	50.44	91	15.12	16.08	17.36	91	20.38	22.01	23.31
6 - 0	91	53.38	54.91	56.40	91	44.08	47.08	50.08	91	15.13	16.12	17.22	91	20.61	21.85	23.19
6 - 6	92	52.71	54.57	55.83	92	43.55	46.52	49.59	92	14.87	16.00	16.89	92	20.58	21.84	22.95
7 - 0	92	52.31	53.99	55.52	92	43.14	45.85	49.46	92	14.87	15.84	16.87	92	20.59	21.79	22.95
7 - 6	88	52.03	53.72	54.90	88	43.03	45.61	49.44	88	14.89	15.72	16.91	88	20.50	21.81	22.94
8 - 0	91	51.75	53.47	54.78	92	42.77	45.22	49.11	92	14.79	15.65	16.73	92	20.40	21.81	22.71
8 - 6	90	51.38	53.23	54.49	90	42.28	44.91	49.48	90	14.82	15.58	16.76	90	20.34	21.69	22.67
9 - 0	92	51.06	52.79	54.24	92	41.94	44.61	49.91	92	14.62	15.71	16.84	92	20.41	21.69	22.68
9 - 6	88	50.70	52.53	53.96	88	41.93	44.79	50.28	88	14.64	15.68	16.89	88	20.38	21.67	22.86
10 - 0	85	50.86	52.34	53.45	85	42.20	44.87	50.30	85	14.66	15.63	17.13	85	20.58	21.77	22.87
10 - 6	78	50.62	51.98	53.26	80	41.11	44.67	50.36	80	14.55	15.57	16.94	80	20.56	21.68	22.99
11 - 0	76	50.11	51.76	53.19	75	41.50	45.07	50.74	76	14.58	15.62	17.26	76	20.28	21.72	22.97
11 - 6	78	50.06	51.49	52.94	77	40.89	44.57	50.27	77	14.68	15.67	17.55	78	20.29	21.60	22.85
12 - 0	70	49.67	51.26	52.86	69	40.84	44.23	50.28	69	14.53	15.50	17.58	70	20.31	21.54	22.75
12 - 6	72	49.80	51.08	52.44	73	40.84	43.89	49.22	73	14.48	15.63	17.16	73	20.42	21.52	22.69
13 - 0	71	48.96	50.95	52.45	70	40.78	44.16	50.53	70	14.70	15.65	17.40	71	20.42	21.46	22.57
13 - 6	69	49.22	50.85	52.44	68	40.20	44.10	49.62	68	14.53	15.56	17.04	69	20.54	21.44	22.51
14 - 0	66	49.16	50.80	52.68	66	41.07	44.03	48.94	66	14.58	15.55	16.86	67	20.15	21.52	22.61
14 - 6	61	48.60	50.71	52.06	61	40.55	43.36	48.29	61	14.63	15.54	17.21	61	20.42	21.48	22.78
15 - 0	55	48.91	51.00	52.46	54	40.63	44.07	50.01	55	14.78	15.73	17.31	55	20.24	21.68	23.06
15 - 6	52	49.08	50.94	52.80	52	40.64	44.24	47.83	52	14.73	15.82	17.61	52	20.46	21.79	23.39
16 - 0	49	49.01	51.25	52.97	49	40.10	43.82	48.54	49	14.90	15.72	17.04	50	20.32	21.87	23.17
16 - 6	37	48.76	51.16	52.58	37	41.00	43.83	48.15	37	14.79	16.04	17.26	37	21.02	22.08	23.33
17 - 0	42	49.40	51.46	52.87	42	40.99	44.37	48.94	41	14.88	15.88	17.39	40	20.76	21.99	23.54
17 - 6	23	50.54	51.92	52.53	22	42.31	44.81	51.55	22	14.89	16.42	18.06	22	21.00	22.21	23.64
18 - 0	33	50.08	51.73	52.57	32	40.70	43.90	49.10	31	14.99	16.05	17.72	32	21.18	22.13	23.24
19 - 0	25	49.87	52.03	52.70	16	40.64	44.53	46.61	16	15.31	16.03	17.15	16	21.13	22.03	23.39
20 - 0	31	50.32	52.02	52.92	15	41.62	44.02	46.25	15	15.10	15.86	17.01	14	21.34	22.39	23.66
21 - 0	35	50.82	52.14	52.74	12	41.16	44.59	46.44	12	15.53	16.07	16.78	12	21.35	22.28	23.56
22 - 0	39	50.44	52.08	53.01	11	41.50	46.47	49.50	12	15.27	16.47	17.22	11	21.49	22.58	23.51
23 - 0	37	50.32	52.19	53.32	13	41.48	45.65	51.26	13	14.77	16.46	17.63	13	21.83	22.66	24.21
24 - 0	34	50.49	52.20	53.32	10	41.73	45.78	50.98	11	15.59	16.49	17.84	11	21.67	23.22	23.90
25 - 0	30	50.58	52.09	53.20	12	41.02	44.52	48.02	12	15.10	16.06	17.32	12	21.58	22.41	23.70

ANTHROPOMETRY

TABLE E-26

Female

Measurements Relative to Height (Measurement/Height X 100)

Age	Sitting Height				Iliac Circumference				Iliac Width				Biacromial Width			
		Percentiles				Percentiles				Percentiles				Percentiles		
Yr. Mo.	N	10th	50th	90th	N	10th	50th	90th	N	10th	50th	90th	N	10th	50th	90th
Supine		Crown-rump length														
Birth	55	64.40	67.90	71.97	56	50.00	54.18	59.82	55	14.73	16.11	18.47	53	20.77	22.58	25.20
0 - 1	63	64.30	66.66	69.03	68	52.20	56.46	61.51	69	15.17	16.37	17.35	58	20.95	23.22	25.64
0 - 2	61	64.70	66.82	68.92	62	53.74	58.62	63.20	62	15.60	16.80	18.56	50	21.64	24.16	26.11
0 - 3	67	64.39	66.83	68.55	67	54.08	59.02	63.66	67	15.58	16.84	18.25	66	21.56	23.26	24.95
0 - 4	59	64.92	66.68	68.46	59	55.23	59.73	64.65	59	15.78	17.08	18.51	46	21.93	23.69	25.61
0 - 5	57	64.55	66.87	68.41	56	55.11	60.26	65.09	57	15.76	16.96	18.92	45	22.15	23.77	25.92
0 - 6	58	64.18	66.36	68.22	61	56.33	60.47	64.63	63	16.16	17.07	18.58	60	21.33	23.42	25.42
0 - 9	59	63.57	65.41	67.09	59	54.42	59.58	63.42	59	15.60	16.76	18.56	55	21.75	23.64	25.35
1 - 0	65	62.31	64.26	66.21	64	52.61	56.36	61.77	66	15.34	16.53	18.18	64	21.41	23.34	24.71
1 - 6	58	60.27	62.52	64.11	45	49.77	53.41	58.65	42	14.91	16.16	17.43	40	19.89	21.95	24.19
2 - 0	43	58.77	60.59	62.45	29	45.26	49.23	53.21	27	14.52	15.85	17.02	29	19.33	21.02	23.51
Erect																
2 - 0	56	58.83	60.09	61.43	56	50.64	54.92	59.34	57	16.12	17.40	18.42	57	22.54	23.64	25.12
2 - 6	71	57.76	58.90	60.45	70	50.45	53.80	57.54	69	16.01	17.06	18.34	70	22.42	23.29	24.95
3 - 0	71	56.73	58.03	59.37	70	49.03	52.38	55.48	71	15.92	17.04	18.18	70	21.82	22.82	24.17
3 - 6	68	55.99	57.28	58.54	68	48.66	51.52	53.96	68	16.06	16.83	18.16	68	21.83	22.71	24.07
4 - 0	77	55.43	56.69	58.15	78	47.70	50.06	53.02	77	15.88	16.62	17.77	76	21.15	22.54	23.68
4 - 6	89	54.75	56.23	57.73	90	46.29	48.98	52.19	90	15.36	16.52	17.52	89	20.32	22.10	23.39
5 - 0	89	54.11	55.82	57.53	89	45.53	48.34	51.37	90	15.09	16.34	17.48	90	20.14	21.98	23.01
5 - 6	90	53.81	55.31	57.16	90	45.11	47.71	51.21	90	15.02	16.16	17.39	90	20.43	21.85	23.14
6 - 0	95	53.18	55.13	56.43	95	44.22	47.16	51.33	95	15.08	16.07	17.22	95	20.51	21.92	22.96
6 - 6	95	52.75	54.81	56.42	95	43.73	46.60	50.18	94	14.94	15.96	17.06	94	20.77	21.90	22.90
7 - 0	90	52.58	54.25	55.70	90	43.49	46.42	51.65	89	14.95	15.88	17.23	90	20.70	21.81	22.91
7 - 6	92	52.28	53.92	55.39	92	43.14	46.12	50.75	91	14.95	15.92	16.99	92	20.55	21.75	22.84
8 - 0	90	51.91	53.42	55.17	90	42.75	45.87	50.32	90	14.80	15.82	16.98	90	20.42	21.70	22.84
8 - 6	90	51.69	53.25	54.97	90	42.52	45.40	50.98	90	14.81	15.91	17.01	90	20.61	21.80	22.78
9 - 0	80	51.30	52.94	54.57	80	42.17	45.24	52.01	80	14.88	15.89	17.25	80	20.50	21.71	22.83
9 - 6	75	50.98	52.59	54.16	75	42.70	45.45	51.40	75	15.07	15.99	16.97	74	20.58	21.57	22.74
10 - 0	76	51.17	52.36	53.59	76	41.92	45.25	53.61	76	15.00	15.96	17.02	76	20.42	21.71	22.69
10 - 6	73	50.87	52.18	53.85	73	41.68	45.13	51.90	73	14.93	15.96	17.48	73	20.36	21.46	22.62
11 - 0	70	50.44	51.90	53.56	69	41.72	45.02	52.62	70	14.94	16.00	17.46	70	20.32	21.47	22.62
11 - 6	67	50.44	51.72	53.05	67	41.65	45.32	51.16	67	15.03	15.94	17.22	66	20.27	21.43	22.36
12 - 0	69	50.09	51.63	53.00	69	41.35	45.43	51.33	69	14.85	15.98	17.36	69	20.24	21.40	22.42
12 - 6	64	50.10	51.62	53.26	64	41.73	45.06	51.24	64	14.98	16.04	17.31	64	20.57	21.32	22.55
13 - 0	68	50.02	51.59	52.91	68	41.92	45.40	50.52	67	14.97	16.00	17.49	67	20.22	21.26	22.45
13 - 6	53	49.92	51.76	53.38	52	41.61	45.15	50.55	53	15.11	16.06	17.39	53	20.20	21.39	22.47
14 - 0	61	50.13	51.88	53.46	60	42.58	46.67	51.20	61	15.44	16.37	17.88	61	20.47	21.48	22.71
14 - 6	43	50.15	52.00	53.60	42	42.85	46.41	50.81	42	15.41	16.52	17.79	42	20.61	21.63	22.19
15 - 0	52	50.46	52.31	53.50	52	43.06	46.51	52.46	51	15.65	16.55	17.97	51	20.48	21.54	22.40
15 - 6	23	50.48	52.46	53.94	22	43.08	45.77	50.66	22	15.54	16.54	17.77	22	20.18	21.54	22.77
16 - 0	57	50.79	52.54	53.86	56	44.11	46.60	53.72	56	15.82	16.64	18.09	57	20.39	21.69	22.56
16 - 6	12	50.52	52.50	53.63	5	-	-	-	5	-	-	-	5	-	-	-
17 - 0	47	51.16	52.64	53.91	43	43.44	47.21	53.24	44	15.92	16.79	18.24	44	20.43	21.82	22.64
17 - 6	18	51.11	52.69	53.68	2	-	-	-	2	-	-	-	2	-	-	-
18 - 0	35	51.42	52.85	53.96	25	44.04	47.78	52.65	25	15.55	17.13	18.96	25	21.01	22.19	22.98
19 - 0	35	51.30	52.77	53.76	19	44.30	48.12	52.75	19	16.45	17.41	18.34	19	20.92	21.95	22.93
20 - 0	36	51.24	52.91	53.88	15	44.73	46.22	52.03	15	15.94	16.93	18.28	15	20.63	21.67	22.80
21 - 0	34	51.04	52.84	54.15	12	45.20	47.13	51.07	12	15.66	16.86	17.90	12	21.33	21.88	22.72
22 - 0	32	51.15	52.80	54.16	10	45.50	47.95	53.86	10	16.36	17.09	18.43	10	21.96	22.25	23.06
23 - 0	30	51.22	52.66	54.07	11	44.82	47.10	51.08	11	16.57	17.12	17.75	11	21.28	22.08	22.59
24 - 0	25	50.98	52.66	53.89	9	-	-	-	9	-	-	-	9	-	-	-
25 - 0	25	50.91	52.85	53.91	8	-	-	-	8	-	-	-	8	-	-	-

ANTHROPOMETRY

TABLE E-27

Male

Measurements Relative to Height (Measurement/Height X 100)

Age	Fronto-occipital Circumference				Xiphisternal Circumference				Xiphisternal Width				Xiphisternal Depth			
		Percentiles				Percentiles				Percentiles				Percentiles		
Yr. Mo.	N	10th	50th	90th	N	10th	50th	90th	N	10th	50th	90th	N	10th	50th	90th
Supine																
Birth	49	66.30	69.04	71.93	49	61.33	64.51	68.48	49	18.20	19.46	20.84	48	16.19	17.63	19.26
0 - 1	62	66.69	68.69	71.15	61	62.72	65.52	68.01	62	19.43	20.92	22.15	62	16.32	17.50	18.74
0 - 2	52	65.73	67.27	70.78	53	63.12	66.23	69.85	52	20.08	21.48	22.97	51	15.52	16.89	18.14
0 - 3	59	64.12	66.49	68.96	57	62.34	65.42	68.81	58	20.22	21.72	23.11	57	15.16	16.33	17.38
0 - 4	49	63.92	65.90	67.77	49	62.71	65.76	68.32	49	20.50	22.21	23.13	49	14.77	15.76	16.76
0 - 5	51	62.62	65.05	67.50	51	62.08	65.24	68.71	51	20.80	22.01	23.51	51	14.46	15.70	17.02
0 - 6	70	61.95	64.79	66.68	70	61.40	63.95	67.71	70	19.78	21.82	23.08	69	14.46	15.59	17.36
0 - 9	53	60.71	63.09	66.09	52	60.03	63.40	67.44	50	20.21	21.30	22.77	51	14.27	15.53	16.91
1 - 0	72	59.11	61.47	64.08	64	58.54	61.75	64.73	64	19.28	20.44	22.06	63	14.06	15.30	16.69
1 - 6	75	56.00	58.69	60.82	46	56.20	59.06	62.25	45	18.54	19.54	21.14	46	13.88	14.82	15.72
2 - 0	69	53.76	55.99	58.61	33	52.59	55.95	58.72	33	17.99	18.77	20.06	31	13.15	13.72	14.69
Erect																
2 - 0	53	54.28	57.08	59.08	51	54.16	56.88	59.05	52	18.25	19.30	20.47	52	12.32	13.61	15.12
2 - 6	60	52.52	54.99	56.74	60	52.50	54.86	57.90	60	17.89	18.84	19.89	59	12.28	13.35	14.58
3 - 0	59	50.50	52.52	54.87	57	50.87	53.34	56.45	58	17.36	18.34	19.48	58	12.17	12.98	13.82
3 - 6	57	49.14	51.42	53.62	55	49.82	52.03	55.73	57	16.93	18.03	19.03	57	11.97	12.74	13.73
4 - 0	74	47.86	49.86	51.90	72	47.93	51.17	54.24	74	16.30	17.60	18.54	73	11.65	12.60	13.70
4 - 6	93	46.36	48.39	50.61	91	47.43	49.73	52.71	93	15.80	16.97	18.05	90	11.35	12.21	13.32
5 - 0	87	45.19	47.22	49.48	87	46.64	49.23	51.83	87	15.64	16.77	17.89	87	11.05	12.00	13.08
5 - 6	91	44.25	45.85	48.00	91	45.78	48.36	51.32	91	15.26	16.36	17.81	91	10.86	11.82	12.85
6 - 0	91	43.11	44.63	46.54	90	45.26	48.05	50.61	91	15.02	16.23	17.48	91	10.81	11.71	12.75
6 - 6	92	42.01	43.73	45.44	91	44.90	47.38	50.68	92	14.92	16.07	17.28	92	10.60	11.58	12.56
7 - 0	92	41.01	42.76	44.55	92	44.34	47.08	50.00	92	14.94	15.83	17.17	92	10.41	11.54	12.66
7 - 6	87	40.31	41.82	43.80	85	43.93	46.75	49.69	88	14.62	15.88	16.96	88	10.23	11.45	12.63
8 - 0	91	39.35	41.04	42.96	91	43.54	46.46	49.60	92	14.57	15.73	17.06	91	10.26	11.39	12.29
8 - 6	87	38.66	40.23	42.39	89	43.56	46.47	49.40	90	14.50	15.71	16.90	90	10.12	11.26	12.38
9 - 0	88	37.96	39.65	41.46	89	43.43	46.39	49.77	92	14.42	15.78	17.04	92	10.06	11.34	12.38
9 - 6	83	37.17	38.84	40.93	87	43.10	46.19	49.67	88	14.48	15.68	16.99	88	9.99	11.31	12.53
10 - 0	82	36.94	38.50	40.20	82	42.89	46.19	50.23	85	14.54	15.78	17.17	85	10.10	11.33	12.48
10 - 6	78	36.18	37.84	39.82	79	43.39	46.02	50.07	80	14.67	15.73	17.05	80	10.00	11.12	12.66
11 - 0	72	35.65	37.31	38.93	76	42.90	45.63	50.15	76	14.50	15.74	17.25	76	9.86	11.16	12.38
11 - 6	74	35.16	36.66	38.45	77	43.07	45.63	50.40	78	14.59	15.77	17.33	78	9.71	11.11	12.61
12 - 0	69	34.63	36.29	38.27	69	42.98	45.66	50.09	70	14.56	15.64	17.33	70	9.90	11.21	12.56
12 - 6	68	33.81	35.77	37.83	73	43.06	45.74	50.17	73	14.42	15.74	17.08	73	9.84	11.24	12.51
13 - 0	66	33.38	34.99	36.76	68	42.71	46.04	50.85	71	14.50	15.88	17.33	71	9.91	11.16	12.66
13 - 6	63	32.79	34.48	36.47	69	42.29	45.67	50.64	69	14.45	15.68	17.35	69	9.97	11.12	12.79
14 - 0	61	32.31	33.55	35.62	67	42.66	45.74	50.20	67	14.35	15.80	17.21	66	9.93	11.21	12.58
14 - 6	59	31.78	33.07	34.72	61	42.81	45.84	51.35	61	14.57	15.82	17.38	61	9.91	11.21	12.72
15 - 0	50	31.25	32.65	34.44	55	43.58	46.12	50.60	55	14.75	16.11	17.48	55	10.00	11.25	12.76
15 - 6	46	31.07	32.40	33.58	49	42.89	46.38	50.95	52	14.97	16.08	17.60	52	10.24	11.28	12.73
16 - 0	47	30.85	32.06	33.62	49	42.50	46.57	51.30	50	14.60	16.06	17.66	50	10.05	11.32	12.56
16 - 6	36	30.60	31.96	33.39	36	43.43	46.79	51.87	37	15.28	16.22	17.70	37	10.49	11.38	12.86
17 - 0	41	30.43	31.90	33.21	41	43.03	47.33	53.58	42	15.13	16.46	18.32	42	10.24	11.33	13.06
17 - 6	23	30.61	32.05	33.03	22	44.68	47.37	56.00	22	15.40	16.82	18.63	22	10.48	11.52	13.75
18 - 0	33	30.44	31.49	33.08	32	44.43	48.31	54.17	32	15.01	16.75	19.22	32	10.27	11.52	13.38
19 - 0	25	30.53	31.23	32.99	17	44.02	47.11	53.80	16	14.86	16.28	18.57	16	10.37	11.41	13.49
20 - 0	31	30.54	31.77	33.02	15	43.58	47.97	53.88	15	15.40	16.69	18.24	15	10.40	11.09	12.84
21 - 0	35	30.63	31.92	32.86	12	44.96	49.04	51.47	12	15.98	16.46	17.84	12	10.40	11.48	12.36
22 - 0	39	30.57	32.00	33.17	12	43.18	50.16	54.60	13	15.91	16.69	18.12	12	9.32	11.77	13.72
23 - 0	37	30.60	32.03	33.22	13	43.10	49.69	57.69	14	15.70	16.72	18.79	13	9.68	12.04	14.32
24 - 0	33	30.49	31.86	33.17	11	42.20	51.00	54.82	11	14.74	17.69	18.15	11	10.60	11.91	13.95
25 - 0	30	30.38	31.83	34.00	12	43.54	48.14	51.40	12	15.77	16.40	17.98	12	10.35	11.67	12.15

ANTHROPOMETRY

TABLE E-28

Female

Measurements Relative to Height (Measurement/Height X 100)

Age	Fronto-occipital Circumference				Xiphisternal Circumference				Xiphisternal Width				Xiphisternal Depth			
		Percentiles				Percentiles				Percentiles				Percentiles		
Yr. Mo.	N	10th	50th	90th	N	10th	50th	90th	N	10th	50th	90th	N	10th	50th	90th
Supine																
Birth	55	66.48	69.15	71.30	55	63.13	65.69	68.90	55	18.69	19.74	20.96	56	16.11	17.41	18.87
0 - 1	69	66.30	68.59	71.90	67	62.63	65.58	68.52	69	18.99	20.68	22.02	69	16.04	17.40	18.89
0 - 2	62	64.91	68.29	70.87	61	63.12	65.92	69.04	62	19.66	21.15	22.69	62	16.02	16.81	18.12
0 - 3	67	64.53	66.57	69.18	65	61.89	65.22	68.74	66	19.69	21.14	22.93	66	15.44	16.27	17.72
0 - 4	58	64.25	66.33	68.39	57	61.88	65.66	69.21	58	20.27	21.80	23.60	58	15.12	16.24	17.45
0 - 5	57	62.78	65.54	67.34	56	61.74	64.92	68.48	56	20.55	21.86	23.40	56	14.80	16.00	17.21
0 - 6	63	62.37	64.76	68.30	60	62.02	64.61	69.15	63	20.47	21.65	23.41	63	14.69	16.00	17.22
0 - 9	61	61.21	63.12	66.52	58	60.58	63.42	67.01	58	19.59	21.22	22.68	57	14.48	15.51	16.75
1 - 0	73	59.23	61.86	64.91	63	58.79	61.87	64.80	59	18.96	20.40	21.85	58	14.40	15.30	16.54
1 - 6	73	55.76	58.50	61.54	46	55.80	58.41	62.04	42	18.40	19.53	21.01	38	13.34	14.67	15.72
2 - 0	68	52.67	55.72	58.12	27	52.69	54.96	57.39	28	17.22	18.51	19.44	26	12.37	13.42	14.70
Erect																
2 - 0	58	53.58	56.73	59.15	53	53.89	56.09	58.94	57	17.86	19.11	20.33	55	12.51	13.70	14.77
2 - 6	71	51.87	54.75	57.17	69	52.16	54.22	56.50	70	17.46	18.62	19.51	70	11.95	13.06	14.17
3 - 0	71	49.75	52.65	55.47	67	50.46	52.42	55.05	71	16.80	18.04	19.19	71	11.87	12.68	13.79
3 - 6	68	47.89	50.93	53.33	67	49.47	51.25	53.48	68	16.58	17.47	18.69	68	11.82	12.66	13.60
4 - 0	78	46.68	49.31	51.79	77	47.85	49.98	52.33	77	15.96	17.21	18.01	76	11.46	12.37	13.20
4 - 6	91	45.26	47.76	50.56	87	46.90	48.84	51.46	90	15.56	16.72	17.59	91	11.15	12.02	12.95
5 - 0	90	44.19	46.59	48.98	88	46.08	48.12	50.74	90	15.10	16.45	17.39	90	10.90	11.86	12.95
5 - 6	90	43.16	45.52	47.70	90	45.26	47.57	49.82	90	15.03	16.12	17.26	90	10.79	11.70	12.58
6 - 0	95	42.14	44.28	46.83	95	44.64	46.90	49.34	95	14.87	15.93	16.95	95	10.58	11.46	12.45
6 - 6	95	40.99	43.36	45.78	95	43.97	46.48	48.69	95	14.62	15.78	16.85	95	10.45	11.44	12.27
7 - 0	90	40.40	42.34	44.65	90	43.63	45.99	48.88	90	14.52	15.64	16.53	90	10.29	11.30	12.17
7 - 6	88	39.48	41.38	43.83	92	43.30	45.72	48.53	92	14.53	15.61	16.64	92	10.08	11.23	12.17
8 - 0	85	38.96	40.75	42.96	90	43.17	45.64	48.83	90	14.31	15.40	16.65	90	10.06	11.21	12.20
8 - 6	85	38.30	40.32	42.42	88	42.64	45.38	48.86	90	14.28	15.41	16.53	90	10.17	11.07	12.18
9 - 0	79	37.51	39.35	41.84	80	42.78	45.12	49.10	80	14.48	15.21	16.72	80	10.05	11.02	12.30
9 - 6	72	36.62	38.85	41.06	75	42.68	45.15	49.03	75	14.32	15.31	16.39	75	10.23	11.03	12.07
10 - 0	72	36.12	38.36	40.54	76	42.62	44.78	48.93	76	14.19	15.18	16.55	75	10.11	10.98	12.38
10 - 6	73	35.63	37.69	39.74	73	41.92	44.61	49.54	73	14.01	15.20	16.78	73	9.92	10.89	12.29
11 - 0	67	35.11	36.80	39.12	70	41.47	44.37	49.70	70	14.11	15.23	16.62	70	9.90	10.96	12.30
11 - 6	67	33.89	35.97	37.98	67	41.73	44.11	48.07	67	14.00	14.99	16.31	67	10.00	11.00	12.46
12 - 0	67	33.34	35.22	37.54	69	41.15	43.79	48.56	69	14.00	15.07	16.50	69	9.70	10.84	12.22
12 - 6	63	33.21	34.61	36.80	64	41.18	43.51	47.32	64	13.96	14.98	16.14	64	9.63	10.79	11.90
13 - 0	66	32.52	34.03	36.14	67	40.77	43.10	46.72	68	13.97	15.04	16.13	68	9.64	10.62	12.10
13 - 6	47	32.28	34.05	35.80	51	40.84	43.01	47.72	53	13.97	15.09	16.32	53	9.64	10.76	12.08
14 - 0	53	32.07	33.45	35.22	61	40.88	43.15	48.33	61	14.19	15.31	16.67	61	9.42	10.69	11.95
14 - 6	41	32.05	33.34	35.15	42	40.83	43.17	46.90	42	14.41	15.22	16.27	42	9.56	10.78	12.26
15 - 0	50	31.44	32.89	34.64	52	40.12	43.07	47.64	51	14.07	15.00	16.30	52	9.51	10.69	12.08
15 - 6	23	31.44	33.25	34.89	22	40.25	42.99	46.65	22	13.80	14.67	16.50	22	9.68	10.76	11.98
16 - 0	55	31.62	33.04	34.51	57	40.47	43.83	48.27	57	14.15	15.29	16.92	57	9.74	10.78	12.49
16 - 6	12	32.19	33.15	34.79	5	-	-	-	5	-	-	-	5	-	-	-
17 - 0	47	31.39	32.97	34.46	44	39.82	43.73	48.12	43	13.91	15.24	17.02	44	9.79	10.72	12.09
17 - 6	18	32.30	32.91	35.05	2	-	-	-	2	-	-	-	2	-	-	-
18 - 0	35	31.25	32.78	34.65	25	40.90	43.81	49.46	25	14.37	15.42	17.05	25	10.06	10.89	12.75
19 - 0	35	31.61	32.90	34.33	19	40.99	44.79	49.75	19	14.56	15.60	17.01	19	10.12	11.31	13.21
20 - 0	35	31.59	33.05	34.66	15	40.36	44.63	48.66	15	13.78	15.61	16.99	15	10.37	10.81	12.70
21 - 0	33	31.76	33.06	34.69	12	41.48	43.92	48.64	12	14.75	15.59	16.96	12	10.39	11.11	12.12
22 - 0	32	31.67	32.98	34.40	10	41.97	45.31	49.49	10	14.78	16.15	17.15	11	10.82	11.17	12.23
23 - 0	30	31.93	33.13	34.80	11	42.44	45.38	47.08	11	14.98	16.07	17.28	10	10.79	11.17	11.93
24 - 0	25	31.78	32.99	34.17	9	-	-	-	9	-	-	-	9	-	-	-
25 - 0	25	31.94	33.43	34.46	8	-	-	-	8	-	-	-	8	-	-	-

ANTHROPOMETRY

TABLE E-29

Increments in Height and Weight
Based on Increments of Individuals

Age	Male											
	Height (cm.)						Weight (kg.)					
					Range						Range	
Yr. Mo. Yr. Mo.	N	Mean	S.D.	Median	Min.	Max.	N	Mean	S.D.	Median	Min.	Max.
Supine												
Birth to 0-1	51	4.16	1.123	4.07	1.60	6.70	52	0.75	0.261	0.73	0.15	1.43
0-1 to 0-2	55	3.93	1.237	4.07	0.80	6.60	55	1.08	0.291	1.07	0.57	1.92
0-2 to 0-3	55	3.17	1.040	3.22	1.10	5.80	55	0.88	0.231	0.88	0.38	1.48
0-3 to 0-4	54	2.48	0.987	2.36	0.10	4.30	54	0.69	0.209	0.71	0.19	1.02
0-4 to 0-5	52	2.40	0.921	2.37	0.40	4.70	52	0.64	0.202	0.64	0.11	1.10
0-5 to 0-6	53	1.93	0.872	1.82	0.20	4.30	53	0.60	0.233	0.59	0.09	1.02
0-6 to 0-9	53	4.44	0.960	4.38	2.00	6.50	54	1.21	0.350	1.23	0.12	1.97
0-9 to 1-0	55	3.87	1.144	3.92	1.30	6.60	56	0.87	0.348	0.85	0.17	1.71
1-0 to 1-6	67	6.30	1.214	6.21	3.50	9.10	74	1.34	0.410	1.34	0.34	2.49
1-6 to 2-0	70	5.50	1.112	5.64	2.70	7.60	91	1.09	0.446	1.06	-0.12	2.27
Erect												
2-0 to 2-6	58	4.57	0.636	4.50	2.90	6.10	95	1.11	0.384	1.09	0.12	2.27
2-6 to 3-0	64	4.30	0.734	4.28	2.70	5.60	97	1.01	0.351	0.98	0.23	2.11
3-0 to 3-6	61	3.70	0.740	3.68	1.90	5.20	94	1.00	0.416	1.01	-0.20	2.04
3-6 to 4-0	63	3.59	0.668	3.57	1.90	5.40	97	0.92	0.384	0.92	-0.23	1.81
4-0 to 4-6	78	3.54	0.815	3.54	0.90	5.60	95	1.12	0.486	1.09	0.17	2.61
4-6 to 5-0	97	3.35	0.763	3.25	1.70	5.50	96	1.05	0.556	1.05	-0.46	2.61
5-0 to 5-6	93	3.46	0.707	3.37	1.70	5.20	91	1.21	0.581	1.13	0.11	3.40
5-6 to 6-0	98	3.28	0.626	3.19	1.40	5.10	98	1.12	0.725	1.07	0.22	5.67
6-0 to 6-6	97	3.20	0.749	3.17	1.10	5.30	97	1.34	0.722	1.29	-0.20	4.42
6-6 to 7-0	97	3.03	0.705	3.02	0.50	5.10	96	1.24	0.714	1.25	-2.15	2.95
7-0 to 7-6	95	3.11	0.582	3.05	1.00	5.50	95	1.41	0.714	1.29	-0.85	3.29
7-6 to 8-0	94	2.85	0.521	2.88	1.30	4.00	94	1.54	0.990	1.42	-0.91	5.44
8-0 to 8-6	95	2.90	0.583	2.90	1.30	4.40	95	1.42	0.883	1.30	-1.25	4.08
8-6 to 9-0	97	2.79	0.646	2.85	0.90	4.20	97	1.69	0.972	1.56	-1.92	4.48
9-0 to 9-6	96	2.71	0.585	2.65	1.20	4.20	95	1.68	1.066	1.51	-1.13	5.44
9-6 to 10-0	93	2.56	0.703	2.55	1.10	4.30	93	1.87	0.961	1.89	-0.79	4.65
10-0 to 10-6	86	2.66	0.603	2.68	1.00	4.70	86	1.39	1.048	1.28	-0.79	4.09
10-6 to 11-0	82	2.48	0.671	2.42	1.00	5.00	81	1.98	1.181	1.87	-1.25	5.89
11-0 to 11-6	80	2.64	0.804	2.58	1.30	5.70	79	1.72	1.196	1.48	-0.68	4.77
11-6 to 12-0	72	2.86	0.939	2.70	1.40	5.80	71	2.19	1.274	2.08	-0.91	5.78
12-0 to 12-6	71	2.72	1.076	2.59	0.50	5.70	70	2.17	1.628	1.99	-1.70	7.03
12-6 to 13-0	71	3.13	1.072	2.82	1.30	6.30	70	2.58	1.774	2.40	-0.57	7.72
13-0 to 13-6	68	3.33	1.266	3.10	0.90	6.40	68	2.74	2.027	2.54	-4.77	8.28
13-6 to 14-0	64	3.74	1.466	3.66	0.60	7.20	64	3.27	1.701	3.08	-1.36	8.05
14-0 to 14-6	59	3.54	1.310	3.44	0.90	6.50	57	3.29	1.902	3.35	-1.70	7.48
14-6 to 15-0	58	3.27	1.425	3.40	0.20	6.20	58	3.12	1.743	2.98	-0.68	9.41
15-0 to 15-6	53	2.81	1.310	2.60	0.10	5.30	53	2.92	1.879	2.75	-0.68	8.16
15-6 to 16-0	51	2.25	1.412	2.21	-0.40	4.90	49	2.52	2.485	2.45	-5.33	12.59
16-0 to 16-6	41	1.98	1.335	1.60	0.30	5.20	41	2.23	2.713	2.22	-2.50	9.52
16-6 to 17-0	39	1.45	1.181	1.33	-0.80	5.10	39	2.33	2.475	2.09	-2.78	7.93
17-0 to 17-6	24	0.92	0.603	0.86	0.20	2.40	24	1.61	2.013	1.81	-3.85	4.53
17-6 to 18-0	15	0.78	0.876	0.61	-0.40	2.80	18	0.39	2.667	0.48	-4.30	5.66
18-0 to 19-0	23	0.86	0.938	0.80	-0.60	3.30	17	1.95	2.704	2.40	-3.63	6.01
19-0 to 20-0	24	0.28	0.632	0.12	-0.50	1.90	12	2.02	2.743	1.95	-2.49	7.37
20-0 to 21-0	28	0.12	0.374	0.18	-1.10	0.70	11	0.00	2.699	0.23	-4.54	4.54
21-0 to 22-0	30	0.02	0.427	-0.03	-1.20	1.00	7	-	-	-	-	-
22-0 to 23-0	26	-0.04	0.378	-0.02	-0.80	0.90	5	-	-	-	-	-
23-0 to 24-0	30	0.11	0.250	0.13	-0.50	0.60	3	-	-	-	-	-
24-0 to 25-0	22	0.01	0.260	0.05	-0.60	0.40	4	-	-	-	-	-

ANTHROPOMETRY

TABLE E-30

Increments in Height and Weight
Based on Increments of Individuals

Age	Female											
	Height (cm.)						Weight (kg.)					
					Range						Range	
Yr. Mo. Yr. Mo.	N	Mean	S.D.	Median	Min.	Max.	N	Mean	S.D.	Median	Min.	Max.
Supine												
Birth to 0-1	55	3.74	1.060	3.83	1.50	6.20	53	0.56	0.249	0.58	-0.11	1.04
0-1 to 0-2	57	3.36	1.068	3.37	0.40	6.30	58	0.87	0.261	0.83	0.45	1.47
0-2 to 0-3	56	3.04	1.054	2.98	0.50	6.00	56	0.74	0.237	0.75	0.23	1.42
0-3 to 0-4	53	2.29	0.977	2.22	0.50	4.00	54	0.69	0.220	0.69	0.11	1.24
0-4 to 0-5	57	2.29	1.007	2.28	0.50	4.30	57	0.60	0.235	0.56	0.22	1.16
0-5 to 0-6	53	1.90	1.002	1.67	0.10	4.40	53	0.57	0.231	0.57	0.17	1.14
0-6 to 0-9	48	4.36	1.143	4.53	0.50	6.20	48	1.21	0.331	1.21	0.49	1.95
0-9 to 1-0	53	3.91	1.052	3.79	1.70	6.50	56	0.96	0.394	0.93	0.11	2.03
1-0 to 1-6	64	6.47	1.269	6.51	3.70	9.00	79	1.28	0.473	1.25	0.21	2.83
1-6 to 2-0	60	5.78	1.087	5.89	2.90	8.40	88	1.17	0.385	1.18	0.23	1.94
Erect												
2-0 to 2-6	62	4.60	0.853	4.51	2.90	6.60	95	1.04	0.362	0.97	0.11	1.93
2-6 to 3-0	71	4.17	0.835	4.14	2.50	7.20	95	1.01	0.384	1.00	0.22	2.00
3-0 to 3-6	73	3.81	0.737	3.82	2.00	5.30	94	1.04	0.390	0.99	0.06	2.49
3-6 to 4-0	72	3.76	0.753	3.73	2.40	6.20	94	1.06	0.453	1.04	-0.23	2.72
4-0 to 4-6	80	3.47	0.752	3.44	1.00	5.20	94	1.04	0.484	1.02	-0.14	2.50
4-6 to 5-0	93	3.49	0.703	3.45	1.20	5.10	92	1.11	0.417	1.07	0.18	2.38
5-0 to 5-6	94	3.38	0.715	3.38	1.50	5.10	93	1.17	0.611	1.05	0.11	3.55
5-6 to 6-0	94	3.24	0.617	3.25	1.70	6.10	94	1.13	0.611	1.04	-0.12	2.95
6-0 to 6-6	97	3.10	0.753	3.10	0.80	5.90	97	1.23	0.645	1.17	-1.48	2.95
6-6 to 7-0	96	2.98	0.685	3.00	1.00	4.40	96	1.36	0.863	1.26	-0.11	6.47
7-0 to 7-6	95	3.05	0.577	3.06	1.90	4.50	95	1.46	0.726	1.38	-0.23	3.63
7-6 to 8-0	92	2.92	0.589	2.88	1.70	4.70	91	1.47	0.929	1.39	-1.02	4.42
8-0 to 8-6	91	2.78	0.664	2.73	1.50	4.50	89	1.67	0.872	1.64	-0.22	4.19
8-6 to 9-0	87	2.91	0.731	2.86	1.20	5.10	86	1.60	1.035	1.54	-0.57	6.47
9-0 to 9-6	77	2.65	0.947	2.63	0.10	5.60	76	1.63	1.043	1.50	-0.45	4.19
9-6 to 10-0	70	2.96	0.834	2.77	1.10	5.40	70	1.77	1.309	1.55	-1.93	5.55
10-0 to 10-6	71	2.79	0.863	2.66	0.70	5.80	70	1.84	1.309	1.64	-1.82	5.56
10-6 to 11-0	69	3.01	0.841	2.83	1.20	5.30	69	1.99	1.290	1.88	-1.93	5.55
11-0 to 11-6	64	3.32	1.088	3.11	1.00	5.60	64	2.18	1.597	2.14	-1.81	8.27
11-6 to 12-0	62	3.30	1.010	3.30	1.10	6.80	61	2.28	1.414	2.14	-1.13	5.90
12-0 to 12-6	66	3.12	1.123	3.16	0.30	5.50	66	2.81	1.516	2.74	-1.25	6.46
12-6 to 13-0	67	2.95	1.171	2.79	0.80	5.40	66	2.18	1.484	2.00	-0.91	4.99
13-0 to 13-6	61	2.67	1.377	2.57	-0.30	5.90	59	2.37	1.378	2.44	-0.91	5.33
13-6 to 14-0	55	2.05	1.274	2.12	-0.90	4.20	54	2.30	1.690	2.45	-2.84	5.67
14-0 to 14-6	41	1.63	0.995	1.55	-0.20	4.10	42	1.66	1.823	1.85	-1.93	5.10
14-6 to 15-0	37	1.00	0.751	0.97	-0.90	2.90	37	1.21	1.043	1.27	-1.59	2.95
15-0 to 15-6	20	0.79	0.822	0.75	-0.30	2.70	20	1.21	1.435	0.98	-1.81	3.96
15-6 to 16-0	22	0.62	0.686	0.60	-0.70	1.90	18	0.77	1.284	1.02	-1.93	2.50
16-0 to 16-6	12	0.11	0.595	0.14	-1.00	0.90	7	-	-	-	-	-
16-6 to 17-0	11	0.23	0.506	0.07	-0.40	1.30	5	-	-	-	-	-
17-0 to 17-6	12	-0.04	0.202	-0.07	-0.40	0.30	1	-	-	-	-	-
17-6 to 18-0	12	-0.12	0.372	-0.10	-1.10	0.20	2	-	-	-	-	-
18-0 to 19-0	28	0.17	0.621	0.09	-1.10	2.00	15	0.44	2.673	0.80	-4.31	3.86
19-0 to 20-0	24	0.00	0.446	-0.05	-1.00	0.90	10	-0.66	2.116	-0.59	-4.88	2.27
20-0 to 21-0	28	0.14	0.466	0.05	-0.40	1.70	6	-	-	-	-	-
21-0 to 22-0	24	-0.15	0.374	-0.11	-1.30	0.40	4	-	-	-	-	-
22-0 to 23-0	24	-0.06	0.391	-0.08	-0.90	0.60	5	-	-	-	-	-
23-0 to 24-0	20	-0.04	0.303	-0.04	-0.90	0.60	5	-	-	-	-	-
24-0 to 25-0	19	0.18	0.306	0.23	-0.20	1.10	4	-	-	-	-	-

ANTHROPOMETRY

TABLE E-31

Skinfold Thickness Measurements in Millimeters

	Male								Female							
	Triceps				Subscapular				Triceps				Subscapular			
		Percentiles				Percentiles				Percentiles				Percentiles		
Yr. Mo.	N	10th	50th	90th	N	10th	50th	90th	N	10th	50th	90th	N	10th	50th	90th
4 - 0	21	6.0	8.8	10.8	21	3.1	4.2	6.2	16	6.6	9.2	11.8	16	3.8	4.8	5.7
4 - 6	23	5.3	8.0	11.8	23	3.2	4.3	6.6	21	8.0	9.8	12.9	21	4.0	5.0	6.7
5 - 0	22	5.4	8.3	10.4	22	2.9	4.4	5.8	21	7.7	9.5	12.2	21	3.7	4.5	5.9
5 - 6	23	5.6	8.6	10.3	23	3.6	4.4	5.6	20	8.2	10.5	13.2	20	3.7	4.9	7.3
6 - 0	22	6.0	7.8	10.8	22	3.4	4.1	5.1	24	6.8	9.7	13.4	24	3.7	4.6	6.9
6 - 6	24	5.4	8.2	12.3	24	3.4	4.2	5.9	26	7.6	9.5	13.5	26	3.4	4.8	6.5
7 - 0	23	5.9	8.1	12.1	23	3.4	4.4	5.7	18	7.5	10.3	17.0	19	3.9	4.8	8.1
7 - 6	22	4.8	7.8	12.3	22	3.4	4.6	6.2	24	7.7	10.5	15.3	24	3.9	5.3	8.8
8 - 0	22	5.3	8.5	11.9	22	3.3	4.5	6.2	24	7.0	11.3	16.2	24	4.1	6.3	11.2
8 - 6	20	4.6	8.0	13.0	20	3.2	4.8	6.0	26	6.1	12.0	19.4	26	4.1	5.0	12.6
9 - 0	22	4.9	9.5	16.1	22	3.3	5.1	7.0	26	5.9	10.2	17.0	26	4.1	5.5	10.8
9 - 6	22	4.8	9.8	15.0	22	3.7	5.3	7.2	23	6.6	10.6	15.4	23	4.0	5.1	11.8
10 - 0	21	4.9	11.5	16.6	21	4.1	5.6	8.8	23	6.5	10.4	18.4	23	4.2	5.2	12.6
10 - 6	20	5.0	9.0	17.5	20	3.4	5.2	12.6	23	6.1	13.4	16.4	23	4.2	6.0	16.1
11 - 0	19	5.7	10.1	17.8	19	4.3	5.7	11.5	24	8.4	12.2	17.9	24	4.6	6.3	14.2
11 - 6	21	5.0	10.6	19.4	21	3.8	5.2	11.2	21	6.1	10.6	17.2	21	4.9	6.1	11.2
12 - 0	21	4.3	10.8	17.4	21	4.2	5.2	15.0	25	6.1	11.8	21.4	25	4.6	7.0	16.8
12 - 6	21	5.3	9.0	17.3	21	4.2	6.0	9.7	19	7.0	12.9	20.4	19	4.9	7.1	17.2
13 - 0	22	4.9	8.0	19.4	22	4.0	5.7	13.3	22	6.2	10.7	21.6	22	5.2	6.9	16.0
13 - 6	21	4.3	8.0	16.4	21	3.9	5.7	19.8	14	6.8	11.7	17.2	14	4.9	6.4	14.0
14 - 0	17	5.0	8.2	17.3	17	4.4	6.2	20.6	19	7.3	13.3	18.3	19	5.4	7.5	13.5
14 - 6	20	3.4	5.2	19.2	20	4.2	6.0	15.2	14	8.9	10.0	17.8	14	6.1	7.5	13.4
15 - 0	14	3.5	5.4	15.4	14	4.9	6.6	16.0	20	7.8	12.1	20.4	20	5.8	7.8	17.0
15 - 6	13	4.6	6.6	13.8	13	5.5	6.7	20.0	8	-	-	-	8	-	-	-
16 - 0	13	3.6	6.7	13.2	13	4.7	7.4	12.8	21	7.7	13.9	22.7	21	6.3	8.7	15.2
16 - 6	15	4.2	5.6	10.0	15	5.4	6.6	11.1	1	-	-	-	1	-	-	-
17 - 0	10	3.8	4.6	10.2	10	6.1	6.7	8.0	18	7.9	15.3	20.6	18	6.2	9.8	22.3
18 - 0	10	4.3	7.7	13.4	10	6.3	7.6	14.8	13	6.4	14.9	21.9	13	6.7	11.3	18.6

Section F

MEASUREMENTS FROM ROENTGENOGRAMS
HEART SIZE
LONG BONE LENGTHS
BONE, MUSCLE AND FAT WIDTHS
SKELETAL MATURATION

MARION M. MARESH

MEASUREMENTS FROM ROENTGENOGRAMS

HEART SIZE

Material

TELEROENTGENOGRAMS of the chest were taken at frequent intervals on all subjects enrolled in the Child Research Council since the beginning of the study with birth dates as early as 1915 for two subjects and as late as 1967 for one baby. Roentgenograms taken before 1932 were on inflammable film and because they were such a potential fire hazard, the decision to destroy them was made in the mid-1930's. Copies were made of several dozen of the infancy films of many of the subjects but copying techniques were not very satisfactory and the effort was abandoned after several weeks. Thus for subjects born between 1915 and 1932, the roentgenograms of the chest now in the files may begin at varying ages through childhood and adolescence. The few successful copies were measured and included in the data. These are the only measurements from roentgenograms that antedate 1932. From over 10,000 roentgenograms of the chest of 313 subjects, the transverse diameter of the heart and the internal diameter of the chest have been measured and recorded together with age, height (or length) and weight of each subject on the day the roentgenogram was taken. The transverse diameter of the heart (TD) was measured as the sum of the greatest horizontal distance from the midline of the thorax to the right cardiac margin and the greatest horizontal distance from the midline to the left cardiac margin. Internal diameter of the chest (ID) was measured horizontally from the right to the left pleural surfaces through the dome of the right side of the diaphragm and parallel to the transverse diameter of the heart. The conditions under which height (or length) and weight were taken are described in the section on Anthropometry.

The measurement technique was described in detail in 1938(1) and again in 1948(2). All measurements were made and checked by M. Maresh. If the second measurement did not agree with the first, a third measurement was made and very occasionally a fourth until two measurements agreed. Usually the recorded measurement was the original one.

Supine posteroanterior roentgenograms were taken at 5 foot focal film distance during infancy and early childhood to about four years of age in most of the subjects born before 1950. Over 2500 roentgenograms of 128 boys and 137 girls are in this block of data. Radiographic technique was described in the 1938(1) publication cited above. Attempts were always made to time the radiographic exposure to the inspiratory phase of respiration. This varied from mid-respiration to the full, deep breath that frequently precedes a loud cry of protest from a baby.

Posteroanterior roentgenograms of the chest were taken in the erect position at 7½ foot focal film distance after 4 years of age in the 1930's and 1940's. Radiographic technique was described in the 1948(2) publication. In the 1950's, erect films were taken at progressively earlier ages as it became apparent that most children were cooperative with this procedure as early as two years of age or occasionally even earlier. Measurements from 3184 erect roentgenograms of 71 boys and 57 girls were reported in the 1948(2) publication cited above. These data are coded separately on the magnetic tapes but are included with the data from 4724 additional roentgenograms of these and other subjects numbering 135 boys and 137 girls in the block of data from roentgenograms taken in the erect position in the statistical summaries in this volume. The technical error (see Introduction for details of the equation) between the measurements published in 1948 and their remeasurement in 1967 was calculated for 100 sets of values recorded midway in the measurement time interval. This value was 0.017 cm for TD and 0.023 cm for ID. For another sample of 100 sets of measurements of the post-1948 roentgenograms, the original and repeat measurements were recorded independently. The technical error calculated from them was 0.012 cm for TD and 0.022 cm for ID. Since the limits of measurement were 0.05 cm for TD and 0.1 cm for ID, the technical errors seemed to warrant the recording of single values rather than the average of two measurements.

Statistical Summaries, Tables and Graphs

The statistical summary program has been described in the Introduction. Age limits of ± 15 days from the stated age were used at 1, 2, and 3 months of age, ± 45 days for the quarter-year ages from 6 months through 19 years, ± 91 days for the half-year ages from 19 through 21 years and ±182 days for the yearly ages from 21 years on. After one year of age the tables F-1, F-2 and F-3 do not include data for the 3 and 9-month intervals for the measurements from either the supine or erect roentgenograms. From 15 through 21 years, only the data for the birthday examination are given. From 22 years through 38 years, the data for the even-numbered birthday examinations (22, 24, 26, etc.) are included in the tables. No data are included after 38 years since the N for each age interval was less than 10. The data not included in the tables are available. In none of the summaries for an age interval do data appear for a given subject more than once. Thus an N of 18 will include measurements from 18 subjects of that sex whose ages at that examination were within the specified limits. Not included in the tables are the summary data for the heights and weights of these subjects. Since all of them are included in the summary data from the anthropometric measurements in Section E, those tables may be considered representative of this subgroup.

Figure F-1 presents the mean data from Tables F-1 and F-3. Means for TD are significantly greater in males than in females (Z test, $P < 0.005$) in both the supine and erect data. After adolescence the difference between the means becomes progressively greater and the average of the yearly mean TD values for males from 21 through 38 years is 16 percent greater than the average for females from 21 through 37 years.

In Figure F-1 when the mean values for the TD/ID ratios are compared for males and females, no significant sex difference is found for the majority of the age intervals. From 6½ through 12 years, the ratios for females were consistently larger than for the males; in 5 of the 12 age intervals the differences between the means were statistically significant at or below the 0.05 level of confidence. For the younger and older age groups few determinations were significantly larger for either sex and the data were essentially linear after 14 years of age with mean values near 0.40.

LONG BONES

A. Measured Lengths

Material

When this roentgenographic study of the growth in length of the six major long bones was begun in 1935, the available information about segmental linear growth had been derived from anthropometric measurements. The comparison of anthropometric measurements with bone lengths measured from roentgenograms in a report by M. Maresh and J. Deming(3) on a group of newborn infants at Crittenton Home presented evidence that bone lengths could be measured with greater accuracy from roentgenograms than was possible using external measurements and anthropometric techniques. In that same year (1935) roentgenographic studies of the long bones of the left arm and leg on most of the Child Research Council subjects who were preadolescent were started. Many of these early films were eliminated from the data as the radiographic technique was standardized.

In 1967 there were seriatim roentgenograms from 123 male and 121 female subjects giving 5980 sets of measurements. All subjects born since 1940 had their initial roentgenograms in the first six months of life. Earlier-born subjects had their initial films at from 1 to 11½ years. The schedule of roentgen examinations since 1941 has been at 2, 4 and 6 months of age and the birthday and half-year examinations thereafter until long bone growth was judged to be complete on the roentgenograms. This was as early as 14 or 15 years for some of the girls and as late as 19 or 20 for some of the boys. Obviously the late-born subjects were still infants when the study was terminated and had had less than 5 sets of measurements. Twenty-six of the older subjects had 40 or more sets of measurements. The mean number of measurements per subject was 24.5 and on two-thirds of the subjects there were between 15 and 40 sets of measurements for each subject. In the spring of 1941, in an effort to conserve x-ray film, it was decided to take roentgenograms of the forearm and thigh only (the slowest growing and the most rapidly growing of the long bones) on subjects over 12 years of age. By the fall of 1943 the film shortage had eased and the full long bone roentgenograms were reinstituted on these subjects. This time interval was responsible for gaps in the humerus, tibia and fibula lengths on ten of the older boys and girls (born before 1931) and is the reason for 210 of the 229 blanks in the long bone data on the tapes.

Technique

The radiographic technique and method of measuring bone lengths were described in detail in 1943(4) and in 1955(5). All measurements were made and checked by the same person, M. Maresh, until 1957. After 1957 either C. Hansman or M. Maresh did the measuring and the checking of each measurement. If the second measurement agreed within 0.05 cm, the original measurement was used. If there was 0.1 cm difference in the two measurements, a third and, very occasionally, a fourth measurement was made until two values agreed.

Cassette size was appropriate to the size of the subject. Since unossified epiphyses could not be included in the length measurements of infants and young children, two sets of data are presented in Tables F-4 through F-9. From 2 months through 12 years, the length was measured parallel to the long axis of the bone from the most proximal edge to the most distal edge of the diaphysis. From 10 years through adolescence, length measurements were from the most proximal edge of the epiphysis at one end of the bone to the most distal edge of the epiphysis at the opposite end of the bone, care being taken to keep the ruler parallel to the long axis of the bone. From 10 through 12 years there are therefore two sets of measurements, (1) diaphysis and

(2) diaphysis and epiphyses including the cartilaginous portion of the epiphyseal plate. No correction has been made for magnification or distortion factors although these have been calculated from dried bone specimens as magnification of 1 to 1.5 percent with the bone in contact with the cassette and as much as 2 to 3 percent with the bone in a simulated body position with respect to the cassette surface. The measurements are not to be considered as anatomical lengths but the changes in length from age to age are probably consistent with the rate of growth.

Statistical Summaries, Tables and Graphs

Tables F-4 through F-9 present the N for each age interval, mean, standard deviation, 10th, 50th and 90th percentile values for both males and females for diaphyseal lengths from two months through 12 years and for the lengths including the epiphyses from 10 years through 18 years in the males and through 17 years in females. The left half of Figure F-2 shows the median values for the humerus, radius, femur and tibia lengths for males and females. The values for the ulna and fibula were omitted from the graph to avoid duplication in these segments. Since these are graphed on a common vertical scale, the differential growth rates of the bones in the arm and leg are obvious. Also obvious is the greater length of all bones for the males after adolescence (Z test, $P<0.001$). From two months through early adolescence there is no statistically significant sex difference between the mean values for the humerus, femur or tibia. For the radius (and ulna) the lengths for males are consistently larger than for females from infancy (Z test, $P<0.01$) except for the 11 to 13 year period when the earlier adolescence of the females negates the sex difference so apparent at other ages. The longer forearm bones in the male than in the female are the most obvious distinguishing segmental characteristic between the sexes prior to adolescence. As Deming and Washburn(6) demonstrated in body length measurements, there is some difference in the slope of the growth curves for the long bones during infancy; the curves for girls and boys reach the same asymptote with different acceleration constants.

B. Lengths Relative to Height

Since it is obvious that the longest bone lengths are usually those of the tallest subjects, any estimate of segmental proportions should be independent of height. "Relative bone length" is such an expression since each bone length is presented as a percent of height, and the "long-legged" individual is not necessarily above average height(7).

Material

The anthropometric measurements of height (or length of the infants) are part of the recorded data of each subject on the day of the roentgen examination. Therefore the material for the relative bone lengths is from the same subject population described in the preceding section.

Statistical Summaries, Tables and Graphs

Tables F-10 through F-15 present the selections from the statistical summary program for the relative bone lengths of each of the 6 major long bones of the extremities that correspond with the selections for the measured bone lengths for each age interval for males and females. The data are again in two sections: (1) the relative bone lengths when using the diaphyseal lengths from two months through 12 years as the dividend in the computation and (2) the relative length from 10 years through adolescence using the length including the ossified epiphyses as the dividend.

The right half of Figure F-2 shows the median values for the relative lengths of the humerus, radius, femur and tibia for males and for females in graphic form. Before adolescence only the forearm bones have mean values that are significantly different in males and females. The relatively longer radius in the males (Z test, $P<0.01$) is evidence that the longer measured bone length in the males is independent of any possible difference in height between males and females. After adolescence the relative bone lengths of all bones are much greater in the males (Z test, $P < 0.005$).

An interesting observation is the decrease in relative lengths of the femur, tibia and fibula after adolescence, especially in the female. In the data for the individual subjects, this decrease is more obvious and is also evident in the relative length of the arm bones for the earlier maturing subjects. The reason for this decrease is that after long bone growth ceases, further increase in height due to growth of the spine results in a lowering of the relative bone lengths.

BONE, MUSCLE AND FAT MEASUREMENTS

Interest in body composition in recent years has led to many different approaches in investigations. In 1940 Stuart and his co-workers(8) presented a method for studying the growth of bone, muscle and overlying subcutaneous tissue from roentgenograms of the leg in children. Since then other roentgenographic studies have added to the evaluation of changes in body composition in the growing child and the adult.

Material

The roentgenograms of the arm and leg which were made for the measurement of long bone lengths (preceding section) were the source material for the measurement of tissue widths in this study. From these films, 3239 sets of bone, muscle and fat widths were measured on 140 subjects, 75 male and 65 female. Of the 126 subjects who had their initial roentgenograms of the extremities in the first year of life, 114 had these first roentgenograms at 2 months of age. These were the subjects born since 1940 and a few of the last-born were still infants when the study was terminated. The other 14 subjects were older (2½ to 11½ years) when the long bone roentgenograms were started; thirteen were male and they are the fathers or uncles of one to four of the younger subjects.

Technique

Roentgenographic technique was described in the publications(4,5) cited previously. The levels of tissue measurement and method of measuring these shadows have been described(9,10,11).

The seventeen measurements – total width as well as bone, muscle and fat widths at the maximum width of the forearm, mid-length level of the femur and maximum calf width, two additional fat widths at the level of the deltoid insertion on the arm and at the maximum hip bulge, mid-length bone widths of the humerus, radius and tibia – together with height, weight and age in days on the day of the roentgen examination, made up the data for each subject at each age interval. Bone widths and the fat measurements at the deltoid insertion and the maximum hip bulge were direct caliper measurements. For the muscle measurements, the bone width was subtracted from the measured bone and muscle width. For the other fat measurements, the combined bone and muscle width was subtracted from total widths measured at the forearm, thigh and calf. Tissue measurements were recorded to the nearest 0.1 mm on the Vernier scale of the calipers. Each measurement was made and checked by M. Maresh. Although each measurement was checked, only one value was recorded since, as with measurements from the roentgenograms of the chest, the technical error (see Introduction) between 343 pairs of duplicate measurements recorded independently ranged from 0.042 mm to 0.068 mm. If the check measurement was within 0.1 mm of the original measurement, the first measurement was the recorded value. If the second measurement differed more than 0.1 mm, a third or very occasionally a fourth measurement was made until two agreed. There were 123 blanks in the original data of 3239 sets with 20 values in each set. Of these 121 were in the data of 5 of the 13 older males and they were largely due to absence of films for these segments (for details see preceding section of the documentation for the long bone data).

Statistical Summaries, Tables and Graphs

In selecting data from the statistical summary sheets for the

Tables F-16 through F-26, the means and standard deviations were omitted because of the skewed nature of some of the distributions, especially for the fat measurements. For the different levels of tissue measurements and for combinations of tissue measurements in the tables, only the 10th, 50th and 90th percentiles are presented for each sex at each age interval. Full data for all measurements including means, standard deviations, maximum and minimum values and 25th and 75th percentiles are available. The greater fat width measurements for females are evident at all ages in these percentiles. In the full data, maximum values in fat widths for males were at essentially the same level as the females, sometimes even greater than the females' maximums until after adolescence, but minimum values for males were always lower than the minimums for females. Graphed to the same scale in Figure F-3 are the median values for bone, muscle and fat widths at the forearm, thigh and calf and the medians for fat width at the maximum hip bulge for males and females. Of interest are the sex difference in median values for muscle widths in the forearm after six years of age which is not present in the muscle widths at the calf or thigh, and the progressively larger female median values for fat widths after adolescence.

SKELETAL MATURATION

Material

As a part of the study of skeletal growth, estimates of the level of skeletal maturation were made from roentgenograms of the left hand and wrist.

Since 1947 roentgenograms of the hand and wrist were taken at the birthday and half-year examinations as part of the roentgen study of the long bones. Before that date hand films were taken at irregular and less frequent intervals. A total of 3449 roentgenograms taken between the ages of 1 and 20 years were available for study. These were from 205 subjects, 100 female and 105 male. The number of roentgenograms for each subject ranged from 1 to 36. There were 28 females and 42 males who had had less than 10 roentgenograms of the hand; the other 135 subjects had an average of 23.2 roentgenograms each.

Assessment of Skeletal Age

The Greulich-Pyle Atlas(12) was the standard of reference used in the evaluation of skeletal age. In making these estimates one can elect to use an arithmetic average of the assigned skeletal age of each individual center of ossification of the hand and wrist or one can decide on a skeletal age that seems to best represent the maturational level after a careful overall inspection of the hand and wrist. For a group of 32 adolescent boys and girls, the skeletal ages were determined by both methods. The technical error calculated from the differences between the two sets of measurements was 0.25 years.

C. Hansman and M. Maresh have used the overall inspection method of assessing skeletal age in the collection of these data. In making the assessments, it was accepted that individual differences in maturational sequences and the psychological or even the physiological state of the assessor at a given time may result in assessments that vary by as much as 3 or 4 months from the skeletal ages by the same or different equally trained assessors on different days or different times of the same day. In the preparation for a publication by Hansman and Maresh in 1961(13) skeletal ages were assessed independently by both authors from 1710 roentgenograms. These were seriatim roentgenograms of the hand and wrist of 71 girls (928) and 61 boys (782). Differences between the two assessments of 3 months or less were found in 75.5 percent of the girls and 80.9 percent of the boys. Differences of 6 months or less were found in 90.0 percent of the girls and 93.7 percent of the boys. There was no consistent tendency toward higher or lower levels for either assessor and the assigned skeletal ages agreed on over half the films. Using the same test for technical error as before, a value of less than 3 months was found.

When the second edition of the Greulich-Pyle Atlas(14) was published in 1959, duplicate skeletal age assessments were done independently by Hansman and Maresh for all the roentgenograms of 6 boys and 6 girls, each using both editions of the Atlas. The analysis of variance for the four variables [(1) 1950 Atlas, Hansman; (2) 1959 Atlas, Hansman; (3) 1950 Atlas, Maresh and (4) 1959 Atlas, Maresh] showed that the change in standards did not significantly affect the assessments.

It is not to be assumed that the stated skeletal ages for individual data or in the summary statistics are "true" skeletal ages. They do represent the best approximation to an exact skeletal age that could be determined by Hansman and Maresh. It is their opinion that when a skeletal age is assigned to a given roentgenogram of the hand and wrist, a potential error of plus or minus 3 months may be assumed to be present.

Statistical Summaries, Tables and Graphs

The age limits for each interval were set at ± 15 days from the stated age. Those subjects who were born prematurely were omitted from the data. Table F-27 presents the number of subjects included in each half-year age interval, the median skeletal age and the range in skeletal ages at each age for males (1 through 18 years) and females (1 through 17 years). The 10th, 25th, 75th and 90th percentiles, the means and standard deviations as well as a more detailed description of the tests for accuracy of the data are also available.

Figure F-4 illustrates the median, the minimum and the maximum skeletal ages at each indicated chronological age for boys and for girls compared to a diagonal line representing a theoretical norm on which skeletal age is equal to chronological age. Only in girls from 1 to 2½ years and in boys at one year of age do the medians for skeletal age equal or exceed the chronological age prior to adolescence. At all other ages the median values are less than the chronological age, as far below the chronological age as 11 months in girls at 9½ years. In late adolescence the medians for skeletal age are closer to chronological age for the girls than for boys. The range for skeletal ages for both sexes is narrowest in early childhood and becomes increasingly wider during the childhood years. In girls from 10 through 13 years the difference between the highest and lowest skeletal ages was between 5 and 6 years, e.g., at 11 years the maximum skeletal age was 13 years 9 months and the minimum was 7 years 10 months.

REFERENCES

1. Maresh, M.M., and Washburn, A.H.: Size of the heart in healthy children. Amer J Dis Child, 56:33, 1938.
2. Maresh, M.M.: Growth of the heart related to bodily growth during childhood and adolescence. Pediatrics, 2:382, 1948.
3. Maresh, M.M., and Deming, J.: The growth of the long bones in 80 infants. Child Develop, 10:91, 1939.
4. Maresh, M.M.: Growth of major long bones in healthy children. Amer J Dis Child, 66:227, 1943.
5. Maresh, M.M.: Linear growth of long bones of extremities from infancy through adolescence. Amer J Dis Child, 89:725, 1955.
6. Deming, J., and Washburn, A.H.: Application of the Jenss curve to the observed pattern of growth during the first eight years of life in forty boys and forty girls. Hum Biol, 35:484, 1963.
7. Maresh, M.M.: Linear body proportions. Amer J Dis Child, 98:27, 1959.
8. Stuart, H.C.; Hill, P., and Shaw, C.: The growth of bone, muscle and overlying tissue as revealed by studies of roentgenograms of the leg area. Monogr Soc Res Child Develop, 1940, vol. V, no. 3.
9. Maresh, M.M.: Bone, muscle and fat measurements. Longitudinal measurements of the bone, muscle and fat widths from roentgenograms of the extremities during the first six years of life. Pediatrics, 28:971, 1961.
10. Maresh, M.M.: Tissue changes in the individual during growth from x-rays of the extremities. Ann NY Acad Sci, 110:465, 1963.
11. Maresh, M.M.: Changes in tissue widths during growth. Amer J Dis Child, 111:142, 1966.
12. Greulich, W.W., and Pyle, S.I.: Radiographic Atlas of Skeletal Development of the Hand and Wrist. Stanford, Calif., Stanford Univ. Press, 1950.
13. Hansman, C.F., and Maresh, M.M.: A longitudinal study of skeletal maturation. Amer J Dis Child, 101:305, 1961.
14. Greulich, W.W., and Pyle, S.I.: Radiographic Atlas of Skeletal Development of the Hand and Wrist, 2nd ed. Stanford, Calif., Stanford Univ. Press, 1959.

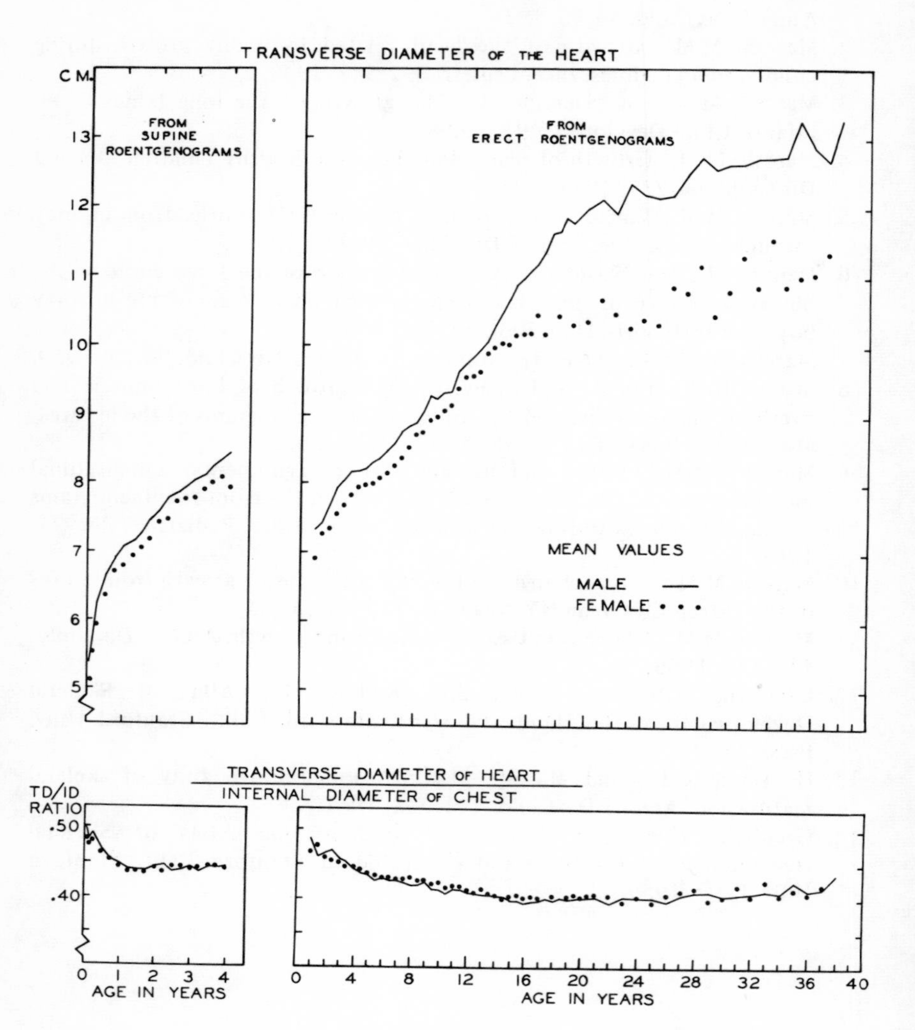

TRANSVERSE DIAMETER OF THE HEART
CM.
FROM SUPINE ROENTGENOGRAMS
FROM ERECT ROENTGENOGRAMS
13
12
11
10
9
8
7
6
5
MEAN VALUES
MALE
FEMALE
TRANSVERSE DIAMETER OF HEART
INTERNAL DIAMETER OF CHEST
TD/ID RATIO
.50
.40
0 1 2 3 4
AGE IN YEARS
0 4 8 12 16 20 24 28 32 36 40
AGE IN YEARS

FIG. F-1

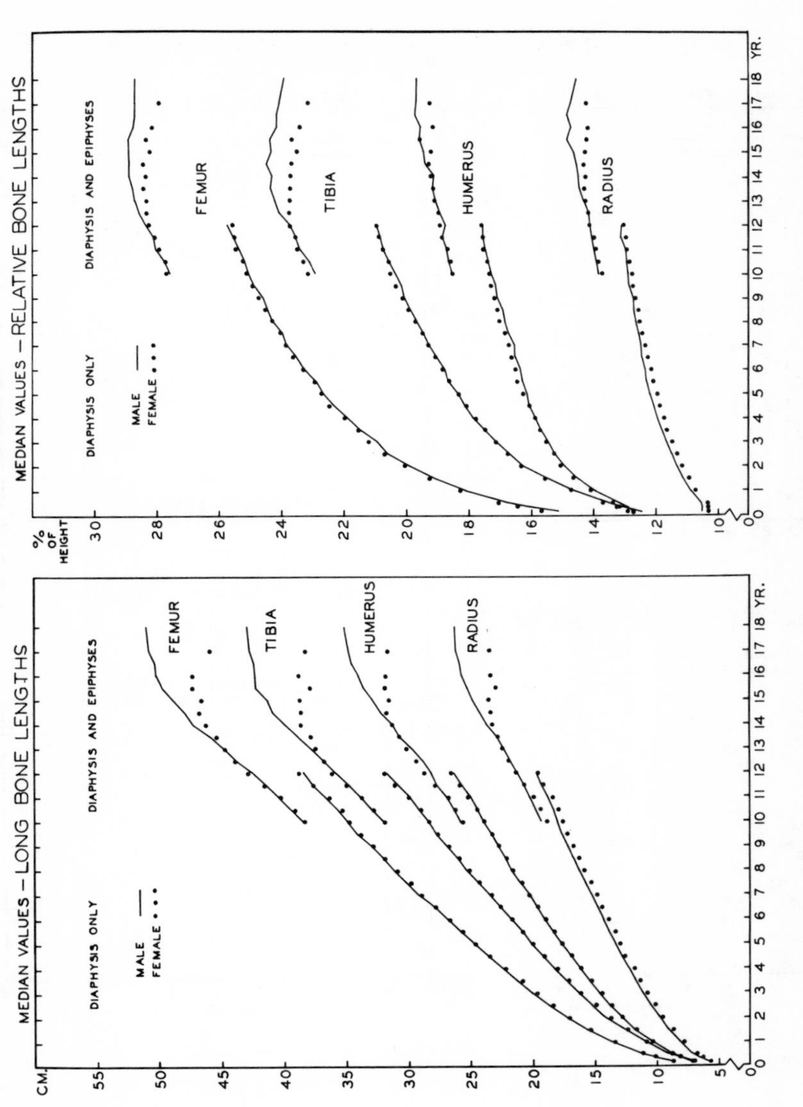
MEDIAN VALUES – LONG BONE LENGTHS
CM.
55
50
45
40
35
30
25
20
15
10
5
0
DIAPHYSIS ONLY
DIAPHYSIS AND EPIPHYSES
MALE
FEMALE
FEMUR
TIBIA
HUMERUS
RADIUS
0 1 2 3 4 5 6 7 8 9 10 11 12 13 14 15 16 17 18 YR.
MEDIAN VALUES – RELATIVE BONE LENGTHS
% OF HEIGHT
30
28
26
24
22
20
18
16
14
12
10
0
DIAPHYSIS ONLY
DIAPHYSIS AND EPIPHYSES
MALE
FEMALE
FEMUR
TIBIA
HUMERUS
RADIUS
0 1 2 3 4 5 6 7 8 9 10 11 12 13 14 15 16 17 18 YR.

FIG. F-2

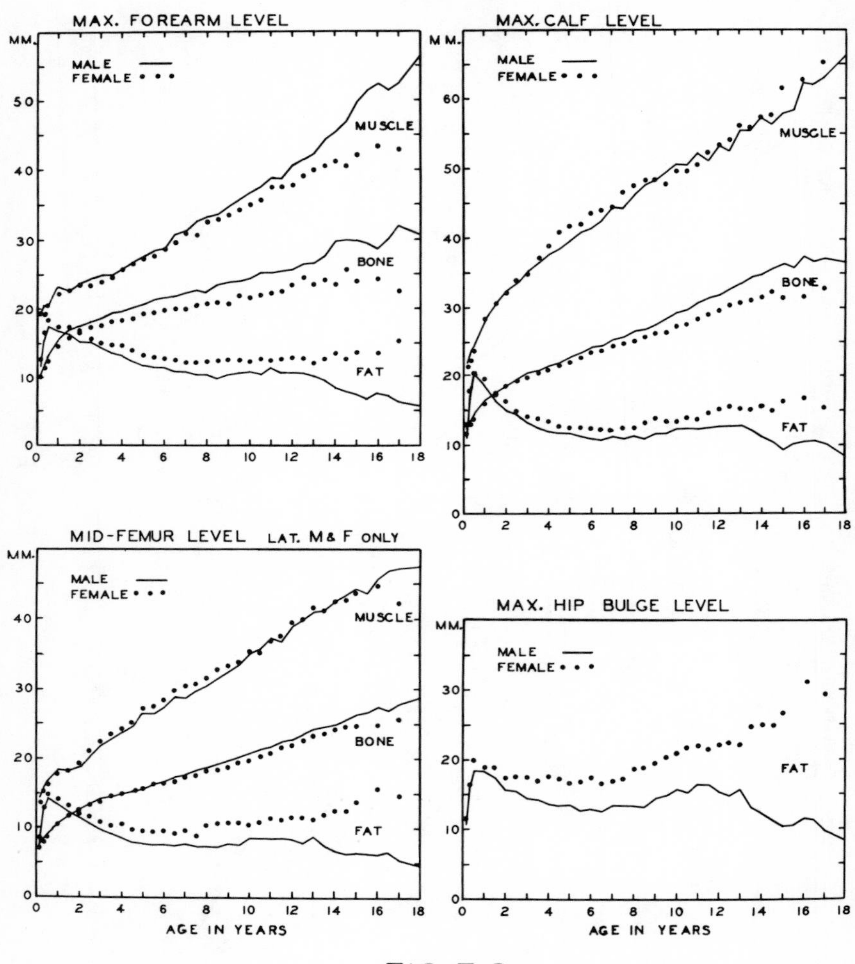
TISSUE WIDTHS FROM ROENTGENOGRAMS
MEDIAN VALUES
MAX. FOREARM LEVEL
MM.
MALE
FEMALE
MUSCLE
BONE
FAT
50
40
30
20
10
0
0 2 4 6 8 10 12 14 16 18
MAX. CALF LEVEL
MM.
MALE
FEMALE
MUSCLE
BONE
FAT
60
50
40
30
20
10
0
0 2 4 6 8 10 12 14 16 18
MID-FEMUR LEVEL LAT. M & F ONLY
MM.
MALE
FEMALE
MUSCLE
BONE
FAT
40
30
20
10
0
0 2 4 6 8 10 12 14 16 18
AGE IN YEARS
MAX. HIP BULGE LEVEL
MM.
MALE
FEMALE
FAT
30
20
10
0
0 2 4 6 8 10 12 14 16 18
AGE IN YEARS

FIG. F-3

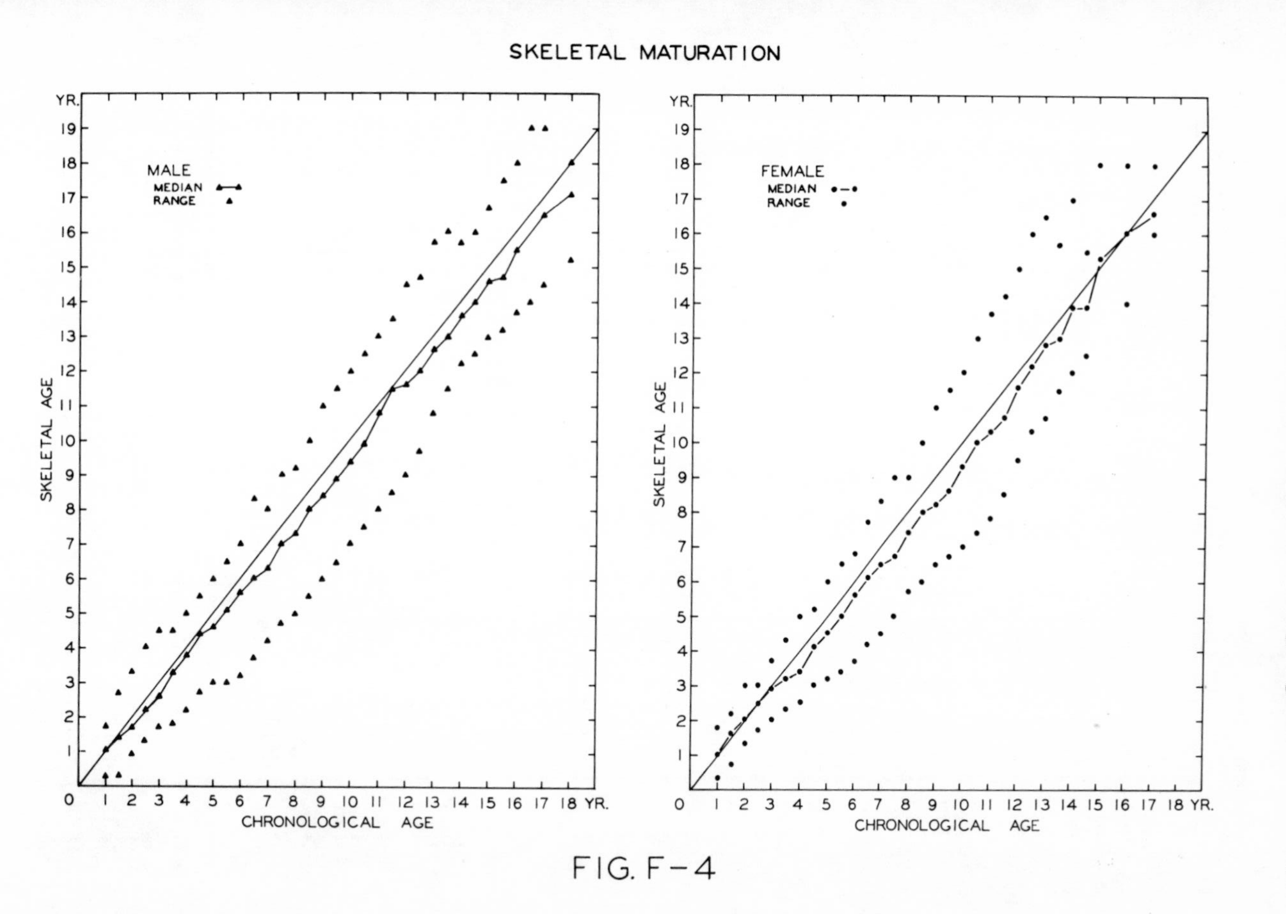
SKELETAL MATURATION
MALE
MEDIAN
RANGE
FEMALE
MEDIAN
RANGE
SKELETAL AGE
CHRONOLOGICAL AGE
YR.

FIG. F-4

MEASUREMENTS FROM ROENTGENOGRAMS

TABLE F-1

Transverse Diameter of the Heart in Centimeters

Age	Male						Female					
				Percentiles						Percentiles		
Yr. Mo.	N	Mean	S.D.	10th	50th	90th	N	Mean	S.D.	10th	50th	90th
Supine												
0 - 1	102	5.38	.45	4.73	5.33	5.94	104	5.11	.41	4.55	5.08	5.64
0 - 2	37	5.71	.41	5.13	5.71	6.18	39	5.54	.42	5.06	5.52	6.16
0 - 3	73	6.23	.54	5.57	6.19	7.11	92	5.92	.49	5.26	5.88	6.48
0 - 6	91	6.72	.66	5.90	6.70	7.56	103	6.36	.51	5.71	6.40	6.99
0 - 9	68	6.90	.59	6.18	6.81	7.63	85	6.70	.57	5.92	6.71	7.38
1 - 0	90	7.08	.60	6.38	7.03	7.87	98	6.79	.58	6.05	6.78	7.53
1 - 6	75	7.25	.57	6.45	7.26	8.02	86	7.06	.67	6.13	7.14	7.83
2 - 0	71	7.57	.62	6.74	7.51	8.44	78	7.42	.68	6.46	7.49	8.24
2 - 6	62	7.81	.55	6.97	7.91	8.43	70	7.71	.56	7.04	7.76	8.38
3 - 0	64	8.02	.53	7.27	8.06	8.67	62	7.78	.59	7.07	7.81	8.55
3 - 6	59	8.23	.44	7.73	8.30	8.66	56	8.00	.55	7.27	8.05	8.71
4 - 0	23	8.44	.50	7.76	8.53	8.99	17	7.91	.39	7.44	7.91	8.35
Erect												
1 - 0	19	7.32	.58	6.48	7.28	8.02	15	6.90	.38	6.30	6.91	7.45
1 - 6	27	7.41	.60	6.69	7.30	8.17	27	7.28	.50	6.55	7.28	7.76
2 - 0	33	7.67	.57	6.94	7.59	8.29	33	7.32	.71	6.36	7.41	8.23
2 - 6	43	7.91	.63	7.15	7.92	8.73	38	7.56	.57	6.83	7.61	8.30
3 - 0	42	8.03	.47	7.43	8.00	8.71	45	7.68	.54	6.93	7.70	8.31
3 - 6	43	8.16	.60	7.52	8.22	8.97	47	7.82	.49	7.22	7.87	8.47
4 - 0	79	8.17	.47	7.53	8.18	8.74	89	7.94	.51	7.30	7.93	8.53
4 - 6	96	8.20	.45	7.66	8.24	8.81	96	7.96	.51	7.27	8.00	8.51
5 - 0	101	8.30	.53	7.68	8.27	8.99	97	7.98	.57	7.17	8.01	8.73
5 - 6	106	8.34	.61	7.56	8.30	9.16	95	8.07	.61	7.35	8.11	8.80
6 - 0	97	8.49	.59	7.68	8.49	9.23	102	8.13	.56	7.42	8.11	8.85
6 - 6	102	8.60	.61	7.79	8.64	9.43	103	8.26	.62	7.44	8.23	9.14
7 - 0	100	8.75	.56	8.04	8.72	9.49	108	8.36	.60	7.50	8.40	9.04
7 - 6	98	8.83	.62	7.98	8.87	9.67	101	8.51	.67	7.64	8.48	9.54
8 - 0	91	8.90	.66	8.05	8.93	9.69	99	8.71	.64	7.87	8.68	9.53
8 - 6	95	9.04	.76	8.04	9.05	10.04	98	8.76	.66	7.83	8.66	9.59
9 - 0	98	9.28	.79	8.18	9.25	10.31	99	8.94	.67	8.07	8.91	9.83
9 - 6	98	9.24	.77	8.24	9.20	10.28	97	8.98	.66	8.22	8.91	9.91
10 - 0	96	9.32	.70	8.48	9.21	10.41	96	9.08	.73	8.15	9.04	10.14
10 - 6	97	9.34	.68	8.44	9.35	10.27	92	9.14	.80	8.06	9.09	10.15
11 - 0	96	9.63	.77	8.47	9.69	10.51	93	9.39	.75	8.40	9.33	10.33
11 - 6	96	9.74	.76	8.70	9.73	10.75	93	9.54	.84	8.45	9.54	10.64
12 - 0	96	9.83	.86	8.68	9.88	10.97	91	9.58	.91	8.43	9.49	10.72
12 - 6	95	9.94	.83	8.88	9.86	11.05	87	9.61	.79	8.62	9.58	10.66
13 - 0	92	10.07	.85	8.97	10.11	11.18	86	9.90	.82	8.91	9.78	10.80
13 - 6	93	10.30	.88	9.21	10.21	11.56	83	9.98	.87	8.86	9.83	11.22
14 - 0	93	10.48	.95	9.18	10.45	11.74	82	10.03	.93	8.98	9.90	11.29
14 - 6	86	10.67	1.04	9.34	10.60	12.10	62	10.01	.85	8.96	9.95	11.19
15 - 0	79	10.83	.97	9.69	10.74	12.14	73	10.15	.82	9.11	10.19	11.28
16 - 0	78	11.07	.94	9.83	11.04	12.34	69	10.17	.87	9.12	10.09	11.47
17 - 0	71	11.36	.93	10.18	11.33	12.57	60	10.18	.76	9.16	10.08	11.20
18 - 0	51	11.62	.91	10.56	11.61	12.77	46	10.42	.86	9.34	10.30	11.54
19 - 0	38	11.78	.95	10.54	11.76	12.84	38	10.30	.98	9.04	10.22	11.61
20 - 0	34	11.99	1.01	10.75	11.92	13.33	35	10.35	.97	9.19	10.16	11.89
21 - 0	38	12.10	1.03	10.73	12.20	13.63	34	10.66	1.01	9.28	10.70	11.99
22 - 0	35	11.91	1.11	10.46	11.62	13.39	36	10.48	.94	9.30	10.34	11.66
24 - 0	32	12.20	1.04	11.08	12.04	13.52	21	10.39	1.16	9.05	10.38	12.00
26 - 0	30	12.18	1.08	10.94	12.01	13.84	19	10.85	1.11	9.32	10.73	12.33
28 - 0	26	12.71	.96	11.36	12.82	13.96	15	11.14	.70	10.32	11.12	12.07
30 - 0	23	12.62	1.01	11.23	12.66	13.91	15	10.79	.94	9.67	10.93	12.08
32 - 0	23	12.70	.98	11.46	13.00	13.88	10	10.84	.93	9.60	10.92	12.10
34 - 0	18	12.74	.96	11.42	12.65	13.88	10	10.89	.98	10.06	10.38	12.25
36 - 0	14	12.88	1.12	11.12	13.06	14.32	8	11.02	-	-	-	-
38 - 0	10	13.27	1.16	12.01	13.15	14.67	4	-	-	-	-	-

MEASUREMENTS FROM ROENTGENOGRAMS TABLE F-2

Internal Diameter of the Chest in Centimeters

Age	Male						Female					
				Percentiles						Percentiles		
Yr. Mo.	N	Mean	S.D.	10th	50th	90th	N	Mean	S.D.	10th	50th	90th
Supine												
0 - 1	102	10.78	.65	9.96	10.73	11.71	104	10.55	.64	9.81	10.52	11.39
0 - 2	37	11.85	.95	10.63	12.10	12.85	39	11.68	.61	10.83	11.74	12.50
0 - 3	73	12.70	.73	11.80	12.54	13.68	92	12.33	.67	11.41	12.33	13.14
0 - 6	91	14.33	.83	13.22	14.22	15.43	103	13.76	.79	12.72	13.75	14.88
0 - 9	68	15.22	.89	14.07	15.24	16.43	85	14.76	.90	13.68	14.64	15.76
1 - 0	90	15.78	.86	14.75	15.72	16.98	98	15.28	.75	14.26	15.25	16.23
1 - 6	75	16.54	.84	15.42	16.50	17.79	86	16.10	.89	14.89	16.08	17.39
2 - 0	71	17.06	.78	16.14	17.01	18.20	78	16.79	.84	15.69	16.73	17.92
2 - 6	62	17.80	.86	16.69	17.79	18.67	70	17.38	.87	16.14	17.44	18.51
3 - 0	64	18.09	.79	17.04	18.04	19.20	62	17.66	.84	16.62	17.54	18.76
3 - 6	59	18.48	.84	17.29	18.47	19.41	56	17.93	.87	16.83	17.85	19.23
4 - 0	23	18.91	.72	17.97	18.97	19.72	17	17.91	1.10	16.34	18.14	18.96
Erect												
1 - 0	19	15.02	.80	14.06	14.84	15.92	15	14.82	.88	13.78	14.82	16.26
1 - 6	27	16.08	.82	14.98	16.12	16.85	27	15.36	1.00	13.96	15.40	16.66
2 - 0	33	16.49	.84	15.47	16.51	17.60	33	15.92	.82	14.85	15.90	16.90
2 - 6	43	16.86	.77	15.86	16.77	17.88	38	16.58	.80	15.68	16.43	17.79
3 - 0	42	17.50	1.01	16.15	17.35	18.97	45	17.00	.88	15.86	16.95	18.04
3 - 6	43	18.05	.88	17.01	17.87	19.39	47	17.49	.79	16.33	17.56	18.38
4 - 0	79	18.49	.88	17.35	18.54	19.58	89	17.79	.84	16.78	17.70	18.93
4 - 6	96	18.79	.86	17.74	18.75	19.98	96	18.05	.83	17.02	18.15	19.19
5 - 0	101	19.09	.88	17.91	19.13	20.27	97	18.27	.87	17.07	18.26	19.43
5 - 6	106	19.52	.91	18.42	19.40	20.86	95	18.61	.91	17.44	18.68	19.84
6 - 0	97	19.74	.93	18.61	19.71	21.08	102	18.92	.94	17.82	18.93	20.28
6 - 6	102	20.14	.99	18.80	20.20	21.41	103	19.19	.97	17.84	19.20	20.47
7 - 0	100	20.48	.93	19.28	20.63	21.60	108	19.54	.95	18.42	19.55	20.99
7 - 6	98	20.87	1.02	19.51	20.94	22.24	101	19.84	.96	18.67	19.74	21.23
8 - 0	91	21.20	1.02	19.86	21.20	22.42	99	20.20	1.05	18.81	20.14	21.79
8 - 6	95	21.53	1.11	20.08	21.64	23.02	98	20.54	1.09	19.09	20.40	21.97
9 - 0	98	21.93	1.16	20.33	21.91	23.59	99	20.91	1.08	19.63	20.78	22.53
9 - 6	98	22.34	1.15	20.62	22.36	23.71	97	21.31	1.16	19.92	21.26	23.00
10 - 0	96	22.65	1.16	20.92	22.72	24.14	96	21.43	1.24	19.68	21.53	23.07
10 - 6	97	22.87	1.28	20.86	22.92	24.36	92	21.89	1.36	20.16	21.74	24.02
11 - 0	96	23.25	1.35	21.24	23.19	25.12	93	22.45	1.44	20.52	22.44	24.42
11 - 6	96	23.61	1.25	21.66	23.68	25.05	93	22.75	1.49	20.56	22.72	24.76
12 - 0	96	23.99	1.42	21.89	24.10	25.85	91	23.20	1.58	21.03	23.13	25.50
12 - 6	95	24.34	1.47	22.44	24.35	26.11	87	23.56	1.61	21.31	23.52	25.47
13 - 0	92	24.86	1.59	22.76	24.77	27.03	86	24.03	1.56	21.93	23.98	26.26
13 - 6	93	25.37	1.70	23.08	25.37	27.81	83	24.49	1.54	22.36	24.42	26.52
14 - 0	93	26.06	1.79	23.75	25.98	28.64	82	24.87	1.54	22.74	24.81	26.96
14 - 6	86	26.53	1.77	24.08	26.65	28.86	62	24.97	1.52	22.99	24.81	27.14
15 - 0	79	27.17	1.67	25.08	27.00	29.53	73	25.12	1.37	23.38	24.88	27.26
16 - 0	78	28.13	1.80	25.62	28.28	30.47	69	25.30	1.35	23.54	25.35	27.42
17 - 0	71	28.62	1.85	26.22	28.73	31.08	60	25.43	1.33	23.64	25.40	27.18
18 - 0	51	29.16	1.83	26.58	29.16	31.55	46	25.74	1.40	24.04	25.46	27.59
19 - 0	38	29.47	2.03	26.63	29.59	32.18	38	25.49	1.49	23.68	25.35	27.70
20 - 0	33	29.83	1.92	27.19	29.71	32.25	35	25.69	1.56	23.56	25.72	27.90
21 - 0	38	30.08	1.70	27.74	30.05	32.50	34	26.10	1.59	23.93	26.28	28.25
22 - 0	35	30.14	1.72	27.53	30.28	32.31	36	25.84	1.59	23.66	25.72	27.90
24 - 0	32	30.31	1.99	27.41	30.33	32.85	21	25.85	2.01	23.15	25.67	28.54
26 - 0	30	30.61	1.97	27.83	30.71	32.87	19	26.52	1.94	24.07	26.46	28.95
28 - 0	26	30.90	1.69	28.00	31.12	33.00	15	26.80	1.78	24.32	26.98	29.08
30 - 0	23	30.99	1.68	28.23	31.25	33.08	15	26.75	1.90	24.34	26.50	29.06
32 - 0	23	31.00	1.68	28.09	31.67	32.70	10	26.89	1.98	24.40	27.34	29.41
34 - 0	18	31.04	1.52	28.49	30.70	32.75	10	26.89	2.32	24.20	27.36	29.49
36 - 0	14	31.12	1.65	29.20	31.44	32.97	8	27.08	-	-	-	-
38 - 0	10	30.39	1.82	28.36	30.14	32.94	4	-	-	-	-	-

MEASUREMENTS FROM ROENTGENOGRAMS

TABLE F-3

Ratio of Transverse Diameter of Heart to Internal Diameter of Chest

Age	Male						Female					
				Percentiles						Percentiles		
Yr. Mo.	N	Mean	S.D.	10th	50th	90th	N	Mean	S.D.	10th	50th	90th
Supine												
0 - 1	102	.499	.034	.458	.497	.548	104	.484	.032	.436	.485	.523
0 - 2	37	.484	.034	.446	.481	.524	39	.475	.028	.437	.472	.515
0 - 3	73	.491	.035	.448	.485	.533	92	.480	.037	.432	.477	.527
0 - 6	91	.469	.041	.414	.470	.520	103	.463	.041	.412	.460	.522
0 - 9	68	.454	.034	.413	.452	.498	85	.455	.037	.408	.455	.499
1 - 0	90	.449	.039	.396	.447	.503	98	.445	.039	.394	.443	.500
1 - 6	75	.439	.031	.392	.439	.475	86	.439	.038	.385	.439	.485
2 - 0	71	.444	.033	.404	.441	.484	78	.442	.040	.391	.447	.487
2 - 6	62	.439	.032	.387	.443	.472	70	.444	.033	.403	.443	.485
3 - 0	64	.444	.031	.403	.444	.481	62	.441	.032	.396	.439	.482
3 - 6	59	.446	.028	.418	.447	.479	56	.446	.029	.408	.441	.485
4 - 0	23	.446	.026	.410	.448	.479	17	.442	.021	.415	.433	.467
Erect												
1 - 0	19	.488	.032	.428	.490	.524	15	.467	.032	.424	.476	.493
1 - 6	27	.461	.036	.415	.464	.511	27	.476	.045	.418	.472	.549
2 - 0	33	.466	.036	.422	.463	.511	33	.460	.043	.399	.461	.503
2 - 6	43	.470	.040	.418	.468	.525	38	.457	.035	.415	.451	.496
3 - 0	42	.460	.026	.427	.458	.488	45	.452	.032	.413	.449	.487
3 - 6	43	.453	.035	.412	.452	.494	47	.447	.026	.405	.448	.478
4 - 0	79	.442	.027	.413	.441	.474	89	.447	.026	.409	.448	.485
4 - 6	96	.437	.027	.399	.436	.468	96	.441	.026	.405	.438	.479
5 - 0	101	.435	.028	.396	.436	.467	97	.437	.028	.401	.440	.469
5 - 6	106	.428	.032	.387	.428	.470	95	.434	.030	.385	.438	.471
6 - 0	97	.430	.028	.389	.430	.463	102	.430	.029	.393	.431	.467
6 - 6	102	.427	.030	.389	.424	.461	103	.431	.034	.388	.429	.470
7 - 0	100	.428	.028	.390	.429	.462	108	.428	.026	.391	.432	.461
7 - 6	98	.424	.028	.386	.424	.458	101	.429	.031	.388	.428	.468
8 - 0	91	.420	.029	.386	.419	.455	99	.431	.030	.386	.431	.468
8 - 6	95	.420	.033	.380	.418	.466	98	.427	.028	.387	.426	.464
9 - 0	98	.424	.032	.384	.421	.466	99	.428	.029	.387	.426	.466
9 - 6	98	.414	.031	.373	.412	.457	97	.422	.028	.384	.421	.457
10 - 0	96	.412	.027	.375	.411	.445	96	.424	.032	.381	.423	.465
10 - 6	97	.409	.027	.376	.404	.448	92	.418	.030	.379	.415	.458
11 - 0	96	.415	.031	.374	.411	.458	93	.419	.031	.382	.420	.455
11 - 6	96	.413	.030	.368	.411	.451	93	.419	.029	.378	.420	.454
12 - 0	96	.410	.030	.367	.408	.450	91	.413	.031	.375	.412	.454
12 - 6	95	.409	.028	.367	.410	.442	87	.409	.031	.368	.409	.449
13 - 0	92	.406	.030	.361	.404	.443	86	.413	.029	.373	.412	.453
13 - 6	93	.406	.028	.371	.403	.443	83	.408	.032	.358	.406	.450
14 - 0	93	.402	.028	.364	.400	.439	82	.404	.032	.359	.404	.443
14 - 6	86	.403	.035	.357	.399	.448	62	.401	.030	.356	.401	.442
15 - 0	79	.399	.030	.354	.399	.438	73	.404	.028	.369	.399	.442
16 - 0	78	.394	.031	.352	.395	.433	69	.402	.030	.366	.402	.440
17 - 0	71	.397	.030	.358	.394	.438	60	.401	.029	.362	.397	.446
18 - 0	51	.399	.030	.363	.393	.440	46	.405	.033	.359	.401	.451
19 - 0	38	.400	.027	.363	.398	.435	38	.405	.036	.355	.402	.453
20 - 0	33	.402	.028	.363	.402	.438	35	.403	.031	.368	.397	.454
21 - 0	38	.403	.033	.356	.403	.446	34	.408	.031	.369	.406	.449
22 - 0	35	.395	.029	.356	.397	.432	36	.406	.035	.366	.400	.455
24 - 0	32	.403	.024	.367	.405	.432	21	.403	.043	.359	.396	.469
26 - 0	30	.398	.030	.358	.396	.439	19	.409	.033	.371	.413	.451
28 - 0	26	.412	.030	.369	.418	.448	15	.417	.033	.371	.423	.451
30 - 0	23	.407	.026	.373	.404	.438	15	.404	.033	.349	.408	.440
32 - 0	23	.410	.027	.373	.411	.440	10	.404	.028	.373	.392	.438
34 - 0	18	.411	.034	.367	.406	.447	10	.407	.041	.353	.413	.459
36 - 0	14	.414	.034	.368	.422	.444	8	.408	-	-	-	-
38 - 0	10	.438	.042	.389	.430	.498	4	-	-	-	-	-

MEASUREMENTS FROM ROENTGENOGRAMS

TABLE F-4

Humerus Length in Centimeters

Age	Male						Female					
				Percentiles						Percentiles		
Yr. Mo.	N	Mean	S.D.	10th	50th	90th	N	Mean	S.D.	10th	50th	90th
Diaphyseal Length												
0 - 2	59	7.24	.45	6.57	7.29	7.75	69	7.18	.36	6.77	7.22	7.62
0 - 4	59	8.06	.48	7.31	8.08	8.64	65	8.02	.38	7.52	8.09	8.51
0 - 6	67	8.84	.50	8.26	8.90	9.48	78	8.68	.46	7.99	8.75	9.16
1 - 0	72	10.55	.52	9.93	10.49	11.21	81	10.36	.48	9.73	10.40	10.91
1 - 6	68	11.88	.54	11.16	11.85	12.58	84	11.70	.51	11.04	11.69	12.27
2 - 0	68	13.00	.55	12.31	12.95	13.82	84	12.77	.58	11.97	12.81	13.52
2 - 6	71	13.90	.59	13.10	13.90	14.62	82	13.69	.61	12.98	13.62	14.46
3 - 0	71	14.75	.67	13.88	14.70	15.62	79	14.53	.67	13.64	14.43	15.35
3 - 6	73	15.50	.78	14.66	15.48	16.29	78	15.34	.71	14.31	15.24	16.21
4 - 0	72	16.27	.69	15.28	16.20	17.12	80	16.09	.77	15.10	16.07	17.07
4 - 6	71	16.98	.74	16.06	16.90	18.03	78	16.91	.83	15.80	16.91	18.07
5 - 0	77	17.74	.82	16.78	17.75	18.92	80	17.63	.87	16.54	17.57	18.87
5 - 6	73	18.46	.81	17.52	18.44	19.43	74	18.26	.90	17.12	18.23	19.54
6 - 0	71	19.09	.76	18.17	19.02	20.06	75	19.00	.96	17.76	18.98	20.42
6 - 6	72	19.73	.81	18.76	19.60	20.85	81	19.67	.97	18.49	19.58	20.99
7 - 0	71	20.36	.87	19.41	20.22	21.42	86	20.26	1.00	19.00	20.24	21.55
7 - 6	76	21.04	.89	19.87	21.02	22.23	83	20.93	1.05	19.60	20.88	22.49
8 - 0	70	21.73	.98	20.53	21.68	23.04	85	21.63	1.04	20.18	21.55	23.09
8 - 6	72	22.25	.92	21.19	22.07	23.45	82	22.13	1.12	20.68	22.02	23.69
9 - 0	76	22.87	.96	21.72	22.73	24.15	83	22.80	1.18	21.20	22.72	24.42
9 - 6	78	23.51	1.07	22.27	23.40	25.08	83	23.42	1.29	21.78	23.32	25.27
10 - 0	77	24.10	1.03	22.79	23.97	25.57	84	23.98	1.32	22.26	23.92	25.81
10 - 6	76	24.58	1.10	23.22	24.44	26.11	75	24.59	1.46	22.76	24.48	26.70
11 - 0	75	25.17	1.07	23.79	24.98	26.56	76	25.19	1.47	23.17	25.08	27.48
11 - 6	76	25.74	1.19	24.31	25.71	27.30	75	25.91	1.53	23.91	25.86	28.15
12 - 0	73	26.30	1.28	24.72	26.30	28.04	71	26.56	1.56	24.46	26.50	28.64
Length including Epiphyses												
10 - 0	76	25.83	1.12	24.43	25.78	27.26	83	25.61	1.46	23.72	25.58	27.61
10 - 6	76	26.37	1.16	24.96	26.24	27.91	75	26.29	1.61	24.26	26.22	28.39
11 - 0	75	27.00	1.15	25.48	26.93	28.51	76	26.96	1.64	24.88	26.71	29.25
11 - 6	77	27.63	1.27	25.95	27.60	28.95	75	27.85	1.73	25.60	27.81	30.18
12 - 0	76	28.20	1.38	26.58	28.10	29.89	75	28.75	1.82	26.38	28.67	31.36
12 - 6	67	28.92	1.31	27.16	28.89	30.60	65	29.40	1.77	27.18	29.34	31.60
13 - 0	69	29.66	1.53	27.70	29.70	31.56	69	30.10	1.75	27.74	30.00	32.43
13 - 6	69	30.50	1.66	28.29	30.60	32.40	62	30.57	1.74	28.34	30.70	32.90
14 - 0	69	31.33	1.68	29.11	31.18	33.50	64	31.17	1.67	29.01	31.14	33.53
14 - 6	64	32.14	1.76	30.01	32.15	34.18	42	31.49	1.71	29.22	31.61	33.85
15 - 0	60	32.90	1.67	30.64	32.87	34.97	57	31.56	1.70	29.39	31.44	33.68
15 - 6	52	33.65	1.65	31.40	33.52	36.03	12	32.32	1.96	29.96	31.80	35.49
16 - 0	60	34.10	1.45	32.24	34.00	36.17	40	31.65	1.85	29.03	31.66	34.29
16 - 6	38	34.34	1.53	32.45	34.51	36.26	3	-	-	-	-	-
17 - 0	50	34.71	1.46	32.86	34.78	36.56	18	31.54	1.73	29.20	31.56	33.65
18 - 0	28	35.06	1.56	33.30	35.04	37.28	4	-	-	-	-	-

MEASUREMENTS FROM ROENTGENOGRAMS

TABLE F-5

Radius Length in Centimeters

Age	Male						Female					
				Percentiles						Percentiles		
Yr. Mo.	N	Mean	S.D.	10th	50th	90th	N	Mean	S.D.	10th	50th	90th
Diaphyseal Length												
0 - 2	59	5.97	.33	5.53	5.94	6.40	69	5.78	.28	5.44	5.74	6.13
0 - 4	59	6.60	.33	6.17	6.63	7.02	65	6.34	.28	5.98	6.34	6.68
0 - 6	67	7.08	.35	6.61	7.10	7.55	78	6.76	.34	6.37	6.78	7.15
1 - 0	72	8.26	.40	7.80	8.21	8.75	81	7.89	.34	7.47	7.88	8.30
1 - 6	68	9.14	.44	8.58	9.14	9.69	83	8.75	.40	8.18	8.69	9.21
2 - 0	68	9.86	.47	9.28	9.86	10.49	84	9.50	.45	8.89	9.54	10.03
2 - 6	71	10.52	.48	9.89	10.51	11.06	82	10.14	.50	9.49	10.15	10.74
3 - 0	71	11.16	.53	10.49	11.16	11.76	79	10.77	.52	10.02	10.80	11.42
3 - 6	73	11.69	.62	10.98	11.73	12.47	78	11.38	.55	10.58	11.42	12.11
4 - 0	72	12.31	.56	11.57	12.27	12.95	80	11.92	.57	11.10	11.91	12.61
4 - 6	71	12.82	.56	12.04	12.86	13.56	78	12.52	.66	11.58	12.55	13.36
5 - 0	77	13.38	.61	12.57	13.40	14.17	80	13.02	.69	12.02	12.98	13.84
5 - 6	73	13.89	.64	12.97	13.92	14.78	74	13.46	.72	12.55	13.33	14.39
6 - 0	71	14.38	.59	13.55	14.40	15.05	75	14.00	.74	12.96	13.92	14.98
6 - 6	72	14.83	.64	13.99	14.80	15.70	81	14.47	.78	13.40	14.46	15.45
7 - 0	71	15.30	.67	14.44	15.25	16.18	86	14.93	.80	13.88	14.83	15.98
7 - 6	76	15.79	.69	14.84	15.75	16.59	83	15.43	.84	14.32	15.36	16.57
8 - 0	70	16.29	.71	15.38	16.30	17.20	85	15.89	.87	14.76	15.85	17.07
8 - 6	72	16.68	.66	15.79	16.72	17.49	82	16.28	.88	15.10	16.13	17.54
9 - 0	76	17.13	.74	16.28	17.10	18.05	83	16.76	.93	15.59	16.72	18.04
9 - 6	78	17.61	.77	16.82	17.60	18.61	83	17.22	1.02	15.90	17.11	18.70
10 - 0	77	18.05	.79	17.14	18.02	19.04	84	17.68	1.04	16.33	17.52	19.03
10 - 6	76	18.44	.84	17.43	18.42	19.60	75	18.18	1.18	16.82	17.99	19.74
11 - 0	75	18.87	.85	17.92	18.74	20.01	76	18.60	1.17	17.13	18.44	20.17
11 - 6	76	19.30	.92	18.26	19.23	20.64	75	19.20	1.21	17.66	19.13	20.81
12 - 0	74	19.74	.96	18.65	19.68	21.08	71	19.69	1.27	18.06	19.62	21.34
Length including Epiphyses												
10 - 0	76	19.30	.81	18.31	19.28	20.15	83	18.93	1.14	17.39	18.82	20.44
10 - 6	76	19.77	.89	18.74	19.82	20.86	75	19.50	1.30	17.88	19.36	21.18
11 - 0	75	20.26	.89	19.26	20.20	21.39	76	20.00	1.30	18.24	19.94	21.84
11 - 6	77	20.73	.97	19.65	20.71	21.96	75	20.67	1.35	18.78	20.65	22.45
12 - 0	77	21.23	1.03	20.06	21.20	22.61	75	21.35	1.42	19.23	21.29	23.23
12 - 6	71	21.80	1.02	20.58	21.76	23.18	67	21.88	1.42	19.76	21.91	23.59
13 - 0	73	22.37	1.18	20.94	22.31	23.95	70	22.36	1.31	20.53	22.39	23.98
13 - 6	73	23.02	1.29	21.48	22.93	24.68	63	22.78	1.27	21.00	22.70	24.33
14 - 0	75	23.69	1.35	22.10	23.68	25.54	65	23.14	1.18	21.51	23.16	24.57
14 - 6	69	24.28	1.41	22.70	24.24	26.47	42	23.35	1.17	21.73	23.40	24.52
15 - 0	61	24.87	1.34	23.31	24.87	26.74	57	23.45	1.17	21.88	23.50	24.90
15 - 6	52	25.50	1.28	24.14	25.28	27.34	12	23.74	1.52	22.26	22.88	26.14
16 - 0	61	25.77	1.17	24.31	25.67	27.44	40	23.50	1.18	21.92	23.37	24.95
16 - 6	38	25.98	1.13	24.61	25.93	27.84	3	-	-	-	-	-
17 - 0	50	26.18	1.12	24.78	26.14	27.41	18	23.38	1.18	21.95	23.45	25.33
18 - 0	28	26.32	1.28	25.02	26.21	27.86	4	-	-	-	-	-

MEASUREMENTS FROM ROENTGENOGRAMS

TABLE F-6

Ulna Length in Centimeters

Age	Male						Female					
				Percentiles						Percentiles		
Yr. Mo.	N	Mean	S.D.	10th	50th	90th	N	Mean	S.D.	10th	50th	90th
Diaphyseal Length												
0 - 2	59	6.70	.35	6.28	6.72	7.14	69	6.53	.31	6.14	6.49	6.90
0 - 4	59	7.38	.34	6.94	7.35	7.80	65	7.12	.31	6.70	7.15	7.52
0 - 6	67	7.91	.37	7.43	7.93	8.36	78	7.57	.38	7.07	7.61	8.03
1 - 0	71	9.26	.44	8.74	9.24	9.78	81	8.90	.40	8.41	8.93	9.38
1 - 6	68	10.23	.46	9.59	10.26	10.70	83	9.89	.44	9.31	9.90	10.50
2 - 0	68	10.97	.49	10.39	10.91	11.52	84	10.71	.48	10.06	10.74	11.36
2 - 6	71	11.66	.52	10.99	11.63	12.15	82	11.38	.52	10.72	11.45	12.01
3 - 0	71	12.34	.56	11.64	12.34	12.96	79	12.06	.54	11.31	12.06	12.72
3 - 6	73	12.91	.64	12.03	12.94	13.64	78	12.72	.57	11.94	12.73	13.45
4 - 0	72	13.56	.56	12.79	13.55	14.27	80	13.31	.58	12.44	13.33	14.04
4 - 6	71	14.10	.56	13.34	14.07	14.91	78	13.93	.66	13.04	13.95	14.72
5 - 0	77	14.70	.61	13.93	14.66	15.52	80	14.46	.71	13.54	14.46	15.36
5 - 6	73	15.26	.67	14.33	15.26	16.18	74	14.91	.72	13.96	14.78	15.84
6 - 0	71	15.75	.62	14.94	15.76	16.49	75	15.49	.74	14.47	15.41	16.49
6 - 6	72	16.22	.68	15.39	16.22	17.05	81	15.99	.79	15.05	15.91	17.08
7 - 0	71	16.73	.70	15.79	16.77	17.58	86	16.48	.83	15.42	16.44	17.63
7 - 6	76	17.22	.74	16.39	17.18	18.16	83	17.01	.85	15.92	16.93	18.16
8 - 0	70	17.73	.74	16.88	17.70	18.58	85	17.49	.87	16.42	17.45	18.63
8 - 6	72	18.16	.71	17.29	18.16	19.10	82	17.91	.88	16.86	17.77	19.21
9 - 0	76	18.64	.79	17.67	18.63	19.60	83	18.43	.95	17.18	18.32	19.80
9 - 6	78	19.17	.83	18.16	19.18	20.11	83	18.97	1.04	17.64	18.83	20.45
10 - 0	77	19.62	.85	18.66	19.54	20.57	84	19.44	1.06	18.04	19.32	20.94
10 - 6	76	20.04	.88	18.97	20.05	21.12	75	20.00	1.24	18.60	19.77	21.55
11 - 0	75	20.51	.92	19.49	20.38	21.73	76	20.47	1.20	18.98	20.34	22.24
11 - 6	76	20.98	.99	19.84	20.95	22.27	75	21.13	1.31	19.42	21.08	22.79
12 - 0	74	21.45	1.02	20.22	21.44	22.80	70	21.64	1.33	19.91	21.57	23.31
Length including Epiphyses												
10 - 0	76	20.22	.90	19.18	20.25	21.28	83	20.38	1.23	18.78	20.32	22.10
10 - 6	76	20.80	.97	19.69	20.78	21.91	75	21.02	1.38	19.27	20.89	22.90
11 - 0	75	21.33	1.02	20.15	21.24	22.55	76	21.55	1.33	19.85	21.49	23.36
11 - 6	77	21.95	1.13	20.56	21.97	23.38	75	22.26	1.38	20.50	22.23	24.17
12 - 0	77	22.49	1.17	21.03	22.53	23.93	75	22.97	1.47	21.03	22.82	24.92
12 - 6	71	23.15	1.18	21.66	23.19	24.59	67	23.54	1.44	21.49	23.52	25.30
13 - 0	73	23.79	1.32	22.13	23.92	25.48	70	24.00	1.33	22.17	23.96	25.76
13 - 6	73	24.51	1.39	22.72	24.56	26.14	63	24.44	1.31	22.56	24.40	26.16
14 - 0	75	25.23	1.46	23.47	25.32	27.10	65	24.81	1.21	23.23	24.84	26.50
14 - 6	69	25.90	1.47	24.28	25.84	28.00	42	25.02	1.18	23.49	24.99	26.81
15 - 0	61	26.51	1.40	25.00	26.51	28.43	57	25.10	1.22	23.58	25.00	26.82
15 - 6	52	27.19	1.31	25.60	26.95	29.02	12	25.50	1.51	23.77	25.08	27.73
16 - 0	61	27.48	1.22	26.02	27.26	29.26	40	25.23	1.20	23.71	25.14	26.98
16 - 6	38	27.73	1.21	26.19	27.70	29.57	3	-	-	-	-	-
17 - 0	50	27.94	1.17	26.39	27.94	29.30	17	25.02	1.23	23.28	24.94	26.84
18 - 0	28	28.16	1.35	26.69	27.97	30.08	4	-	-	-	-	-

MEASUREMENTS FROM ROENTGENOGRAMS TABLE F-7

Femur Length in Centimeters

Age	Male						Female					
				Percentiles						Percentiles		
Yr. Mo.	N	Mean	S.D.	10th	50th	90th	N	Mean	S.D.	10th	50th	90th
Diaphyseal Length												
0 - 2	59	8.60	.54	7.94	8.58	9.27	68	8.72	.43	8.13	8.67	9.18
0 - 4	59	10.07	.48	9.41	10.06	10.74	65	10.08	.36	9.56	10.08	10.58
0 - 6	67	11.22	.50	10.45	11.30	11.82	78	11.11	.46	10.52	11.16	11.66
1 - 0	72	13.66	.58	12.94	13.68	14.30	81	13.46	.49	12.80	13.48	13.96
1 - 6	68	15.54	.68	14.66	15.53	16.33	84	15.39	.64	14.52	15.38	16.36
2 - 0	68	17.24	.73	16.43	17.19	18.11	84	17.08	.71	16.19	17.06	18.08
2 - 6	72	18.72	.78	17.80	18.77	19.65	82	18.52	.77	17.53	18.43	19.69
3 - 0	71	20.03	.85	19.09	20.06	21.16	79	19.84	.87	18.75	19.76	21.14
3 - 6	73	21.21	1.14	20.02	21.24	22.60	78	21.11	1.00	19.88	20.94	22.53
4 - 0	72	22.41	.99	21.38	22.41	23.72	80	22.32	1.01	20.97	22.15	23.84
4 - 6	71	23.57	1.05	22.25	23.53	25.03	78	23.55	1.14	21.89	23.45	25.07
5 - 0	77	24.75	1.11	23.60	24.70	26.34	80	24.70	1.15	23.34	24.59	26.16
5 - 6	73	25.82	1.17	24.42	25.73	27.48	74	25.70	1.22	24.22	25.54	27.38
6 - 0	71	26.97	1.20	25.65	26.90	28.82	75	26.89	1.35	25.21	26.56	28.78
6 - 6	72	28.03	1.26	26.52	27.90	29.78	81	27.90	1.38	26.11	27.77	29.67
7 - 0	71	29.11	1.33	27.48	29.08	30.82	86	28.88	1.36	27.30	28.89	30.80
7 - 6	76	30.12	1.35	28.51	30.04	31.99	83	29.98	1.52	28.04	29.73	31.92
8 - 0	70	31.21	1.46	29.37	31.04	33.12	85	30.98	1.56	28.95	30.92	33.10
8 - 6	72	32.10	1.46	30.20	31.99	34.06	82	31.89	1.58	29.80	31.92	34.10
9 - 0	76	33.04	1.46	31.28	32.90	34.92	83	32.87	1.68	30.51	32.86	35.18
9 - 6	78	34.00	1.58	31.90	34.01	35.90	83	33.88	1.86	31.42	33.76	36.65
10 - 0	77	34.93	1.57	33.06	34.92	37.16	84	34.79	1.91	32.42	34.70	37.36
10 - 6	76	35.74	1.62	33.77	35.55	37.76	75	35.65	2.14	33.01	35.21	38.88
11 - 0	75	36.70	1.65	34.89	36.55	38.98	76	36.70	2.24	33.86	36.34	40.20
11 - 6	76	37.58	1.81	35.31	37.63	40.00	75	37.80	2.34	34.59	37.54	41.21
12 - 0	74	38.61	1.90	36.41	38.46	40.98	71	38.76	2.29	35.92	38.77	41.62
Length including Epiphyses												
10 - 0	76	38.51	1.70	36.49	38.41	40.71	83	38.28	2.11	35.51	38.11	41.23
10 - 6	76	39.42	1.79	37.14	39.36	41.75	75	39.26	2.37	36.32	39.02	42.80
11 - 0	75	40.52	1.79	38.35	40.38	43.00	76	40.35	2.48	37.42	40.16	43.86
11 - 6	77	41.48	1.94	39.11	41.31	43.92	75	41.54	2.52	38.22	41.41	45.07
12 - 0	77	42.56	2.06	40.01	42.46	45.13	74	42.79	2.52	39.31	42.81	46.18
12 - 6	71	43.71	1.96	41.02	43.58	46.33	67	43.79	2.39	40.45	43.80	47.01
13 - 0	73	44.74	2.15	41.80	44.71	47.50	69	44.72	2.41	41.51	44.65	47.93
13 - 6	73	45.84	2.40	42.70	45.80	48.74	63	45.31	2.20	42.30	45.30	48.33
14 - 0	75	47.08	2.41	43.74	47.17	49.91	64	45.99	2.25	42.65	46.14	48.74
14 - 6	69	47.89	2.52	44.54	47.91	51.50	41	46.45	2.08	43.89	46.62	49.61
15 - 0	61	48.90	2.35	45.60	48.79	52.20	57	46.44	2.14	43.46	46.50	49.32
15 - 6	52	49.85	2.34	46.80	49.67	53.08	12	47.15	2.60	43.93	47.20	50.55
16 - 0	60	50.28	2.28	47.54	50.18	53.67	40	46.67	2.40	43.58	47.19	50.02
16 - 6	38	50.45	2.49	47.72	50.21	53.88	3	-	-	-	-	-
17 - 0	50	50.89	2.32	48.30	50.68	54.10	18	46.29	2.62	43.20	45.78	50.46
18 - 0	28	51.17	2.44	48.57	51.00	54.83	4	-	-	-	-	-

MEASUREMENTS FROM ROENTGENOGRAMS

TABLE F-8

Tibia Length in Centimeters

Age	Male						Female					
				Percentiles						Percentiles		
Yr. Mo.	N	Mean	S.D.	10th	50th	90th	N	Mean	S.D.	10th	50th	90th
Diaphyseal Length												
0 - 2	59	7.08	.54	6.31	7.01	7.79	69	7.03	.46	6.47	7.04	7.62
0 - 4	58	8.19	.53	7.58	8.10	8.87	65	8.08	.46	7.46	8.09	8.72
0 - 6	67	9.10	.52	8.44	9.07	9.81	78	8.89	.53	8.16	8.90	9.56
1 - 0	72	11.03	.52	10.40	11.00	11.74	81	10.85	.48	10.26	10.83	11.58
1 - 6	68	12.61	.60	11.89	12.56	13.32	84	12.40	.56	11.68	12.42	13.16
2 - 0	68	14.01	.65	13.21	14.02	14.85	84	13.82	.65	12.98	13.74	14.66
2 - 6	72	15.25	.68	14.40	15.25	16.12	82	15.01	.70	14.10	14.96	16.08
3 - 0	72	16.35	.77	15.46	16.28	17.31	79	16.11	.82	15.13	16.11	17.21
3 - 6	73	17.28	.98	16.17	17.32	18.48	78	17.12	.87	15.95	17.17	18.29
4 - 0	72	18.28	.90	17.22	18.31	19.44	80	18.08	.95	16.85	18.04	19.36
4 - 6	71	19.18	.92	18.09	19.19	20.46	78	19.09	1.05	17.73	19.08	20.53
5 - 0	77	20.14	.99	18.92	20.11	21.42	80	19.99	1.14	18.39	19.90	21.58
5 - 6	73	21.03	1.07	19.71	20.87	22.32	74	20.79	1.25	19.19	20.75	22.45
6 - 0	71	21.89	1.00	20.73	21.75	23.23	75	21.74	1.26	20.07	21.60	23.50
6 - 6	72	22.78	1.16	21.53	22.57	24.30	81	22.63	1.36	20.92	22.53	24.55
7 - 0	71	23.62	1.18	22.23	23.50	25.07	86	23.41	1.41	21.58	23.26	25.38
7 - 6	76	24.42	1.24	23.07	24.30	25.87	83	24.32	1.50	22.40	24.22	26.59
8 - 0	70	25.33	1.29	23.62	25.31	26.82	85	25.17	1.56	23.02	25.06	27.52
8 - 6	72	26.06	1.23	24.49	25.95	27.77	82	25.91	1.56	23.88	25.82	28.20
9 - 0	76	26.87	1.34	25.24	26.88	28.56	83	26.75	1.71	24.45	26.64	29.22
9 - 6	78	27.69	1.44	25.86	27.67	29.61	83	27.66	1.87	25.23	27.56	30.45
10 - 0	77	28.49	1.42	26.73	28.34	30.39	84	28.43	1.93	25.82	28.30	31.25
10 - 6	76	29.20	1.51	27.14	29.08	31.17	75	29.24	2.14	26.55	28.91	32.30
11 - 0	75	29.98	1.50	28.11	29.83	31.97	76	30.08	2.12	27.30	29.98	33.18
11 - 6	76	30.68	1.65	28.65	30.73	32.70	75	31.05	2.14	28.22	31.03	34.17
12 - 0	73	31.59	1.70	29.29	31.59	33.78	71	31.82	2.17	28.96	31.79	34.87
Length including Epiphyses												
10 - 0	76	32.00	1.57	30.00	31.96	33.77	83	32.11	2.17	29.25	31.96	35.11
10 - 6	76	32.89	1.70	30.63	32.94	34.89	75	33.09	2.37	30.05	32.70	36.47
11 - 0	75	33.86	1.71	31.65	33.84	36.02	76	34.01	2.31	31.06	33.70	37.41
11 - 6	77	34.74	1.85	32.31	34.69	36.97	75	35.04	2.32	31.97	34.92	38.53
12 - 0	76	35.73	1.91	33.22	35.79	38.18	75	36.09	2.38	32.95	36.04	39.45
12 - 6	67	36.75	1.86	34.04	36.72	38.97	65	36.73	2.30	33.60	36.68	39.87
13 - 0	69	37.67	2.06	34.96	37.75	40.34	69	37.45	2.22	34.44	37.34	40.62
13 - 6	69	38.82	2.20	35.84	38.90	41.76	62	37.90	2.18	34.96	37.70	40.76
14 - 0	69	39.74	2.19	36.92	39.92	42.56	64	38.43	2.14	35.42	38.56	41.01
14 - 6	64	40.60	2.31	37.73	40.84	43.51	42	38.69	2.05	35.94	38.54	41.42
15 - 0	60	41.22	2.15	38.51	41.21	44.14	57	38.57	2.08	35.81	38.59	41.24
15 - 6	52	42.05	2.23	39.24	42.11	44.63	12	39.05	2.85	35.73	37.84	42.15
16 - 0	60	42.26	2.18	39.68	42.15	44.72	40	38.68	2.26	35.69	38.65	41.54
16 - 6	38	42.51	2.42	39.71	42.36	45.07	3	-	-	-	-	-
17 - 0	50	42.65	2.32	40.06	42.64	45.14	18	38.07	2.36	35.36	38.03	41.38
18 - 0	28	42.95	2.56	39.80	42.94	45.49	4	-	-	-	-	-

MEASUREMENTS FROM ROENTGENOGRAMS

TABLE F-9

Fibula Length in Centimeters

Age	Male						Female					
				Percentiles						Percentiles		
Yr. Mo.	N	Mean	S.D.	10th	50th	90th	N	Mean	S.D.	10th	50th	90th
Diaphyseal Length												
0 - 2	59	6.81	.53	6.12	6.83	7.54	69	6.68	.44	6.10	6.72	7.26
0 - 4	58	7.86	.49	7.29	7.81	8.57	65	7.71	.41	7.16	7.68	8.26
0 - 6	67	8.72	.48	8.08	8.71	9.41	78	8.49	.52	7.74	8.57	9.12
1 - 0	72	10.71	.55	10.00	10.66	11.49	81	10.50	.51	9.80	10.48	11.17
1 - 6	68	12.39	.62	11.61	12.40	13.09	84	12.13	.59	11.31	12.09	12.82
2 - 0	68	13.81	.67	13.07	13.76	14.63	84	13.60	.68	12.71	13.55	14.52
2 - 6	72	15.07	.71	14.20	15.05	16.01	82	14.79	.71	13.83	14.73	15.75
3 - 0	72	16.21	.77	15.23	16.22	17.19	79	15.94	.79	14.94	15.88	16.98
3 - 6	73	17.16	.96	16.07	17.21	18.16	78	16.96	.83	15.87	16.98	18.12
4 - 0	72	18.18	.87	17.13	18.13	19.28	80	17.95	.91	16.68	17.93	19.15
4 - 6	71	19.08	.88	17.98	19.13	20.17	78	18.94	1.02	17.56	18.82	20.36
5 - 0	77	20.04	.96	18.92	20.06	21.14	80	19.86	1.11	18.44	19.86	21.34
5 - 6	73	20.90	1.02	19.78	20.80	22.18	74	20.65	1.17	19.22	20.52	22.32
6 - 0	71	21.75	.96	20.56	21.70	22.92	75	21.60	1.22	19.94	21.47	23.33
6 - 6	72	22.60	1.05	21.33	22.54	23.99	81	22.43	1.34	20.78	22.30	24.37
7 - 0	71	23.42	1.13	22.06	23.38	24.96	86	23.21	1.34	21.47	23.03	25.05
7 - 6	76	24.21	1.18	22.67	24.24	25.70	83	24.08	1.45	22.22	24.04	26.10
8 - 0	70	25.10	1.24	23.49	25.02	26.73	85	24.88	1.48	22.93	24.83	27.02
8 - 6	72	25.77	1.18	24.21	25.78	27.30	82	25.61	1.52	23.72	25.63	27.81
9 - 0	76	26.56	1.30	24.99	26.54	28.34	83	26.37	1.63	24.26	26.30	28.72
9 - 6	78	27.38	1.38	25.63	27.35	29.19	83	27.22	1.76	25.10	27.17	29.87
10 - 0	77	28.13	1.39	26.33	28.11	29.94	84	27.94	1.83	25.71	27.77	30.63
10 - 6	76	28.78	1.46	26.84	28.81	30.69	75	28.72	2.04	26.17	28.51	31.75
11 - 0	75	29.49	1.46	27.73	29.35	31.38	76	29.44	1.98	27.05	29.35	32.45
11 - 6	76	30.17	1.60	28.12	30.08	32.17	75	30.38	2.07	27.76	30.23	33.50
12 - 0	73	31.01	1.64	28.90	30.94	33.20	71	31.11	2.08	28.26	30.89	34.21
Length including Epiphyses												
10 - 0	76	31.04	1.52	29.20	31.04	33.04	83	30.79	1.95	28.28	30.64	33.59
10 - 6	76	31.80	1.62	29.67	31.83	33.86	75	31.67	2.18	28.94	31.54	34.47
11 - 0	75	32.62	1.59	30.69	32.51	34.54	76	32.47	2.15	29.72	32.28	35.48
11 - 6	77	33.40	1.76	31.01	33.41	35.58	74	33.46	2.21	30.57	33.25	36.68
12 - 0	76	34.28	1.80	31.90	34.36	36.69	75	34.46	2.27	31.36	34.24	37.61
12 - 6	67	35.19	1.68	32.56	35.26	37.20	65	35.10	2.22	32.08	34.91	37.90
13 - 0	69	36.02	1.98	33.32	35.96	38.55	69	35.85	2.19	32.92	35.90	38.84
13 - 6	69	37.11	2.14	34.07	37.18	40.13	62	36.34	2.14	33.64	36.20	39.24
14 - 0	69	38.03	2.13	35.24	37.92	41.05	64	36.79	2.06	33.92	37.04	39.54
14 - 6	64	38.85	2.25	36.16	38.78	42.08	42	36.89	2.15	34.38	36.80	39.88
15 - 0	60	39.53	2.15	37.01	39.52	42.24	57	37.02	2.00	34.34	37.12	39.86
15 - 6	52	40.44	2.21	37.70	40.48	43.44	12	37.57	2.58	34.33	37.07	41.01
16 - 0	60	40.63	2.17	38.20	40.46	43.56	40	37.24	2.15	34.43	37.28	40.08
16 - 6	38	40.86	2.28	38.23	40.85	43.68	3	-	-	-	-	-
17 - 0	50	41.04	2.26	38.24	40.83	44.02	18	36.68	2.42	33.76	36.55	40.06
18 - 0	28	41.28	2.42	38.44	41.50	44.14	4	-	-	-	-	-

MEASUREMENTS FROM ROENTGENOGRAMS

TABLE F-10

Relative Humerus Length (% of Height)

Age Yr. Mo.	Male						Female					
	N	Mean	S.D.	Percentiles 10th	50th	90th	N	Mean	S.D.	Percentiles 10th	50th	90th
Diaphyseal Length/Height x 100												
0 - 2	59	12.69	.65	11.68	12.72	13.45	69	12.87	.56	12.18	12.92	13.60
0 - 4	59	12.84	.65	11.94	12.90	13.68	65	13.12	.58	12.38	13.16	13.81
0 - 6	67	13.18	.56	12.41	13.18	13.91	78	13.34	.52	12.52	13.41	13.93
1 - 0	72	13.99	.51	13.34	13.97	14.72	81	14.11	.51	13.53	14.11	14.79
1 - 6	68	14.60	.50	14.08	14.56	15.28	84	14.68	.45	14.06	14.66	15.27
2 - 0	68	15.04	.45	14.46	14.98	15.76	84	15.02	.42	14.45	15.06	15.56
2 - 6	71	15.30	.43	14.71	15.25	15.90	82	15.29	.44	14.74	15.28	15.86
3 - 0	71	15.47	.46	14.87	15.47	16.14	79	15.50	.43	14.94	15.55	16.00
3 - 6	73	15.69	.42	15.15	15.71	16.30	78	15.71	.44	15.12	15.73	16.22
4 - 0	72	15.90	.44	15.30	15.88	16.50	80	15.86	.45	15.17	15.86	16.41
4 - 6	71	16.05	.46	15.42	16.06	16.63	78	16.08	.47	15.42	16.09	16.68
5 - 0	77	16.23	.49	15.67	16.17	16.90	80	16.23	.50	15.49	16.26	16.93
5 - 6	73	16.38	.45	15.78	16.30	16.98	74	16.36	.52	15.63	16.43	17.03
6 - 0	71	16.46	.45	15.97	16.40	17.08	75	16.50	.55	15.77	16.50	17.16
6 - 6	72	16.55	.43	16.00	16.55	17.15	81	16.64	.53	15.91	16.62	17.27
7 - 0	71	16.63	.47	16.02	16.56	17.32	86	16.74	.51	16.01	16.74	17.33
7 - 6	76	16.74	.46	16.18	16.73	17.38	83	16.81	.52	16.16	16.84	17.41
8 - 0	70	16.89	.49	16.33	16.82	17.54	85	16.98	.50	16.37	17.02	17.57
8 - 6	72	16.94	.48	16.46	16.89	17.62	82	17.04	.55	16.25	17.05	17.63
9 - 0	76	17.04	.46	16.44	17.06	17.63	83	17.15	.58	16.38	17.19	17.81
9 - 6	78	17.16	.50	16.54	17.14	17.86	83	17.24	.55	16.55	17.26	17.94
10 - 0	77	17.25	.49	16.58	17.29	17.87	84	17.30	.56	16.62	17.35	17.97
10 - 6	76	17.31	.52	16.57	17.37	17.95	75	17.40	.57	16.66	17.40	18.04
11 - 0	75	17.38	.51	16.64	17.44	17.98	76	17.46	.57	16.72	17.52	18.07
11 - 6	76	17.48	.52	16.73	17.56	18.05	75	17.50	.56	16.74	17.54	18.03
12 - 0	73	17.48	.52	16.75	17.53	18.13	71	17.59	.60	16.86	17.58	18.24
Length including Epiphyses/Height x 100												
10 - 0	76	18.50	.52	17.77	18.51	19.14	83	18.49	.57	17.82	18.53	19.17
10 - 6	76	18.56	.53	17.83	18.61	19.29	75	18.59	.58	17.86	18.57	19.21
11 - 0	75	18.64	.52	17.93	18.71	19.25	76	18.68	.57	17.98	18.68	19.38
11 - 6	77	18.75	.55	18.00	18.82	19.47	75	18.80	.57	18.04	18.84	19.40
12 - 0	76	18.76	.53	18.08	18.77	19.42	75	18.96	.61	18.16	18.93	19.74
12 - 6	67	18.90	.53	18.22	18.92	19.61	65	19.01	.64	18.19	18.98	19.73
13 - 0	69	19.03	.55	18.26	19.05	19.79	69	19.07	.62	18.27	19.08	19.80
13 - 6	69	19.12	.55	18.29	19.17	19.82	62	19.14	.67	18.30	19.13	19.80
14 - 0	69	19.16	.57	18.41	19.08	20.02	64	19.21	.64	18.46	19.21	19.96
14 - 6	64	19.32	.57	18.54	19.38	20.07	42	19.28	.67	18.55	19.26	20.01
15 - 0	60	19.39	.58	18.59	19.42	20.22	57	19.21	.70	18.46	19.21	20.03
15 - 6	52	19.54	.57	18.68	19.58	20.23	12	19.44	.62	18.82	19.58	19.99
16 - 0	60	19.54	.57	18.67	19.57	20.34	40	19.09	.68	18.11	19.16	19.83
16 - 6	38	19.58	.58	18.78	19.70	20.30	3	-	-	-	-	-
17 - 0	50	19.62	.56	18.77	19.68	20.38	18	19.14	.65	18.12	19.24	19.85
18 - 0	28	19.59	.52	18.81	19.64	20.20	4	-	-	-	-	-

MEASUREMENTS FROM ROENTGENOGRAMS

TABLE F-11

Relative Radius Length (% of Height)

Age	Male						Female					
				Percentiles						Percentiles		
Yr. Mo.	N	Mean	S.D.	10th	50th	90th	N	Mean	S.D.	10th	50th	90th
Diaphyseal Length/Height x 100												
0 - 2	59	10.47	.38	10.01	10.53	10.88	69	10.36	.43	9.83	10.34	10.87
0 - 4	59	10.52	.33	10.09	10.51	10.97	65	10.36	.42	9.80	10.34	10.88
0 - 6	67	10.56	.40	10.04	10.57	11.02	78	10.39	.40	9.96	10.33	10.86
1 - 0	72	10.96	.41	10.41	10.94	11.55	81	10.75	.40	10.23	10.76	11.24
1 - 6	68	11.23	.41	10.71	11.20	11.78	83	10.98	.38	10.56	10.98	11.39
2 - 0	68	11.41	.38	10.97	11.37	11.94	84	11.17	.39	10.62	11.20	11.60
2 - 6	71	11.58	.38	11.11	11.50	12.08	82	11.32	.39	10.88	11.34	11.78
3 - 0	71	11.70	.38	11.20	11.68	12.23	79	11.49	.39	10.95	11.49	11.98
3 - 6	73	11.83	.36	11.38	11.80	12.35	78	11.66	.38	11.12	11.65	12.13
4 - 0	72	12.03	.39	11.56	11.98	12.55	80	11.75	.38	11.28	11.76	12.20
4 - 6	71	12.12	.38	11.67	12.08	12.63	78	11.90	.40	11.36	11.89	12.37
5 - 0	77	12.23	.39	11.77	12.21	12.80	80	11.99	.39	11.48	11.99	12.44
5 - 6	73	12.33	.37	11.82	12.33	12.84	74	12.06	.40	11.48	12.07	12.53
6 - 0	71	12.40	.36	11.95	12.37	12.90	75	12.16	.40	11.68	12.16	12.62
6 - 6	72	12.45	.38	12.04	12.43	12.98	81	12.24	.41	11.70	12.24	12.69
7 - 0	71	12.49	.37	12.06	12.46	12.98	86	12.34	.41	11.85	12.37	12.82
7 - 6	76	12.57	.40	12.05	12.56	13.12	83	12.39	.40	11.87	12.42	12.84
8 - 0	70	12.66	.38	12.20	12.62	13.19	85	12.48	.41	11.93	12.49	12.96
8 - 6	72	12.70	.35	12.29	12.71	13.15	82	12.53	.41	11.93	12.57	12.99
9 - 0	76	12.76	.38	12.31	12.73	13.31	83	12.61	.42	12.11	12.65	13.05
9 - 6	78	12.85	.41	12.33	12.85	13.41	83	12.67	.41	12.11	12.71	13.14
10 - 0	77	12.92	.39	12.47	12.88	13.45	84	12.76	.39	12.22	12.79	13.22
10 - 6	76	12.98	.41	12.47	12.93	13.56	75	12.85	.43	12.30	12.87	13.37
11 - 0	75	13.03	.43	12.50	12.99	13.60	76	12.89	.42	12.31	12.94	13.37
11 - 6	76	13.11	.43	12.63	13.11	13.68	75	12.96	.41	12.42	12.98	13.44
12 - 0	74	13.13	.42	12.63	13.08	13.68	71	13.04	.44	12.46	13.05	13.53
Length including Epiphyses/Height x 100												
10 - 0	76	13.82	.40	13.37	13.81	14.30	83	13.67	.41	13.12	13.72	14.20
10 - 6	76	13.92	.42	13.41	13.88	14.46	75	13.79	.45	13.17	13.81	14.28
11 - 0	75	13.99	.44	13.46	13.97	14.59	76	13.85	.43	13.29	13.90	14.39
11 - 6	77	14.07	.44	13.50	14.04	14.62	75	13.95	.43	13.40	13.99	14.50
12 - 0	77	14.13	.44	13.59	14.10	14.75	75	14.07	.44	13.47	14.10	14.54
12 - 6	71	14.25	.44	13.72	14.17	14.92	67	14.13	.46	13.56	14.16	14.59
13 - 0	73	14.34	.47	13.71	14.31	14.98	70	14.17	.43	13.61	14.24	14.68
13 - 6	73	14.46	.46	13.89	14.42	15.07	63	14.25	.45	13.63	14.27	14.76
14 - 0	75	14.50	.48	13.96	14.45	15.19	65	14.26	.46	13.65	14.24	14.74
14 - 6	69	14.62	.47	14.04	14.56	15.23	42	14.30	.48	13.77	14.30	14.84
15 - 0	61	14.67	.49	14.10	14.62	15.30	57	14.27	.48	13.61	14.26	14.90
15 - 6	52	14.81	.48	14.18	14.80	15.44	12	14.28	.52	13.70	14.20	14.83
16 - 0	61	14.78	.48	14.20	14.71	15.46	40	14.18	.47	13.66	14.19	14.77
16 - 6	38	14.82	.45	14.28	14.81	15.43	3	-	-	-	-	-
17 - 0	50	14.80	.45	14.28	14.76	15.42	18	14.19	.50	13.52	14.22	14.73
18 - 0	28	14.71	.50	14.19	14.58	15.51	4	-	-	-	-	-

MEASUREMENTS FROM ROENTGENOGRAMS

TABLE F-12

Relative Ulna Length (% of Height)

Age	Male						Female					
				Percentiles						Percentiles		
Yr. Mo.	N	Mean	S.D.	10th	50th	90th	N	Mean	S.D.	10th	50th	90th
Diaphyseal Length/Height x 100												
0 - 2	59	11.75	.39	11.27	11.76	12.26	69	11.71	.46	11.15	11.72	12.26
0 - 4	59	11.76	.36	11.36	11.74	12.26	65	11.63	.46	11.05	11.63	12.27
0 - 6	67	11.80	.40	11.31	11.80	12.29	78	11.63	.44	11.07	11.60	12.26
1 - 0	71	12.28	.41	11.76	12.25	12.86	81	12.12	.44	11.62	12.12	12.67
1 - 6	68	12.58	.40	12.09	12.59	13.09	83	12.41	.40	11.90	12.39	12.91
2 - 0	68	12.70	.40	12.25	12.64	13.21	84	12.60	.40	12.13	12.57	13.09
2 - 6	71	12.83	.38	12.37	12.78	13.30	82	12.71	.40	12.25	12.71	13.17
3 - 0	71	12.95	.38	12.45	12.94	13.44	79	12.87	.39	12.37	12.86	13.36
3 - 6	73	13.07	.36	12.63	13.00	13.52	78	13.03	.39	12.56	13.01	13.49
4 - 0	72	13.26	.37	12.82	13.18	13.85	80	13.12	.38	12.63	13.11	13.61
4 - 6	71	13.33	.37	12.89	13.32	13.77	78	13.24	.38	12.76	13.23	13.68
5 - 0	77	13.44	.38	12.94	13.40	13.98	80	13.31	.40	12.77	13.28	13.86
5 - 6	73	13.54	.39	13.04	13.49	14.14	74	13.35	.39	12.79	13.36	13.84
6 - 0	71	13.58	.37	13.12	13.51	14.12	75	13.45	.38	12.97	13.47	13.92
6 - 6	72	13.62	.40	13.17	13.56	14.20	81	13.52	.41	13.00	13.52	14.00
7 - 0	71	13.66	.36	13.24	13.62	14.14	86	13.61	.39	13.08	13.62	14.09
7 - 6	76	13.71	.41	13.21	13.66	14.24	83	13.66	.40	13.14	13.66	14.12
8 - 0	70	13.78	.39	13.33	13.73	14.31	85	13.73	.40	13.19	13.76	14.19
8 - 6	72	13.84	.37	13.43	13.78	14.36	82	13.78	.38	13.22	13.80	14.23
9 - 0	76	13.89	.40	13.41	13.85	14.44	83	13.87	.39	13.31	13.86	14.31
9 - 6	78	13.99	.45	13.41	13.98	14.52	83	13.96	.40	13.37	13.97	14.45
10 - 0	77	14.05	.44	13.49	14.01	14.65	84	14.03	.37	13.52	14.05	14.51
10 - 6	76	14.11	.42	13.64	14.08	14.66	75	14.15	.43	13.58	14.12	14.62
11 - 0	75	14.16	.48	13.63	14.05	14.81	76	14.19	.42	13.62	14.16	14.70
11 - 6	76	14.25	.46	13.70	14.24	14.80	75	14.27	.42	13.70	14.28	14.77
12 - 0	74	14.26	.46	13.72	14.19	14.84	70	14.34	.44	13.76	14.33	14.83
Length including Epiphyses/Height x 100												
10 - 0	76	14.49	.47	13.94	14.45	15.08	83	14.71	.44	14.11	14.73	15.22
10 - 6	76	14.64	.48	14.06	14.61	15.26	75	14.86	.48	14.29	14.85	15.45
11 - 0	75	14.73	.53	14.09	14.66	15.49	76	14.94	.45	14.36	14.96	15.49
11 - 6	77	14.90	.52	14.23	14.83	15.60	75	15.03	.44	14.52	15.04	15.52
12 - 0	77	14.96	.52	14.34	14.95	15.64	75	15.14	.47	14.57	15.15	15.60
12 - 6	71	15.14	.53	14.56	15.14	15.86	67	15.20	.46	14.66	15.21	15.65
13 - 0	73	15.25	.53	14.64	15.21	15.93	70	15.21	.45	14.69	15.21	15.75
13 - 6	73	15.40	.52	14.80	15.33	16.04	63	15.29	.46	14.74	15.32	15.77
14 - 0	75	15.45	.53	14.86	15.37	16.16	65	15.29	.47	14.71	15.29	15.88
14 - 6	69	15.60	.51	14.95	15.51	16.22	42	15.32	.49	14.68	15.32	15.78
15 - 0	61	15.64	.52	15.04	15.55	16.30	57	15.28	.51	14.65	15.27	15.92
15 - 6	52	15.79	.50	15.20	15.76	16.42	12	15.34	.51	14.81	15.41	15.80
16 - 0	61	15.76	.51	15.19	15.73	16.41	40	15.22	.46	14.61	15.28	15.75
16 - 6	38	15.82	.49	15.21	15.74	16.55	3	-	-	-	-	-
17 - 0	50	15.80	.49	15.19	15.73	16.48	17	15.21	.41	14.67	15.29	15.70
18 - 0	28	15.74	.54	15.18	15.53	16.55	4	-	-	-	-	-

MEASUREMENTS FROM ROENTGENOGRAMS — TABLE F-13

Relative Femur Length (% of Height)

Age Yr. Mo.	Male N	Male Mean	Male S.D.	Male Percentiles 10th	Male Percentiles 50th	Male Percentiles 90th	Female N	Female Mean	Female S.D.	Female Percentiles 10th	Female Percentiles 50th	Female Percentiles 90th
Diaphyseal Length/Height x 100												
0 - 2	59	15.08	.74	14.02	15.17	15.94	68	15.63	.71	14.75	15.68	16.47
0 - 4	59	16.05	.55	15.43	16.02	16.81	65	16.48	.52	15.80	16.44	17.19
0 - 6	67	16.74	.58	15.98	16.73	17.45	78	17.07	.48	16.44	17.04	17.70
1 - 0	72	18.13	.57	17.41	18.11	18.88	81	18.33	.48	17.65	18.32	18.98
1 - 6	68	19.10	.59	18.28	19.14	19.79	84	19.31	.55	18.68	19.25	20.05
2 - 0	68	19.95	.56	19.20	19.93	20.76	84	20.09	.51	19.44	20.05	20.79
2 - 6	72	20.58	.59	19.85	20.61	21.30	82	20.68	.51	19.96	20.70	21.35
3 - 0	71	21.01	.58	20.27	20.98	21.79	79	21.16	.53	20.44	21.22	21.81
3 - 6	73	21.47	.64	20.67	21.47	22.26	78	21.62	.58	20.88	21.56	22.43
4 - 0	72	21.90	.64	21.00	21.91	22.83	80	22.00	.53	21.32	21.99	22.68
4 - 6	71	22.28	.64	21.40	22.31	23.06	78	22.39	.58	21.61	22.48	23.11
5 - 0	77	22.64	.64	21.78	22.61	23.55	80	22.74	.55	21.94	22.75	23.38
5 - 6	73	22.91	.62	22.05	22.88	23.66	74	23.01	.59	22.22	22.93	23.85
6 - 0	71	23.24	.66	22.30	23.27	23.99	75	23.35	.57	22.59	23.32	24.12
6 - 6	72	23.52	.66	22.59	23.54	24.36	81	23.60	.61	22.75	23.63	24.31
7 - 0	71	23.76	.69	22.77	23.82	24.58	86	23.87	.62	23.03	23.85	24.71
7 - 6	76	23.97	.61	23.14	23.98	24.73	83	24.08	.62	23.34	24.04	24.88
8 - 0	70	24.25	.70	23.30	24.26	25.14	85	24.32	.64	23.60	24.33	25.14
8 - 6	72	24.44	.68	23.51	24.42	25.28	82	24.54	.61	23.70	24.55	25.33
9 - 0	76	24.62	.64	23.78	24.59	25.48	83	24.73	.68	23.83	24.75	25.55
9 - 6	78	24.81	.70	23.76	24.84	25.78	83	24.94	.70	24.07	24.94	25.82
10 - 0	77	25.00	.69	24.05	25.02	25.86	84	25.10	.65	24.31	25.11	25.96
10 - 6	76	25.15	.67	24.33	25.15	25.99	75	25.21	.70	24.28	25.21	26.18
11 - 0	75	25.34	.69	24.38	25.35	26.21	76	25.43	.73	24.51	25.45	26.37
11 - 6	76	25.52	.74	24.53	25.54	26.43	75	25.52	.72	24.64	25.46	26.42
12 - 0	74	25.66	.76	24.64	25.71	26.63	71	25.67	.70	24.80	25.65	26.60
Length including Epiphyses/Height x 100												
10 - 0	76	27.58	.70	26.57	27.57	28.55	83	27.64	.66	26.84	27.67	28.47
10 - 6	76	27.75	.72	26.73	27.76	28.58	75	27.76	.68	26.99	27.69	28.65
11 - 0	75	27.97	.74	26.79	28.00	28.93	76	27.96	.70	27.05	27.94	28.83
11 - 6	77	28.15	.74	27.26	28.10	29.15	75	28.05	.69	27.15	28.05	28.93
12 - 0	77	28.32	.77	27.16	28.36	29.29	74	28.22	.66	27.35	28.23	29.07
12 - 6	71	28.58	.74	27.54	28.59	29.43	67	28.29	.68	27.34	28.29	29.13
13 - 0	73	28.68	.75	27.63	28.72	29.56	69	28.33	.70	27.40	28.31	29.24
13 - 6	73	28.80	.78	27.76	28.79	29.86	63	28.35	.65	27.50	28.41	29.03
14 - 0	75	28.83	.78	27.77	28.86	30.00	64	28.33	.70	27.33	28.36	29.22
14 - 6	69	28.84	.76	27.74	28.85	30.00	41	28.41	.67	27.62	28.41	29.11
15 - 0	61	28.84	.80	27.89	28.88	30.00	57	28.27	.62	27.62	28.21	29.07
15 - 6	52	28.95	.77	27.91	28.92	30.10	12	28.36	.68	27.34	28.35	29.12
16 - 0	60	28.84	.76	27.88	28.75	29.89	40	28.15	.69	27.44	28.14	29.10
16 - 6	38	28.76	.75	27.76	28.67	29.70	3	-	-	-	-	-
17 - 0	50	28.76	.76	27.81	28.69	29.88	18	28.08	.67	27.33	27.94	29.22
18 - 0	28	28.59	.72	27.66	28.69	29.63	4	-	-	-	-	-

MEASUREMENTS FROM ROENTGENOGRAMS TABLE F-14

Relative Tibia Length (% of Height)

Age	Male						Female					
				Percentiles						Percentiles		
Yr. Mo.	N	Mean	S.D.	10th	50th	90th	N	Mean	S.D.	10th	50th	90th
Diaphyseal Length/Height x 100												
0 - 2	59	12.42	.76	11.13	12.44	13.39	69	12.61	.78	11.40	12.73	13.56
0 - 4	58	13.05	.64	12.19	13.03	13.92	65	13.21	.68	12.40	13.22	14.04
0 - 6	67	13.57	.59	12.83	13.56	14.37	78	13.66	.60	12.73	13.76	14.37
1 - 0	72	14.64	.52	13.91	14.67	15.28	81	14.78	.49	14.15	14.74	15.42
1 - 6	68	15.50	.50	14.91	15.52	16.17	84	15.56	.49	14.94	15.58	16.18
2 - 0	68	16.21	.45	15.64	16.23	16.83	84	16.25	.47	15.57	16.30	16.87
2 - 6	72	16.76	.42	16.28	16.75	17.34	82	16.77	.49	16.10	16.76	17.50
3 - 0	72	17.14	.46	16.60	17.16	17.76	79	17.18	.52	16.51	17.14	17.89
3 - 6	73	17.49	.51	16.87	17.52	18.18	78	17.53	.53	16.92	17.49	18.31
4 - 0	72	17.86	.54	17.15	17.85	18.60	80	17.81	.54	17.10	17.80	18.50
4 - 6	71	18.13	.50	17.52	18.14	18.82	78	18.14	.54	17.46	18.10	18.90
5 - 0	77	18.41	.53	17.80	18.38	19.16	80	18.40	.58	17.66	18.34	19.13
5 - 6	73	18.66	.53	18.00	18.62	19.37	74	18.61	.64	17.74	18.62	19.50
6 - 0	71	18.87	.49	18.25	18.80	19.48	75	18.88	.60	18.10	18.85	19.68
6 - 6	72	19.11	.60	18.41	19.02	19.84	81	19.13	.64	18.36	19.06	19.98
7 - 0	71	19.28	.56	18.54	19.26	19.98	86	19.33	.64	18.60	19.28	20.18
7 - 6	76	19.43	.56	18.78	19.44	20.14	83	19.53	.63	18.75	19.46	20.35
8 - 0	70	19.68	.57	18.96	19.66	20.35	85	19.75	.66	18.97	19.71	20.67
8 - 6	72	19.84	.52	19.13	19.84	20.49	82	19.93	.62	19.17	19.93	20.78
9 - 0	76	20.02	.57	19.31	20.02	20.75	83	20.12	.68	19.30	20.09	21.02
9 - 6	78	20.20	.61	19.37	20.17	20.90	83	20.35	.68	19.45	20.36	21.27
10 - 0	77	20.39	.57	19.63	20.35	21.14	84	20.50	.68	19.74	20.48	21.42
10 - 6	76	20.55	.60	19.75	20.57	21.29	75	20.67	.73	19.88	20.58	21.69
11 - 0	75	20.70	.62	19.82	20.72	21.40	76	20.83	.70	19.99	20.76	21.86
11 - 6	76	20.83	.66	20.03	20.82	21.74	75	20.96	.68	20.24	20.82	21.92
12 - 0	73	20.99	.66	20.16	20.95	21.80	71	21.06	.72	20.29	20.97	22.08
Length including Epiphyses/Height x 100												
10 - 0	76	22.88	.59	22.07	22.90	23.58	83	23.18	.76	22.25	23.18	24.22
10 - 6	76	23.14	.65	22.30	23.14	24.00	75	23.39	.77	22.39	23.28	24.45
11 - 0	75	23.38	.66	22.51	23.40	24.18	76	23.56	.72	22.68	23.50	24.60
11 - 6	77	23.57	.69	22.69	23.53	24.42	75	23.65	.70	22.76	23.53	24.67
12 - 0	76	23.76	.70	22.83	23.75	24.61	75	23.79	.72	22.90	23.72	24.83
12 - 6	67	24.01	.70	23.10	24.09	24.81	65	23.74	.69	22.91	23.77	24.69
13 - 0	69	24.16	.73	23.22	24.20	25.02	69	23.73	.76	22.72	23.74	24.85
13 - 6	69	24.33	.74	23.31	24.35	25.23	62	23.72	.77	22.72	23.72	24.79
14 - 0	69	24.30	.78	23.22	24.27	25.36	64	23.68	.79	22.76	23.70	24.63
14 - 6	64	24.40	.74	23.37	24.44	25.36	42	23.69	.80	22.70	23.68	24.80
15 - 0	60	24.30	.76	23.35	24.31	25.24	57	23.47	.79	22.54	23.50	24.53
15 - 6	52	24.41	.76	23.50	24.38	25.27	12	23.48	.98	21.98	23.64	24.64
16 - 0	60	24.21	.83	23.08	24.18	25.22	40	23.33	.84	22.50	23.39	24.50
16 - 6	38	24.23	.82	23.24	24.14	25.36	3	-	-	-	-	-
17 - 0	50	24.10	.77	23.14	24.05	25.07	18	23.10	.82	21.91	23.14	23.89
18 - 0	28	23.99	.88	22.93	23.89	25.36	4	-	-	-	-	-

MEASUREMENTS FROM ROENTGENOGRAMS — TABLE F-15

Relative Fibula Length (% of Height)

Age Yr. Mo.	Male N	Male Mean	Male S.D.	Male Percentiles 10th	Male Percentiles 50th	Male Percentiles 90th	Female N	Female Mean	Female S.D.	Female Percentiles 10th	Female Percentiles 50th	Female Percentiles 90th
Diaphyseal Length/Height x 100												
0 - 2	59	11.94	.77	10.83	12.04	12.81	69	11.99	.72	11.00	12.04	12.84
0 - 4	58	12.52	.61	11.71	12.59	13.36	65	12.61	.58	12.00	12.57	13.32
0 - 6	67	13.01	.51	12.43	13.01	13.65	78	13.03	.58	12.19	13.13	13.74
1 - 0	72	14.21	.51	13.64	14.18	14.90	81	14.30	.50	13.66	14.31	14.96
1 - 6	68	15.23	.53	14.54	15.25	15.95	84	15.22	.49	14.54	15.22	15.81
2 - 0	68	15.98	.48	15.44	15.91	16.68	84	15.98	.49	15.33	15.99	16.57
2 - 6	72	16.56	.44	16.01	16.55	17.20	82	16.52	.48	15.88	16.52	17.18
3 - 0	72	17.00	.47	16.49	17.01	17.65	79	17.00	.50	16.29	17.00	17.63
3 - 6	73	17.37	.50	16.84	17.39	18.00	78	17.37	.49	16.76	17.36	17.94
4 - 0	72	17.76	.53	17.10	17.73	18.44	80	17.69	.51	17.00	17.68	18.34
4 - 6	71	18.03	.48	17.49	18.04	18.64	78	18.00	.54	17.27	18.00	18.74
5 - 0	77	18.32	.51	17.72	18.31	18.98	80	18.28	.56	17.48	18.30	18.99
5 - 6	73	18.55	.48	18.05	18.52	19.15	74	18.49	.58	17.72	18.47	19.30
6 - 0	71	18.74	.46	18.18	18.72	19.40	75	18.75	.57	17.93	18.77	19.51
6 - 6	72	18.96	.49	18.34	18.86	19.65	81	18.96	.61	18.23	18.97	19.76
7 - 0	71	19.12	.52	18.55	19.15	19.85	86	19.17	.60	18.37	19.17	19.96
7 - 6	76	19.26	.50	18.63	19.26	19.88	83	19.34	.60	18.54	19.35	20.10
8 - 0	70	19.50	.52	18.87	19.47	20.22	85	19.53	.62	18.83	19.53	20.34
8 - 6	72	19.62	.49	19.05	19.62	20.27	82	19.70	.60	18.95	19.66	20.43
9 - 0	76	19.78	.54	19.04	19.77	20.50	83	19.83	.64	18.99	19.83	20.70
9 - 6	78	19.97	.56	19.30	19.94	20.70	83	20.03	.63	19.18	20.07	20.88
10 - 0	77	20.13	.55	19.43	20.12	21.04	84	20.15	.63	19.37	20.16	21.00
10 - 6	76	20.26	.58	19.47	20.27	21.09	75	20.30	.69	19.48	20.23	21.30
11 - 0	75	20.36	.60	19.64	20.37	21.11	76	20.40	.67	19.50	20.38	21.23
11 - 6	76	20.49	.62	19.71	20.46	21.38	75	20.50	.65	19.70	20.48	21.37
12 - 0	73	20.60	.62	19.84	20.57	21.43	71	20.59	.68	19.73	20.61	21.50
Length including Epiphyses/Height x 100												
10 - 0	76	22.22	.60	21.50	22.18	23.12	83	22.22	.63	21.41	22.24	23.03
10 - 6	76	22.38	.64	21.62	22.36	23.34	75	22.39	.68	21.58	22.30	23.31
11 - 0	75	22.52	.63	21.72	22.54	23.32	76	22.49	.66	21.70	22.46	23.29
11 - 6	77	22.66	.66	21.87	22.61	23.57	74	22.60	.64	21.91	22.60	23.40
12 - 0	76	22.80	.66	21.96	22.75	23.60	75	22.71	.65	21.89	22.75	23.49
12 - 6	67	23.00	.64	22.19	22.92	23.84	65	22.68	.64	21.84	22.78	23.42
13 - 0	69	23.10	.71	22.11	23.03	24.04	69	22.71	.69	21.84	22.72	23.54
13 - 6	69	23.26	.71	22.38	23.18	24.22	62	22.74	.71	21.76	22.79	23.54
14 - 0	69	23.25	.73	22.35	23.23	24.04	64	22.67	.72	21.62	22.72	23.51
14 - 6	64	23.35	.68	22.50	23.32	24.22	42	22.59	.91	21.57	22.56	23.69
15 - 0	60	23.30	.74	22.45	23.24	24.25	57	22.53	.71	21.59	22.58	23.34
15 - 6	52	23.48	.75	22.62	23.42	24.63	12	22.59	.83	21.26	22.70	23.48
16 - 0	60	23.28	.85	22.28	23.26	24.41	40	22.46	.77	21.49	22.50	23.46
16 - 6	38	23.29	.78	22.45	23.22	24.36	3	-	-	-	-	-
17 - 0	50	23.19	.79	22.39	23.12	24.42	18	22.25	.86	20.99	22.32	23.21
18 - 0	28	23.06	.82	22.14	23.00	24.21	4	-	-	-	-	-

MEASUREMENTS FROM ROENTGENOGRAMS

Table F-16

Bone Widths in Millimeters - Male

Age Yr. Mo.	N	Max. Forearm (F) Percentiles 10th	50th	90th	Mid-thigh (T) Percentiles 10th	50th	90th	Max. Calf (C) Percentiles 10th	50th	90th	Sum of F, T, C Percentiles 10th	50th	90th
0 - 2	55	9.34	10.35	11.54	6.50	7.36	8.14	9.88	12.11	13.96	26.18	29.76	33.25
0 - 4	55	10.67	11.95	13.56	7.40	8.25	9.16	10.41	13.26	15.17	29.15	33.55	37.19
0 - 6	58	11.52	13.07	14.50	8.14	8.95	9.89	12.26	14.65	16.06	32.35	36.77	39.59
1 - 0	61	13.41	15.56	17.04	9.58	10.56	11.74	14.03	16.12	18.18	37.73	41.98	46.34
1 - 6	59	14.32	16.91	18.75	11.01	11.85	12.96	15.86	17.56	20.02	42.00	46.27	50.44
2 - 0	57	15.44	17.54	19.52	11.83	12.75	13.88	16.64	18.46	20.60	43.94	48.63	52.85
2 - 6	59	15.90	18.10	20.60	12.32	13.41	14.67	17.49	19.40	21.40	46.47	50.84	55.54
3 - 0	57	16.69	18.87	21.04	12.84	14.10	15.32	18.42	20.32	22.01	48.76	53.56	57.50
3 - 6	56	16.82	19.40	21.97	13.36	14.37	15.94	19.26	20.74	22.77	49.81	54.43	58.84
4 - 0	52	17.29	19.69	22.14	13.82	14.96	16.20	19.46	21.29	23.23	52.01	56.40	60.54
4 - 6	54	18.22	20.04	22.48	14.14	15.30	16.90	20.17	21.95	23.53	53.28	57.38	61.86
5 - 0	55	18.21	20.70	23.38	14.54	15.75	17.12	20.69	22.72	24.32	54.10	59.09	64.37
5 - 6	51	18.77	21.33	23.66	15.03	16.36	17.71	21.14	23.37	24.76	55.53	60.74	65.36
6 - 0	50	19.06	21.58	24.47	15.37	16.64	18.28	21.64	24.22	25.66	57.23	62.03	67.58
6 - 6	49	18.63	21.82	24.22	15.67	17.22	18.32	22.41	24.54	26.20	57.60	63.34	68.71
7 - 0	48	18.02	22.16	25.47	16.49	17.64	19.35	22.78	25.30	27.43	59.07	64.92	71.53
7 - 6	48	18.99	22.70	26.66	16.89	18.15	19.78	23.42	25.86	28.02	61.13	66.67	72.35
8 - 0	46	18.52	22.33	26.89	17.42	18.74	20.46	24.12	26.56	28.89	61.77	67.59	74.27
8 - 6	44	19.96	23.18	26.89	17.52	19.15	21.42	24.46	26.98	29.48	62.85	69.66	74.74
9 - 0	45	19.30	23.85	27.62	17.98	19.90	21.76	25.13	27.53	29.91	64.37	71.12	77.81
9 - 6	47	20.09	23.97	27.75	18.29	20.10	22.49	25.40	28.51	30.94	65.49	72.53	78.90
10 - 0	45	19.67	24.35	28.62	18.64	20.82	23.03	26.48	29.16	31.60	67.24	74.18	81.62
10 - 6	46	19.62	25.05	28.10	19.16	21.35	22.81	26.68	29.86	32.51	67.72	75.13	82.65
11 - 0	42	19.36	25.07	29.12	19.51	21.72	23.64	27.70	30.70	33.48	67.08	76.47	84.76
11 - 6	44	20.63	25.32	29.67	19.43	22.42	24.21	27.60	31.34	34.04	70.44	77.45	85.06
12 - 0	44	20.18	25.52	29.47	20.05	22.78	24.64	28.09	31.80	35.07	70.46	79.36	87.07
12 - 6	41	22.42	26.17	30.80	20.67	23.45	25.39	28.95	32.72	36.33	73.02	82.30	91.77
13 - 0	44	20.02	26.48	31.81	21.22	24.10	26.13	29.53	33.40	36.97	74.82	82.24	93.06
13 - 6	40	22.05	27.63	31.56	21.20	24.47	27.03	29.58	34.28	37.28	74.26	86.68	93.12
14 - 0	39	24.85	29.73	33.39	22.17	24.90	27.22	30.90	34.95	38.40	80.74	88.90	96.95
14 - 6	35	20.97	29.93	33.66	22.32	25.58	27.93	30.44	35.74	39.04	76.75	90.11	99.25
15 - 0	31	24.79	29.86	34.14	22.99	26.19	28.27	31.76	36.10	40.18	82.61	92.37	101.17
15 - 6	25	24.0C	29.24	33.52	23.59	26.53	29.92	32.42	35.81	41.33	80.28	92.70	99.26
16 - 0	28	22.75	28.60	34.13	24.62	27.36	30.86	34.07	37.35	41.59	85.62	94.28	103.48
16 - 6	16	23.83	30.11	34.67	24.53	26.94	29.34	33.98	36.75	40.05	82.82	93.45	102.05
17 - 0	25	24.20	31.98	35.74	24.53	27.86	29.71	35.29	37.03	41.54	86.62	97.05	103.14
18 - 0	12	23.34	30.65	33.88	24.72	28.72	29.67	34.61	36.60	40.26	86.21	97.27	102.51

MEASUREMENTS FROM ROENTGENOGRAMS TABLE F-17

Bone Widths in Millimeters - Female

Age	N	Max. Forearm (F)			Mid-thigh (T)			Max. Calf (C)			Sum of F, T, C		
		Percentiles			Percentiles			Percentiles			Percentiles		
Yr. Mo.		10th	50th	90th	10th	50th	90th	10th	50th	90th	10th	50th	90th
0 - 2	59	9.17	10.06	11.01	6.39	7.09	7.78	9.15	11.72	12.93	25.65	28.44	31.58
0 - 4	55	10.07	11.45	12.44	7.18	7.84	8.81	10.94	12.91	14.24	29.27	31.71	35.37
0 - 6	61	10.84	12.24	13.10	7.65	8.53	9.54	11.53	13.56	15.19	30.88	33.92	36.96
1 - 0	58	12.72	14.66	16.11	8.92	10.40	11.24	13.27	15.85	17.87	35.74	40.82	44.37
1 - 6	58	13.67	15.83	17.50	10.42	11.71	12.74	14.54	17.13	19.05	39.26	45.29	48.77
2 - 0	56	13.41	16.33	18.66	11.12	12.62	13.79	15.80	18.30	20.36	41.43	47.96	50.68
2 - 6	58	15.25	17.16	19.79	11.86	13.28	14.60	16.84	19.04	21.02	44.43	49.97	53.98
3 - 0	57	15.69	17.48	19.98	12.54	13.71	15.19	17.49	19.63	21.74	45.71	51.50	54.88
3 - 6	57	15.79	18.03	20.24	12.93	14.41	15.70	18.14	20.24	22.41	47.26	52.62	57.13
4 - 0	56	16.37	18.16	20.19	13.50	14.79	16.20	18.43	20.65	22.76	49.10	54.13	58.45
4 - 6	55	16.40	18.57	20.98	13.93	15.21	16.75	19.16	21.32	23.20	50.57	55.33	60.20
5 - 0	53	17.03	19.14	21.60	14.46	15.68	17.27	19.72	21.96	23.81	52.01	56.58	61.83
5 - 6	48	17.11	19.30	21.92	14.75	16.12	17.70	20.39	22.55	24.41	52.32	58.46	63.32
6 - 0	50	18.00	19.74	22.11	15.04	16.48	17.98	21.12	23.21	25.06	54.55	59.14	65.02
6 - 6	51	16.70	19.95	22.78	15.54	16.83	18.42	21.13	23.55	25.63	54.40	60.02	65.12
7 - 0	52	17.21	19.99	22.70	15.88	17.17	19.06	21.79	24.08	26.33	56.44	62.03	66.51
7 - 6	47	16.86	20.32	23.32	16.33	17.53	19.34	22.31	24.72	26.74	56.84	62.88	66.98
8 - 0	45	17.25	20.70	23.89	16.71	18.06	19.88	22.74	25.00	27.15	58.39	63.56	69.50
8 - 6	45	15.95	20.85	23.99	17.21	18.31	20.22	23.03	25.63	27.75	57.23	64.19	70.59
9 - 0	44	16.90	20.75	24.21	17.36	18.82	20.94	23.24	26.09	28.66	59.40	65.56	71.61
9 - 6	45	16.78	21.74	24.80	17.61	19.22	21.51	24.00	26.37	29.15	60.82	66.10	73.90
10 - 0	44	16.59	21.52	25.94	18.03	19.68	21.99	24.17	27.05	29.74	61.42	68.10	75.77
10 - 6	41	17.48	21.96	25.25	18.69	20.09	22.71	24.85	27.38	30.26	63.84	69.84	74.23
11 - 0	40	16.83	22.09	25.07	19.24	20.71	23.27	25.20	28.15	30.74	65.97	68.99	75.96
11 - 6	38	18.73	22.16	26.05	19.63	21.26	23.92	26.19	28.97	31.41	66.35	71.52	78.76
12 - 0	36	16.94	23.20	27.81	20.41	21.88	24.12	26.60	29.41	32.57	67.14	74.41	82.22
12 - 6	33	16.77	24.32	28.19	20.60	22.44	25.04	27.24	30.25	32.53	67.54	76.84	82.81
13 - 0	33	17.04	23.33	28.37	21.41	23.08	24.99	27.74	30.62	34.14	70.01	77.15	84.32
13 - 6	27	16.71	24.01	28.59	21.88	23.51	25.52	28.23	31.00	34.06	70.33	78.84	86.81
14 - 0	27	17.91	23.43	28.69	22.33	24.05	25.56	28.63	31.33	34.40	71.97	80.16	87.07
14 - 6	19	19.14	25.66	28.25	23.44	24.38	25.64	29.59	32.14	34.81	74.88	82.61	88.54
15 - 0	24	16.28	23.96	30.04	22.57	24.54	26.05	29.09	31.33	34.69	71.48	79.49	90.35
16 - 0	17	19.18	24.04	28.68	23.16	24.72	26.43	29.67	31.48	35.39	71.66	82.52	86.02
17 - 0	10	18.74	22.31	30.13	23.94	25.42	26.53	29.25	32.72	34.45	76.47	79.45	88.10

MEASUREMENTS FROM ROENTGENOGRAMS TABLE F-18

Muscle Widths in Millimeters - Male

Age		Max. Forearm (F)			Mid-thigh (T) (Lateral half)			Max. Calf (C)			Sum of F, T, C		
		Percentiles			Percentiles			Percentiles			Percentiles		
Yr. Mo.	N	10th	50th	90th	10th	50th	90th	10th	50th	90th	10th	50th	90th
0 - 2	55	16.42	19.52	23.47	11.87	14.22	17.19	19.48	21.91	25.15	48.97	56.21	64.06
0 - 4	55	17.82	20.64	23.54	12.61	15.55	17.83	19.77	23.59	28.60	52.26	59.60	68.06
0 - 6	58	17.23	20.16	24.58	13.06	16.58	19.40	20.27	24.58	28.67	52.79	61.27	69.83
1 - 0	61	19.95	23.06	25.63	15.01	18.43	21.59	23.73	28.24	32.84	61.03	70.02	77.69
1 - 6	59	19.58	22.72	26.12	15.85	18.26	22.21	27.64	30.60	35.31	64.47	71.78	82.24
2 - 0	57	20.22	23.80	27.24	15.93	18.93	22.29	28.71	32.34	36.79	67.24	75.60	85.04
2 - 6	59	20.56	24.23	27.34	17.34	20.10	24.10	29.12	33.57	38.82	69.36	77.80	88.98
3 - 0	57	21.18	24.96	28.75	19.02	21.93	25.49	31.59	35.35	40.86	73.15	82.16	92.99
3 - 6	56	21.23	24.90	29.55	19.82	22.81	26.26	31.90	36.50	42.20	75.56	84.78	94.76
4 - 0	52	21.96	25.54	29.88	20.28	23.82	27.19	33.27	37.78	43.76	77.97	87.00	96.94
4 - 6	54	22.90	26.69	29.98	21.24	24.67	28.83	34.72	38.38	45.26	81.01	90.90	98.79
5 - 0	55	23.75	27.30	31.06	23.56	26.43	29.62	34.40	39.82	45.44	83.13	94.00	103.31
5 - 6	51	24.56	28.19	32.37	23.09	26.32	30.55	35.86	40.99	47.72	87.01	95.44	108.26
6 - 0	50	25.46	28.87	33.28	23.51	27.12	32.27	36.14	41.28	48.03	89.78	97.33	109.02
6 - 6	49	26.99	30.81	35.17	23.89	28.83	31.40	37.41	42.51	49.68	91.50	102.30	113.10
7 - 0	48	27.24	31.13	35.85	24.50	28.70	32.84	38.06	44.59	50.64	92.92	102.33	116.61
7 - 6	48	28.18	32.75	36.55	25.84	29.80	35.08	38.79	44.42	50.89	96.26	105.92	119.27
8 - 0	46	29.32	33.24	37.35	26.62	30.58	34.55	40.75	46.14	51.86	97.74	109.90	121.31
8 - 6	44	29.94	33.76	37.79	27.06	31.55	37.00	41.02	47.65	53.50	101.39	112.35	124.80
9 - 0	45	31.64	34.80	40.67	27.43	32.25	38.43	42.58	48.14	54.59	105.17	116.30	126.68
9 - 6	47	32.17	35.88	39.51	28.04	33.33	38.31	42.02	49.49	56.47	105.55	119.60	129.66
10 - 0	45	32.87	36.84	40.32	30.49	35.03	39.90	43.77	50.62	55.38	111.44	119.61	134.74
10 - 6	46	32.90	37.38	42.30	30.11	35.86	40.93	43.65	50.56	58.12	110.62	123.33	136.82
11 - 0	42	33.92	38.79	43.05	31.20	37.10	41.36	42.77	52.06	57.37	112.47	126.08	139.69
11 - 6	44	34.21	38.68	45.43	31.62	36.81	41.90	44.11	51.14	58.68	112.70	127.80	140.59
12 - 0	44	35.55	40.60	45.55	34.44	38.92	44.73	45.37	53.08	60.24	119.00	131.58	148.71
12 - 6	41	36.04	41.46	47.36	34.64	39.82	45.28	46.20	52.55	62.51	118.62	132.66	153.38
13 - 0	44	36.26	42.20	48.93	35.00	40.95	47.54	46.54	55.35	64.18	124.14	137.82	159.42
13 - 6	40	38.00	44.30	51.05	35.44	41.05	49.04	45.34	55.36	66.84	125.04	139.63	165.10
14 - 0	39	38.39	45.33	52.02	36.32	42.33	49.56	47.27	57.25	68.02	125.24	143.47	168.68
14 - 6	35	40.16	46.79	54.97	37.54	43.09	50.26	48.51	56.36	69.22	129.19	146.52	169.75
15 - 0	31	43.37	49.72	57.52	38.11	44.05	50.65	50.30	57.90	71.20	134.63	150.77	178.83
15 - 6	25	44.78	51.35	58.51	37.69	43.49	49.93	51.06	58.36	70.31	136.62	152.32	172.33
16 - 0	28	47.00	52.35	59.57	38.66	45.65	53.94	52.91	62.11	70.40	147.58	160.46	179.53
16 - 6	16	49.26	51.48	61.49	41.15	46.88	51.82	55.54	62.07	71.51	149.28	159.41	181.48
17 - 0	25	49.82	52.32	59.64	42.38	47.05	51.29	54.22	63.06	71.48	150.84	162.24	176.68
18 - 0	12	52.08	56.44	62.37	39.07	47.35	51.53	56.03	66.08	72.84	155.42	167.30	182.78

MEASUREMENTS FROM ROENTGENOGRAMS

TABLE F-19

Muscle Widths in Millimeters - Female

Age Yr. Mo.	N	Max. Forearm (F) Percentiles 10th	50th	90th	Mid-thigh (T) (Lateral half) Percentiles 10th	50th	90th	Max. Calf (C) Percentiles 10th	50th	90th	Sum of F, T, C Percentiles 10th	50th	90th
0 - 2	59	16.72	19.27	21.86	10.84	13.52	16.30	17.55	21.05	25.04	47.68	54.15	62.00
0 - 4	55	16.00	19.22	21.63	11.80	15.20	18.11	19.14	22.03	26.35	50.04	56.56	63.17
0 - 6	61	17.16	20.47	22.84	13.60	16.09	18.87	20.85	23.60	27.28	53.56	60.78	66.76
1 - 0	58	19.74	22.16	24.85	15.03	17.85	21.12	25.08	28.31	31.60	61.82	68.81	75.84
1 - 6	58	19.83	22.85	25.12	15.72	18.06	21.59	26.60	30.58	33.89	65.32	71.42	78.63
2 - 0	56	20.67	23.41	27.04	15.92	19.13	24.00	28.98	31.98	35.54	67.91	75.38	83.28
2 - 6	58	20.45	23.15	26.05	17.39	20.96	24.28	30.10	33.95	36.53	71.07	77.79	83.90
3 - 0	57	21.41	23.86	26.86	18.97	22.26	25.75	31.58	34.86	38.97	75.91	80.82	89.72
3 - 6	57	21.86	24.50	27.64	19.38	23.43	27.24	33.21	37.08	42.00	77.40	84.72	93.05
4 - 0	56	23.25	25.71	28.10	21.42	24.11	27.58	34.25	38.93	42.74	80.75	88.35	97.21
4 - 6	55	23.87	26.53	29.29	21.28	25.12	28.80	36.22	40.97	45.21	83.59	92.11	100.91
5 - 0	53	23.95	27.08	31.04	23.02	27.10	30.16	36.57	41.69	45.76	86.06	96.12	104.36
5 - 6	48	23.77	27.54	31.74	23.71	27.35	31.23	37.48	41.96	46.40	88.11	96.76	105.76
6 - 0	50	24.88	28.66	32.14	22.90	28.30	31.80	38.69	43.60	47.62	89.56	99.88	107.88
6 - 6	51	24.85	29.48	34.25	24.95	29.72	32.81	38.43	43.94	49.04	93.13	102.63	112.27
7 - 0	52	25.80	30.89	34.94	25.66	30.55	34.16	40.39	44.28	50.74	94.79	106.42	116.44
7 - 6	47	27.16	30.59	36.09	25.01	30.75	35.08	39.90	46.53	54.03	95.28	107.63	119.08
8 - 0	45	28.56	32.44	37.88	27.05	31.48	36.36	41.22	47.48	51.74	100.49	112.66	122.85
8 - 6	45	29.41	32.86	37.99	27.78	32.99	37.87	41.62	48.06	54.16	102.07	113.86	125.79
9 - 0	44	30.00	33.30	38.24	29.22	33.23	37.68	40.95	48.20	57.24	103.09	116.42	127.84
9 - 6	45	29.79	34.03	38.55	29.43	33.72	39.38	43.32	47.82	56.69	104.81	116.99	131.78
10 - 0	44	30.13	34.99	39.56	30.46	35.10	40.68	42.28	49.50	57.05	106.32	120.32	130.42
10 - 6	41	31.18	35.56	40.45	31.92	35.11	41.72	43.24	49.59	58.95	109.72	122.00	137.05
11 - 0	40	32.58	37.27	40.90	32.28	36.69	43.81	43.44	50.51	61.20	112.88	124.55	142.06
11 - 6	38	31.70	37.30	41.76	32.76	37.43	42.78	44.45	52.06	61.44	114.10	126.54	143.49
12 - 0	36	33.53	37.75	41.77	33.44	39.38	43.99	44.73	53.13	61.80	115.61	130.31	146.81
12 - 6	33	35.09	39.01	43.29	35.76	39.70	45.10	46.40	54.05	64.83	120.45	132.83	148.80
13 - 0	33	35.72	39.91	45.96	36.35	41.27	45.70	47.04	56.08	65.32	124.29	138.67	151.23
13 - 6	27	35.19	40.47	46.81	33.84	41.10	46.11	47.02	55.81	70.12	121.57	137.04	151.88
14 - 0	27	36.94	41.01	45.93	36.44	42.15	48.17	52.30	57.31	70.07	130.28	142.88	158.61
14 - 6	19	35.21	40.36	46.26	37.62	42.13	45.75	50.44	57.61	67.14	132.43	140.70	152.56
15 - 0	24	35.83	42.08	47.27	37.65	43.52	48.04	52.79	61.40	71.31	133.88	146.30	161.64
16 - 0	17	39.21	43.21	47.66	36.98	44.60	50.46	56.23	62.60	73.40	137.41	151.66	163.78
17 - 0	10	41.86	42.89	49.58	35.65	42.10	52.85	61.42	65.22	74.59	149.27	153.98	161.83

MEASUREMENTS FROM ROENTGENOGRAMS

TABLE F-20

Fat Widths in Millimeters - Male

Age Yr. Mo.	N	Max. Forearm (F) Percentiles 10th	50th	90th	Mid-thigh (T) (Lateral half) Percentiles 10th	50th	90th	Max. Calf (C) Percentiles 10th	50th	90th	Sum of F, T, C Percentiles 10th	50th	90th
0 - 2	55	8.91	11.58	16.24	5.32	7.56	10.97	8.82	11.00	16.38	23.83	30.67	42.90
0 - 4	55	11.64	15.05	19.40	7.92	12.21	16.99	12.55	16.61	21.99	32.47	43.58	56.98
0 - 6	58	14.12	17.54	22.13	9.46	14.04	19.17	15.00	20.16	24.97	39.00	51.59	66.01
1 - 0	61	13.28	16.83	21.65	9.11	13.27	20.97	15.46	18.62	24.71	38.56	47.86	65.32
1 - 6	59	12.98	16.35	21.73	8.58	12.10	17.06	12.78	16.41	22.11	35.18	45.68	59.77
2 - 0	57	12.25	15.24	19.82	7.39	11.34	17.14	11.69	14.99	19.82	32.51	41.68	56.49
2 - 6	59	12.03	15.13	19.44	7.16	10.42	15.89	11.50	14.26	18.97	31.64	39.48	53.44
3 - 0	57	11.18	14.31	18.53	6.54	9.85	14.32	10.20	13.09	17.00	28.30	37.15	49.20
3 - 6	56	11.46	13.62	17.41	6.13	9.03	13.63	9.30	12.56	16.19	26.89	35.62	46.64
4 - 0	52	10.62	13.17	16.65	5.87	8.59	13.01	9.11	11.95	15.90	25.40	34.01	44.49
4 - 6	54	9.40	12.25	16.30	5.26	7.99	11.44	8.62	11.76	15.20	24.86	32.69	42.99
5 - 0	55	9.31	11.86	15.61	5.14	7.83	11.08	8.38	11.66	14.45	23.62	31.83	40.09
5 - 6	51	9.13	11.50	14.89	4.84	7.52	11.22	8.09	11.19	14.90	22.51	30.48	40.44
6 - 0	50	8.87	11.42	15.37	5.11	7.56	12.08	8.24	10.98	14.64	22.91	29.89	39.60
6 - 6	49	8.14	10.91	13.71	4.95	7.26	11.37	8.17	10.82	14.71	21.75	29.32	39.42
7 - 0	48	8.41	10.80	14.16	4.64	7.57	11.46	8.49	11.04	14.93	21.91	29.54	39.94
7 - 6	48	7.89	10.21	13.93	4.86	7.27	11.60	8.01	10.99	14.99	21.87	28.49	37.59
8 - 0	46	7.68	10.22	15.63	4.69	7.30	11.62	8.01	11.20	15.83	21.17	28.85	42.37
8 - 6	44	7.80	9.84	15.97	4.78	7.18	11.96	7.57	10.95	14.80	21.18	27.98	39.54
9 - 0	45	7.34	10.12	14.90	4.71	7.78	13.24	8.03	11.58	16.02	21.05	30.20	44.36
9 - 6	47	7.82	10.64	14.66	4.59	7.59	13.27	7.90	11.73	15.52	20.80	29.89	41.52
10 - 0	45	7.54	10.90	15.47	4.47	8.37	14.08	8.77	12.17	16.95	21.27	31.60	42.69
10 - 6	46	7.82	10.25	15.75	3.87	8.51	13.59	8.41	12.38	16.22	21.00	30.32	44.09
11 - 0	42	7.47	11.14	15.54	4.57	8.41	14.92	8.91	12.21	16.93	20.62	31.75	47.08
11 - 6	44	7.36	10.68	15.05	4.12	8.55	14.55	8.71	12.50	15.21	20.58	32.45	44.26
12 - 0	44	7.54	10.48	15.12	4.18	8.16	15.06	8.18	12.84	17.47	23.09	32.21	48.28
12 - 6	41	7.29	10.38	14.99	4.51	7.87	16.00	8.75	12.88	17.87	22.15	32.18	43.66
13 - 0	44	7.25	9.95	14.58	4.72	8.75	15.02	7.89	12.97	17.91	20.50	31.27	46.84
13 - 6	40	5.90	9.22	13.60	4.27	7.39	15.61	7.96	12.03	17.54	19.81	28.29	47.50
14 - 0	39	5.79	8.00	12.94	4.19	6.92	14.00	7.84	11.12	16.32	18.70	26.69	44.67
14 - 6	35	5.40	7.78	13.47	3.66	6.31	15.93	7.07	10.39	17.35	16.98	24.91	46.22
15 - 0	31	5.04	7.22	13.05	3.94	6.60	14.12	6.45	9.31	16.61	18.14	24.61	43.06
15 - 6	25	5.53	6.82	11.86	4.42	6.33	10.49	6.99	10.12	14.76	17.38	23.20	38.48
16 - 0	28	5.38	7.45	12.75	3.95	6.09	13.20	6.40	10.55	15.70	17.21	23.68	44.60
16 - 6	16	4.88	7.02	11.04	4.38	6.52	10.56	6.18	10.74	14.30	16.61	24.72	39.48
17 - 0	25	4.91	6.27	9.83	3.52	5.45	9.95	7.20	10.15	13.19	16.78	21.51	34.92
18 - 0	12	4.44	5.71	8.15	3.00	4.68	10.42	5.73	8.32	14.52	12.83	16.65	33.77

MEASUREMENTS FROM ROENTGENOGRAMS — TABLE F-21

Fat Widths in Millimeters - Female

Age	N	Max. Forearm (F)			Mid-thigh (T) (Lateral half)			Max. Calf (C)			Sum of F, T, C		
		Percentiles			Percentiles			Percentiles			Percentiles		
Yr. Mo.		10th	50th	90th	10th	50th	90th	10th	50th	90th	10th	50th	90th
0 - 2	59	10.72	12.57	15.72	6.05	8.58	12.90	10.07	12.86	16.09	27.52	34.56	44.19
0 - 4	55	12.31	16.26	20.29	9.05	12.50	17.60	14.38	17.56	21.52	37.42	46.12	57.13
0 - 6	61	14.01	18.23	21.57	10.78	14.72	20.90	15.37	20.32	25.25	40.93	54.10	65.22
1 - 0	58	14.24	17.32	21.80	10.46	14.12	19.47	15.26	19.16	23.84	41.58	51.25	63.95
1 - 6	58	13.72	17.27	20.68	9.66	13.06	19.13	13.65	17.09	20.89	37.34	46.90	58.84
2 - 0	56	12.92	16.73	20.55	8.55	12.01	18.45	12.27	16.10	20.02	34.17	44.24	57.04
2 - 6	58	12.72	15.31	19.08	8.06	11.50	15.92	11.99	14.88	18.28	32.52	41.72	52.76
3 - 0	57	12.38	15.00	19.30	7.81	10.83	14.84	11.42	13.96	17.68	31.59	39.85	51.36
3 - 6	57	11.91	14.74	17.89	7.11	10.17	15.16	10.77	13.67	16.90	30.52	38.35	49.94
4 - 0	56	11.46	14.60	17.16	7.34	10.39	14.41	10.05	13.16	16.55	29.36	38.20	47.41
4 - 6	55	11.00	13.99	16.79	6.74	9.89	14.54	10.22	12.64	16.35	29.19	36.09	46.71
5 - 0	53	10.66	13.12	16.17	6.85	9.45	14.29	9.88	12.28	15.97	28.11	34.90	44.95
5 - 6	48	10.06	12.91	16.04	6.47	9.42	13.98	9.47	12.26	17.02	26.81	35.28	46.18
6 - 0	50	9.70	12.70	15.95	6.14	9.44	14.00	9.66	12.14	16.10	26.58	33.77	46.08
6 - 6	51	9.22	12.36	15.21	5.84	9.06	13.70	9.29	12.09	16.42	25.76	32.88	44.24
7 - 0	52	9.34	12.06	14.87	5.90	9.67	15.18	9.38	12.01	17.62	25.53	33.18	47.00
7 - 6	47	8.78	12.06	15.88	5.83	8.82	16.04	9.22	12.18	17.37	24.13	32.35	47.84
8 - 0	45	8.96	12.09	15.72	6.08	10.22	17.12	9.64	12.28	18.52	26.55	33.91	49.18
8 - 6	45	8.74	12.21	16.34	6.52	10.70	17.08	9.71	13.02	18.06	24.83	35.83	51.05
9 - 0	44	9.59	12.49	16.26	6.21	10.75	17.86	9.99	13.80	19.47	25.96	36.31	52.58
9 - 6	45	9.32	12.22	16.84	6.70	10.77	17.99	9.93	13.26	19.64	27.74	35.64	54.50
10 - 0	44	9.43	12.12	16.67	6.56	10.18	16.20	10.29	13.15	18.96	27.51	35.51	51.39
10 - 6	41	8.80	12.45	15.76	6.65	10.76	17.53	10.18	13.86	19.48	26.55	37.22	52.83
11 - 0	40	8.99	12.30	17.42	7.40	11.24	17.03	10.64	13.59	19.93	29.20	36.88	52.48
11 - 6	38	8.82	12.54	16.20	6.86	11.09	16.71	11.33	14.36	19.39	28.69	37.30	49.37
12 - 0	36	8.59	12.89	17.70	7.64	11.49	17.89	11.27	15.03	20.94	28.44	39.19	54.66
12 - 6	33	8.74	12.58	17.28	7.53	11.29	18.86	11.66	15.28	21.47	28.85	39.49	56.60
13 - 0	33	9.66	11.90	15.58	7.50	11.11	18.90	12.03	15.02	20.84	29.82	37.70	54.09
13 - 6	27	8.57	12.50	16.64	7.77	11.98	19.94	11.50	15.02	22.26	30.66	38.86	55.52
14 - 0	27	9.67	13.20	17.30	7.61	12.30	21.14	12.52	15.44	22.24	30.94	40.50	57.77
14 - 6	19	9.29	12.48	17.54	8.19	12.38	18.77	12.06	14.94	22.40	29.72	39.97	58.46
15 - 0	24	8.77	13.42	16.91	8.36	13.57	22.55	13.03	16.13	21.09	32.29	43.20	58.24
16 - 0	17	10.62	13.54	19.05	9.04	15.60	21.49	13.18	16.85	24.94	33.99	48.20	61.98
17 - 0	10	10.84	15.07	18.83	11.15	14.65	25.15	13.78	15.07	22.81	37.64	45.18	66.95

MEASUREMENTS FROM ROENTGENOGRAMS

TABLE F-22

Bone Widths at Mid-length Levels in Millimeters - Male

Age Yr. Mo.	N	Humerus (1)			Radius (2)			Femur (3) (same as column T in Table F-16)			Tibia (4)		
		Percentiles			Percentiles			Percentiles			Percentiles		
		10th	50th	90th	10th	50th	90th	10th	50th	90th	10th	50th	90th
0 - 2	55	6.05	6.88	7.96	3.87	4.58	5.37	6.50	7.36	8.14	6.42	7.06	7.98
0 - 4	55	7.80	8.38	9.51	4.85	5.58	6.31	7.40	8.25	9.16	7.45	8.04	9.71
0 - 6	58	8.27	9.17	10.20	5.58	6.30	6.80	8.14	8.95	9.89	7.72	8.66	9.84
1 - 0	61	9.92	11.08	12.01	6.63	7.22	8.00	9.58	10.56	11.74	8.91	10.04	11.43
1 - 6	59	10.73	11.79	12.96	7.09	8.01	8.70	11.01	11.85	12.96	10.15	11.09	12.93
2 - 0	57	10.98	12.41	13.43	7.46	8.15	8.84	11.83	12.75	13.88	10.47	11.62	13.37
2 - 6	59	11.58	12.66	14.07	7.39	8.32	9.27	12.32	13.41	14.67	10.85	12.08	13.52
3 - 0	57	11.63	13.02	14.07	7.82	8.59	9.52	12.84	14.10	15.32	11.39	12.47	14.02
3 - 6	56	11.80	13.16	14.22	8.07	8.86	9.96	13.36	14.37	15.94	11.82	12.75	14.34
4 - 0	52	12.32	13.29	14.40	8.34	9.19	10.54	13.82	14.96	16.20	12.00	13.16	14.69
4 - 6	54	12.72	13.56	15.05	8.57	9.54	10.52	14.14	15.30	16.90	12.61	13.52	14.99
5 - 0	55	12.79	13.91	15.22	8.77	9.88	10.82	14.54	15.75	17.12	12.94	13.99	15.29
5 - 6	51	12.91	14.37	15.66	9.00	10.25	11.23	15.03	16.36	17.71	13.29	14.52	15.72
6 - 0	50	13.26	14.56	15.98	9.30	10.52	11.60	15.37	16.64	18.28	13.77	14.72	16.32
6 - 6	49	13.21	14.77	16.39	9.60	10.63	11.70	15.67	17.22	18.32	14.00	15.32	16.57
7 - 0	48	13.72	14.92	16.51	9.85	11.04	11.94	16.49	17.64	19.35	14.51	15.86	17.22
7 - 6	48	13.89	15.39	17.10	9.92	11.04	12.55	16.89	18.15	19.78	14.90	16.26	17.59
8 - 0	46	14.05	15.50	17.62	10.21	11.10	12.71	17.42	18.74	20.46	15.50	16.64	18.14
8 - 6	44	14.56	15.95	17.95	10.14	11.58	13.17	17.52	19.15	21.42	15.86	17.11	18.61
9 - 0	45	14.67	16.09	18.13	10.50	11.88	13.51	17.98	19.90	21.76	16.26	17.66	19.12
9 - 6	47	14.52	16.48	18.50	10.74	11.88	13.47	18.29	20.10	22.49	16.57	18.34	19.53
10 - 0	45	15.10	16.79	19.22	10.90	12.35	13.82	18.64	20.82	23.03	16.97	18.71	20.17
10 - 6	46	15.36	16.98	18.89	10.86	12.54	14.23	19.16	21.35	22.81	17.18	19.13	20.80
11 - 0	42	15.64	17.56	19.31	10.75	12.98	14.46	19.51	21.72	23.64	18.10	19.74	21.71
11 - 6	44	15.68	17.92	19.72	11.22	12.92	14.75	19.43	22.42	24.21	18.34	20.36	22.23
12 - 0	44	16.16	18.04	20.10	11.40	13.22	14.70	20.05	22.78	24.64	18.40	20.45	22.70
12 - 6	39	16.73	18.78	20.88	11.45	13.54	15.09	20.67	23.45	25.39	18.98	20.92	23.59
13 - 0	41	16.70	19.14	21.42	11.82	13.67	15.38	21.22	24.10	26.13	19.32	21.28	23.99
13 - 6	39	17.04	19.39	22.00	11.91	13.95	15.74	21.20	24.47	27.03	19.58	22.37	24.27
14 - 0	37	17.46	20.16	22.69	12.45	14.68	16.27	22.17	24.90	27.22	20.17	22.66	24.71
14 - 6	34	17.50	20.57	23.08	12.27	14.43	16.50	22.32	25.58	27.93	20.33	22.90	25.80
15 - 0	30	18.70	20.88	23.49	13.48	15.18	17.29	22.99	26.19	28.27	21.04	23.91	25.96
15 - 6	25	18.18	21.04	24.12	12.88	15.36	17.38	23.59	26.53	29.92	21.06	24.02	27.31
16 - 0	28	19.82	22.40	24.84	13.62	15.30	17.52	24.62	27.36	30.86	21.92	24.33	27.96
16 - 6	16	19.94	21.60	23.70	13.79	15.12	17.50	24.53	26.94	29.34	21.83	23.87	26.65
17 - 0	25	20.35	22.02	24.84	14.12	16.04	17.35	24.53	27.86	29.71	21.99	24.45	27.26
18 - 0	12	20.52	21.92	24.88	14.61	15.62	17.34	24.72	28.72	29.67	21.81	24.70	26.17

MEASUREMENTS FROM ROENTGENOGRAMS

TABLE F-23

Bone Widths at Mid-length Levels in Millimeters - Female

Age	N	Humerus (1)			Radius (2)			Femur (3) (same as column T in Table F-17)			Tibia (4)		
		Percentiles			Percentiles			Percentiles			Percentiles		
Yr. Mo.		10th	50th	90th	10th	50th	90th	10th	50th	90th	10th	50th	90th
0 - 2	59	6.01	6.78	7.64	4.10	4.57	5.06	6.39	7.09	7.78	6.30	6.97	7.89
0 - 4	55	7.09	7.99	9.18	4.63	5.30	5.92	7.18	7.84	8.81	6.79	7.78	8.48
0 - 6	61	7.93	8.93	9.72	5.14	5.70	6.51	7.65	8.53	9.54	7.43	8.30	9.17
1 - 0	58	9.32	10.74	11.68	5.98	6.68	7.66	8.92	10.40	11.24	8.25	9.85	11.26
1 - 6	58	10.19	11.56	12.70	6.69	7.57	8.25	10.42	11.71	12.74	9.40	10.93	12.67
2 - 0	56	10.41	12.30	13.05	6.78	7.72	8.72	11.12	12.62	13.79	9.93	11.48	12.88
2 - 6	58	10.65	12.25	13.33	7.05	7.99	8.89	11.86	13.28	14.60	10.23	11.99	13.55
3 - 0	57	11.16	12.57	13.66	7.40	8.19	9.08	12.54	13.71	15.19	10.83	12.41	13.81
3 - 6	57	11.24	12.74	13.68	7.55	8.71	9.70	12.93	14.41	15.70	11.17	12.65	14.16
4 - 0	56	11.48	12.98	14.44	7.86	8.93	9.90	13.50	14.79	16.20	11.80	13.16	14.52
4 - 6	55	11.67	13.38	14.64	8.01	9.15	10.14	13.93	15.21	16.75	12.18	13.58	14.88
5 - 0	53	11.89	13.52	14.92	8.37	9.67	10.42	14.46	15.68	17.27	12.44	13.99	15.51
5 - 6	48	12.17	13.80	15.02	8.45	9.63	10.80	14.75	16.12	17.70	12.97	14.36	15.96
6 - 0	50	12.50	14.09	15.25	8.74	9.81	11.21	15.04	16.48	17.98	13.32	14.83	16.17
6 - 6	51	12.61	14.41	15.52	9.01	10.02	11.21	15.54	16.83	18.42	13.45	15.22	16.64
7 - 0	52	12.90	14.61	15.94	9.18	10.41	11.42	15.88	17.17	19.06	14.11	15.78	17.08
7 - 6	47	12.72	14.86	16.50	9.10	10.62	11.78	16.33	17.53	19.34	14.32	15.96	17.18
8 - 0	45	13.16	15.19	16.71	9.44	10.70	11.82	16.71	18.06	19.88	14.73	16.36	17.64
8 - 6	45	13.46	15.34	16.89	9.31	10.87	11.99	17.21	18.31	20.22	15.11	16.68	18.34
9 - 0	44	13.51	15.61	17.25	9.75	10.88	12.49	17.36	18.82	20.94	15.31	17.15	18.79
9 - 6	45	13.72	15.89	17.24	9.55	11.23	12.72	17.61	19.22	21.51	15.62	17.44	19.60
10 - 0	44	13.90	16.03	17.70	9.91	11.38	12.79	18.03	19.68	21.99	15.92	17.69	19.72
10 - 6	41	14.48	16.15	17.95	9.97	11.52	13.00	18.69	20.09	22.71	16.12	18.16	20.17
11 - 0	40	14.57	16.40	18.38	10.28	11.77	13.32	19.24	20.71	23.27	16.79	18.45	21.15
11 - 6	38	15.03	16.86	19.16	10.66	12.07	13.46	19.63	21.26	23.92	17.19	18.84	21.15
12 - 0	36	15.53	17.32	19.03	10.40	12.06	13.52	20.41	21.88	24.12	17.75	19.18	21.95
12 - 6	33	16.09	17.69	19.73	10.74	12.11	13.58	20.60	22.44	25.04	18.02	19.60	22.79
13 - 0	33	16.31	18.20	20.22	10.92	12.37	13.87	21.41	23.08	24.99	18.31	19.72	23.46
13 - 6	27	16.52	18.17	20.48	11.12	12.64	14.13	21.88	23.51	25.52	18.67	20.31	24.03
14 - 0	27	16.75	18.94	20.38	11.13	12.52	14.15	22.33	24.05	25.56	19.34	20.63	23.59
14 - 6	19	17.44	19.22	20.47	11.34	12.74	14.26	23.44	24.38	25.64	19.97	21.04	23.16
15 - 0	24	17.29	19.26	20.41	11.03	12.61	14.23	22.57	24.54	26.05	19.18	20.55	23.42
16 - 0	17	17.21	19.76	21.03	11.42	12.94	14.58	23.16	24.72	26.43	19.90	21.15	22.77
17 - 0	10	17.74	19.22	20.58	11.46	12.89	13.71	23.94	25.42	26.53	20.32	21.22	22.84

EASUREMENTS FROM ROENTGENOGRAMS

TABLE F-24

Additional Fat Widths in Millimeters

	Level of Deltoid Insertion (D)								Level of Max. Hip Bulge (H)							
	Male				Female				Male				Female			
Age		Percentiles				Percentiles				Percentiles				Percentiles		
r. Mo.	N	10th	50th	90th	N	10th	50th	90th	N	10th	50th	90th	N	10th	50th	90th
0 - 2	55	7.50	9.21	11.98	59	8.57	10.02	11.72	55	7.45	10.56	15.64	59	8.81	11.62	15.28
0 - 4	55	9.18	11.26	13.58	55	9.82	12.03	13.74	55	11.77	15.80	21.37	55	13.50	16.34	21.88
0 - 6	58	10.25	12.52	14.95	61	10.31	12.96	15.22	58	13.18	18.44	25.21	61	14.34	19.87	26.71
1 - 0	61	9.68	11.83	14.69	58	9.75	12.60	15.49	61	13.19	18.40	25.89	58	14.46	18.95	25.08
1 - 6	59	9.53	11.65	14.49	58	9.62	12.45	15.50	59	11.82	17.41	21.83	58	13.02	18.76	25.51
2 - 0	57	8.62	11.38	13.45	56	9.23	12.34	15.21	57	11.01	15.84	21.34	56	13.13	17.30	24.30
2 - 6	59	8.76	11.42	13.57	58	9.36	12.30	14.60	59	11.21	15.26	20.64	58	11.88	17.48	22.72
3 - 0	57	8.77	10.65	13.14	57	9.14	11.98	14.94	57	9.95	14.47	19.87	57	12.21	17.25	21.80
3 - 6	56	8.27	10.42	12.87	57	9.36	11.76	14.08	56	10.40	14.07	19.80	57	11.11	16.98	22.21
4 - 0	52	7.57	10.25	13.00	56	8.82	11.59	15.38	52	9.71	13.72	19.20	56	11.42	17.43	22.28
4 - 6	54	7.82	9.96	12.09	55	8.78	11.19	15.26	54	9.33	13.33	18.15	55	11.34	17.16	22.58
5 - 0	55	6.94	9.98	12.28	53	8.85	10.81	15.53	55	8.79	13.45	17.19	53	11.20	16.63	23.20
5 - 6	51	7.30	9.58	12.00	48	7.96	11.01	16.02	51	7.85	12.87	17.71	48	10.48	16.71	23.96
6 - 0	50	6.75	9.34	12.53	50	7.91	10.65	16.84	50	8.07	12.99	17.84	50	10.28	17.41	24.20
6 - 6	49	6.49	9.21	12.14	51	7.29	10.78	15.18	49	8.52	12.57	18.52	51	10.11	16.66	24.97
7 - 0	48	6.50	9.16	12.81	52	8.06	10.72	16.20	48	7.83	13.19	18.74	52	9.85	16.94	24.08
7 - 6	48	6.45	8.74	12.45	47	7.73	11.32	17.86	48	7.45	13.28	17.84	47	9.72	17.03	27.53
8 - 0	46	6.28	9.55	14.54	45	7.76	11.07	18.38	46	7.00	13.42	20.47	45	11.14	18.86	29.82
8 - 6	44	5.94	8.87	13.88	45	8.26	11.88	18.46	44	7.14	13.16	20.64	45	11.36	18.88	31.27
9 - 0	45	6.05	9.24	15.58	44	8.15	12.20	19.93	45	8.06	14.37	25.54	44	11.36	19.62	32.56
9 - 6	47	6.32	9.78	15.71	45	8.69	12.84	19.62	47	7.78	14.93	24.00	45	12.78	20.22	32.58
0 - 0	45	6.62	10.12	16.32	44	7.99	12.84	20.38	45	9.14	15.79	25.26	44	12.22	20.96	32.15
0 - 6	46	6.66	9.97	16.72	41	8.57	12.86	19.42	45	8.40	15.11	28.73	41	12.57	21.79	32.28
1 - 0	42	6.65	10.54	16.77	40	9.01	12.93	19.97	42	7.13	16.37	26.38	40	13.02	21.93	30.62
1 - 6	44	6.34	10.05	16.33	38	9.05	14.36	19.95	44	7.93	16.28	26.24	38	13.37	21.49	30.81
2 - 0	44	6.69	10.82	18.42	36	9.26	13.77	20.83	44	7.92	15.35	29.24	36	13.74	22.12	34.40
- 6	39	7.22	10.13	19.29	33	9.47	14.12	21.93	41	8.24	14.95	30.56	32	13.73	22.24	33.44
3 - 0	41	6.90	11.43	20.30	33	8.76	14.30	21.26	43	7.29	15.67	29.40	33	15.14	22.17	33.39
3 - 6	39	6.38	8.91	17.07	27	9.14	13.26	21.69	40	6.86	13.06	25.53	27	15.38	24.59	35.72
4 - 0	37	5.29	8.90	16.72	27	9.78	14.44	21.70	39	6.88	12.27	24.99	27	13.63	24.91	34.61
4 - 6	34	4.58	7.33	20.81	19	9.57	13.25	20.62	35	5.82	11.24	28.16	19	15.25	24.99	33.61
5 - 0	30	4.72	7.38	18.96	24	10.31	15.06	22.63	30	5.64	10.54	29.56	24	17.64	26.74	36.67
5 - 6	25	4.24	6.95	16.59	6	-	-	-	23	5.42	10.60	18.25	6	-	-	-
6 - 0	28	4.00	6.39	20.14	17	10.99	16.14	23.92	27	5.46	11.22	33.39	17	19.43	31.36	40.51
6 - 6	16	4.82	7.54	14.67	2	-	-	-	15	7.77	11.18	19.21	2	-	-	-
7 - 0	25	4.18	6.30	13.22	10	13.58	20.70	27.82	24	5.44	9.85	15.14	10	21.35	29.05	52.15
8 - 0	12	3.89	6.10	9.56	7	-	-	-	11	4.24	8.41	14.46	7	-	-	-

MEASUREMENTS FROM ROENTGENOGRAMS

TABLE F-25

Sums of Other Combinations of Widths in Millimeters - Male

Age	Sum of 5 Fat Widths (FTCDH - Tables F-20, F-24)				Sum of 4 Mid-length Bone Widths (1,2,3,4 - Table F-22)				Sum of 3 Bone plus Muscle Widths (FTC - Tables F-16 and F-18)			
		Percentiles				Percentiles				Percentiles		
Yr. Mo.	N	10th	50th	90th	N	10th	50th	90th	N	10th	50th	90th
0 - 2	55	39.35	50.61	68.95	55	23.60	26.00	29.24	55	78.83	85.82	95.38
0 - 4	55	54.22	71.23	91.78	55	27.72	30.50	33.62	55	85.95	92.94	100.93
0 - 6	58	60.81	82.85	105.92	58	30.48	33.01	35.80	58	90.11	97.08	107.21
1 - 0	61	64.20	77.82	104.26	61	35.65	38.86	42.60	61	100.79	111.76	122.66
1 - 6	59	57.03	73.98	95.28	59	39.67	42.94	46.84	59	109.08	116.75	130.22
2 - 0	57	53.91	69.02	90.61	57	41.49	45.02	48.73	57	114.54	123.43	136.91
2 - 6	59	52.54	65.55	86.47	59	43.36	46.56	50.73	59	119.51	128.38	141.87
3 - 0	57	47.80	62.19	80.47	57	44.38	48.22	52.28	57	123.76	135.33	150.64
3 - 6	56	47.90	60.26	76.86	56	45.82	49.21	53.86	56	127.83	138.92	153.98
4 - 0	52	44.17	58.85	75.56	52	47.47	50.71	54.71	52	134.07	141.48	155.26
4 - 6	54	41.73	56.51	72.10	54	48.99	52.10	55.65	54	138.14	146.81	158.52
5 - 0	55	41.41	56.30	69.90	55	49.68	53.53	57.53	55	140.58	153.24	164.56
5 - 6	51	39.35	52.86	66.93	51	51.20	55.26	59.56	51	146.66	156.34	170.77
6 - 0	50	40.13	52.11	68.16	50	52.15	56.66	61.23	50	148.58	159.66	174.34
6 - 6	49	38.99	51.18	68.06	49	53.78	57.98	62.45	49	151.90	163.09	178.98
7 - 0	48	38.36	52.10	70.62	48	55.75	59.26	65.20	48	157.76	168.52	184.82
7 - 6	48	37.97	50.89	64.98	48	57.15	60.95	66.56	48	160.41	173.14	188.70
8 - 0	46	36.11	52.90	73.59	46	58.22	61.70	68.04	46	163.74	177.67	193.68
8 - 6	44	35.54	50.57	72.92	44	59.41	64.01	69.72	44	168.54	180.82	197.87
9 - 0	45	36.50	52.32	82.70	45	60.82	65.55	71.78	45	172.76	186.29	203.29
9 - 6	47	37.68	56.15	78.19	47	61.62	66.98	72.53	47	175.09	192.05	206.97
10 - 0	45	36.54	56.66	84.28	45	63.62	68.58	75.09	45	181.63	195.54	209.78
10 - 6	45	36.16	55.29	89.60	46	63.64	69.79	75.97	46	181.29	200.28	218.01
11 - 0	42	37.55	59.57	88.55	42	65.85	72.35	78.22	42	186.19	204.28	219.03
11 - 6	44	36.69	58.07	84.07	44	66.32	73.43	80.20	44	188.04	205.68	224.22
12 - 0	44	37.27	58.41	94.22	44	68.31	74.37	82.52	44	195.35	211.34	236.23
12 - 6	39	39.51	58.14	89.48	39	70.01	76.40	83.99	39	195.65	215.60	240.59
13 - 0	40	37.99	55.02	98.11	41	70.54	78.05	86.43	40	200.82	218.23	248.23
13 - 6	39	36.19	50.52	89.34	39	70.78	80.72	87.96	39	200.17	224.16	254.42
14 - 0	36	33.09	46.24	78.08	37	74.40	82.29	90.45	36	209.40	234.52	260.72
14 - 6	34	28.19	42.25	100.75	34	73.36	83.30	93.24	34	211.30	235.82	261.54
15 - 0	29	29.40	41.94	97.81	30	78.27	87.57	93.22	29	219.33	243.01	273.13
15 - 6	23	28.96	39.17	70.53	25	76.96	87.98	95.20	23	226.64	247.13	266.49
16 - 0	27	28.82	41.49	94.19	28	82.06	89.72	102.10	27	235.50	255.47	273.98
16 - 6	15	32.26	43.65	72.56	16	81.22	87.99	93.80	15	236.48	252.41	277.02
17 - 0	24	27.92	37.56	61.68	24	83.49	91.10	96.23	24	244.84	257.35	274.03
18 - 0	11	21.46	35.09	54.64	12	83.96	91.86	96.85	12	251.14	263.82	279.79

MEASUREMENTS FROM ROENTGENOGRAMS — TABLE F-26

Sums of Other Combinations of Widths in Millimeters - Female

Age	Sum of 5 Fat Widths (FTCDH - Tables F-21, F-24)				Sum of 4 Mid-length Bone Widths (1,2,3,4 - Table F-23)				Sum of 3 Bone plus Muscle Widths (FTC - Tables F-17, F-19)			
		Percentiles				Percentiles				Percentiles		
Yr. Mo.	N	10th	50th	90th	N	10th	50th	90th	N	10th	50th	90th
0 - 2	59	46.80	57.08	71.14	59	23.30	25.22	27.72	59	75.31	82.97	91.16
0 - 4	55	61.58	74.64	90.67	55	26.74	28.66	31.72	55	80.67	88.34	94.95
0 - 6	61	66.95	89.14	107.41	61	28.66	31.47	34.38	61	86.18	94.77	102.41
1 - 0	58	67.23	82.07	102.18	58	33.01	38.07	41.18	58	98.64	108.90	117.89
1 - 6	58	60.62	80.18	98.86	58	36.81	41.84	45.59	58	107.29	116.16	125.34
2 - 0	56	57.78	74.26	94.45	56	39.17	44.30	48.02	56	112.04	122.94	132.32
2 - 6	58	55.47	72.15	89.75	58	40.95	45.79	49.80	58	117.22	127.17	136.09
3 - 0	57	54.04	69.65	88.36	57	42.22	47.55	50.45	57	124.16	132.73	143.64
3 - 6	57	50.19	68.08	84.73	57	43.44	48.84	52.47	57	127.39	138.26	148.13
4 - 0	56	50.76	68.75	82.57	56	44.95	50.37	53.92	56	133.02	141.94	152.27
4 - 6	55	49.79	64.16	83.77	55	46.51	51.94	55.23	55	136.52	147.30	158.08
5 - 0	53	48.24	62.20	83.76	53	48.10	53.20	56.66	53	140.74	153.33	162.10
5 - 6	48	45.99	62.56	84.72	48	48.83	54.34	58.47	48	142.19	155.15	167.25
6 - 0	50	45.32	60.11	85.99	50	50.44	55.20	59.96	50	147.02	158.05	172.03
6 - 6	51	43.76	60.72	79.14	51	51.22	56.44	60.86	51	151.78	162.55	175.18
7 - 0	52	44.76	62.28	86.35	52	52.50	58.23	62.22	52	154.46	167.43	181.72
7 - 6	47	42.73	62.01	96.59	47	53.70	59.12	63.94	47	157.25	170.02	186.00
8 - 0	45	45.28	64.38	95.37	45	55.12	60.41	65.27	45	160.20	175.14	188.93
8 - 6	45	46.94	67.38	99.64	45	55.64	61.15	66.22	45	164.02	178.65	193.68
9 - 0	44	48.63	69.84	102.23	44	56.49	62.24	68.87	44	167.18	181.75	197.77
9 - 6	45	51.39	71.14	107.35	45	57.91	64.27	69.78	45	169.00	184.10	201.27
10 - 0	44	48.15	70.72	100.09	44	58.76	64.70	71.60	44	170.90	187.05	201.06
10 - 6	41	49.18	73.06	99.32	41	60.47	65.65	72.63	41	175.69	189.87	211.07
11 - 0	40	53.97	73.07	98.80	40	61.65	67.33	75.14	40	180.87	195.00	216.33
11 - 6	38	52.90	75.58	98.18	38	63.86	69.11	76.78	38	181.95	200.07	221.01
12 - 0	36	51.37	77.59	107.06	36	66.29	69.81	78.38	36	189.33	203.65	227.10
12 - 6	32	53.94	76.66	106.63	33	66.04	71.71	79.03	33	194.34	210.69	231.60
13 - 0	33	53.71	75.48	107.67	33	67.07	73.34	81.80	33	198.28	214.96	229.78
13 - 6	27	55.05	79.75	111.33	27	69.32	74.91	81.58	27	198.27	216.50	234.72
14 - 0	27	56.20	81.35	118.29	27	70.24	76.83	81.90	27	207.98	224.32	234.83
14 - 6	19	54.54	77.60	108.22	19	74.32	77.87	80.65	19	211.76	222.09	234.20
15 - 0	24	58.88	86.08	120.62	24	71.13	77.59	81.98	24	212.99	226.54	240.25
16 - 0	17	68.23	98.07	120.52	17	73.44	79.44	82.37	17	221.74	230.92	242.46
17 - 0	10	72.58	90.12	147.13	10	73.24	79.40	81.92	10	225.65	235.32	243.92

MEASUREMENTS FROM ROENTGENOGRAMS

TABLE F-27

Skeletal Maturation

Chronological Age	Male				Female			
	Skeletal Age				Skeletal Age			
Yr. Mo.	N	50th Percentile Yr. Mo.	Range Yr. Mo.	Range Yr. Mo.	N	50th Percentile Yr. Mo.	Range Yr. Mo.	Range Yr. Mo.
1 - 0	53	1 - 0	0 - 3	1 - 8	64	1 - 0	0 - 3	1 - 10
1 - 6	43	1 - 5	0 - 4	2 - 8	58	1 - 8	0 - 9	2 - 3
2 - 0	54	1 - 9	0 - 9	3 - 4	68	2 - 2	1 - 4	3 - 0
2 - 6	55	2 - 3	1 - 4	4 - 0	68	2 - 6	1 - 8	3 - 0
3 - 0	54	2 - 8	1 - 8	4 - 6	67	2 - 10	2 - 0	3 - 9
3 - 6	37	3 - 3	1 - 10	4 - 6	46	3 - 3	2 - 4	4 - 4
4 - 0	51	3 - 10	2 - 3	5 - 0	66	3 - 5	2 - 6	5 - 0
4 - 6	40	4 - 5	2 - 9	5 - 6	48	4 - 1	3 - 0	5 - 6
5 - 0	50	4 - 7	3 - 0	6 - 0	59	4 - 6	3 - 2	6 - 0
5 - 6	38	5 - 1	3 - 0	6 - 6	52	5 - 0.5	3 - 5	6 - 6
6 - 0	39	5 - 7	3 - 3	7 - 0	54	5 - 7	3 - 9	6 - 10
6 - 6	40	6 - 0	3 - 9	8 - 4	53	6 - 2	4 - 2	7 - 9
7 - 0	46	6 - 4	4 - 3	8 - 0	53	6 - 7	4 - 6	8 - 4
7 - 6	41	7 - 0	4 - 9	9 - 0	57	6 - 9	5 - 0	9 - 0
8 - 0	42	7 - 3.5	5 - 0	9 - 2	53	7 - 4	5 - 9	9 - 0
8 - 6	42	7 - 11	5 - 6	10 - 0	54	7 - 11	6 - 0	10 - 0
9 - 0	43	8 - 4	6 - 0	11 - 0	52	8 - 2	6 - 6	11 - 0
9 - 6	39	8 - 11	6 - 6	11 - 6	49	8 - 7	6 - 9	11 - 6
10 - 0	43	9 - 5	7 - 0	12 - 0	54	9 - 3	7 - 0	12 - 0
10 - 6	42	9 - 11	7 - 6	12 - 6	54	10 - 0	7 - 5	13 - 0
11 - 0	41	10 - 10	8 - 0	13 - 0	49	10 - 4	7 - 10	13 - 9
11 - 6	45	11 - 6	8 - 6	13 - 6	49	10 - 9	8 - 6	14 - 3
12 - 0	43	11 - 7	9 - 0	14 - 6	49	11 - 7	9 - 6	15 - 0
12 - 6	40	12 - 0	9 - 9	14 - 9	45	12 - 3	10 - 4	16 - 0
13 - 0	42	12 - 8	10 - 10	15 - 9	46	12 - 9	10 - 9	16 - 6
13 - 6	40	13 - 1	11 - 6	16 - 0	33	13 - 0.5	11 - 6	15 - 9
14 - 0	37	13 - 7	12 - 2	15 - 9	40	13 - 11	12 - 0	17 - 0
14 - 6	40	14 - 1	12 - 6	16 - 0	22	13 - 11	12 - 6	15 - 6
15 - 0	36	14 - 7	13 - 0	16 - 9	33	15 - 4	13 - 4	18 - 0
15 - 6	34	14 - 8	13 - 3	17 - 6	8	-	-	-
16 - 0	35	15 - 6	13 - 8	18 - 0	25	16 - 1	14 - 0	18 - 0
16 - 6	21	15 - 5	14 - 0	19 - 0	1	-	-	-
17 - 0	28	16 - 6	14 - 6	19 - 0	10	16 - 7	16 - 0	18 - 0
18 - 0	16	17 - 1	15 - 3	18 - 0	1	-	-	-

Section G

HEMATOLOGY

ALDULA J. MEYERS

HEMATOLOGY

Outline of Study

HEMATOLOGY studies, started in July, 1935, have included all subjects born since August, 1934. The group is composed of 87 males and 101 females from 110 families. Thirty-six families have 2 siblings being studied, thirteen have 3, and five have 4. Ages at the last blood count for subjects are:

	Males	Females
5 years or less	19	22
6-10 years	16	19
11-15 years	15	16
16-20 years	10	19
Over 20 years	27	25

Until 1947 counts were done at the physical examination visits at 1, 2, 3, 6, 9 and 12 months, and thereafter at each physical examination visit (see Introduction). Starting in 1947 counts were discontinued at the 3- and 9-month visits after 3 years unless there was a clinical need for a blood count.

Because of the importance of knowing the hematologic picture at birth for understanding the rapid changes within the first few months of life, a blood count on the third day of life was started in August, 1948. Blood was drawn at the hospital in which the infant was delivered.

In all, 5749 samples of blood have been studied. All but 346 of the analyses were by the present investigator. The number of counts per subject varies from 1 to 72, as follows:

	Number of subjects	
Number of counts	Male	Female
Less than 10	9	10
10-19	17	21
20-29	12	19
30-39	20	24
40-49	17	16
50-59	7	7
60-69	4	4
70-79	1	0

Not all determinations were performed on each sample of blood. The actual number of analyses for each variable is:

Variable	No. determinations
Erythrocyte sedimentation rate	4489
Hematocrit (packed cell volume)	5598
Hemoglobin concentration	5571
Erythrocyte count	5042
Reticulocyte percent	3799
Total leucocyte count	5215
Differential leucocyte count	5118

Methods

Collection of blood sample:

1. *Peripheral blood:* The heel, toe, or finger was rubbed with alcohol and a thin film of vaseline spread over the spot to be pricked. (This facilitated blood collection by keeping the blood in round drops.) A puncture wound deep enough to give a free flow

of blood was made with a spring lancet, and between ¼ and ½ cc of blood was collected into a small vial which contained a dried thin film of heparin (0.15 mg of 110 unit heparin). The sample thus collected was used for determinations of hemoglobin, erythrocyte count, hematocrit and sedimentation rate. Leucocyte dilutions, differential smears, and reticulocyte smears were taken directly from the bleeding point. From the same prick blood was collected for plasma protein studies (see Section H).

Sometimes two, and very occasionally three, pricks were necessary to obtain sufficient blood for analysis, and very rarely it was impossible to obtain enough for all determinations.

2. *Venous blood:* With the advent of Tiselius analysis of serum in July, 1949 (see Section H), larger blood samples were required. Venous blood was drawn from the antecubital vein with a minimum of stasis. The age at which this procedure replaced collection of peripheral blood varied with the subject, being dependent both upon his cooperation and the size of his veins. In general, venipunctures could be started at about 4 years of age. After initial misgivings, many subjects preferred venipuncture to pricking of the finger; the cooperation of most subjects at a very early age was remarkable.

Approximately ½ to 1 cc of venous blood for hematology was placed in a shell vial containing 0.30 mg of 110 unit heparin as a dried thin film. All analyses were made from this heparinized sample. Studies by Andresen and Mugrage(1) showed no difference in erythrocyte values between venous and peripheral samples provided no stasis was used in obtaining the venous blood. This was confirmed by later comparisons of group data from peripheral and venous samples at the same ages. The median differences (venous minus peripheral) were: hemoglobin + 0.05 grams; erythrocyte count + 0.12 million per cubic millimeter; hematocrit + 0.70 percent. The 67 venous samples where stasis had been used were compared with the median at each age of the venous values where no stasis had been employed. The median differences were:

Hemoglobin + 0.40 grams, significant at the 0.05 level
Hematocrit + 1.70 percent, significant at the 0.01 level

No other significant differences were found. If leucocyte dilutions and smears were made within half an hour of the taking of the blood, heparin had no significant effect on the leucocyte or differential count. (In practice these dilutions and smears were always made within 15 minutes.) The median differences between samples without heparin and those with heparin were: total leucocyte count + 200 cells; neutrophils + 0.1 percent; lymphocytes – 0.8 percent; eosinophils + 0.1 percent; and monocytes + 0.1 percent.

Analysis of samples:

For each of the variables to be discussed technical errors have been calculated. In most instances the method used was that described in the Introduction. However, some variables required different treatment.

The technical error of a percent (reticulocyte and relative differential leucocyte counts) was calculated from the equation(2):

$$V = \frac{p\ (1 - p)}{N}$$

where V is the variance (technical error squared)
p is the observed proportion
N is the number of cells counted

For the product of two determinations, each with its technical error (absolute differential counts), the equation is(3):

$$Va = (Vp \times L^2) + (Vl \times P^2) - VpVl$$

where Va is the variance of the absolute differential count
Vp is the variance of the relative differential count
Vl is the variance of the total leucocyte count
P is the relative differential count
L is the total leucocyte count

Technical error is the square root of the variance.

In determining the equivalent of technical errors for quotients (mean corpuscular constants), a quadratic equation is used to obtain the confidence limits for X/Y(4):

$$A^2 (Y^2 - t^2 Vy) - 2A (XY - t^2 Ey Ex Rxy) + (X^2 - t^2 Vx) = 0$$

where A is the confidence limit
Y is the divisor
X is the dividend
Vx and Vy are the respective variances
Ex and Ey are the respective technical errors
Rxy is the coefficient of correlation between X and Y
t is the Student's number for the desired confidence limit (1.96 for 95% confidence limit, and 2.59 for 99%)

1. *Erythrocyte sedimentation rate (E.S.R.)* (Tables G-1 and G-2): The procedure has been described in detail by Meyers et al(5). Determinations were done in the Smith(6) tube, which has an internal diameter of about 2.5 mm and a height of 50 mm.

Starting in February, 1944, readings in tenths of millimeters of the descent of the erythrocyte column were made every 5 minutes for one hour, the greatest fall in any interval being designated as the E.S.R. For a single determination the technical error is ± 0.12 mm.

Three hundred forty-nine rates were determined in a tube set at a 45-degree angle rather than vertically; these were converted to their equivalent vertical values using the nomogram of Washburn and Meyers(7). Inasmuch as the technical error involved in these transpositions is ± 0.27 mm, over twice that for a vertical determination, all values obtained by this method are so labeled on the magnetic tape but are included in the analyses presented herewith.

Previous to 1944 there were 504 E.S.R. determinations in which readings were taken every 15 minutes rather than every 5 minutes. These were converted to their equivalent 5-minute values by multiplying by a factor of 0.39. The error introduced by this conversion, ± 0.15 mm, is only slightly greater than that of the routine method.

Meyers et al(5) have shown that the E.S.R. is influenced chiefly by the hematocrit and the plasma proteins. Since clinical interest centers on its fluctuations with the latter, elimination of the hematocrit as an influencing factor is desirable. Therefore a correction based on the prediction formula of these workers was used to convert each observed E.S.R. to what it would have been with a hematocrit of 40 percent. The formula for this conversion is:

$$\text{Corrected E.S.R.} = \left[\frac{3 \times \text{hematocrit in \%}}{2 \times (100 - \text{hematocrit})} \times (\text{Obs. E.S.R.} + 1.33)\right] - 1.33$$

Both the observed and corrected rates are presented in the tables.

Results from E.S.R. determinations by the method described above can be converted to values obtained by 15-minute readings in a Wintrobe tube by multiplying by 3.6. The technical error of the resultant value is ± 0.68 mm.

2. *Hematocrit* (Table G-3): The Smith tube was centrifuged for one hour at a relative centrifugal force of 1575 times gravity. The height in millimeters of the column of packed red blood cells was divided by the height in millimeters of the entire sample to obtain the hematocrit, reported in percent. No correction was made for plasma trapped between the cells. The technical error for a single determination is ± 0.30 percent.

3. *Hemoglobin concentration* (Table G-4): Until March, 1948, hemoglobin determinations were done with a Hellige solid standard hemoglobinometer which was periodically checked against results of Van Slyke analyses of oxygen-carrying capacity of blood. A total of 2090 values was obtained by this method, usually done in duplicate. Technical error when the average of two values is used is ± 0.13 grams per 100 cc of blood.

After March, 1948, the hemoglobin determinations were done using a photoelectric colorimeter calibrated by this investigator. Once again, periodic checks were made against Van Slyke analyses, or later against standard Hemotrol solutions. Sodium carbonate (0.1%) was used to convert hemoglobin to oxyhemoglobin. Usually only one determination was made; its technical error is ± 0.17 grams per 100 cc of blood.

4. *Erythrocyte count* (Table G-5): Hayem's diluting fluid was used, and U. S. certified pipets and counting chambers were always utilized. Two drops were counted by the standard method; if they differed by more than 20 counted cells (200,000 cells per cu mm) the procedure was repeated using two more drops from

the same or a second pipet. The recorded value is the average of the last two counted; technical error for this average is ± 6.9 counted cells, or ± 69,000 cells per cu mm of blood.

5. *Mean corpuscular constants* (Tables G-6 and G-7): Mean corpuscular volume in cubic microns is obtained by dividing the hematocrit in percent by the erythrocyte count in millions per cu mm of blood and multiplying by 10.

Mean corpuscular hemoglobin concentration in percent is obtained by dividing the hemoglobin in gm per 100 cc of blood by the hematocrit in percent and multiplying by 100.

Confidence limits for these quotients vary with the levels of the two factors involved. At a hemoglobin of 15.0 grams, erythrocyte count of 5.00 million per cu mm, and a hematocrit of 45.0 percent, the confidence intervals are:

	Confidence interval	
	95%	99%
Mean corpuscular volume	90.04 ± 1.88	90.08 ± 2.47
Mean corpuscular hemoglobin concentration	33.33 ± 0.38	33.33 ± 0.50

Correlation coefficients used in the above calculations were computed on all data at all ages, and are: erythrocyte count and hematocrit + 0.6604; hemoglobin and hematocrit + 0.9194.

6. *Reticulocytes* (Table G-8): The method, using brilliant cresyl blue, was described by Washburn(8). Five thousand erythrocytes were counted and the number of reticulocytes in each 1000 recorded. The average of these numbers, divided by ten, was recorded as the reticulocyte percent. Technical error for this type of determination varies with the percent:

% Reticulocytes	Technical Error (%)
0.5	±0.100
1.0	±0.141
4.0	±0.277
7.0	±0.361

7. *Total leucocyte count* (Table G-9): One percent acetic acid was used as diluent. The procedure was identical with that described for the erythrocyte counts. Technical error for the average of two counts is ± 5.2 counted cells, or ± 260 cells per cu mm. In the percentiles listed, results are rounded to the nearest 50 cells.

8. *Differential leucocyte count* (Tables G-10 through G-13): The two-cover-slip method was used and the smears stained with Wright's stain. Five hundred cells were counted in groups of 100; the percent of each type in each 100 cells was recorded and the average used. Technical errors computed by the formula described above (theoretical) with those computed by the method described in the Introduction (observed) show close agreement:

Average Percent	Theoretical T.E. (%)	Observed T.E. (%)
0.0 - 4.9	±0.70	±0.75
5.0 - 9.9	±1.18	±1.10
10.0 - 14.9	±1.48	±1.45
15.0 - 19.9	±1.70	±1.73
20.0 - 24.9	±1.87	±1.87
25.0 - 29.9	±2.00	±1.93
30.0 - 34.9	±2.10	±2.04
35.0 - 39.9	±2.16	±2.14
40.0 - 44.9	±2.21	±2.18
45.0 - 49.9	±2.23	±2.09
50.0 - 54.9	±2.23	±2.22
55.0 - 59.9	±2.21	±2.14
60.0 - 64.9	±2.16	±2.08
65.0 - 69.9	±2.10	±2.05
70.0 - 74.9	±2.00	±2.09

75.0 - 79.9	±1.87	±1.90
80.0 - 84.9	±1.70	±1.79
85.0 - 89.9	±1.48	±1.48
90.0 - 94.9	±1.18	—
95.0 - 99.9	±0.70	—

The absolute differential count (percent of each type times the total leucocyte count) is more meaningful biologically than the percent itself. Technical errors are presented in Figure G-1. An example showing use of this graph would be: if the total leucocyte count is 10,000 and there are 50 percent lymphocytes, the technical error of the absolute lymphocyte count (5,000) is obtained by locating on the abscissa the 50 percent point, going up to the intersection with the curve for a total leucocyte count of 10,000, then across to the intercept of this point on the ordinate. Reading from the scale shows the technical error to be ±290 cells per cu mm.

Treatment of data:

1. *Age limits:* For the cross-sectional analysis of data, these age limits were set:

Ages listed		Age included
Yr. Mo. to Yr. Mo.		
3 days	---	22 - 81 hours
0 - 1	0 - 9	Stated age ± 15 days
1 - 0	15 - 0	Stated age ± 45 days
16 - 0	---	16 years minus 127 days to 16 years plus 182 days
17 - 0	20 - 0	Stated age ± 182 days
23 - 6	38 - 6	Stated age ± 2-1/2 years

N is the number of individuals. Each subject appears only once in any age group. If more than one determination was available in a given age span, the one nearest the stated age was used unless there was a more complete analysis available at an age further removed from the stated age but still within the age span. Statistical summaries for some ages are not included in the tables but are available on request. In no instance did the omitted value vary appreciably from that which could be interpolated between the ages shown in the tables.

2. *Percentile calculations:* With two exceptions, percentile calculations were done by computer as described in the Introduction. Because of the extreme skewness of distribution in the E.S.R. and eosinophilic leucocyte values, division into 10 cells was inadequate to describe the data. Therefore, the values were divided into varying numbers of cells (from 15 to 150) to insure that less than 10 percent of the values fell within the range of the lowest cell.

3. *Smoothing of percentiles:* Smoothing was accomplished by three-point smoothing twice(9).

4. *Means and standard deviations:* These were calculated for all variables, but the skewness of data on reticulocytes, E.S.R., total leucocyte and differential leucocyte counts makes these values misleading, and they are omitted from the tables.

5. *Exclusion of data:* No attempt was made to exclude values which might be associated with illness in a subject. The number of such values at any given age is not large enough to influence results significantly.

Sixty-seven determinations were omitted from the erythrocyte data because stasis had been employed in obtaining the blood sample. (See Collection of blood sample, above.) Five others were omitted because the subject had been staying at an altitude of 9,000 feet or more for some time immediately before the sample was taken.

Analysis of eosinophil data revealed that the 27 allergic subjects had values averaging significantly higher than those of non-allergic subjects (Figure G-2). This was a sufficient number to influence percentiles, so values from allergic subjects (Group A) were excluded from the eosinophil data. Also omitted were values on

16 younger subjects whose allergic status could not be evaluated because of their age (Group B), and values on 2 non-allergic subjects during pinworm infestations (Group C). The total numbers of omitted determinations were:

	No. Subjects			No. Determinations		
	Male	Female	Total	Male	Female	Total
Group A	15	12	27	612	205	817
Group B	8	8	16	49	85	134
Group C	1	1	2	3	4	7
Total omitted	24	21	45	664	294	958

Data from these subjects were included in other percentile calculations since it was determined that they had no significant influence on results obtained.

In 1959 it was decided to use heparinized blood for leucocyte and differential counts on peripheral blood as was being done on venous blood. Preliminary comparisons showed no significant differences between heparinized and non-heparinized samples. Furthermore, as described above, there is no significant difference in median values on our subjects between venous (heparinized) and peripheral (non-heparinized) blood. After 167 leucocyte and differential counts had been done on peripheral heparinized blood, it was apparent that, contrary to our previous findings, there were marked differences between these counts and those done on blood taken directly from the bleeding point. Values from each heparinized peripheral sample were compared with the medians at that age of all non-heparinized samples, with these average differences:

	Heparin minus non-heparin	Probability
Total leucocytes	- 1300 per cu mm	<0.001
Neutrophils	- 849	<0.001
Eosinophils	- 105	<0.001
Monocytes	- 154	<0.001
Lymphocytes	- 100	Insig.

Because of these differences all leucocyte and differential counts from peripheral heparinized blood have been completely discarded.

A number of observations have not been included in the data presented here. The percent of subjects in whom these findings occurred was:

	% occurrence	% occurrence	Range
	at 3 days	at later ages	(all ages)
Immature neutrophils*	100	80	0 - 13.0%
Basophils	69	80	0 - 3.2%
Blast-like cells†	84	67	0 - 4.9%
Unclassified leucocytes	81	25	0 - 2.5%
Nucleated erythrocytes	68	1	0 - 294/cu mm
Polychromatophilia	44	0.4	
Anisocytosis	24	‡	
Poikilocytosis	8	<1	
Achromia	<1	<1	

*These were included with mature forms in tabulations for this presentation.
†This category includes very immature forms of any type of leucocyte.
‡Incidence of anisocytosis shows a gradual decline, with none noted after 18 years.

Lymphocyte classification into 4 types based on size and morphology was done on 2509 of the differential smears.

Non-analytic Factors which might Influence Results

To test each possibly influential non-analytic factor, a sample age was chosen at which the number of counts was about equally divided with respect to that factor. Differences in medians between the groups were tested for significance.

Comparisons of venous and peripheral blood and of venous blood drawn with and without stasis have already been considered.

With these factors no differences significant at or below the 5 percent level were found: winter versus summer, and subjects who bled well versus those who bled poorly.

Comparison of afternoon with morning counts at three different ages gave discrepant results:

Afternoon minus Morning

	Age 5-1/2 years		Age 5 years		Age 9 months	
	Med. diff.	**Prob.**	**Med. diff.**	**Prob.**	**Med. diff.**	**Prob.**
Total leucocytes	+ 1800	<0.001	Insignificant		Insignificant	
Neutrophils	+ 933	<0.001	+ 427	<0.01	Insignificant	
Lymphocytes	+ 720	<0.01	Insignificant		+ 1892	<0.01

Subjects whose behavior during blood-taking was described as "crying and fighting" had these values significantly higher than those on subjects whose behavior was "good":

	Prob.
Erythrocyte count	<0.02
Hematocrit	<0.05
Monocytes	<0.01
Neutrophils	<0.01

A detailed description of our classification of subject behavior is given in Section H.

Because of the findings described above, time of day, behavior, and the presence or absence of stasis are coded on the tape. Erythrocyte values on venous blood obtained with stasis were excluded from percentiles, as discussed above. No other differentiation was made in the analyses presented in this publication.

Sex Differences

No significant sex differences appear in any constituent of the blood until adolescence. Nevertheless there are some consistent, though small, differences apparent by comparison of the median values of each sex at each age.

1. Lymphocytes – females slightly higher at all ages.
2. Eosinophils – females slightly lower at all ages
3. Monocytes – females slightly lower at all ages.
4. Erythrocyte count – females slightly lower from 3 years of age.
5. Reticulocytes – females slightly lower beginning at about 10 years of age.
6. Mean corpuscular volume – females slightly higher at most ages, starting at 3 years.
7. Mean corpuscular hemoglobin concentration – females slightly lower beginning at about 6 years of age.

At adolescence the erythrocyte values of males increase quite sharply to levels significantly higher than those of females (see Figure G-3 and Tables G-3 through G-5). The age at which an individual male's values rise seems to be related in timing to other adolescent changes and varies considerably between subjects.

Neutrophil and Lymphocyte Counts

Changes with age in the percents of neutrophils and lymphocytes are shown in Figure G-4. From a median level of 55 percent at three days the neutrophils drop to 22 percent at 1 month and 19 percent at 2 and 3 months. Thereafter the percent of neutrophils rises gradually as the percent of lymphocytes decreases. Neutrophils do not become preponderant until almost 8 years of age. This is in contrast to average values published(10,11) showing a preponderance of neutrophils by 4 years of age. Unfortunately, neither of these sources describes the subjects on whom their figures are based. Use of means rather than medians on the Child Research Council data raises the neutrophil percent only slightly during the 4- to 8-year period, and does not change the age of first preponderance of neutrophils.

REFERENCES

1. Andresen, M.I., and Mugrage, E.R.: Venous and peripheral red blood cell values. Am J Clin Path, 8:46, 1938.
2. Croxton, F.E., and Cowden, D.J.: Applied General Statistics. Prentice-Hall, Inc., New York, 1945, p. 332.
3. Goodman, L.A.: On the exact variance of products. J Amer Statist Ass, 55:708, 1960.
4. Fieller, E.C.: A fundamental formula in the statistics of biological assay, and some applications. Quart J Pharm Pharmacol, 17:117, 1944.
5. Meyers, A.J.; Trevorrow, V.; Washburn, A.H., and Mugrage, E.R.: Quantitative studies of the influence of plasma proteins and hematocrit on the erythrocyte sedimentation rate. Blood, 8:893, 1953.
6. Smith, C.H.: A method for determining the sedimentation rate and red cell volume in infants and children with the use of capillary blood. Amer J Med Sci, 192:73, 1936.
7. Washburn, A.H., and Meyers, A.J.: The sedimentation of erythrocytes at an angle of 45 degrees. Lab Clin Med, 49:318, 1957.
8. Washburn, A.H.: Blood cells in healthy young infants. IV. Postnatal readjustments of the red blood cells in individual babies. Amer J Dis Child, 62:530, 1941.
9. Croxton, F.E., and Cowden, D.J.: op. cit., p. 386.
10. Nelson, W.E.: Textbook of Pediatrics. Philadelphia, W. B. Saunders and Co., 1959, p. 932.
11. Holt, L. E., and McIntosh, R.: Holt Pediatrics. New York, Appleton-Century-Crofts, Inc., 1953, p. 631.

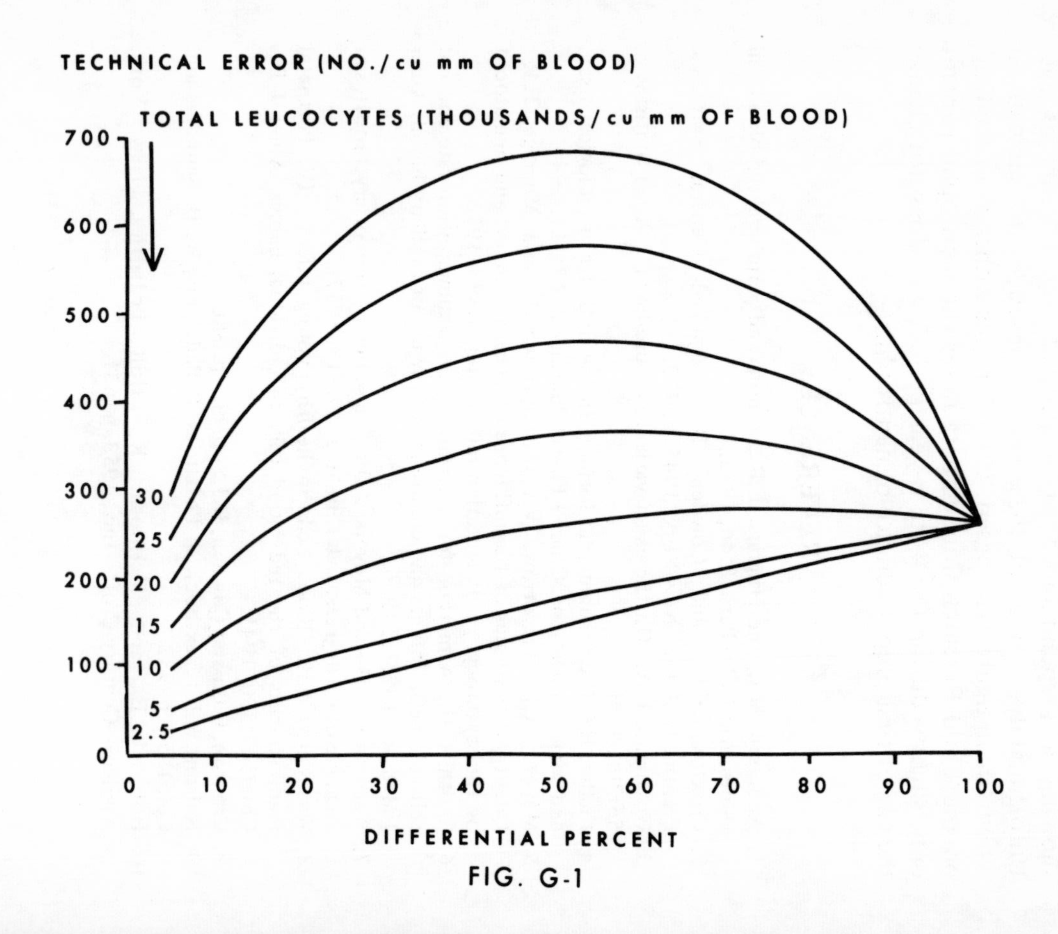
TECHNICAL ERROR (NO./cu mm OF BLOOD)
TOTAL LEUCOCYTES (THOUSANDS/cu mm OF BLOOD)
700
600
500
400
300
200
100
0
30
25
20
15
10
5
2.5
0
10
20
30
40
50
60
70
80
90
100
DIFFERENTIAL PERCENT

FIG. G-1

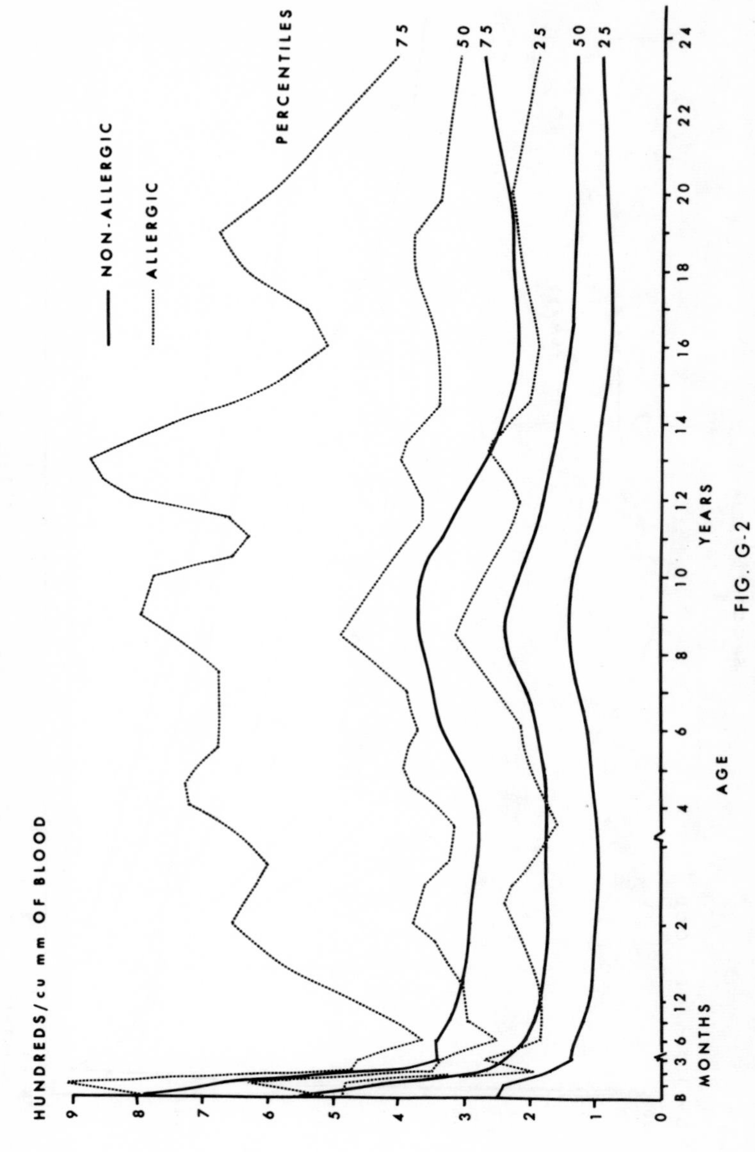
EOSINOPHILS IN ALLERGIC AND NON-ALLERGIC SUBJECTS
HUNDREDS/cu mm OF BLOOD
NON-ALLERGIC
ALLERGIC
PERCENTILES
75
50
75
25
50
25
0
1
2
3
4
5
6
7
8
9
B
3
6
12
MONTHS
2
4
6
8
10
12
14
16
18
20
22
24
YEARS
AGE

FIG. G-2

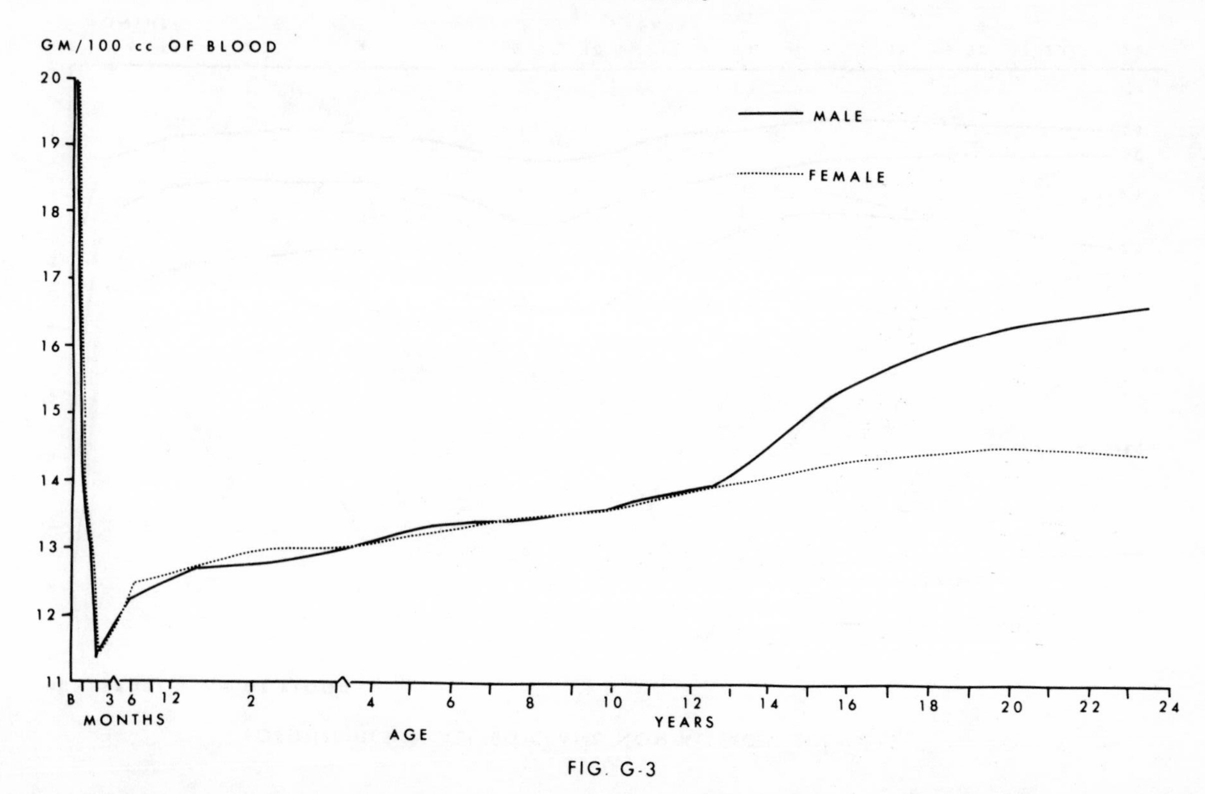
HEMOGLOBIN VALUES
SMOOTHED MEDIANS
GM/100 cc OF BLOOD
MALE
FEMALE
20
19
18
17
16
15
14
13
12
11
B 3 6 12
MONTHS
2 4 6 8 10 12 14 16 18 20 22 24
YEARS
AGE

FIG. G-3

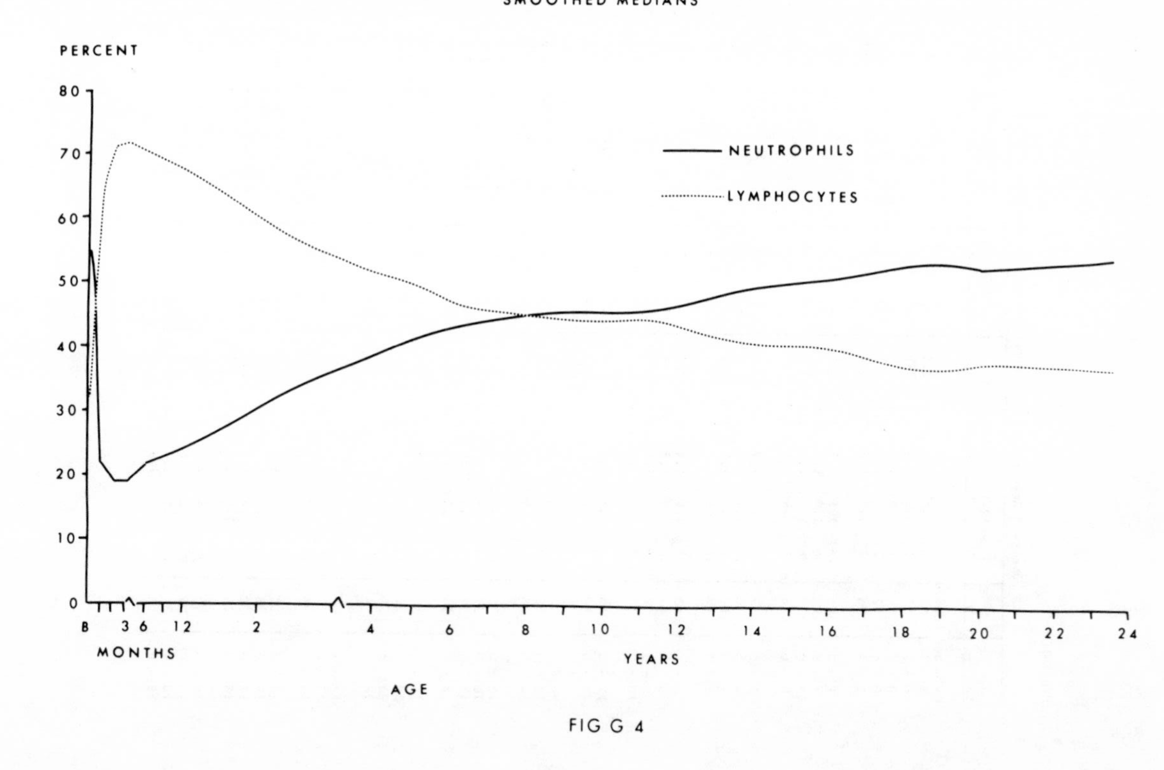
LYMPHOCYTE AND NEUTROPHIL PERCENTS
SMOOTHED MEDIANS
PERCENT
80
70
60
50
40
30
20
10
0
NEUTROPHILS
LYMPHOCYTES
B
3 6 12
2
4
6
8
10
12
14
16
18
20
22
24
MONTHS
YEARS
AGE

FIG G 4

HEMATOLOGY

TABLE G-1

Observed Erythrocyte Sedimentation Rate in mm. per 5 Minutes

Age		Observed Percentiles					Range		Smoothed Percentiles				
Yr. Mo.	N	10th	25th	50th	75th	90th	Min.	Max.	10th	25th	50th	75th	90th
Male and Female													
0 - 1	88	.3	.7	1.0	1.6	2.5	.1	5.7					
0 - 2	88	.7	1.0	1.5	2.3	2.9	.4	4.3					
0 - 3	80	.6	.9	1.5	2.3	3.0	.3	5.0					
0 - 6	82	.7	.9	1.3	2.1	3.1	.2	9.4	.7	.9	1.4	2.2	3.1
0 - 9	95	.7	1.0	1.5	2.2	3.2	.4	5.5	.7	1.0	1.5	2.1	3.0
1 - 0	105	.9	1.1	1.5	1.9	2.8	.3	6.0	.8	1.0	1.5	2.1	2.9
1 - 6	105	.8	1.0	1.5	2.0	2.4	.3	4.7	.8	1.0	1.5	2.0	2.6
2 - 0	103	.8	1.0	1.4	2.1	2.6	.4	4.4	.8	1.0	1.4	2.0	2.6
2 - 6	106	.7	.9	1.3	1.8	2.6	.4	4.5	.8	1.0	1.4	1.9	2.6
3 - 0	99	.8	1.0	1.4	2.0	2.6	.3	6.0	.7	1.0	1.4	1.9	2.6
4 - 0	110	.8	1.1	1.6	2.0	2.7	.3	3.7	.7	1.0	1.5	1.9	2.6
5 - 0	109	.7	.9	1.3	1.8	2.6	.4	4.8	.7	.9	1.4	1.8	2.5
6 - 0	98	.7	1.0	1.4	1.9	2.5	.3	8.5	.7	1.0	1.4	1.9	2.5
7 - 0	97	.7	1.0	1.4	1.9	2.7	.4	5.6	.7	.9	1.4	1.9	2.7
8 - 0	89	.6	.9	1.2	1.8	2.4	.3	5.0	.7	.9	1.3	1.8	2.4
9 - 0	92	.6	.8	1.2	1.7	2.1	.2	4.2	.6	.8	1.2	1.7	2.1
10 - 0	74	.7	.8	1.1	1.7	2.1	.5	4.7	.6	.8	1.1	1.7	2.1
11 - 0	84	.6	.8	1.2	1.8	2.1	.3	4.0	.6	.8	1.1	1.7	2.0
12 - 0	80	.5	.7	1.0	1.4	1.9	.3	3.5	.6	.8	1.1	1.6	2.0
Male													
13 - 0	32	.6	.7	1.2	1.7	1.9	.3	2.6	.5	.7	1.0	1.6	1.9
14 - 0	38	.4	.6	.8	1.2	1.8	.2	2.1	.4	.6	.9	1.3	1.8
15 - 0	30	.3	.5	.8	1.1	1.2	.2	2.6	.4	.5	.8	1.1	1.6
16 - 0	27	.3	.4	.7	1.0	1.4	.2	3.6	.3	.5	.8	1.1	1.4
17 - 0	27	.3	.4	.9	1.0	1.5	.1	2.0	.3	.4	.8	1.1	1.4
18 - 0	23	.3	.5	.6	1.1	1.5	.1	2.8	.3	.4	.7	1.0	1.5
19 - 0	21	.2	.4	.7	1.0	1.5	.2	1.6	.3	.4	.7	1.0	1.4
20 - 0	20	.3	.4	.7	1.0	1.4	.2	1.9	.3	.4	.7	1.0	1.4
23 - 6	20	.3	.4	.6	1.0	1.2	.2	1.5					
28 - 6	4			.8			.4	1.9					
Female													
13 - 0	37	.6	.8	1.3	1.7	2.7	.5	4.7	.6	.8	1.2	1.6	2.2
14 - 0	36	.5	.8	1.1	1.7	1.9	.3	2.6	.5	.8	1.1	1.6	2.2
15 - 0	35	.5	.7	1.2	1.5	2.0	.2	3.0	.5	.8	1.2	1.7	2.1
16 - 0	33	.5	.7	1.6	1.8	2.4	.3	3.1	.5	.8	1.4	1.8	2.1
17 - 0	30	.6	.8	1.4	1.9	2.0	.5	2.6	.6	.8	1.4	1.9	2.1
18 - 0	26	.7	1.0	1.4	1.9	2.0	.5	3.0	.6	.8	1.4	1.9	2.1
19 - 0	22	.7	.9	1.4	2.0	2.2	.4	3.0	.6	.8	1.4	1.9	2.1
20 - 0	22	.4	.6	1.6	1.9	2.2	.2	2.7	.6	.8	1.5	1.8	2.1
23 - 6	21	.6	.9	1.4	1.6	2.0	.3	3.0					
28 - 6	8			1.8			.5	2.6					

HEMATOLOGY

TABLE G-2

Corrected Erythrocyte Sedimentation Rate in mm. per 5 Minutes

Age	N	Observed Percentiles					Range		Smoothed Percentiles				
Yr. Mo.		10th	25th	50th	75th	90th	Min.	Max.	10th	25th	50th	75th	90th
Male and Female													
0 - 1	88	.5	.6	.9	1.4	2.3	.1	3.9					
0 - 2	88	.1	.4	.8	1.4	1.6	0	2.3					
0 - 3	80	.2	.5	1.0	1.4	1.9	0	2.9					
0 - 6	82	.3	.6	.9	1.7	2.5	0	6.2	.4	.6	1.0	1.6	2.3
0 - 9	95	.6	.8	1.1	1.6	2.6	.3	4.9	.5	.7	1.1	1.7	2.5
1 - 0	105	.5	.8	1.2	1.8	2.6	.3	4.6	.5	.8	1.2	1.7	2.5
1 - 6	105	.6	.9	1.2	1.7	2.2	.4	4.2	.5	.8	1.2	1.7	2.3
2 - 0	103	.5	.9	1.2	1.6	2.4	.4	3.7	.6	.8	1.2	1.6	2.4
2 - 6	106	.6	.8	1.2	1.6	2.4	.3	4.7	.6	.8	1.2	1.7	2.4
3 - 0	99	.7	.9	1.3	1.8	2.4	.2	5.1	.6	.8	1.3	1.8	2.4
4 - 0	110	.7	.9	1.4	2.0	2.3	.3	3.7	.6	.9	1.3	1.8	2.3
5 - 0	109	.6	.8	1.3	1.7	2.4	.4	4.8	.7	.9	1.3	1.8	2.3
6 - 0	98	.7	.9	1.3	1.9	2.6	.4	6.6	.7	.9	1.3	1.8	2.4
7 - 0	97	.7	1.0	1.3	1.9	2.7	.5	4.5	.7	1.0	1.3	1.9	2.6
8 - 0	89	.6	.9	1.2	1.8	2.5	.4	5.5	.7	.9	1.3	1.8	2.5
9 - 0	92	.7	.8	1.2	1.7	2.2	.3	3.8	.7	.9	1.2	1.7	2.2
10 - 0	74	.7	.9	1.2	1.7	2.4	.5	4.0	.7	.9	1.2	1.8	2.3
11 - 0	84	.7	.9	1.3	2.0	2.4	.3	4.0	.7	.9	1.3	1.9	2.3
12 - 0	80	.7	.9	1.2	1.7	2.2	.4	4.1	.7	.9	1.3	1.8	2.3
13 - 0	69	.8	1.0	1.4	2.0	2.4	.5	5.0	.8	1.0	1.3	1.8	2.4
14 - 0	74	.7	1.0	1.3	1.9	2.3	.5	3.6	.7	1.0	1.3	1.9	2.5
15 - 0	65	.8	1.0	1.4	1.9	2.4	.5	3.6	.8	1.0	1.4	2.0	2.6
16 - 0	60	.8	.9	1.4	2.1	2.9	.6	4.7	.8	1.0	1.4	2.0	2.6
17 - 0	57	1.0	1.1	1.5	2.2	2.6	.8	3.6	.9	1.1	1.5	2.1	2.7
18 - 0	49	.8	1.2	1.6	2.1	2.6	.5	3.6	.9	1.1	1.5	2.1	2.6
19 - 0	43	.9	1.3	1.5	2.2	2.6	.8	4.0	.9	1.2	1.5	2.1	2.6
20 - 0	42	.8	1.1	1.5	2.1	2.8	.4	3.4	.9	1.1	1.5	2.2	2.6
23 - 6	41	.9	1.2	1.5	2.1	2.5	.7	3.1	.9	1.2	1.6	2.2	2.6
28 - 6	12	1.0	1.2	1.8	2.3	2.7	.8	4.1					

HEMATOLOGY

TABLE G-3

Hematocrit in Percent

Age Yr. Mo.	N	Mean	S.D.	Observed Percentiles 10th	25th	50th	75th	90th	Range Min.	Max.	Smoothed Percentiles 10th	25th	50th	75th	90th
Male and Female															
3 days	80	59.42	6.12	51.3	54.4	59.3	64.0	67.4	46.6	76.7					
0 - 1	159	40.84	6.40	32.7	36.2	40.3	44.5	49.5	22.3	63.4					
0 - 2	151	33.37	3.37	29.3	31.1	33.1	35.3	37.5	26.4	51.4					
0 - 3	146	34.61	2.68	31.3	32.9	34.5	36.1	38.4	27.7	43.6					
0 - 6	144	36.86	3.02	32.9	35.0	36.9	38.6	40.8	29.7	47.6					
0 - 9	149	37.46	2.54	34.1	35.9	37.6	38.9	40.4	30.7	44.4	33.8	35.6	37.4	39.0	40.8
1 - 0	161	37.81	2.42	34.6	36.1	37.5	39.4	41.2	32.2	44.4	34.3	36.0	37.7	39.3	41.0
1 - 6	157	38.26	2.33	34.7	36.8	38.4	39.6	41.1	32.7	44.2	34.9	36.6	38.1	39.6	41.1
2 - 0	146	38.19	2.14	35.4	37.0	38.1	39.5	41.0	32.5	47.1	35.4	36.9	38.2	39.7	41.1
2 - 6	144	38.44	2.15	35.8	36.8	38.4	40.0	41.4	33.8	43.7	35.9	37.0	38.4	39.9	41.2
3 - 0	132	38.73	1.89	36.4	37.4	38.7	40.1	41.0	33.4	43.2	36.0	37.2	38.6	40.1	41.2
4 - 0	125	38.96	2.02	35.9	37.7	39.1	40.4	41.5	34.2	43.8	36.2	37.6	39.1	40.5	41.5
5 - 0	115	39.40	2.04	36.8	37.9	39.4	40.9	42.1	34.0	43.7	36.8	37.9	39.4	40.9	42.1
6 - 0	110	39.57	1.93	37.0	38.2	39.5	40.9	42.3	34.9	44.1	37.2	38.3	39.6	41.1	42.3
7 - 0	102	39.95	1.95	37.3	38.6	39.8	41.0	42.7	35.5	45.1	37.2	38.6	39.9	41.3	42.7
8 - 0	93	40.32	2.40	37.3	38.5	40.1	42.0	43.7	33.7	45.6	37.4	38.8	40.2	41.8	43.2
9 - 0	93	40.40	2.10	37.9	38.9	40.2	41.8	43.5	35.2	45.9	37.6	39.0	40.4	42.1	43.5
10 - 0	74	40.75	2.33	37.6	39.1	40.8	42.4	43.8	35.8	45.5	37.9	39.2	40.7	42.4	43.7
11 - 0	89	41.28	2.25	38.3	39.6	41.3	42.9	44.5	35.6	47.0	38.3	39.7	41.2	42.8	44.1
12 - 0	85	41.59	2.03	38.8	40.3	41.7	43.3	44.2	37.1	46.0	38.7	40.2	41.7	43.3	44.4
Male															
13 - 0	35	42.51	2.48	39.4	40.8	42.2	44.4	45.6	38.2	48.9	39.6	40.9	42.3	44.0	45.6
14 - 0	41	44.07	2.47	42.2	42.7	43.6	45.2	47.7	38.8	50.0	41.0	42.2	43.6	45.1	47.5
15 - 0	32	45.10	2.35	42.7	43.5	44.9	46.3	48.5	39.4	49.6	42.6	43.3	44.9	46.4	48.3
16 - 0	34	46.19	1.86	44.2	45.0	46.2	47.4	48.6	41.4	50.6	43.5	44.8	45.9	47.5	49.4
17 - 0	33	47.24	2.79	43.9	45.1	46.8	48.9	51.8	43.1	52.9	44.4	45.4	46.8	48.4	50.3
18 - 0	25	47.63	2.06	45.3	46.4	47.4	49.0	50.4	43.3	52.4	45.2	46.2	47.5	49.1	50.8
19 - 0	24	48.32	2.13	46.0	46.7	48.0	49.7	51.4	45.1	53.2	45.6	46.7	48.1	49.5	51.4
20 - 0	21	49.24	2.10	46.5	48.1	49.3	50.1	51.3	45.9	55.0	45.7	46.9	48.4	49.7	52.1
23 - 6	23	49.38	2.76	46.6	47.5	49.6	50.2	53.2	42.8	54.6					
28 - 6	6					48.6			43.5	53.8					
Female															
13 - 0	36	42.17	2.30	39.4	40.3	41.7	44.1	45.2	37.6	47.2	39.1	40.6	42.1	43.9	45.1
14 - 0	37	42.26	2.26	38.7	40.8	42.7	43.8	44.9	37.2	46.2	39.2	40.6	42.3	44.0	45.4
15 - 0	36	42.23	2.67	38.7	40.3	42.3	44.1	45.6	36.4	46.2	39.4	40.9	42.7	44.2	45.5
16 - 0	34	42.95	2.26	40.0	41.0	43.5	44.6	45.2	38.2	46.8	39.6	41.2	43.1	44.5	45.7
17 - 0	32	43.44	2.40	40.1	42.2	43.5	44.9	46.3	37.6	49.0	39.9	41.7	43.4	44.9	46.3
18 - 0	30	43.43	2.75	39.9	42.1	43.5	45.0	47.2	37.8	48.3	40.1	42.1	43.6	45.2	46.8
19 - 0	25	43.86	2.69	40.4	42.2	43.8	45.8	47.0	37.8	49.5	40.1	42.1	43.7	45.3	47.1
20 - 0	22	44.26	2.71	40.1	42.8	44.1	45.6	48.0	38.8	49.8	39.9	41.8	43.5	45.2	46.9
23 - 6	21	43.23	2.93	39.4	40.6	43.4	45.1	46.4	38.8	49.8					
28 - 6	9					41.9			39.6	48.0					

HEMATOLOGY

TABLE G-4

Hemoglobin in Grams per 100 cc. Blood

Age Yr. Mo.	N	Mean	S.D.	Observed Percentiles 10th	25th	50th	75th	90th	Range Min.	Max.	Smoothed Percentiles 10th	25th	50th	75th	90th
Male and Female															
3 days	83	19.79	2.00	17.3	18.3	19.8	21.2	22.8	15.9	24.2					
0 - 1	167	13.80	1.95	11.3	12.4	13.7	14.9	16.2	7.8	21.0					
0 - 2	159	11.44	1.13	10.0	10.6	11.4	12.2	12.9	8.7	16.4					
0 - 3	160	11.79	1.01	10.5	11.1	11.7	12.5	13.2	9.2	15.0					
0 - 6	156	12.45	1.06	11.1	11.7	12.4	13.1	14.0	9.3	14.9					
0 - 9	154	12.48	1.14	11.2	11.8	12.5	13.2	13.9	9.1	16.2	11.1	11.7	12.4	13.2	13.9
1 - 0	167	12.56	1.09	11.2	11.8	12.6	13.3	14.0	9.4	15.0	11.3	11.9	12.6	13.3	14.0
1 - 6	161	12.81	.94	11.6	12.0	12.9	13.5	14.0	9.7	15.8	11.5	12.1	12.8	13.4	14.0
2 - 0	145	12.86	.88	11.8	12.0	12.9	13.4	14.0	10.4	15.0	11.7	12.3	12.9	13.5	14.0
2 - 6	141	12.88	.84	11.8	12.3	12.9	13.4	13.9	10.9	15.2	11.8	12.4	13.0	13.5	14.0
3 - 0	127	13.02	.83	11.9	12.5	13.0	13.6	14.0	10.8	15.4	11.9	12.4	13.0	13.6	14.0
4 - 0	126	13.05	.74	12.1	12.5	13.0	13.5	14.1	11.0	14.6	12.0	12.6	13.1	13.6	14.1
5 - 0	112	13.19	.83	12.2	12.6	13.2	13.8	14.3	10.4	15.3	12.2	12.7	13.2	13.8	14.3
6 - 0	106	13.33	.77	12.3	12.8	13.2	14.0	14.3	11.6	15.0	12.3	12.8	13.3	13.9	14.4
7 - 0	101	13.39	.82	12.3	12.9	13.4	13.9	14.4	11.1	15.3	12.3	12.9	13.4	14.0	14.5
8 - 0	91	13.43	.88	12.3	12.8	13.4	14.0	14.7	11.4	15.6	12.4	12.9	13.4	14.1	14.6
9 - 0	93	13.61	.85	12.6	13.0	13.5	14.2	14.7	11.8	15.6	12.5	13.0	13.5	14.2	14.7
10 - 0	72	13.63	.92	12.5	13.0	13.4	14.2	14.8	11.7	16.2	12.6	13.1	13.6	14.3	14.8
11 - 0	87	13.79	.80	12.6	13.2	13.7	14.4	14.9	11.9	15.5	12.7	13.2	13.7	14.4	14.9
12 - 0	82	13.91	.78	12.8	13.4	13.8	14.3	15.0	12.1	15.7	12.8	13.3	13.9	14.4	15.0
Male															
13 - 0	34	14.40	.97	13.3	13.6	14.2	14.9	16.0	12.5	16.6	13.1	13.6	14.1	14.8	15.6
14 - 0	41	14.58	.99	13.5	14.1	14.5	15.0	15.9	12.1	17.2	13.4	14.0	14.6	15.2	16.0
15 - 0	30	15.02	.92	14.0	14.2	15.2	15.6	16.2	12.8	16.8	14.0	14.4	15.1	15.7	16.4
16 - 0	31	15.52	.86	14.4	14.8	15.5	16.1	16.5	13.7	17.4	14.3	14.7	15.5	16.2	16.7
17 - 0	33	15.84	1.03	14.7	15.1	15.8	16.7	17.2	13.0	17.7	14.6	15.0	15.8	16.5	17.0
18 - 0	25	16.02	1.14	14.7	15.0	16.0	16.9	17.7	13.7	18.1	14.8	15.2	16.0	16.8	17.4
19 - 0	22	16.13	1.03	15.1	15.5	16.0	16.6	17.2	14.8	19.6	15.1	15.5	16.2	16.9	17.7
20 - 0	21	16.80	1.05	15.6	16.1	16.6	17.4	18.3	14.7	19.0	15.3	15.8	16.3	17.1	18.0
23 - 6	22	16.76	.94	15.7	16.1	16.6	17.2	18.4	15.5	18.8					
28 - 6	6					16.2			15.0	18.9					
Female															
13 - 0	33	13.90	.88	12.6	13.1	13.9	14.5	15.1	12.2	15.7	12.8	13.3	14.0	14.6	15.2
14 - 0	36	14.16	.90	12.8	13.6	14.4	14.8	15.2	12.2	15.8	12.8	13.3	14.1	14.7	15.3
15 - 0	35	14.10	1.03	12.7	13.2	14.2	14.8	15.3	12.2	16.2	12.8	13.4	14.2	14.8	15.3
16 - 0	33	14.14	.91	12.8	13.5	14.3	14.9	15.1	12.4	15.8	12.8	13.6	14.3	14.8	15.4
17 - 0	30	14.44	.94	13.1	14.0	14.6	15.1	15.6	11.9	16.0	12.9	13.7	14.4	14.9	15.5
18 - 0	29	14.21	1.13	12.7	13.5	14.1	14.8	15.8	12.3	16.7	13.0	13.8	14.4	14.9	15.6
19 - 0	23	14.54	.98	13.2	13.8	14.7	15.0	15.6	12.9	16.4	13.1	13.9	14.5	14.9	15.6
20 - 0	26	14.60	.79	13.9	14.2	14.6	15.0	15.4	12.2	16.4	13.1	14.0	14.4	15.1	15.6
23 - 6	21	14.40	1.13	12.6	13.8	14.4	15.2	15.7	12.4	15.9					
28 - 6	9					13.9			13.0	15.3					

HEMATOLOGY

TABLE G-5

Erythrocytes in Millions per cu. mm. of Blood

Age				Observed Percentiles					Range		Smoothed Percentiles				
Yr. Mo.	N	Mean	S.D.	10th	25th	50th	75th	90th	Min.	Max.	10th	25th	50th	75th	90th
Male and Female															
3 days	81	5.766	.690	4.99	5.26	5.66	6.16	6.69	4.56	8.01					
0 - 1	166	4.189	.595	3.45	3.77	4.18	4.60	5.03	2.42	5.84					
0 - 2	159	3.739	.377	3.28	3.49	3.72	3.96	4.24	2.76	4.93					
0 - 3	155	4.095	.397	3.60	3.83	4.05	4.36	4.61	3.16	5.24					
0 - 6	152	4.672	.465	4.04	4.33	4.68	5.04	5.28	3.58	5.79					
0 - 9	147	4.740	.419	4.22	4.47	4.72	4.98	5.31	3.77	5.76	4.15	4.41	4.69	4.99	5.27
1 - 0	160	4.695	.383	4.19	4.42	4.67	4.95	5.22	3.70	5.80	4.20	4.40	4.68	4.96	5.24
1 - 6	154	4.696	.367	4.27	4.47	4.66	4.90	5.22	3.76	6.20	4.21	4.41	4.65	4.90	5.16
2 - 0	139	4.628	.357	4.19	4.40	4.62	4.87	5.11	3.81	5.80	4.19	4.39	4.63	4.87	5.11
2 - 6	132	4.677	.347	4.22	4.40	4.66	4.91	5.13	3.94	5.62	4.21	4.40	4.63	4.87	5.12
3 - 0	112	4.627	.357	4.16	4.39	4.60	4.83	5.08	3.72	5.67	4.21	4.40	4.62	4.86	5.09
4 - 0	110	4.628	.331	4.22	4.44	4.60	4.85	5.12	3.74	5.35	4.22	4.41	4.61	4.86	5.08
5 - 0	101	4.642	.341	4.23	4.38	4.61	4.88	5.07	3.87	5.52	4.24	4.42	4.64	4.90	5.11
6 - 0	92	4.710	.336	4.29	4.42	4.73	4.96	5.14	3.72	5.62	4.28	4.45	4.70	4.95	5.15
7 - 0	85	4.704	.320	4.31	4.47	4.66	4.96	5.14	4.00	5.50	4.27	4.45	4.67	4.93	5.13
8 - 0	79	4.615	.286	4.24	4.42	4.59	4.81	5.00	3.98	5.27	4.25	4.43	4.62	4.87	5.06
9 - 0	81	4.613	.279	4.26	4.45	4.61	4.78	4.97	3.97	5.40	4.24	4.43	4.64	4.87	5.05
10 - 0	75	4.648	.350	4.19	4.38	4.65	4.89	5.15	4.01	5.46	4.26	4.44	4.68	4.91	5.12
11 - 0	79	4.781	.381	4.26	4.49	4.72	4.98	5.25	3.82	5.93	4.28	4.48	4.71	4.96	5.21
Male															
12 - 0	39	4.755	.364	4.27	4.51	4.74	4.99	5.20	4.06	5.74	4.30	4.51	4.76	5.03	5.30
13 - 0	23	4.879	.287	4.43	4.67	4.91	5.08	5.22	4.34	5.46	4.42	4.62	4.85	5.07	5.23
14 - 0	33	4.933	.389	4.51	4.67	4.85	5.13	5.39	4.28	6.08	4.54	4.69	4.90	5.12	5.34
15 - 0	28	5.037	.355	4.59	4.78	5.00	5.25	5.42	4.40	5.90	4.62	4.77	4.96	5.22	5.49
16 - 0	28	5.131	.308	4.84	4.94	5.05	5.15	5.72	4.70	5.83	4.72	4.85	5.05	5.25	5.66
17 - 0	27	5.134	.252	4.78	4.96	5.10	5.28	5.46	4.74	5.74	4.78	4.95	5.13	5.30	5.61
18 - 0	23	5.249	.350	4.77	5.01	5.28	5.44	5.69	4.61	6.08	4.82	5.00	5.21	5.37	5.70
19 - 0	20	5.264	.348	4.89	5.01	5.19	5.39	5.81	4.82	6.24	4.84	5.02	5.24	5.44	5.74
20 - 0	19	5.356	.366	4.86	5.07	5.37	5.54	5.99	4.73	6.12	4.87	5.05	5.25	5.50	5.74
23 - 6	20	5.373	.331	4.97	5.12	5.31	5.69	5.78	4.68	5.94					
28 - 6	4					5.05			4.78	5.14					
Female															
12 - 0	35	4.731	.315	4.35	4.54	4.79	4.94	5.10	4.05	5.48	4.31	4.52	4.71	4.92	5.13
13 - 0	26	4.671	.342	4.24	4.38	4.62	4.94	5.14	4.16	5.36	4.27	4.47	4.72	4.93	5.16
14 - 0	31	4.655	.344	4.18	4.39	4.68	4.88	5.10	4.10	5.44	4.29	4.44	4.73	4.89	5.15
15 - 0	28	4.719	.313	4.33	4.48	4.73	4.92	5.14	4.02	5.38	4.31	4.47	4.70	4.87	5.11
16 - 0	29	4.628	.282	4.31	4.42	4.63	4.80	5.02	4.08	5.12	4.31	4.45	4.68	4.88	5.09
17 - 0	24	4.737	.307	4.36	4.51	4.70	4.97	5.12	4.25	5.56	4.34	4.47	4.69	4.90	5.13
18 - 0	23	4.703	.355	4.29	4.41	4.72	4.85	5.17	4.20	5.43	4.36	4.49	4.71	4.92	5.15
19 - 0	19	4.807	.313	4.46	4.58	4.75	4.98	5.30	4.30	5.40	4.34	4.49	4.72	4.91	5.14
20 - 0	17	4.724	.218	4.40	4.58	4.75	4.91	5.00	4.25	5.12	4.28	4.46	4.68	4.88	5.07
23 - 6	19	4.579	.350	4.09	4.28	4.62	4.86	5.08	3.98	5.15					
28 - 6	7					4.34			4.06	4.80					

HEMATOLOGY

TABLE G-6

Mean Corpuscular Volume in Cubic Microns

Age Yr. Mo.	N	Mean	S.D.	Observed Percentiles 10th	25th	50th	75th	90th	Range Min.	Max.	Smoothed Percentiles 10th	25th	50th	75th	90th
Male and Female															
3 days	79	103.29	7.81	93.6	98.0	104.0	109.3	113.4	76.0	120.2					
0 - 1	156	97.44	8.10	86.7	91.9	97.7	102.9	107.8	72.4	120.3					
0 - 2	149	89.68	7.54	80.0	84.4	89.5	94.9	99.6	68.8	109.9					
0 - 3	141	85.02	6.49	76.0	80.2	85.1	90.3	93.9	67.5	98.6					
0 - 6	138	79.61	6.23	72.3	75.1	79.0	83.9	87.7	64.0	95.3					
0 - 9	142	79.35	6.50	71.5	75.3	79.6	84.1	86.9	55.7	94.3	72.4	76.5	80.0	84.5	87.9
1 - 0	153	81.04	6.51	73.2	77.1	81.3	85.4	89.0	62.8	96.1	72.8	76.9	81.0	85.1	88.2
1 - 6	147	81.97	5.81	73.9	78.3	82.8	86.2	88.7	61.6	95.8	74.3	78.3	82.5	86.1	89.1
2 - 0	135	82.88	5.72	75.4	79.1	83.5	86.5	89.9	66.2	94.7	75.7	79.2	83.2	86.8	90.1
2 - 6	131	82.59	5.27	75.5	79.2	82.9	86.2	89.4	69.0	93.9	76.2	79.6	83.6	86.9	90.0
3 - 0	110	84.36	5.33	78.0	80.8	84.4	87.9	91.1	63.0	101.6	76.9	80.2	83.8	87.4	90.6
4 - 0	109	84.75	5.29	77.9	81.3	84.5	88.4	91.2	73.1	99.5	77.9	80.9	84.5	88.4	91.6
5 - 0	101	85.07	5.81	77.9	80.9	85.3	89.7	92.7	70.5	99.3	77.7	80.6	84.8	88.6	92.4
6 - 0	91	84.44	5.93	76.6	80.3	84.0	88.1	91.3	71.8	105.6	77.5	80.6	84.6	88.5	92.2
7 - 0	85	85.26	5.03	78.7	81.7	85.0	88.6	92.8	72.4	96.1	78.8	81.9	85.2	89.2	92.8
8 - 0	78	86.98	4.46	81.5	84.1	86.9	90.1	92.5	75.1	96.8	80.1	83.1	86.2	90.0	93.5
9 - 0	80	87.90	5.04	81.6	84.1	87.5	91.4	95.0	77.1	101.7	80.6	83.7	86.8	90.5	93.8
10 - 0	55	87.77	5.13	81.7	84.8	88.5	91.2	94.3	73.1	95.2	80.7	84.0	87.5	90.9	93.6
11 - 0	79	87.43	5.69	79.1	83.7	87.8	91.5	94.3	73.8	104.4	80.4	83.7	87.8	91.3	93.9
12 - 0	74	88.05	5.31	81.4	84.7	88.3	92.0	94.6	75.6	104.3	81.5	84.5	88.0	92.0	94.8
13 - 0	49	89.36	5.43	82.9	85.5	88.5	93.3	97.3	78.9	103.2	82.2	85.5	88.7	93.0	96.2
14 - 0	64	90.54	4.74	82.7	88.0	90.8	93.8	96.8	76.5	99.5	82.0	85.9	89.3	93.7	97.1
15 - 0	56	89.99	6.15	80.8	85.7	90.7	94.0	98.4	74.8	100.9	82.5	86.6	90.7	94.1	97.8
16 - 0	57	91.44	5.28	82.9	88.6	92.5	94.6	97.4	76.7	103.0	83.4	87.9	91.6	94.5	98.0
17 - 0	41	91.71	4.88	86.6	88.8	91.9	95.1	97.8	79.9	102.3	84.3	88.5	91.7	95.0	98.5
18 - 0	46	91.75	6.14	83.9	86.8	91.1	95.1	100.6	81.1	107.4	84.8	88.9	91.8	95.5	99.1
19 - 0	39	92.20	5.16	84.5	89.6	91.9	96.0	98.6	80.4	101.7	85.3	88.9	91.9	96.3	99.7
20 - 0	36	92.91	5.68	85.9	88.6	92.4	97.8	99.9	81.6	104.7	85.4	89.0	92.2	96.7	100.4
23 - 6	39	93.68	6.79	85.6	88.6	92.4	98.3	103.6	82.2	111.3	85.8	89.6	92.5	98.2	102.1
28 - 6	11	95.28	5.66	87.8	91.6	93.9	101.1	102.0	86.0	102.6					

HEMATOLOGY

TABLE G-7

Mean Corpuscular Hemoglobin Concentration in Percent

Age	N	Mean	S.D.	Observed Percentiles					Range		Smoothed Percentiles				
Yr. Mo.				10th	25th	50th	75th	90th	Min.	Max.	10th	25th	50th	75th	90th
Male and Female															
3 days	80	33.41	1.56	31.4	32.4	33.3	34.4	35.5	30.0	38.4					
0 - 1	157	33.99	1.83	31.6	32.6	33.8	35.3	36.1	29.0	40.4					
0 - 2	148	34.21	1.72	32.0	32.9	34.2	35.5	36.6	29.0	38.0					
0 - 3	144	34.12	1.65	32.1	33.1	34.1	35.5	36.4	28.1	38.6					
0 - 6	141	33.65	1.66	31.5	32.4	33.4	34.8	36.0	30.0	38.8					
0 - 9	146	33.25	1.67	31.0	32.2	33.1	34.2	35.4	29.5	38.7	31.1	32.2	33.3	34.5	35.5
1 - 0	158	33.21	1.63	30.9	32.1	33.3	34.4	35.3	28.9	37.3	31.1	32.2	33.1	34.5	35.5
1 - 6	153	33.46	1.56	31.4	32.3	33.4	34.7	35.5	29.7	37.3	31.2	32.3	33.4	34.6	35.5
2 - 0	140	33.63	1.71	31.4	32.6	33.6	34.7	35.8	29.8	39.5	31.4	32.4	33.5	34.6	35.6
2 - 6	140	33.46	1.46	31.6	32.4	33.5	34.4	35.3	30.1	37.2	31.6	32.6	33.5	34.6	35.5
3 - 0	125	33.60	1.47	31.7	32.5	33.6	34.5	35.6	30.7	38.0	31.7	32.5	33.5	34.5	35.5
4 - 0	125	33.53	1.48	31.6	32.4	33.5	34.5	35.4	30.8	37.4	31.7	32.5	33.6	34.5	35.5
5 - 0	112	33.51	1.49	31.5	32.5	33.4	34.3	35.7	30.1	37.4	31.8	32.6	33.6	34.5	35.6
6 - 0	105	33.72	1.50	31.7	32.5	33.8	34.6	35.6	30.3	37.5	31.7	32.6	33.7	34.6	35.7
7 - 0	101	33.54	1.41	31.6	32.6	33.4	34.6	35.6	30.7	37.2	31.6	32.6	33.5	34.7	35.6
8 - 0	90	33.38	1.40	31.4	32.5	33.5	34.4	35.1	29.5	36.6	31.6	32.6	33.5	34.5	35.4
9 - 0	92	33.69	1.34	32.1	32.8	33.7	34.6	35.4	30.5	36.8	31.8	32.7	33.5	34.4	35.2
10 - 0	72	33.40	1.42	31.6	32.4	33.1	34.4	35.5	29.8	36.5	31.8	32.6	33.3	34.3	35.1
11 - 0	87	33.40	1.30	31.7	32.5	33.3	34.3	35.2	30.9	36.9	31.8	32.5	33.4	34.3	35.1
12 - 0	82	33.48	1.18	32.2	32.5	33.4	34.2	35.1	31.4	37.8	31.8	32.4	33.4	34.3	35.2
13 - 0	67	33.38	1.33	31.6	32.4	33.3	34.3	35.4	30.8	36.9	31.6	32.4	33.3	34.2	35.2
14 - 0	77	33.26	1.22	31.8	32.4	33.2	34.0	35.0	30.1	36.3	31.7	32.4	33.3	34.2	35.0
15 - 0	65	33.32	1.19	31.9	32.5	33.4	34.2	35.0	30.7	35.7	31.7	32.4	33.3	34.2	35.0
16 - 0	64	33.19	1.27	31.7	32.2	33.1	34.2	34.8	30.3	36.8	31.7	32.4	33.2	34.2	35.1
17 - 0	63	33.39	1.46	31.7	32.5	33.4	34.3	35.1	30.0	37.5	31.6	32.3	33.2	34.2	35.2
18 - 0	53	33.21	1.57	31.2	32.3	33.0	34.2	35.8	30.3	36.6	31.5	32.3	33.2	34.2	35.4
19 - 0	45	33.22	1.29	31.4	32.3	33.3	33.9	35.0	30.4	36.8	31.6	32.3	33.3	34.3	35.6
20 - 0	41	33.61	1.82	31.6	32.1	33.3	34.8	36.4	31.4	38.1	31.6	32.4	33.4	34.3	35.5
23 - 6	43	33.71	1.34	31.8	32.9	34.2	34.7	35.4	30.5	36.2	31.5	32.5	33.4	34.2	35.6
28 - 6	15	33.24	1.51	31.3	32.2	33.1	33.6	35.7	30.4	36.6					

HEMATOLOGY TABLE G-8

Reticulocytes in Percent

Age Yr. Mo.	N	Observed Percentiles 10th	25th	50th	75th	90th	Range Min.	Max.	Smoothed Percentiles 10th	25th	50th	75th	90th
Male and Female													
3 days	78	2.74	3.22	3.66	4.04	4.70	1.40	5.92					
0 - 1	158	.32	.46	.73	1.16	1.76	.22	4.06					
0 - 2	154	1.04	1.46	2.01	2.64	3.33	.66	6.64					
0 - 3	148	.88	1.19	1.59	2.06	2.57	.34	4.38					
0 - 6	134	.65	.86	1.15	1.46	1.83	.40	3.20					
0 - 9	127	.62	.82	1.01	1.35	1.79	.34	2.48	.65	.85	1.10	1.41	1.76
1 - 0	130	.70	.88	1.09	1.42	1.66	.30	2.36	.62	.84	1.08	1.41	1.73
1 - 6	124	.51	.78	1.07	1.44	1.80	.26	2.84	.59	.82	1.07	1.39	1.72
2 - 0	104	.66	.83	1.08	1.44	1.83	.42	2.80	.64	.82	1.06	1.35	1.73
2 - 6	91	.64	.80	1.05	1.34	1.62	.46	2.46	.64	.81	1.05	1.33	1.67
3 - 0	76	.56	.78	1.03	1.33	1.72	.40	2.26	.63	.82	1.06	1.35	1.67
4 - 0	78	.72	.88	1.12	1.48	1.75	.40	3.18	.65	.85	1.10	1.41	1.69
5 - 0	76	.59	.85	1.10	1.36	1.55	.30	2.12	.64	.84	1.09	1.41	1.65
6 - 0	66	.66	.84	1.07	1.34	1.72	.32	2.44	.63	.82	1.04	1.34	1.62
7 - 0	58	.57	.80	1.02	1.23	1.45	.46	2.10	.60	.77	1.00	1.29	1.56
8 - 0	43	.57	.75	.95	1.23	1.44	.40	1.58	.59	.76	1.00	1.33	1.58
9 - 0	44	.67	.80	1.01	1.37	1.50	.42	2.00	.62	.81	1.01	1.32	1.52
10 - 0	30	.58	.70	.82	1.07	1.37	.46	1.70	.62	.79	.95	1.22	1.44
11 - 0	40	.55	.70	.92	1.14	1.50	.44	1.76	.58	.74	.93	1.18	1.47
12 - 0	41	.53	.66	.90	1.11	1.46	.30	1.96	.53	.68	.91	1.15	1.43
13 - 0	33	.49	.64	.79	1.02	1.25	.28	1.46	.49	.63	.84	1.08	1.29
14 - 0	42	.47	.62	.80	1.01	1.16	.30	1.74	.48	.63	.80	1.02	1.22
15 - 0	49	.50	.67	.80	.97	1.26	.26	1.76	.49	.65	.80	1.02	1.24
16 - 0	47	.53	.63	.77	1.02	1.31	.40	1.74	.50	.66	.81	1.03	1.28
17 - 0	41	.51	.70	.85	1.08	1.24	.30	1.52	.51	.67	.84	1.07	1.31
18 - 0	39	.47	.64	.87	1.12	1.42	.12	2.26	.50	.67	.85	1.10	1.37
19 - 0	36	.55	.70	.90	1.10	1.35	.36	1.70	.51	.68	.87	1.13	1.41
20 - 0	32	.48	.64	.82	1.20	1.62	.36	2.98	.52	.69	.88	1.13	1.38
23 - 6	35	.54	.78	.98	1.20	1.42	.24	2.24	.54	.70	.93	1.15	1.41
28 - 6	10	.62	.70	.95	1.12	1.39	.40	1.50					

HEMATOLOGY

TABLE G-9

Total Leucocytes per cu. mm. of Blood

Age	N	Observed Percentiles					Range		Smoothed Percentiles				
Yr. Mo.		10th	25th	50th	75th	90th	Min.	Max.	10th	25th	50th	75th	90th
Male and Female													
3 days	67	7350	9250	11450	14100	18200	4400	28950					
0 - 1	152	7850	9200	11400	13700	15250	5250	30500					
0 - 2	140	6800	8250	9900	11600	13250	4300	21200					
0 - 3	136	6900	8250	10050	12200	14450	5150	20250					
0 - 6	137	7350	8900	11150	14050	16500	4800	25000					
0 - 9	144	7250	8900	11600	14150	16150	5250	20900	7350	8850	11200	13900	16450
1 - 0	151	7450	8800	10800	13500	16650	4700	21200	7000	8450	10750	13500	16050
1 - 6	148	6000	7600	9700	12050	14450	4500	21500	6350	7700	9650	12050	15650
2 - 0	138	6100	7100	8600	10650	12050	4000	13900	6000	7150	8750	10700	13350
2 - 6	129	5600	6600	8050	9800	11200	3500	16750	5650	6800	8250	10000	11900
3 - 0	123	5300	6450	7900	9650	11800	4400	21400	5550	6700	8100	9700	11350
4 - 0	118	5600	6600	7900	9300	10650	3300	13750	5450	6550	7850	9300	10900
5 - 0	115	5450	6450	7700	8900	10600	3800	15750	5400	6500	7850	9200	10700
6 - 0	110	5550	6700	7850	9300	10700	3550	12650	5500	6600	7900	9500	10800
7 - 0	96	5450	6650	8100	9450	10700	4000	16000	5500	6650	7900	9500	10900
8 - 0	88	5300	6400	7500	8650	10450	4750	12550	5450	6600	7800	9100	10850
9 - 0	91	5300	6500	7900	9200	10800	4500	15050	5350	6450	7700	9300	10800
10 - 0	69	5550	6250	7300	9300	11000	5000	14150	5300	6200	7500	9100	10600
11 - 0	86	5200	6100	7300	8550	10000	4050	12400	5150	6050	7300	8650	10050
12 - 0	86	4850	5900	7150	8300	9650	3400	12450	5050	5950	7200	8450	9700
13 - 0	67	5300	6100	7500	8650	10000	4250	12650	5150	5950	7150	8500	9600
14 - 0	73	5150	5800	6950	8000	9250	4050	12900	5100	5850	7000	8250	9350
15 - 0	61	5200	5750	7050	8050	9450	3300	12500	5100	5850	7000	8150	9400
16 - 0	67	5100	5950	7100	8400	9400	3950	12600	5150	5850	7100	8150	9550
17 - 0	60	5050	5950	7050	7900	9700	4350	11300	5150	5900	7150	8200	9600
18 - 0	50	5350	5950	7500	8400	10050	4400	12450	5150	6050	7250	8300	9850
19 - 0	44	4850	6050	7100	8450	9450	4000	11250	5050	6050	7200	8350	9900
20 - 0	42	5100	6450	7300	8500	10750	3750	12600	5150	5950	7100	8250	9700
23 - 6	43	4850	5700	6750	8450	9350	3700	11600	5250	5850	7000	8200	9500
28 - 6	15	5500	5850	7000	7800	9050	4900	10450					

TABLE G-10

Neutrophils

Age		Percent of Total Leucocytes													Number per cu. mm. of Blood											
		Observed Percentiles					Range		Smoothed Percentiles					Observed Percentiles					Range		Smoothed Percentiles					
Yr. Mo.	N	10th	25th	50th	75th	90th	Min.	Max.	10th	25th	50th	75th	90th	10th	25th	50th	75th	90th	Min.	Max.	10th	25th	50th	75th	90th	
Male and Female																										
3 days	67	44.0	47.7	55.0	61.6	66.4	31.2	77.4						3541	4693	6058	8046	10703	2024	22397						
0 - 1	151	12.8	17.0	21.9	27.0	32.3	7.5	47.7						1378	1749	2346	3263	4292	603	8817						
0 - 2	140	12.6	15.2	18.9	23.5	28.2	8.5	48.4						945	1398	1840	2432	3018	476	8180						
0 - 3	136	11.5	14.8	18.7	23.6	30.4	7.2	47.5						975	1345	1850	2579	3620	509	5310						
0 - 6	136	13.1	17.0	21.7	26.9	33.5	7.2	52.8						1136	1738	2451	3416	4655	547	7471						
0 - 9	141	13.6	17.8	22.3	29.5	35.0	6.1	58.1	13.8	17.7	22.5	28.4	34.6	1280	1771	2586	3536	4675	466	8946	1235	1806	2531	3448	4582	
1 - 0	150	14.8	18.4	23.4	28.9	35.3	5.5	56.6	14.8	18.9	23.8	30.1	36.9	1289	1909	2576	3392	4416	462	8178	1292	1862	2603	3492	4550	
1 - 6	147	17.6	22.4	27.2	34.6	42.5	5.4	60.8	17.8	22.0	27.2	34.1	41.1	1394	1961	2808	3744	4886	408	10471	1412	1961	2702	3499	4484	
2 - 0	136	20.8	25.0	31.2	38.9	46.2	7.4	72.5	20.8	25.2	30.6	37.6	45.0	1524	2024	2665	3371	4224	407	6708	1496	2022	2677	3470	4484	
2 - 6	127	24.0	29.2	34.2	42.1	48.0	12.4	68.2	23.0	28.2	33.9	41.0	48.9	1596	2217	2776	3591	4850	762	7797	1524	2088	2735	3655	4856	
3 - 0	120	25.2	31.2	38.6	45.4	52.2	19.7	74.7	24.6	30.0	36.2	43.7	51.4	1527	2029	2918	3975	5353	1192	15986	1612	2184	2843	3741	5024	
4 - 0	117	26.8	31.5	38.3	47.0	53.8	19.8	69.4	27.0	32.4	38.7	46.7	54.1	1789	2356	2868	3811	5004	952	7425	1749	2307	2978	3863	5063	
5 - 0	114	30.4	35.4	41.8	47.5	54.3	23.0	84.5	29.2	35.0	41.2	48.0	54.8	1831	2467	3107	3982	4642	950	13309	1832	2453	3172	4071	4992	
6 - 0	109	28.4	36.6	43.5	50.4	57.5	16.5	76.5	30.1	36.7	43.0	49.8	56.2	1819	2539	3439	4279	5134	884	8075	1908	2557	3374	4248	5216	
7 - 0	96	31.9	38.4	44.8	49.9	54.7	20.8	71.6	31.1	37.7	44.0	50.5	56.7	2098	2751	3519	4350	5290	1118	9737	2040	2656	3457	4342	5437	
8 - 0	87	33.0	38.8	45.1	50.8	57.1	25.2	64.7	33.4	38.7	45.1	51.0	57.1	2078	2642	3331	4119	5227	1361	7117	2115	2719	3476	4350	5427	
9 - 0	90	36.5	38.9	44.9	52.0	58.4	27.7	71.6	35.2	39.7	45.4	51.7	57.4	2141	2773	3552	4420	5244	1683	8804	2091	2703	3476	4356	5345	
10 - 0	68	35.9	40.7	45.8	52.5	58.2	25.8	69.6	34.7	40.0	45.5	51.8	58.1	2110	2625	3346	4251	5628	1566	8769	2062	2610	3371	4226	5284	
11 - 0	84	34.8	40.0	45.5	51.4	56.8	19.8	67.7	34.7	40.0	45.8	51.7	58.1	1948	2548	3273	4005	4871	1166	7142	2074	2573	3248	4065	5028	
12 - 0	82	34.3	41.1	45.6	52.1	57.8	27.5	67.6	35.6	41.2	46.5	53.3	58.7	2106	2609	3285	4096	5103	1662	7072	2152	2608	3318	4151	5086	
13 - 0	66	38.3	43.7	49.3	56.3	61.6	28.8	67.8	36.6	42.4	48.3	55.3	60.6	2337	2916	3664	4455	5502	1622	6727	2136	2688	3460	4316	5362	
14 - 0	73	37.4	42.7	48.3	55.2	62.2	22.7	67.0	37.7	43.4	49.6	55.9	61.9	2081	2604	3235	3999	5334	1203	6914	2066	2649	3437	4284	5417	
15 - 0	59	38.2	43.5	52.4	57.7	62.0	27.5	72.0	37.3	43.1	50.0	56.5	62.6	2319	2673	3535	4374	5477	1244	6688	2159	2645	3447	4240	5372	
16 - 0	65	34.9	41.5	49.2	56.1	63.6	28.0	76.7	37.7	43.6	50.7	57.4	63.3	2242	2655	3503	4083	5399	1416	8195	2304	2725	3532	4275	5345	
17 - 0	60	38.8	44.8	50.7	58.0	63.8	28.0	74.2	39.1	45.0	51.8	58.9	64.6	2304	2724	3508	4387	5041	2024	7160	2372	2825	3629	4504	5382	
18 - 0	50	43.1	48.0	54.3	61.8	65.1	27.5	75.0	40.8	46.5	53.0	60.3	65.8	2683	3159	3958	4699	5537	1815	8018	2452	2972	3766	4687	5517	
19 - 0	44	41.4	47.7	55.1	62.8	70.7	32.0	76.0	41.2	46.8	53.4	60.3	65.6	2265	2953	3682	5140	5963	1807	8056	2461	3033	3782	4826	5603	
20 - 0	39	42.7	48.0	53.2	59.7	64.6	33.5	73.5	39.6	45.8	52.6	58.7	63.5	2641	3265	4041	4949	5636	1909	7472	2463	2948	3677	4526	5345	
23 - 6	43	38.9	44.6	53.9	58.4	62.2	33.3	79.6	39.8	44.0	54.0	59.3	62.8	2401	2867	3385	4330	5147	2013	9234	2543	2968	3672	4383	5126	
28 - 6	15	37.2	39.3	53.7	57.8	61.2	35.8	73.4						2546	2879	3672	4119	4695	2086	5155						

TABLE G-11

Eosinophils

Percent of Total Leucocytes

Age		Observed Percentiles					Range		Smoothed Percentiles				
Yr. Mo.	N	10th	25th	50th	75th	90th	Min.	Max.	10th	25th	50th	75th	90th
Male and Female													
3 days	58	1.4	2.7	4.3	6.1	8.7	.2	17.5					
0 - 1	122	1.8	2.4	3.8	5.0	7.7	.4	20.8					
0 - 2	106	1.3	1.9	2.7	3.7	4.9	.2	10.7					
0 - 3	105	.8	1.3	2.1	3.3	4.2	0	8.0					
0 - 6	107	.9	1.2	1.9	3.1	4.0	.3	11.3					
0 - 9	112	.7	1.0	1.6	2.5	3.6	.1	11.2	.7	1.0	1.7	2.8	4.0
1 - 0	115	.5	.9	1.7	2.7	4.2	0	10.2	.6	1.0	1.7	2.8	4.3
1 - 6	119	.6	1.1	2.0	3.2	5.8	0	11.0	.6	1.1	1.9	3.0	5.1
2 - 0	109	.5	1.0	1.9	3.4	5.2	0	11.0	.6	1.1	2.0	3.4	5.3
2 - 6	106	.8	1.2	2.1	3.7	5.7	.1	10.0	.7	1.2	2.1	3.5	5.6
3 - 0	97	.9	1.3	2.2	3.4	6.1	0	11.6	.7	1.2	2.1	3.5	5.6
4 - 0	94	.8	1.4	2.2	4.0	5.8	0	9.4	.8	1.3	2.2	3.7	5.5
5 - 0	93	.7	1.4	2.2	3.9	5.6	0	13.0	.8	1.4	2.3	3.9	5.6
6 - 0	91	.8	1.3	2.5	4.5	5.5	0	12.7	.9	1.4	2.4	4.3	6.0
7 - 0	73	1.0	1.6	2.3	4.2	7.7	.2	14.0	1.0	1.6	2.6	4.4	6.9
8 - 0	68	1.1	1.9	3.1	4.6	7.6	.5	16.8	1.1	1.8	3.0	4.6	7.3
9 - 0	74	1.5	2.0	3.1	4.9	6.4	1.0	9.6	1.1	1.8	3.1	4.8	7.0
10 - 0	57	.8	1.7	3.0	4.4	6.3	0	9.6	1.0	1.7	3.0	4.6	6.6
11 - 0	67	1.0	1.7	2.6	3.9	5.5	.2	8.0	.9	1.6	2.8	4.2	6.0
12 - 0	63	.8	1.3	2.8	4.1	5.8	0	9.4	.8	1.4	2.5	3.9	5.6
13 - 0	52	.7	1.2	2.1	3.7	4.9	.2	8.5	.8	1.4	2.4	3.8	5.1
14 - 0	56	.6	1.3	2.4	3.9	5.3	0	10.2	.7	1.4	2.3	3.6	4.8
15 - 0	46	.6	1.1	2.1	2.8	4.5	.4	5.8	.6	1.2	2.1	3.1	4.4
16 - 0	52	.5	1.0	1.8	2.7	3.6	.4	21.2	.5	1.1	2.0	2.9	4.2
17 - 0	48	.2	1.0	1.7	2.5	3.8	0	10.0	.5	1.1	1.9	2.8	4.2
18 - 0	38	.8	1.3	2.2	3.3	5.4	.4	7.5	.6	1.2	1.9	3.0	4.4
19 - 0	37	.6	1.1	2.0	3.2	4.1	.3	7.0	.6	1.2	1.9	3.0	4.3
20 - 0	31	.6	1.0	1.6	2.9	4.0	0	6.0	.6	1.3	2.0	3.1	4.5
23 - 6	34	.7	1.3	2.2	3.3	4.3	.5	6.5	.7	1.5	2.3	3.5	5.0
28 - 6	10	.7	1.7	2.4	3.8	5.3	1.0	5.8					

Number per cu. mm. of Blood

Age	Observed Percentiles					Range		Smoothed Percentiles				
Yr. Mo.	10th	25th	50th	75th	90th	Min.	Max.	10th	25th	50th	75th	90th
Male and Female												
3 days	103	253	559	792	1313	35	1987					
0 - 1	162	239	439	677	996	27	1914					
0 - 2	118	168	265	417	644	21	1278					
0 - 3	69	136	225	343	495	0	865					
0 - 6	86	134	201	345	515	30	2079					
0 - 9	80	112	177	300	436	14	1182	78	116	190	319	484
1 - 0	61	103	192	312	502	0	1056	64	106	183	309	507
1 - 6	55	109	182	311	606	0	1683	56	102	174	296	543
2 - 0	38	93	159	303	497	0	1024	54	98	171	291	524
2 - 6	67	97	182	302	478	17	1240	58	94	175	288	506
3 - 0	65	98	166	268	513	0	1235	58	96	173	279	481
4 - 0	62	112	175	276	428	0	722	56	100	169	276	446
5 - 0	57	103	175	307	443	0	1326	61	104	175	301	460
6 - 0	67	103	175	337	477	0	915	66	110	185	331	485
7 - 0	77	119	173	362	519	16	1071	74	126	200	345	506
8 - 0	78	140	238	330	448	35	1142	82	137	235	357	530
9 - 0	129	172	254	339	522	84	720	87	140	238	366	533
10 - 0	51	129	219	347	412	0	758	69	133	217	362	486
11 - 0	56	118	184	299	456	10	585	59	114	193	331	466
12 - 0	57	87	185	316	456	0	658	55	95	177	297	430
13 - 0	59	93	154	275	343	15	405	54	94	164	268	378
14 - 0	43	92	160	274	356	0	801	46	90	154	244	341
15 - 0	36	75	141	215	276	25	412	40	80	147	222	300
16 - 0	41	64	139	197	250	24	1908	37	74	139	216	285
17 - 0	24	77	133	186	241	0	642	37	75	134	215	296
18 - 0	49	81	128	276	426	32	510	42	77	130	227	330
19 - 0	43	79	132	215	310	18	416	42	80	128	221	329
20 - 0	52	72	115	212	338	0	544	43	82	130	231	325
23 - 6	38	100	140	211	333	27	413	54	90	129	271	366
28 - 6	76	88	120	327	340	59	389					

Lymphocytes

Percent of Total Leucocytes

Age Yr. Mo.	N	Observed Percentiles 10th	25th	50th	75th	90th	Range Min.	Max.	Smoothed Percentiles 10th	25th	50th	75th	90th
Male and Female													
3 days	67	18.1	24.1	32.3	38.4	43.5	13.8	58.8					
0 - 1	151	52.5	57.6	64.9	71.2	74.8	43.4	82.8					
0 - 2	140	58.6	65.8	71.1	76.6	79.6	39.2	83.5					
0 - 3	136	59.8	65.2	71.8	77.3	81.9	39.5	88.0					
0 - 6	136	57.2	64.4	70.2	75.2	80.6	28.4	86.6					
0 - 9	141	55.9	62.4	68.6	74.9	79.5	36.5	91.4	55.9	63.0	69.0	74.3	79.4
1 - 0	150	54.4	62.1	68.2	72.8	78.0	37.2	86.4	53.8	61.0	67.5	72.8	78.1
1 - 6	147	48.2	55.8	63.7	69.0	74.6	29.1	88.2	49.8	56.8	64.0	69.6	74.4
2 - 0	136	44.7	52.3	59.6	65.6	71.0	16.9	87.7	46.1	53.1	59.9	65.7	70.7
2 - 6	127	42.6	49.0	55.3	61.5	66.4	28.2	79.8	41.9	49.4	56.5	62.0	67.8
3 - 0	120	37.5	44.9	52.0	58.3	65.2	19.5	72.8	39.4	46.8	53.9	60.1	66.0
4 - 0	117	37.2	43.4	52.9	58.6	64.2	20.8	72.0	36.7	43.8	51.5	57.6	63.4
5 - 0	114	35.6	42.4	48.4	54.0	59.3	12.3	70.0	35.5	42.3	49.7	55.0	60.6
6 - 0	109	33.6	39.4	46.4	53.9	60.6	18.0	73.8	34.4	40.5	46.8	53.6	59.8
7 - 0	96	34.8	40.2	45.8	51.1	57.7	18.4	69.0	33.9	39.5	45.7	52.4	58.6
8 - 0	87	34.2	39.0	44.6	51.4	57.2	27.1	65.2	33.4	38.8	44.6	51.3	56.3
9 - 0	90	33.0	38.7	44.6	50.9	54.5	20.6	65.0	33.6	38.5	44.4	50.7	55.0
10 - 0	68	35.2	38.3	43.5	50.4	54.9	23.0	64.7	33.8	38.3	44.4	50.7	56.2
11 - 0	84	34.7	40.0	45.2	50.9	57.1	24.6	70.3	33.4	38.7	44.7	50.2	57.0
12 - 0	82	34.9	37.9	43.9	49.4	56.0	23.0	62.5	33.0	37.5	43.5	49.1	55.3
13 - 0	66	29.1	33.3	41.0	46.4	52.7	24.2	63.4	30.5	35.3	41.7	48.0	53.5
14 - 0	73	30.4	35.9	41.0	47.7	52.1	23.0	73.7	28.9	35.1	41.0	47.1	52.2
15 - 0	59	28.8	33.5	39.3	46.5	51.9	21.0	64.8	28.7	34.9	40.7	47.1	53.1
16 - 0	65	28.2	35.4	41.8	47.1	56.2	15.2	67.0	28.1	33.9	39.9	46.5	53.0
17 - 0	60	28.1	33.3	39.3	47.3	52.7	19.2	63.8	26.8	32.4	38.6	45.4	51.6
18 - 0	50	24.2	29.5	35.8	41.9	47.4	14.3	64.0	25.6	30.7	37.2	44.0	49.6
19 - 0	44	23.2	28.0	35.2	42.6	47.4	17.6	56.0	25.8	30.4	36.8	44.0	49.1
20 - 0	39	26.4	29.9	37.0	43.8	47.3	17.0	59.5	26.8	31.8	37.8	45.4	51.4
23 - 6	43	28.1	32.4	37.1	45.0	52.6	15.2	57.5	26.1	30.9	36.8	45.5	51.4
28 - 6	15	26.0	30.8	37.4	49.7	54.0	20.7	55.8					

Number per cu. mm. of Blood

Age Yr. Mo.	Observed Percentiles 10th	25th	50th	75th	90th	Range Min.	Max.	Smoothed Percentiles 10th	25th	50th	75th	90th
Male and Female												
3 days	1942	2759	3646	4590	6210	909	7413					
0 - 1	4955	5836	7281	8774	10041	3113	21137					
0 - 2	4548	5645	6681	8264	9961	2627	16536					
0 - 3	4728	5694	7150	8695	10388	3299	13507					
0 - 6	5009	6324	7591	9632	11707	3418	17576					
0 - 9	4724	5826	7809	9788	11461	2880	14082	4801	5968	7517	9517	11547
1 - 0	4669	5753	7152	9132	11473	2924	15391	4424	5512	7095	9054	11100
1 - 6	3709	4647	5874	7454	9171	2318	14227	3789	4704	5963	7675	9297
2 - 0	3100	3889	4964	6613	7683	1031	9911	3296	4067	5064	6428	7602
2 - 6	2926	3528	4298	5353	6486	1855	9530	2930	3608	4474	5646	6648
3 - 0	2505	3152	4030	5247	6247	1542	8861	2710	3365	4213	5266	6261
4 - 0	2621	3263	4032	4724	5748	1215	7926	2513	3143	3946	4814	5742
5 - 0	2439	2964	3627	4327	4933	1279	6520	2396	2978	3758	4558	5317
6 - 0	2188	2815	3612	4506	5296	1270	7413	2316	2866	3686	4520	5269
7 - 0	2588	2898	3628	4106	5106	1518	6693	2399	2845	3591	4268	5236
8 - 0	2328	2778	3197	3883	5008	1920	6136	2342	2767	3375	4114	5109
9 - 0	2236	2695	3364	4119	5126	1213	6968	2250	2722	3364	4070	4941
10 - 0	2264	2720	3311	3923	4822	1833	6266	2180	2675	3351	3999	4806
11 - 0	2130	2584	3268	3885	4811	1415	6468	2114	2580	3236	3882	4717
12 - 0	2062	2530	3115	3823	4350	1687	6712	2066	2505	3060	3763	4476
13 - 0	1847	2316	2914	3781	4419	1211	6014	1913	2386	2922	3661	4297
14 - 0	1871	2295	2807	3436	4104	1440	4979	1814	2276	2821	3457	4038
15 - 0	1721	2222	2757	3211	3756	1050	6587	1817	2254	2810	3428	4002
16 - 0	1914	2292	2951	3616	4023	1237	4845	1794	2209	2785	3401	4046
17 - 0	1769	2141	2616	3421	4329	1191	6146	1741	2133	2687	3304	4050
18 - 0	1558	1980	2662	3049	4068	1056	5072	1712	2079	2618	3242	3991
19 - 0	1698	2006	2348	2921	3529	1512	4478	1715	2057	2549	3220	4080
20 - 0	1890	2182	2695	3422	4378	1297	6780	1703	2050	2651	3343	4124
23 - 6	1603	1900	2571	3351	4448	1245	5405	1609	1937	2671	3266	4235
28 - 6	1666	1930	2781	3397	4188	1138	5831					

TABLE G-13

Monocytes

Percent of Total Leucocytes

Age Yr. Mo.	N	Observed Percentiles 10th	25th	50th	75th	90th	Range Min.	Max.	Smoothed Percentiles 10th	25th	50th	75th	90th
Male and Female													
3 days	67	4.1	5.5	6.8	8.8	10.3	1.8	13.8					
0 - 1	151	3.6	5.3	6.8	9.2	11.9	.5	16.0					
0 - 2	140	3.0	4.4	5.7	7.0	8.5	.8	16.6					
0 - 3	136	2.5	4.2	5.3	6.6	8.1	0	11.3					
0 - 6	136	2.5	3.5	4.5	5.7	7.2	1.2	13.4					
0 - 9	141	2.4	3.4	4.6	6.0	7.5	1.0	14.5	2.6	3.5	4.7	6.0	7.6
1 - 0	150	2.7	3.6	4.9	6.4	8.2	1.3	16.6	2.7	3.6	4.8	6.2	7.7
1 - 6	147	2.7	3.7	4.9	6.5	7.8	1.3	12.6	2.8	3.7	4.9	6.4	7.8
2 - 0	136	2.8	3.7	5.0	6.5	8.1	1.1	12.0	2.9	3.8	5.0	6.5	8.0
2 - 6	127	3.2	4.0	5.1	6.4	8.2	2.0	13.3	3.0	4.0	5.1	6.6	8.0
3 - 0	120	3.1	4.1	5.1	6.8	8.6	1.3	14.0	3.0	4.0	5.1	6.6	8.0
4 - 0	117	2.9	3.7	5.0	6.0	7.4	1.1	10.7	2.8	3.8	5.1	6.3	7.7
5 - 0	114	3.2	4.0	4.8	5.9	7.2	1.8	9.0	2.9	3.8	4.9	6.1	7.3
6 - 0	109	2.7	3.8	5.1	6.3	7.5	.8	14.7	2.8	3.7	4.9	6.1	7.3
7 - 0	96	2.9	3.7	4.8	6.2	7.3	1.0	9.3	2.7	3.6	4.7	5.9	7.0
8 - 0	87	2.7	3.5	4.6	5.6	6.6	1.0	8.7	2.7	3.5	4.7	5.9	6.8
9 - 0	90	3.0	3.8	4.9	6.0	7.2	2.0	9.4	2.7	3.5	4.8	6.0	6.9
10 - 0	68	2.8	3.5	4.4	5.5	6.8	2.0	9.2	2.8	3.6	4.6	5.8	7.0
11 - 0	84	2.8	3.7	4.6	5.7	6.8	1.7	10.0	3.0	3.8	4.8	5.9	7.1
12 - 0	82	2.6	3.9	4.9	6.2	7.3	1.4	12.5	3.0	3.9	4.9	6.1	7.2
13 - 0	66	3.0	3.9	5.0	6.9	8.0	1.0	9.8	3.1	4.0	4.9	6.4	7.5
14 - 0	73	3.3	4.5	5.4	6.4	7.7	2.2	10.8	3.2	4.1	5.1	6.3	7.7
15 - 0	59	3.0	4.1	5.2	6.3	7.6	2.5	10.0	3.2	4.1	5.1	6.4	7.8
16 - 0	65	3.2	4.1	5.2	6.8	8.4	2.8	9.0	3.1	4.0	5.2	6.5	7.9
17 - 0	60	2.9	3.6	4.9	6.3	7.6	2.0	10.0	3.1	3.9	5.1	6.6	7.9
18 - 0	50	3.2	3.7	5.1	6.8	7.9	2.0	11.0	3.2	3.9	5.2	6.6	7.8
19 - 0	44	3.2	4.4	5.6	6.9	7.8	2.0	10.4	3.2	4.0	5.3	6.6	7.5
20 - 0	39	3.4	4.2	5.4	6.3	7.1	1.8	8.6	3.2	4.0	5.3	6.6	7.8
23 - 6	43	3.2	4.3	5.6	6.6	8.0	2.0	10.7	3.3	4.2	5.4	6.9	8.1
28 - 6	15	3.4	4.6	5.6	7.2	8.4	3.0	8.8					

Number per cu. mm. of Blood

Age Yr. Mo.	Observed Percentiles 10th	25th	50th	75th	90th	Range Min.	Max.	Smoothed Percentiles 10th	25th	50th	75th	90th
Male and Female												
3 days	417	577	774	1081	1511	145	2260					
0 - 1	337	499	762	1127	1463	50	2482					
0 - 2	282	390	538	719	899	85	1793					
0 - 3	247	388	532	696	955	0	1533					
0 - 6	224	341	496	702	924	120	1796					
0 - 9	271	388	528	694	879	77	1443	261	369	515	704	913
1 - 0	289	377	521	715	935	141	1584	265	366	500	689	893
1 - 6	241	359	468	644	796	118	1310	244	345	459	637	823
2 - 0	220	305	426	566	708	97	929	225	316	440	589	736
2 - 6	232	310	417	562	686	111	957	228	312	428	573	689
3 - 0	232	313	416	569	710	122	1027	221	309	416	559	694
4 - 0	188	276	368	496	642	112	1092	204	291	388	512	658
5 - 0	224	279	359	473	640	114	1044	210	279	369	487	621
6 - 0	218	299	379	512	614	48	946	213	284	368	489	605
7 - 0	209	282	367	489	612	80	785	204	277	363	473	586
8 - 0	201	253	327	427	543	118	916	203	267	352	454	578
9 - 0	227	293	373	464	592	140	1014	207	269	355	451	582
10 - 0	181	254	348	436	579	126	768	198	263	353	447	565
11 - 0	183	236	347	432	538	109	670	200	261	355	443	551
12 - 0	190	267	355	439	558	78	844	203	271	356	439	543
13 - 0	211	312	402	476	565	83	693	202	283	366	450	549
14 - 0	225	293	370	445	588	126	800	208	278	359	449	568
15 - 0	193	271	365	466	538	142	664	206	274	356	466	578
16 - 0	209	286	364	491	630	136	817	206	272	352	478	599
17 - 0	192	235	306	492	577	115	833	210	267	344	489	605
18 - 0	232	283	368	467	657	138	880	221	276	354	495	616
19 - 0	237	288	364	540	618	178	660	220	277	359	495	601
20 - 0	227	306	392	496	573	146	692	208	277	358	483	600
23 - 6	202	268	372	466	583	127	845	206	294	373	481	602
28 - 6	183	332	380	511	565	147	625					

Section H

SERUM PROTEINS

VIRGINIA E TREVORROW

SERUM AND PLASMA PROTEINS

Subjects and Methods

PLASMA protein studies were started in 1942 on all active subjects then less than 8 years of age. All subjects enrolled from 1942 through 1965 have been included in the protein study. The total group is made up of 182 individuals in 106 families, including 35 families with 2 enrolled children, 13 with 3, and 5 with 4:

Age of subject at last analysis	Number of subjects
Under 5	34
5 - 9	37
10 - 14	31
15 - 19	29
20 - 24	28
25 - 32	23
Total	182

Number of exams. per subject	Number of subjects	
	Male	Female
Under 10	12	9
10 - 19	18	19
20 - 29	11	23
30 - 39	28	32
40 - 49	17	13
Total	86	96

In addition to the above regularly studied individuals, 34 older Child Research Council subjects who were not studied as children have been followed for varying periods of their adult life; the oldest of these was last seen at age 45 years.

Blood was collected as described in Section G. Throughout the study total protein determination has been done by Kjeldahl analysis, corrected for non-protein nitrogen either by actual determination or, more commonly, by a standard correction of 25 mg/100 cc. When plasma was used, the recorded total is for serum, calculated as plasma total minus NPN and fibrinogen.

Three methods of separation have been used. Originally, fractionation of capillary blood plasma was done by the Howe method, a salting-out procedure, as described by us in 1941(1). The method was discontinued in 1955. Serum or plasma was used the day blood was drawn. Single determinations were done except for an occasional set of duplicates.

In 1949 Tiselius separation was started(2), using serum in barbital buffer, pH 8.6. Sera were used immediately or frozen for use within a two-week period. Both ascending and descending patterns were divided by dropping a perpendicular to the base at the low point between fractions. For each of the four patterns, the fractional and total protein areas were measured by planimeter. From this, the mean percent of the total contributed by each fraction was calculated, and this percent of the total grams, as determined by Kjeldahl, was recorded as the concentration for each fraction, in gm/100 cc. Single determinations were done on serum obtained by venipuncture. Because of the necessity of using venous blood in order to obtain an adequate sample of serum (0.6 cc), Tiselius analyses were not done on subjects under 4 years of age.

Paper electrophoresis of 0.1 cc samples of capillary blood serum was used for all subjects from birth to 4 years of age starting in April, 1954. Separation was effected in the Durrum cell(3). Quantitation was by Kjeldahl according to Levin and Oberholzer(4), modified by heat fixation of protein fractions on paper (120°C for 2 hours) and washing in 10 percent aqueous acetic acid. Of a total of 694 analyses, 385 were done in duplicate (2 strips run and analyzed at the same time) and the mean value recorded. Total protein was determined in 516 as an additional check on the analysis. Assuming the total to be correct, recovery from paper was 97.5 percent ± 4.3 percent.

The technical errors, determined as described in the Introduction, are as follows:

Fraction	Technical Error Gm/100 cc	Number of duplicates used in calculation
Total	± 0.0698	100
Howe		
Albumin	± 0.0755	99
Globulin	± 0.0371	100
Fibrinogen	± 0.0087	100
Tiselius		
Albumin	± 0.0400	19
Alpha-1	± 0.0243	19
Alpha-2	± 0.0247	19
Beta	± 0.0250	19
Gamma	± 0.0246	19
Paper		
Albumin	± 0.0581	100
Alpha-1	± 0.0200	100
Alpha-2	± 0.0395	100
Beta	± 0.0345	100
Gamma	± 0.0698	100

In all, 5014 blood samples have been analyzed. The following table indicates the planned schedule of examination. Occasionally, a visit was missed or a blood sample was hemolyzed or inadequate in amount, and analysis omitted. A few 3- or 9-month samples were obtained when the prior visit was missed. Each individual is not included at every age within the span of years during which he was being studied. The mean number of missed visits for the Howe and paper electrophoresis methods is about one in 9 and for Tiselius electrophoresis, about one for each 7 scheduled examinations.

Schedule of Examinations

1942-1946	1, 2, 3 months
	Each 3 months to adolescence
1947-1949	1, 2, 3 months
	Each 3 months to 3 years
	Each 6 months to end of adolescence
	Yearly in adults
1949-1966	As above plus examination at 3 days

Analysis	No. Analyses Regular Subjects	Years	Source of Blood*	Ages of Examinations
Total	3663	1942-1946	P	All scheduled
Protein	182 subjects	1947-1949	P	examinations
		1949-1966	P, V	
Howe	2843	1942-1949	P	All scheduled
	133 subjects	1949-1955	P, V	examinations
Tiselius	1666	1949-1966	V	Start at 4 years
	141 subjects			
Paper	694	1954-1966	P	3 days to
	51 subjects			4 years

* P = peripheral blood. V = venous blood.

Comparison of Different Methods

A named fraction obtained by one method is neither qualitatively nor quantitatively identical with the same fraction obtained by a different method. In general, the Howe "albumin" approximates in amount the sum of the "albumin," "alpha-1" and "alpha-2" by the other methods, and the Howe "globulin" approximates the sum of the "beta" plus "gamma." Between Tiselius and paper electrophoresis, the situation is complex due in part to the role of lipid in influencing the Tiselius patterns. Examples of the discrepancies in levels observed are shown for "beta" and "gamma" globulin in Figure H-1. A series of bloods with both Tiselius and paper electrophoresis showed the Tiselius "beta" globulin to average 0.24 gm higher and the "gamma" about 0.20 gm lower than corresponding fractions by paper electrophoresis.

Non-analytical Factors Which May Influence Serum Proteins

1. *Age:* A definite age trend is apparent in some fractions during all or part of the age span studied. All data are listed in the tables (H-1 through H-14) by age, but the listings are abbreviated over an age span where no age trend is found. The data listed are judged to be representative.

2. *Sex:* Although sex differences occur at individual ages in all protein fractions, these differences are not significant for any individual age at the level P = 0.01. Nevertheless the differences, although minor, do persist over time in two instances: (a) girls tend to higher albumin levels in the preadolescent years; after adolescence, the boys tend to be higher and (b) both sexes show a minor rise in gamma globulin in the adolescent years with the girls showing this change at an earlier age, resulting in a separation with the female level higher from age 12 to age 15 years. These differences are shown graphically (Figure H-2).

3. *Health:* All subjects were ambulatory and not acutely ill except for an occasional cold. Deviations in protein values may have been present as a result of past illness or immunizations (illness and immunization are recorded on tape; see Section A). Values have not been deleted from the group data because of illness.

4. *Venous vs. Peripheral Blood, Use of Stasis:* When the study of venous blood was started, 26 non-subject individuals, age 6-31 years, were studied with both venous and peripheral samples analyzed. Stasis was used for all venous samples. In this group, the venous bloods showed higher protein content (t test, $P<0.001$). A second series of 20 individuals was studied in the same manner except that no stasis was used for the venous samples. In these, the difference was not significant (albumin, $P = 0.17$; globulin, $P = 0.09$). In the subject group stasis has been avoided except in 61 of 1666 venous samples. Each sample is identified on the tape as to type and presence or absence of stasis. The relatively rare use of stasis was deemed to be insignificant for group data, therefore all blood analyses are included.

5. *Behavior of Child:* Behavior of the child while blood was taken has been coded on the tape for most children up to 9 years of age, after which few have shown any serious objection except for fear which is generally well controlled. In the early years there is marked variation in behavior from visit to visit. At ages 1 and 2 years, statistical analyses show albumin to be higher in those who are crying hard and/or fighting than in those who are "good" (Chi Square $P = 0.05$, and $0.05<0.02$). All values are included in the group data since this behavior is "normal" at this age. Whether our group shows more or less objection because of frequent blood taking, or training, is not known. A chart of behavior is shown graphically (Figure H-3). Infrequent variations, such as faintness, fear with trembling, strenuous exercise within 1 hour, etc. are not graphed.

6. *Nature of Bleeding from Capillary Prick:* Some children bleed well, some poorly, and some vary from visit to visit. Analysis of results on 60 individuals who "bled well" on one visit and "bled poorly" on another visit within a 1-year interval showed no significant difference in protein concentration. This is not coded on tape.

7. *Hemolysis:* The presence of hemoglobin in serum will falsely increase the total protein and the fraction with which it separates. This does not present a problem with venous samples for no serum was analyzed when hemolysis was noted (the presence of hemolysis was judged by visual examination only, but

a very small amount can be seen). With capillary blood, precautions were taken to avoid hemolysis, but this was not always successful. No sample was used which was grossly red. It is estimated that hemoglobin may have contributed 0.02 gm/100 cc in some samples. In the Howe separation, this would appear as "albumin." In paper electrophoresis the position of hemoglobin varies with the amount of haptoglobin in the serum. At birth, when haptoglobin is virtually absent, hemoglobin separates in the beta globulin fraction. As haptoglobin appears, the hemoglobin shifts to the alpha-2 globulin area. Each paper was carefully examined before staining for the presence of a faint brownish area which would indicate the presence and position of hemoglobin. Detectable hemoglobin was noted in the beta areas in 11 percent of samples at birth and at 1 month, and in 4 percent of children 2 months or older. Because of the small error introduced, these samples have been included. Hemolysis is not coded on tape.

8. *Haptoglobin Type:* The haptoglobin type of the subject appears to influence the level of alpha-2 globulin characteristic of that individual. All of the subjects have not been typed. Findings on 66 subjects are as follows:

	Number of Individuals		
Haptoglobin type	1 - 1	2 - 1	2 - 2
Mean Alpha-2 above group median	9	22	9
Mean Alpha-2 below group median	3	8	15

For group data this might be of significance only in a population with a distinctly different distribution of the haptoglobin genes. Haptoglobin types are coded in the record of "demographic data."

9. *Time of Day:* This has been coded for each blood sample. No relation has been found between time of day and protein concentration.

10. *Season of Year:* A cross-sectional study of non-Child Research Council subjects has been reported by us(5) to show a

seasonal variation in albumin concentration. This trend was found in the present study only in the years 1945-1947, all other years showing completely random fluctuations with season. We have not identified any single factor responsible for the original finding; apparently the differences reported did not result directly from seasonal weather changes. Dates of examinations are on tape.

Definitions of Tabulated Data

1. *Age:* As in Section G.
2. *N:* As in Section G.
3. *Percentiles:* Calculated as described in the general introduction.
4. *Range:* Absolute values for age.
5. *Smoothed Percentiles:* The tabulated "smoothed percentiles" have been constructed using raw percentiles for all ages. The median was first smoothed. If the progression is a curve, smoothing was done visually using French curves; if a straight line described the data, this line was calculated. In some instances, as with the Tiselius gamma globulin, a series of lines were used. This smoothed median was checked against a scatter chart of the individual raw data. If the over-all error exceeded 2 percent (48 percent on one side, 52 percent on the other), adjustments were made as indicated. An age trend of the width of the distribution was judged by the width of the middle 50 percent of the group using the original percentiles. For any span in which this showed no regular progression, each individual value was calculated as a deviation from the smoothed median. An ogive of the deviations was drawn, and percentiles calculated from the ogive. If a regular expansion or constriction of the middle 50 percent was observed, the 10th, 25th, 75th and 90th percentiles were smoothed in the same manner as was the median. In the younger ages the calculated percentiles frequently define the trend adequately and no smoothing was attempted. In the older age groups the data were often inadequate to define the trend with any degree of confidence.

Data Not Included

1. *Mean and Standard Deviation:* Because of skewness in most fractions, the mean and standard deviation have not been included.

2. *Group Data for Ages Not Listed:* No data are listed in Tables H, 1 through 14, for ages between birthday visits beyond 4 years, and some birthday visits are omitted in intervals where no age trend is apparent.

REFERENCES

1. Hill, R.M., and Trevorrow, V.: Plasma albumin, globulin and fibrinogen in healthy individuals from birth to adult life. I. A system of microanalysis. J Lab Clin Med, 26:1838, 1941.
2. Moore, D.H., and White, J.U.: A new conpact Tiselius electrophoresis apparatus. Rev Sci Instrum, 19:700, 1948.
3. Williams, F.G., Jr.; Pickels, E.G., and Durrum, E.L.: Improved hanging-strip paper electrophoresis technique. Science, 121:829, 1955.
4. Levin, B., and Oberholzer, V.G.: Paper electrophoresis of serum proteins with micro-Kjeldahl nitrogen analysis of the protein fractions. Amer J Clin Path, 23:205, 1953.
5. Trevorrow, V.; Kaser, M.; Patterson, J.P., and Hill, R.M.: Plasma albumin, globulin, and fibrinogen in healthy individuals from birth to adulthood. II. "Normal" values. J Lab Clin Med, 27:1, 1942.

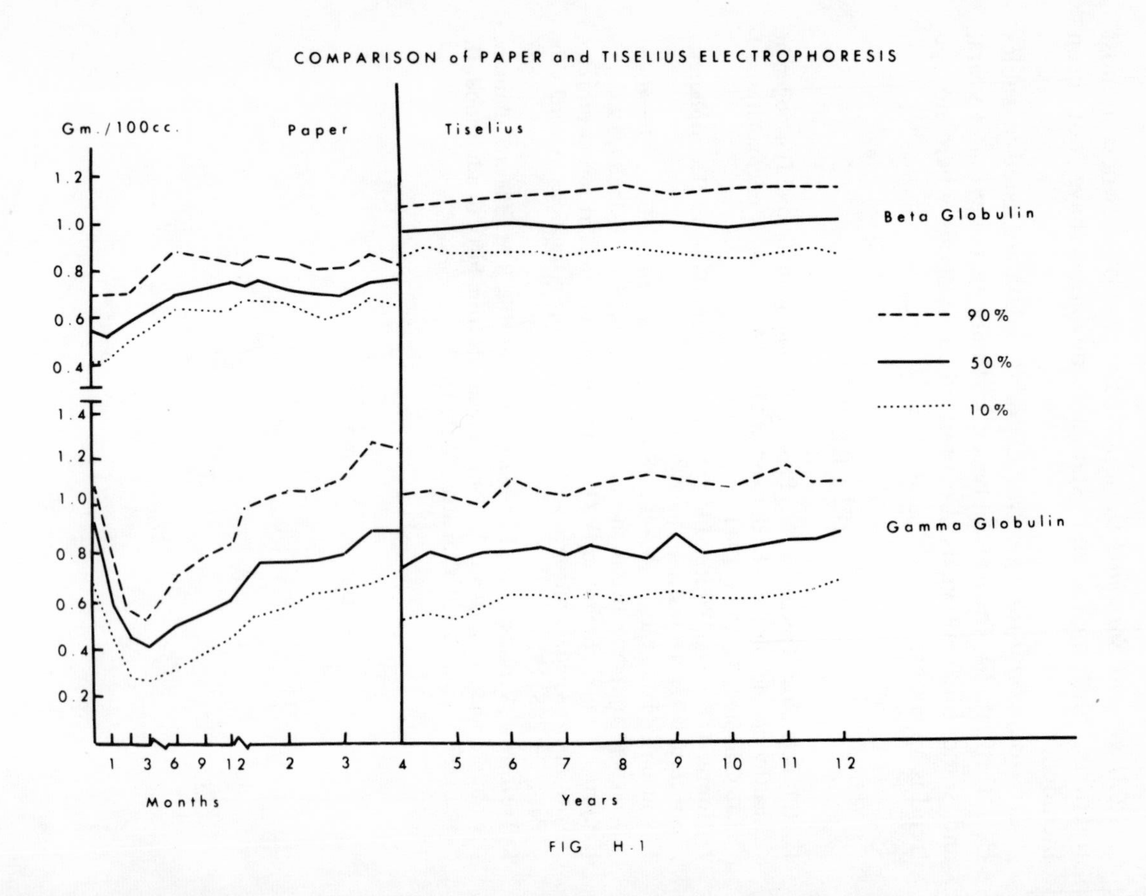
COMPARISON of PAPER and TISELIUS ELECTROPHORESIS
Gm./100cc.
Paper
Tiselius
Beta Globulin
90%
50%
10%
Gamma Globulin
1.2
1.0
0.8
0.6
0.4
1.4
1.2
1.0
0.8
0.6
0.4
0.2
1 3 6 9 12
Months
2 3 4 5 6 7 8 9 10 11 12
Years

FIG H.1

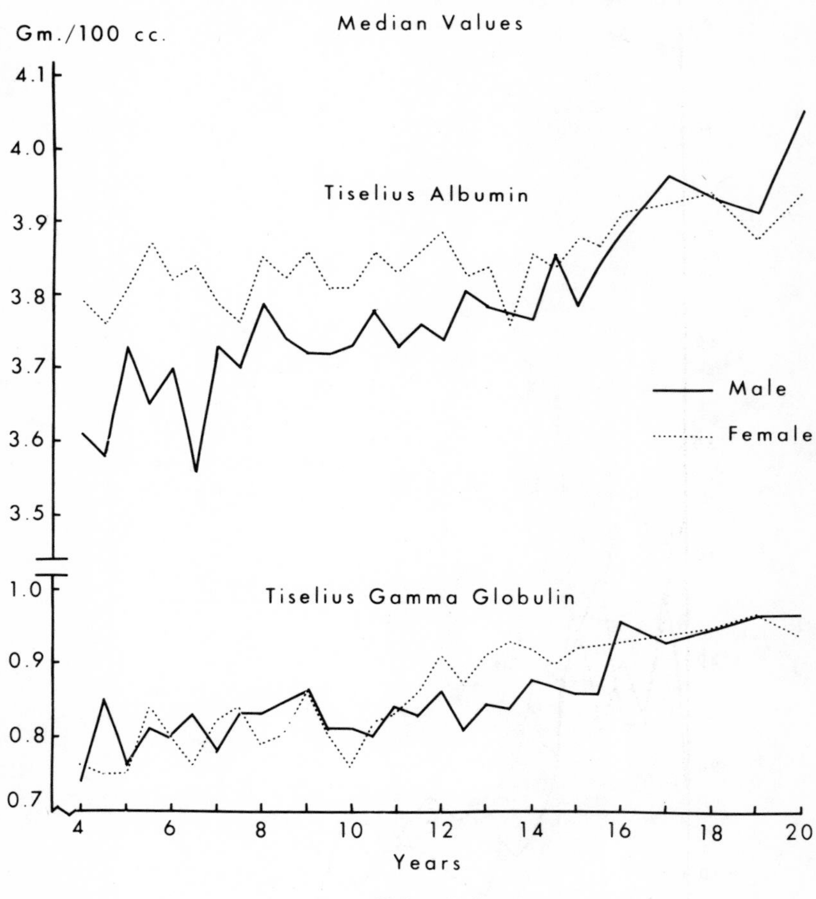
SEX DIFFERENCES in SERUM PROTEINS
Median Values
Gm./100 cc.
4.1
4.0
3.9
3.8
3.7
3.6
3.5
1.0
0.9
0.8
0.7
Tiselius Albumin
Tiselius Gamma Globulin
Male
Female
4
6
8
10
12
14
16
18
20
Years

FIG. H-2

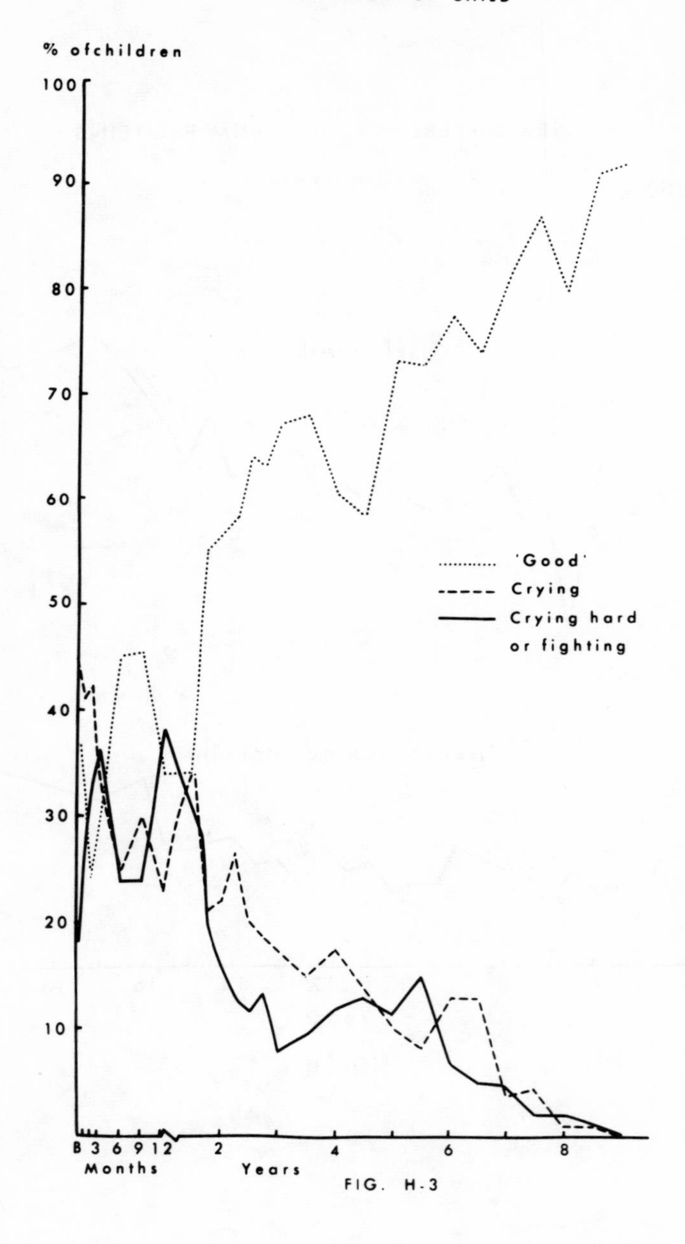
BEHAVIOR of CHILD
% of children
100
90
80
70
60
50
40
30
20
10
'Good'
Crying
Crying hard or fighting
B 3 6 9 12
Months
2
Years
4
6
8

FIG. H-3

SERUM AND PLASMA PROTEINS - MALE AND FEMALE COMBINED

TABLE H-1

Total Protein, Serum, in Gm./100 cc.

Age Yr. Mo.	N	Percentiles 10th	25th	50th	75th	90th	Range Min.	Max.	Smoothed Percentiles 10th	25th	50th	75th	90th
3 days	29	5.079	5.273	5.634	5.889	6.150	4.56	6.32					
0 - 1	51	4.882	5.075	5.322	5.580	5.732	4.52	6.18					
0 - 2	76	5.008	5.228	5.467	5.659	5.783	4.66	6.87					
0 - 3	71	5.312	5.490	5.643	5.807	6.018	4.95	6.39					
0 - 6	65	5.588	5.767	6.032	6.238	6.481	5.30	6.69					
0 - 9	74	5.643	5.874	6.109	6.335	6.492	5.19	6.66	5.73	5.90	6.14	6.35	6.53
1 - 0	77	5.879	6.037	6.226	6.440	6.632	5.63	7.20	5.81	5.99	6.21	6.42	6.61
1 - 6	84	5.887	6.060	6.359	6.641	6.839	5.63	7.27	5.91	6.09	6.32	6.53	6.71
2 - 0	80	6.021	6.184	6.417	6.633	6.775	5.51	6.97	5.98	6.15	6.39	6.60	6.77
2 - 6	89	5.954	6.141	6.349	6.509	6.697	5.56	7.18	6.02	6.19	6.43	6.65	6.82
3 - 0	88	6.086	6.213	6.446	6.727	6.926	5.85	7.19	6.05	6.22	6.47	6.68	6.87
3 - 6	83	6.027	6.228	6.432	6.644	6.816	5.86	7.46	6.08	6.26	6.51	6.72	6.92
4 - 0	96	6.128	6.334	6.557	6.766	7.002	5.88	7.52	6.11	6.29	6.54	6.75	6.96
5 - 0	103	6.157	6.350	6.565	6.842	7.045	5.86	7.30	6.16	6.36	6.60	6.81	7.02
6 - 0	94	6.171	6.367	6.607	6.908	7.069	5.65	7.70	6.22	6.41	6.65	6.87	7.08
7 - 0	101	6.243	6.417	6.670	6.921	7.166	6.02	7.89	6.26	6.45	6.69	6.91	7.13
8 - 0	85	6.266	6.512	6.712	6.980	7.212	6.00	7.64	6.29	6.48	6.71	6.94	7.17
9 - 0	95	6.257	6.461	6.721	6.960	7.216	5.87	7.68	6.30	6.50	6.73	6.95	7.19
10 - 0	82	6.235	6.455	6.644	6.934	7.112	5.98	7.64	6.32	6.51	6.74	6.96	7.20
11 - 0	84	6.385	6.547	6.733	6.994	7.240	6.10	7.59	6.33	6.52	6.76	6.97	7.22
12 - 0	87	6.383	6.550	6.786	6.983	7.255	6.02	7.65	6.34	6.53	6.77	6.99	7.24
13 - 0	75	6.433	6.545	6.795	7.055	7.294	6.13	7.62	6.35	6.55	6.79	7.00	7.25
14 - 0	74	6.392	6.584	6.798	7.019	7.337	5.91	8.10	6.37	6.56	6.80	7.03	7.27
15 - 0	66	6.222	6.498	6.845	7.107	7.294	5.90	8.00	6.38	6.58	6.86	7.09	7.31
16 - 0	67	6.446	6.702	6.999	7.228	7.412	6.08	7.79	6.42	6.63	6.92	7.16	7.39
17 - 0	64	6.490	6.737	7.021	7.298	7.498	6.30	8.38	6.46	6.67	6.97	7.23	7.46
18 - 0	56	6.535	6.739	7.077	7.283	7.439	6.15	7.67	6.50	6.72	7.03	7.30	7.54
19 - 0	49	6.499	6.757	7.036	7.278	7.687	6.30	7.81	6.55	6.77	7.09	7.36	7.61
20 - 0	43	6.645	6.851	7.150	7.456	7.693	6.05	8.00	6.59	6.82	7.15	7.43	7.67
23 - 6	43	6.543	6.715	6.940	7.238	7.434	6.01	8.10	Decrease after 20 years ?				
28 - 6	32	6.510	6.663	6.936	7.198	7.381	6.09	8.00					
33 - 6	24	6.359	6.839	7.039	7.163	7.275	6.25	7.61					
38 - 6	15	6.771	6.827	6.919	7.159	7.435	6.39	7.62					

Fibrinogen in Gm./100 cc.

TABLE H-2

Age Yr. Mo.	N	Percentiles 10th	25th	50th	75th	90th	Range Min.	Max.	Smoothed Percentiles 10th	25th	50th	75th	90th
3 days	27	.172	.210	.253	.305	.322	.150	.400					
0 - 1	69	.139	.162	.208	.240	.287	.113	.379					
0 - 2	66	.110	.138	.174	.222	.270	.086	.340					
0 - 3	70	.105	.130	.164	.222	.269	.083	.336					
0 - 6	75	.106	.131	.163	.193	.245	.077	.461	.116	.137	.165	.199	.242
1 - 0	76	.105	.121	.150	.197	.244	.040	.361	.117	.138	.166	.200	.243
2 - 0	75	.121	.139	.180	.212	.245	.082	.310	.118	.139	.167	.201	.244
3 - 0	62	.125	.145	.170	.204	.254	.097	.374	.120	.141	.169	.203	.246
4 - 0	67	.114	.141	.167	.211	.262	.081	.395	.122	.143	.171	.205	.248
5 - 0	74	.125	.148	.180	.211	.250	.077	.426	.123	.144	.172	.206	.249
6 - 0	66	.121	.141	.168	.212	.270	.093	.366	.125	.146	.174	.208	.251
7 - 0	63	.127	.147	.176	.202	.234	.096	.354	.127	.148	.176	.210	.253
8 - 0	46	.130	.144	.168	.204	.248	.106	.369	.128	.149	.177	.211	.254
9 - 0	52	.122	.149	.172	.203	.238	.108	.275	.130	.151	.179	.213	.256
10 - 0	44	.125	.151	.175	.207	.259	.084	.339	.131	.152	.180	.214	.257
11 - 0	46	.133	.152	.188	.214	.254	.108	.286	.133	.154	.182	.216	.259
12 - 0	48	.148	.163	.186	.216	.250	.125	.343	.135	.156	.184	.218	.261
13 - 0	31	.129	.157	.182	.222	.251	.110	.293	.136	.157	.185	.219	.262
14 - 0	33	.142	.160	.173	.205	.234	.129	.282	.138	.159	.187	.221	.264
15 - 0	26	.135	.150	.177	.236	.277	.112	.313	.140	.161	.189	.223	.266
16 - 0	27	.141	.167	.200	.232	.307	.131	.324	.143	.164	.192	Increasing	
17 - 0	21	.140	.164	.193	.263	.302	.116	.352	.145	.166	.194	spread ?	

SERUM AND PLASMA PROTEINS - MALE AND FEMALE COMBINED

TABLE H-3

Albumin, Howe Method, in Gm./100 cc.

Age		Percentiles					Range		Smoothed Percentiles				
Yr. Mo.	N	10th	25th	50th	75th	90th	Min.	Max.	10th	25th	50th	75th	90th
3 days	33	3.456	3.620	3.832	4.086	4.299	3.230	4.510	3.59	3.71	3.86	4.03	4.19
0 - 1	73	3.672	3.858	3.995	4.163	4.295	3.42	4.80	3.72	3.84	4.00	4.16	4.32
0 - 2	67	3.921	4.040	4.199	4.349	4.512	3.62	4.96	3.92	4.04	4.19	4.35	4.52
0 - 3	74	4.067	4.265	4.420	4.586	4.767	3.89	4.89	4.15	4.27	4.42	4.59	4.75
0 - 6	78	4.278	4.445	4.609	4.760	4.992	4.04	5.26	4.35	4.42	4.62	4.79	4.95
0 - 9	71	4.383	4.557	4.744	4.922	5.092	4.26	5.48	4.42	4.54	4.70	4.86	5.02
1 - 0	77	4.458	4.579	4.741	4.860	5.054	4.11	5.20	4.47	4.60	4.75	4.91	5.08
1 - 6	75	4.416	4.579	4.756	4.895	5.012	4.08	5.17	4.50	4.62	4.78	4.94	5.10
2 - 0	71	4.353	4.584	4.747	4.918	5.041	4.19	5.38	4.45	4.57	4.72	4.89	5.05
2 - 6	67	4.359	4.473	4.643	4.792	4.977	4.09	5.34	4.43	4.55	4.70	4.87	5.03
3 - 0	65	4.419	4.556	4.696	4.932	5.037	4.13	5.25	4.41	4.53	4.69	4.85	5.01
4 - 0	69	4.389	4.486	4.635	4.774	4.988	4.12	5.29	4.38	4.50	4.65	4.81	4.98
5 - 0	73	4.366	4.482	4.624	4.845	4.986	4.11	5.32	4.38	4.50	4.66	4.82	4.98
6 - 0	67	4.417	4.517	4.644	4.802	4.947	4.08	5.18	4.38	4.50	4.66	4.82	4.98
7 - 0	64	4.417	4.544	4.713	4.858	4.992	4.09	5.10	4.39	4.51	4.66	4.82	4.99
8 - 0	47	4.386	4.505	4.627	4.829	5.094	4.27	5.26	4.39	4.51	4.66	4.83	4.99
9 - 0	52	4.450	4.551	4.666	4.776	4.958	4.33	5.24	4.39	4.51	4.67	4.83	4.99
10 - 0	45	4.374	4.460	4.633	4.779	4.899	4.23	5.36	4.39	4.51	4.67	4.83	4.99
11 - 0	46	4.453	4.592	4.732	4.901	5.094	4.34	5.23	4.40	4.52	4.67	4.83	5.00
12 - 0	48	4.459	4.571	4.708	4.911	5.077	4.29	5.44	4.40	4.52	4.68	4.84	5.00
13 - 0	30	4.418	4.585	4.693	4.895	5.010	4.29	5.25	4.42	4.54	4.70	4.86	5.02
14 - 0	33	4.406	4.549	4.723	4.914	5.080	4.31	5.18	4.46	4.58	4.73	4.90	5.06
15 - 0	26	4.420	4.561	4.809	4.972	5.043	4.05	5.51	4.50	4.62	4.77	4.93	5.10
16 - 0	27	4.498	4.630	4.810	4.941	5.138	4.41	5.39	4.53	4.65	4.81	4.97	5.13
17 - 0	22	4.651	4.725	4.867	5.129	5.359	4.59	5.42	4.57	4.69	4.85	5.01	5.17

Globulin, Howe Method, in Gm./100 cc.

TABLE H-4

Age		Percentiles					Range		Smoothed Percentiles				
Yr. Mo.	N	10th	25th	50th	75th	90th	Min.	Max.	10th	25th	50th	75th	90th
3 days	31	1.240	1.385	1.466	1.627	1.713	1.13	1.78					
0 - 1	72	.994	1.084	1.177	1.293	1.430	.76	1.84					
0 - 2	65	.909	.991	1.058	1.161	1.282	.81	1.41					
0 - 3	73	.839	.963	1.049	1.138	1.248	.71	1.34					
0 - 6	75	.908	1.010	1.158	1.294	1.409	.77	1.69		1.06	1.16	1.26	
0 - 9	73	1.026	1.130	1.256	1.372	1.544	.88	2.00		1.13	1.25	1.36	
1 - 0	78	1.129	1.212	1.314	1.466	1.646	.93	1.75	1.11	1.19	1.32	1.44	1.65
1 - 6	75	1.204	1.283	1.390	1.540	1.637	1.01	1.89	1.18	1.29	1.42	1.56	1.75
2 - 0	75	1.253	1.382	1.515	1.632	1.748	1.11	1.99	1.24	1.36	1.49	1.65	1.83
2 - 6	68	1.276	1.411	1.521	1.657	1.787	1.13	1.99	1.30	1.42	1.54	1.71	1.89
3 - 0	66	1.309	1.435	1.590	1.744	2.008	1.17	2.35	1.32	1.46	1.59	1.76	1.94
4 - 0	69	1.429	1.536	1.667	1.841	2.007	1.17	2.36	1.40	1.50	1.65	1.84	2.01
5 - 0	73	1.410	1.553	1.748	1.951	2.108	1.29	3.10	1.44	1.54	1.70	1.88	2.05
6 - 0	67	1.431	1.602	1.754	1.894	2.108	1.23	2.55	1.46	1.57	1.72	1.90	2.07
7 - 0	64	1.477	1.577	1.751	1.936	2.102	1.40	2.61	1.48	1.58	1.74	1.92	2.09
8 - 0	47	1.496	1.628	1.770	2.058	2.176	1.41	2.33	1.50	1.60	1.75	1.94	2.10
9 - 0	52	1.482	1.607	1.770	1.999	2.164	1.34	2.23	1.51	1.61	1.76	1.95	2.12
10 - 0	45	1.446	1.604	1.717	1.986	2.126	1.37	2.22	1.52	1.63	1.78	1.96	2.13
11 - 0	46	1.502	1.570	1.766	1.958	2.046	1.28	2.36	1.54	1.64	1.79	1.98	2.15
12 - 0	48	1.568	1.653	1.822	1.974	2.086	1.32	2.51	1.55	1.66	1.81	1.99	2.16
13 - 0	30	1.641	1.787	1.854	2.023	2.209	1.57	2.28	1.57	1.67	1.82	2.01	2.18
14 - 0	33	1.561	1.681	1.883	2.029	2.123	1.40	2.31	1.58	1.69	1.84	2.02	2.19
15 - 0	26	1.550	1.720	1.850	1.982	2.190	1.37	2.37	1.60	1.70	1.85	2.04	2.20
16 - 0	27	1.591	1.767	1.929	2.101	2.200	1.30	2.32	1.61	1.72	1.87	2.05	2.22
17 - 0	22	1.601	1.738	1.934	2.130	2.278	1.50	2.34	1.62	1.73	1.88	2.06	2.24

SERUM AND PLASMA PROTEINS - MALE AND FEMALE COMBINED

TABLE H-5

Albumin, Tiselius, in Gm./100 cc.

Age		Percentiles					Range		Smoothed Percentiles				
Yr. Mo.	N	10th	25th	50th	75th	90th	Min.	Max.	10th	25th	50th	75th	90th
4 - 0	37	3.403	3.485	3.664	3.789	3.970	3.09	4.17	3.45	3.60	3.74	3.88	4.01
5 - 0	49	3.402	3.608	3.744	3.878	3.969	3.25	4.18	3.46	3.60	3.75	3.88	4.02
6 - 0	53	3.469	3.627	3.740	3.877	4.039	3.25	4.27	3.46	3.61	3.76	3.89	4.03
7 - 0	61	3.429	3.580	3.747	3.894	4.046	3.16	4.27	3.47	3.62	3.77	3.90	4.04
8 - 0	55	3.413	3.703	3.836	3.974	4.126	3.21	4.37	3.48	3.63	3.78	3.91	4.05
9 - 0	64	3.528	3.651	3.773	3.971	4.124	3.27	4.37	3.49	3.64	3.78	3.92	4.06
10 - 0	61	3.556	3.660	3.773	3.899	3.981	3.19	4.18	3.50	3.65	3.79	3.93	4.07
11 - 0	66	3.589	3.681	3.783	3.932	4.102	3.35	4.17	3.51	3.66	3.80	3.94	4.08
12 - 0	65	3.505	3.685	3.825	3.970	4.093	3.29	4.41	3.52	3.67	3.81	3.95	4.09
13 - 0	66	3.468	3.658	3.805	3.957	4.088	3.21	4.32	3.53	3.68	3.82	3.96	4.10
14 - 0	63	3.521	3.638	3.828	3.976	4.132	3.36	4.40	3.55	3.70	3.84	3.98	4.12
15 - 0	58	3.503	3.712	3.864	4.030	4.165	3.30	4.35	3.58	3.73	3.87	4.01	4.14
16 - 0	63	3.659	3.752	3.915	4.069	4.213	3.45	4.43	3.60	3.75	3.90	4.03	4.17
17 - 0	61	3.676	3.796	3.956	4.085	4.207	3.43	4.59	3.63	3.78	3.92	4.06	4.20
18 - 0	55	3.631	3.795	3.926	4.092	4.195	3.35	4.39	3.64	3.79	3.94	4.07	4.21
19 - 0	45	3.629	3.783	3.921	4.087	4.275	3.45	4.55	3.66	3.81	3.95	4.09	4.22
20 - 0	42	3.566	3.851	4.015	4.204	4.410	3.41	4.67	3.67	3.82	3.96	4.10	4.24
23 - 6	43	3.619	3.747	3.929	4.161	4.326	3.32	4.48	Decrease after 20 years ?				
28 - 6	31	3.562	3.728	3.908	4.062	4.238	3.14	4.33					
33 - 6	24	3.713	3.801	3.934	4.046	4.147	3.57	4.41					
38 - 6	15	3.408	3.577	3.811	4.067	4.145	3.33	4.37					

Alpha-1 Globulin, Tiselius, in Gm./100 cc.

TABLE H-6

Age Yr. Mo.	N	10th	25th	50th	75th	90th	Min.	Max.	Smoothed 10th	Smoothed 25th	Smoothed 50th	Smoothed 75th	Smoothed 90th
4 - 0	37	.331	.359	.385	.411	.445	.30	.53	.33	.35	.38	.41	.44
6 - 0	53	.322	.348	.382	.417	.446	.28	.59	↓	↓	↓	↓	↓
8 - 0	55	.345	.361	.384	.419	.454	.28	.51					
10 - 0	62	.344	.360	.382	.410	.436	.30	.46					
12 - 0	67	.336	.352	.370	.395	.422	.28	.47					
14 - 0	63	.331	.358	.381	.412	.428	.28	.53					
16 - 0	63	.315	.335	.362	.384	.416	.28	.53					
18 - 0	55	.318	.341	.368	.406	.461	.29	.53					
20 - 0	42	.331	.345	.368	.386	.403	.30	.43					
23 - 6	43	.324	.344	.356	.384	.410	.30	.45					
28 - 6	31	.307	.333	.370	.402	.436	.29	.51					
33 - 6	24	.320	.335	.380	.400	.415	.30	.45	.33	.35	.38	.41	.44

Alpha-2 Globulin, Tiselius, in Gm./100 cc.

TABLE H-7

Age Yr. Mo.	N	10th	25th	50th	75th	90th	Min.	Max.	Smoothed 10th	Smoothed 25th	Smoothed 50th	Smoothed 75th	Smoothed 90th
4 - 0	37	.686	.746	.803	.868	.939	.64	1.26	.71	.76	.81	.88	.95
5 - 0	50	.674	.727	.791	.891	.949	.58	1.05	.70	.75	.80	.87	.94
6 - 0	54	.711	.753	.801	.858	.919	.63	1.00	.69	.74	.79	.86	.93
7 - 0	61	.677	.723	.781	.829	.946	.65	1.01	.68	.73	.78	.85	.92
8 - 0	55	.670	.698	.748	.838	.922	.61	1.09	.67	.72	.77	.84	.91
9 - 0	64	.662	.705	.767	.828	.885	.57	1.00	.66	.71	.76	.83	.90
10 - 0	61	.648	.690	.738	.808	.881	.57	.96	.66	.71	.76	.83	.90
11 - 0	66	.654	.700	.761	.840	.880	.61	.97	.65	.70	.75	.82	.89
12 - 0	68	.652	.702	.745	.798	.878	.58	.95	.65	.70	.75	.82	.89
13 - 0	66	.665	.706	.740	.816	.905	.57	1.00	.64	.70	.75	.82	.88
14 - 0	63	.630	.674	.728	.795	.887	.57	.96	.64	.69	.74	.81	.88
15 - 0	58	.620	.679	.730	.782	.863	.55	.96	.64	.69	.74	.81	.88
16 - 0	63	.651	.697	.750	.821	.888	.56	1.01	.64	.69	.74	.81	.88
17 - 0	61	.645	.693	.769	.835	.872	.58	.90	.64	.69	.74	.81	.88
18 - 0	55	.641	.680	.747	.819	.924	.57	1.02	.63	.68	.74	.80	.87
19 - 0	45	.642	.672	.760	.835	.912	.59	1.04	.63	.68	.73	.80	.87
20 - 0	42	.641	.687	.740	.791	.837	.60	.88	.63	.68	.73	.80	.87
23 - 6	43	.610	.657	.722	.789	.836	.56	.92	Decrease after 20 years ?				
28 - 6	32	.589	.617	.699	.759	.813	.53	1.05					
33 - 6	24	.595	.655	.690	.724	.795	.58	.83					
38 - 6	15	.593	.633	.709	.789	.869	.55	1.13					

SERUM AND PLASMA PROTEINS - MALE AND FEMALE COMBINED

TABLE H-8

Beta Globulin, Tiselius, in Gm./100 cc.

Age		Percentiles					Range		Smoothed Percentiles				
Yr. Mo.	N	10th	25th	50th	75th	90th	Min.	Max.	10th	25th	50th	75th	90th
4 - 0	37	.861	.902	.955	1.010	1.048	.79	1.21	.83	.90	.96	1.03	1.10
5 - 0	50	.855	.898	.973	1.040	1.090	.80	1.17	.85	.92	.99	1.06	1.13
6 - 0	54	.869	.933	.997	1.079	1.123	.83	1.26	.86	.93	.99	1.07	1.14
7 - 0	61	.860	.906	.979	1.063	1.121	.79	1.29	↓	↓	↓	↓	↓
8 - 0	55	.879	.924	.994	1.078	1.145	.83	1.23					
10 - 0	61	.838	.894	.969	1.064	1.147	.77	1.31					
12 - 0	68	.858	.940	.995	1.047	1.134	.76	1.34					
14 - 0	63	.875	.911	.982	1.068	1.170	.74	1.39					
16 - 0	63	.841	.909	.991	1.069	1.130	.74	1.35					
18 - 0	55	.866	.917	1.003	1.074	1.159	.76	1.34	.86	.93	.99	1.07	1.14
20 - 0	42	.911	.979	1.048	1.129	1.213	.81	1.39	Increase after 18 years ?				
23 - 6	43	.859	.915	.991	1.109	1.214	.73	1.31					
28 - 6	32	.868	.934	1.027	1.187	1.253	.78	1.33					
33 - 6	24	.940	1.000	1.080	1.200	1.290	.90	1.40					
38 - 6	15	1.002	1.051	1.147	1.239	1.303	.97	1.40					

Gamma Globulin, Tiselius, in Gm./100 cc.

TABLE H-9

Age Yr. Mo.	N	10th	25th	50th	75th	90th	Min.	Max.	Smoothed 10th	25th	50th	75th	90th
4 - 0	37	.516	.643	.744	.916	1.049	.47	1.22	.52	.62	.74	.86	1.00
5 - 0	50	.525	.637	.765	.879	1.027	.45	1.50	.57	.67	.79	.91	1.05
6 - 0	54	.619	.689	.795	.906	1.098	.53	1.39	.59	.69	.81	.93	1.06
7 - 0	61	.601	.672	.788	.897	1.042	.50	1.35	.59	.69	.81	.93	1.07
8 - 0	55	.586	.692	.803	.973	1.102	.51	1.19	.59	.69	.81	.93	1.07
9 - 0	64	.629	.733	.868	.955	1.111	.54	1.38	.59	.69	.81	.94	1.07
10 - 0	61	.603	.671	.807	.948	1.071	.52	1.34	.60	.70	.82	.94	1.08
11 - 0	66	.623	.711	.849	.974	1.159	.48	1.34	.62	.72	.84	.96	1.09
12 - 0	68	.681	.751	.886	.987	1.100	.58	1.47	.64	.74	.86	.98	1.11
13 - 0	66	.654	.768	.870	1.008	1.122	.55	1.40	.66	.76	.88	1.00	1.13
14 - 0	63	.656	.790	.900	.999	1.215	.53	1.33	.67	.77	.89	1.01	1.15
15 - 0	58	.662	.823	.899	1.020	1.214	.50	1.55	.69	.79	.91	1.03	1.17
16 - 0	63	.726	.823	.939	1.030	1.157	.54	1.38	.71	.81	.93	1.05	1.18
17 - 0	61	.715	.795	.943	1.077	1.224	.58	1.34	.73	.83	.95	1.07	1.20
18 - 0	55	.710	.823	.934	1.072	1.140	.56	1.36		.84	.96	1.08	
19 - 0	45	.729	.801	.974	1.072	1.160	.59	1.35		.85	.97	1.09	
20 - 0	42	.671	.817	.948	1.067	1.182	.60	1.44		.83	.95	1.07	
23 - 6	43	.664	.762	.874	1.010	1.176	.54	1.56					
28 - 6	32	.704	.758	.857	1.052	1.202	.58	1.69					
33 - 6	24	.705	.789	.855	.922	1.025	.58	1.15					
38 - 6	15	.674	.761	.863	1.089	1.136	.58	1.21					

SERUM AND PLASMA PROTEINS - MALE AND FEMALE COMBINED

TABLE H-10

Albumin, Paper Electrophoresis, in Gm./100 cc.

Age Yr. Mo.	N	Percentiles 10th	25th	50th	75th	90th	Range Min.	Max.	Smoothed Percentiles 10th	25th	50th	75th	90th
3 days	41	2.570	2.852	3.083	3.287	3.446	2.26	4.53	2.65	2.87	3.08	3.28	3.46
0 - 1	42	2.837	2.959	3.090	3.250	3.455	2.53	3.54	2.68	2.90	3.11	3.30	3.49
0 - 2	47	2.953	3.121	3.305	3.580	3.696	2.52	3.84	2.85	3.07	3.28	3.48	3.66
0 - 3	42	3.168	3.306	3.429	3.573	3.719	2.57	3.96	2.92	3.14	3.35	3.54	3.73
0 - 6	39	3.178	3.347	3.444	3.756	3.897	3.04	3.99	3.06	3.28	3.48	3.68	3.86
0 - 9	42	2.922	3.218	3.510	3.699	3.880	2.68	4.19	3.14	3.36	3.57	3.76	3.95
1 - 0	41	3.120	3.379	3.649	3.876	4.043	2.87	4.34	3.20	3.43	3.64	3.83	4.01
1 - 3	38	3.386	3.526	3.702	3.979	4.114	3.11	4.39	3.25	3.47	3.68	3.88	4.06
1 - 6	35	3.179	3.459	3.757	3.978	4.131	3.06	4.42	3.28	3.51	3.72	3.91	4.09
1 - 9	41	3.271	3.502	3.745	3.892	3.980	2.98	4.41	3.30	3.53	3.74	3.93	4.11
2 - 0	37	3.327	3.590	3.780	3.935	4.060	2.97	4.20	3.30	3.52	3.72	3.92	4.10
2 - 3	38	3.343	3.519	3.678	3.817	3.972	2.82	4.16	3.29	3.51	3.72	3.92	4.10
2 - 6	41	3.112	3.351	3.581	3.784	4.017	2.94	4.29	3.28	3.50	3.71	3.90	4.09
2 - 9	38	3.324	3.602	3.731	4.031	4.107	3.13	4.15	3.27	3.49	3.70	3.90	4.08
3 - 0	34	3.286	3.465	3.664	3.855	4.054	3.03	4.23	3.26	3.49	3.70	3.89	4.07
3 - 6	26	2.861	3.189	3.602	3.787	4.070	2.76	4.32	3.25	3.47	3.68	3.88	4.06
4 - 0	24	3.285	3.571	3.733	3.885	4.014	2.97	4.40	3.24	3.46	3.66	3.86	4.04

Alpha-1 Globulin, Paper Electrophoresis, in Gm./100 cc. TABLE H-11

Age Yr. Mo.	N	10th	25th	50th	75th	90th	Min.	Max.	Smoothed 10th	25th	50th	75th	90th
3 days	44	.171	.212	.253	.309	.360	.14	.78					
0 - 1	45	.132	.157	.201	.229	.281	.11	.41	.15	.18	.21	.25	.30
0 - 2	47	.129	.167	.199	.239	.324	.09	.41	↓	↓	↓	↓	↓
0 - 3	42	.152	.189	.220	.258	.350	.13	.39					
0 - 6	42	.140	.190	.230	.274	.358	.12	.41					
1 - 0	41	.164	.183	.211	.250	.319	.14	.38					
2 - 0	36	.153	.182	.218	.251	.280	.08	.38					
3 - 0	34	.146	.169	.203	.256	.289	.13	.36					
4 - 0	25	.160	.182	.208	.244	.300	.15	.35	.15	.18	.21	.25	.30

Alpha-2 Globulin, Paper Electrophoresis, in Gm./100 cc. TABLE H-12

Age Yr. Mo.	N	10th	25th	50th	75th	90th	Min.	Max.	Smoothed 10th	25th	50th	75th	90th
3 days	43	.471	.509	.564	.615	.703	.34	.75			.57		
0 - 1	45	.455	.505	.560	.620	.724	.36	.92			.56		
0 - 2	47	.527	.576	.652	.747	.809	.41	.90			.66		
0 - 3	44	.628	.725	.780	.853	.897	.48	1.08			.78		
0 - 6	40	.723	.780	.907	.990	1.090	.69	1.19			.91		
0 - 9	43	.716	.770	.851	.992	1.127	.68	1.35			.88		
1 - 0	40	.676	.777	.882	.960	1.047	.61	1.14			.86		
1 - 3	41	.675	.776	.833	.907	.987	.60	1.13	.72	.78	.84	.92	1.01
1 - 6	38	.662	.758	.867	.964	1.074	.55	1.32	.70	.77	.82	.90	1.00
1 - 9	41	.675	.767	.826	.912	.969	.47	1.21	.69	.75	.81	.89	.98
2 - 0	36	.730	.793	.834	.890	.962	.64	1.01	.68	.75	.80	.88	.98
2 - 3	40	.694	.723	.774	.847	.928	.56	1.23	.68	.74	.80	.88	.97
2 - 6	40	.675	.723	.792	.852	1.011	.64	1.17	.67	.74	.80	.88	.97
2 - 9	38	.678	.749	.801	.868	.931	.62	.99	.67	.73	.79	.87	.96
3 - 0	35	.681	.729	.784	.840	.964	.60	1.14	.67	.73	.79	.87	.96
3 - 6	25	.654	.714	.777	.879	1.038	.62	1.16	.67	.73	.79	.87	.96
4 - 0	25	.687	.738	.781	.882	.946	.58	.97	.67	.73	.79	.87	.96

SERUM AND PLASMA PROTEINS - MALE AND FEMALE COMBINED

TABLE H-13

Beta Globulin, Paper Electrophoresis, in Gm./100 cc.

Age		Percentiles					Range		Smoothed Percentiles				
Yr. Mo.	N	10th	25th	50th	75th	90th	Min.	Max.	10th	25th	50th	75th	90th
3 days	44	.426	.475	.538	.628	.692	.34	.88	.44	.49	.54	.60	.66
0 - 1	44	.419	.459	.515	.606	.703	.39	.98	.41	.46	.51	.57	.63
0 - 2	46	.495	.522	.579	.641	.699	.45	.88	.48	.53	.58	.64	.70
0 - 3	44	.540	.566	.621	.722	.779	.50	.85	.54	.58	.63	.69	.75
0 - 6	42	.630	.650	.706	.779	.870	.50	.93	.60	.65	.70	.76	.85
0 - 9	43	.628	.669	.720	.795	.859	.55	1.02	.64	.68	.73	.78	.85
1 - 0	39	.619	.686	.747	.801	.841	.60	.90	↓	↓	↓	↓	↓
1 - 3	40	.657	.682	.738	.779	.816	.57	.86	↓	↓	↓	↓	↓
1 - 6	37	.670	.703	.761	.834	.866	.56	.89	↓	↓	↓	↓	↓
2 - 0	36	.647	.682	.727	.776	.827	.57	.90	↓	↓	↓	↓	↓
2 - 6	39	.601	.636	.699	.757	.814	.56	.98	↓	↓	↓	↓	↓
3 - 0	35	.612	.651	.700	.775	.816	.57	.91	↓	↓	↓	↓	↓
3 - 6	26	.669	.715	.748	.793	.868	.64	.98	↓	↓	↓	↓	↓
4 - 0	25	.646	.698	.750	.792	.821	.53	.84	.64	.68	.73	.78	.85

Gamma Globulin, Paper Electrophoresis, in Gm./100 cc.

TABLE H-14

Age Yr. Mo.	N	10th	25th	50th	75th	90th	Min.	Max.	10th	25th	50th	75th	90th
3 days	44	.670	.785	.932	1.072	1.170	.51	1.26					
0 - 1	45	.461	.510	.585	.680	.796	.31	.93					
0 - 2	47	.294	.402	.436	.502	.564	.24	.64					
0 - 3	44	.269	.361	.413	.470	.521	.17	.79					
0 - 6	42	.317	.379	.491	.576	.691	.28	1.07	.31	.38	.47	.62	
0 - 9	44	.377	.441	.543	.677	.785	.32	.97	.38	.45	.54	.69	
1 - 0	40	.441	.496	.616	.700	.846	.34	1.26	.44	.52	.60	.75	
1 - 3	41	.501	.585	.671	.805	.979	.43	1.12	.50	.57	.66	.81	.96
1 - 6	38	.550	.635	.747	.883	1.020	.39	1.39	.54	.61	.70	.85	1.00
1 - 9	40	.534	.616	.695	.809	1.047	.48	1.16	.57	.64	.73	.88	1.03
2 - 0	36	.570	.687	.756	.894	1.060	.48	1.17	.58	.66	.76	.90	1.06
2 - 3	40	.589	.688	.765	.952	1.058	.49	1.15	.60	.68	.77	.92	1.07
2 - 6	41	.613	.687	.769	.893	1.061	.46	1.47	.62	.69	.79	.93	1.08
2 - 9	39	.660	.722	.813	.991	1.092	.50	1.34	.63	.71	.80	.95	1.10
3 - 0	35	.629	.713	.798	.981	1.125	.57	1.25	.64	.72	.82	.96	1.12
3 - 6	26	.658	.761	.891	1.140	1.274	.53	1.64	.69	.76	.85	1.00	1.15
4 - 0	25	.707	.776	.894	1.019	1.226	.50	1.33	.74	.80	.90	1.04	1.20

Section J

SERUM CHOLESTEROL

VIRGINIA A. LEE

VIRGINIA E TREVORROW

SERUM CHOLESTEROL

Subjects

ANALYSIS of total and free cholesterol in venous serum was started in July, 1953 on all Child Research Council subjects between 4 and 19 years of age who were then included in the hematology and serum protein study. Older subjects who were seen for other facets of the Child Research Council program were gradually included in the cholesterol study with addition of older subjects being made as late as 1966. Younger subjects were studied when peripheral blood was available and were followed regularly after they reached the age for venipuncture (about 4 years). Since babies at 3 days and at 1 month of age rarely bled well enough to furnish serum for cholesterol, a separate group of healthy infants in the Colorado General Hospital newborn nursery and at the Crittenton Home was studied. These data are appended to Table J-1.

Blood was taken at 3 days, 1, 2 and 3 months, at 3-month intervals to 3 years, 6-monthly to adolescence and yearly in postadolescent subjects. Twenty-five boys and 24 girls were followed continuously from 1953-54 through 1966.

Starting in 1958, alpha- and beta-lipoprotein cholesterol were also determined in the same samples of venous serum and occasionally in samples of peripheral serum from younger subjects.

In all, 2267 sera from 196 subjects have been analyzed:

Age at last analysis	Number of subjects Male	Female
Under 5 years	9	10
5- <10	14	10
10- <15	12	16
15- <20	12	19
20- <25	17	13
25- <30	8	13
30- <35	9	5
35 and over	20	9
Total	101	95

Number of exams. per subject	Number of subjects Male	Female
1 - 5	20	23
6 - 10	38	25
11 - 15	11	17
16 - 20	15	15
21 - 25	11	14
26 - 28	6	1
Total	101	95

Methods

Blood was obtained as previously described (Section G). After standing at room temperature for one hour the blood was centrifuged and serum removed. All samples were analyzed the day blood was drawn, or the serum was frozen for use within 3 months. Once frozen, the serum was not thawed until used; when thawed, it was well mixed before use. Comparison of analyses done the day blood was drawn and after varying periods of freezing up to 3 months showed no significant difference.

Total and free cholesterol were measured by the Schoenheimer-Sperry method(1) as modified by Sperry and Webb(2) using 0.2 cc of serum for each analysis. All determinations were done in triplicate, the results averaged and recorded as mg/100 cc.

Measurement of cholesterol associated with alpha- and beta-lipoprotein as separated by paper electrophoresis was done by a modification of the method of Boyd(3). The position of the two lipoprotein fractions after electrophoresis of 0.1 cc of serum on paper was located in relation to the proteins stained with bromphenolblue on a separate strip run simultaneously. Initially, this position was determined from a series of analyses in which two unstained strips from each serum, dried in an oven at 90° to 100°C, were cut into one centimeter segments for individual cholesterol determination. Each curve, plotted by centimeters, showed two broad peaks of cholesterol concentration with the low point between them falling at the space between alpha-1 and alpha-2 globulin as determined on a separate sample of the same serum run simultaneously. The alpha-lipoprotein extended from this point through the albumin. The beta-lipoprotein included the area of alpha-2, beta, and one centimeter into the gamma globulin. All succeeding strips were divided according to these measurements, each in relation to the protein distribution of the same serum run at the same time. A section of paper of approximately the same length as the lipoprotein segments was cut from the unused end of each strip for a blank. All determinations were done in duplicate, averaged and recorded as mg/100 cc.

Although technical error for cholesterol determinations is usually reported as percent of the total value, we found that the error did not increase with increasing cholesterol values within the range of values encountered in this work. Technical errors for these data are:

Precipitation method:

Total cholesterol (triplicates) ± 3.88 mg/100 cc
Free cholesterol (triplicates) ± 1.99 mg/100 cc

Paper electrophoresis:
Alpha-lipoprotein (duplicates) ± 1.96 mg/100 cc
Beta-lipoprotein (duplicates) ± 2.41 mg/100 cc

Data Given

Tables J-1 through J-4 list the mean and range of values by age for total cholesterol and each fraction. Total cholesterol in the age span from 3 days to 4 years is given for the combined group, boys and girls, since the number of subjects is very small. The low values at 3 days and 1 month have been substantiated by study of a group of healthy nursery babies; these results are appended to the table of Child Research Council subject data. Cholesterol fractions were not determined in a meaningful number of subjects under 3 years of age, and have been omitted.

Childhood and adolescent values for total and fractional cholesterol are tabulated separately for male and female subjects. The groups studied are not large enough either to establish or to disprove the significance of a sex difference; therefore the data are also listed for the combined group. Yearly age groups are listed except for free cholesterol which shows little change with age.

In adult subjects, the sex difference is more consistently suggestive of a real trend with a significant (P = 0.01) sex difference in alpha- and beta-lipoprotein cholesterol at 33 years 6 months. The data are listed separately for males and females. Smoothed mean values for males and females are graphed in Figure J-1.

Age and N are defined in Section G, with the addition of yearly listings from 20 to 25 years, each defined as the stated birthday ± 182 days.

The standard deviation of the means is omitted since the data appear to show both skewness and kurtosis.

Percentile distribution is omitted because of the inexactness of values calculated for small groups.

REFERENCES

1. Schoenheimer, R., and Sperry, W.M.: A micromethod for the

determination of free and combined cholesterol. J Biol Chem, 106:745, 1934.

2. Sperry, W.M., and Webb, M.: A revision of the Schoenheimer-Sperry method for cholesterol determinations. J Biol Chem, 187:97, 1950.
3. Boyd, G.S.: The estimation of serum lipoprotein. A micromethod based on zone electrophoresis and cholesterol estimation. Biochem J, 58:680, 1954.

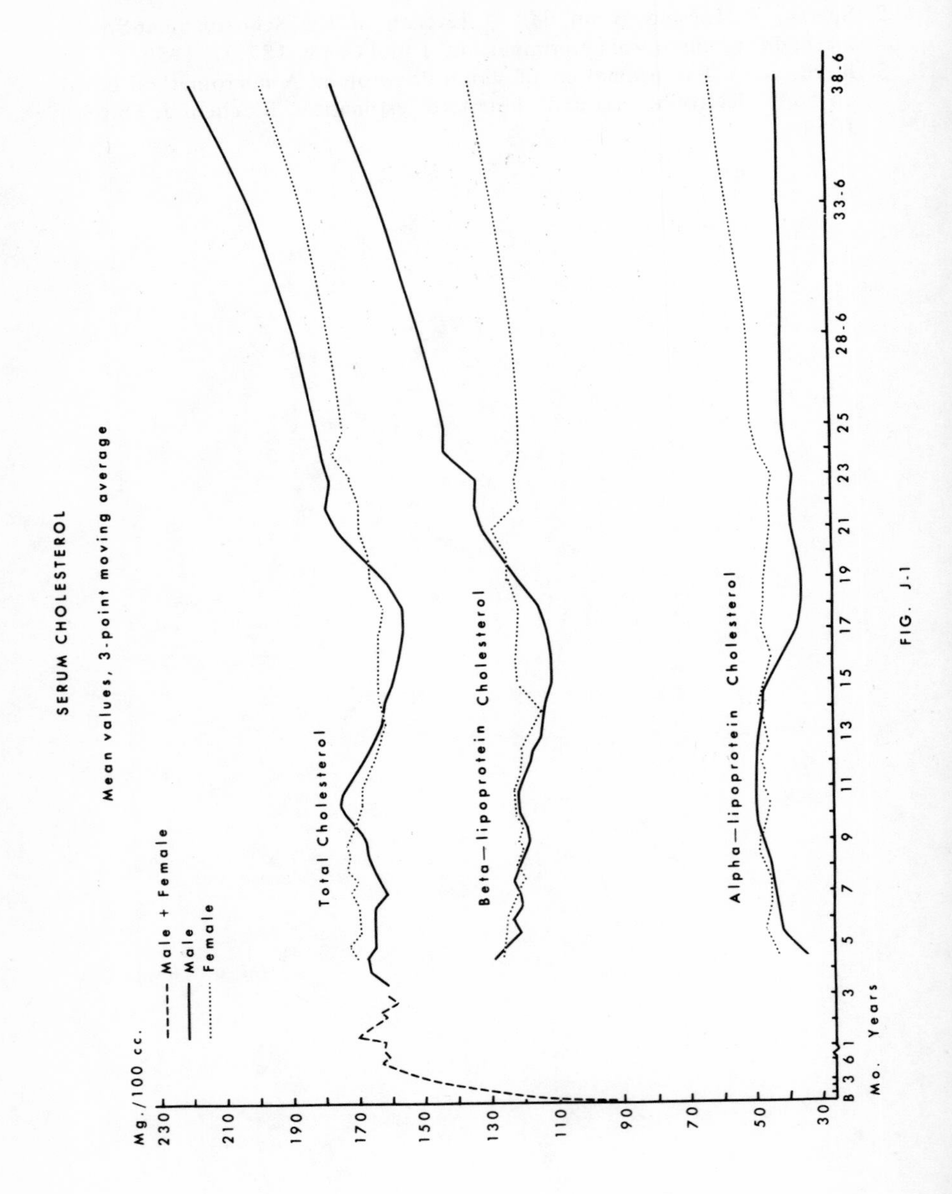
SERUM CHOLESTEROL
Mean values, 3-point moving average
Male + Female
Male
Female
Total Cholesterol
Beta—lipoprotein Cholesterol
Alpha—lipoprotein Cholesterol
Mg./100 cc.
230
210
190
170
150
130
110
90
70
50
30
B 3 6 1 3 5 7 9 11 13 15 17 19 21 23 25 28-6 33-6 38-6
Mo. Years

FIG. J-1

SERUM CHOLESTEROL

TABLE J-1

Total Cholesterol, Mg./100 cc.

Age Yr. Mo.	Male and Female N	Mean	Range Min.	Range Max.	Male N	Mean	Range Min.	Range Max.	Female N	Mean	Range Min.	Range Max.
3 days*	3	93.3	68.6	114.2								
0 - 1*	3	120.2	111.4	127.4								
0 - 2	8	132.7	114.8	155.2								
0 - 3	7	148.6	114.9	176.6								
0 - 6	9	169.2	142.6	211.4								
1 - 0	6	136.0	117.0	168.0								
1 - 6	15	172.7	130.3	234.4								
2 - 0	9	163.6	120.1	228.0								
3 - 0	21	156.3	94.7	246.4								
4 - 0	37	169.4	129.7	222.8	24	169.6	136.7	222.8	13	169.2	129.7	215.7
5 - 0	45	167.3	117.9	208.7	25	163.3	117.9	198.7	20	172.3	133.8	208.7
6 - 0	43	167.6	118.5	225.9	22	168.7	118.5	225.9	21	166.5	140.5	223.0
7 - 0	58	165.0	126.7	249.3	26	161.6	126.7	249.3	32	167.7	129.0	221.0
8 - 0	47	168.8	114.8	229.4	24	169.4	134.0	229.4	23	168.2	114.8	208.9
9 - 0	55	169.7	134.4	223.1	23	167.2	134.4	223.1	32	171.5	134.4	215.8
10 - 0	51	170.2	106.6	229.2	26	171.5	136.4	229.2	25	168.8	106.6	225.9
11 - 0	58	171.4	127.3	223.6	28	173.5	127.3	221.2	30	169.5	128.5	223.6
12 - 0	58	165.3	113.9	227.3	32	166.1	125.6	227.3	26	164.2	113.9	205.3
13 - 0	58	163.3	122.9	217.5	29	165.6	137.2	217.5	29	161.1	122.9	207.8
14 - 0	57	162.0	114.0	225.7	28	162.1	123.4	225.7	29	161.9	114.0	202.7
15 - 0	54	161.3	107.7	247.8	27	157.6	107.7	206.2	27	165.0	123.8	247.8
16 - 0	56	160.4	101.5	230.1	27	156.7	125.0	194.3	29	163.8	101.5	230.1
17 - 0	59	157.5	102.6	228.2	28	154.5	114.8	205.4	31	160.2	102.6	228.2
18 - 0	52	160.5	106.0	237.1	24	155.5	110.9	190.6	28	164.7	106.0	237.1
19 - 0	47	156.9	102.1	218.3	20	153.9	125.5	192.1	27	159.2	102.1	218.3
20 - 0					20	168.9	125.3	217.2	24	171.3	97.1	235.3
21 - 0					17	180.6	134.3	248.2	14	166.8	142.2	187.7
22 - 0					16	175.0	142.5	246.2	16	165.7	140.8	209.5
23 - 0					12	179.6	145.2	226.2	12	172.6	114.6	214.5
24 - 0					13	173.7	123.8	229.1	8	173.4	135.8	221.7
25 - 0					9	185.5	140.9	235.8	10	182.2	107.1	228.7
28 - 6					24	180.6	118.7	254.9	14	171.6	121.7	218.1
33 - 6					24	199.7	132.0	263.8	11	185.0	142.0	242.6
38 - 6					14	218.3	151.5	289.5	8	196.1	133.2	266.7
*Unenrolled babies												
0 - 5 days	27	83.3	43.8	134.3								
20 - 30 days	17	120.7	102.3	147.0								

Free Cholesterol, Mg./100 cc.

TABLE J-2

Age Yr. Mo.	Male and Female N	Mean	Range Min.	Range Max.	Male N	Mean	Range Min.	Range Max.	Female N	Mean	Range Min.	Range Max.
3 - 0	13	46.4	34.9	62.9								
5 - 0	42	49.9	35.9	64.8	24	49.4	35.9	61.3	18	50.7	40.6	64.8
7 - 0	55	49.0	36.2	71.8	24	48.3	36.6	71.8	31	49.6	36.2	63.4
9 - 0	53	50.5	35.0	68.6	22	50.5	41.1	68.6	31	50.5	35.0	63.5
11 - 0	58	50.4	36.4	64.0	28	50.9	37.2	63.7	30	49.9	36.4	64.0
13 - 0	58	47.6	36.0	63.7	29	48.3	36.0	63.7	29	47.0	37.8	62.8
15 - 0	52	48.5	33.0	69.9	26	48.3	34.4	67.2	26	48.7	33.0	69.9
17 - 0	59	46.6	32.8	68.1	28	45.7	34.9	60.8	31	47.5	32.8	68.1
19 - 0	45	46.1	31.1	62.5	18	45.0	38.6	51.7	27	46.9	31.1	62.5
21 - 0	30	50.2	34.5	76.5	17	51.2	34.5	76.5	13	48.8	41.9	56.6
23 - 0	24	51.4	32.6	69.6	12	53.2	41.8	69.6	12	49.5	32.6	61.6
25 - 0	17	53.6	32.2	77.0	7	55.0	44.5	77.0	10	52.6	32.2	64.7
28 - 6	38	52.4	33.2	79.0	24	53.9	33.2	79.0	14	49.9	35.6	63.4
33 - 6	35	60.4	39.0	88.0	24	62.0	44.5	88.0	11	56.9	39.0	75.2
38 - 6	22	64.5	41.3	100.7	14	67.2	47.2	100.7	8	59.7	41.3	81.7

SERUM CHOLESTEROL TABLE J-3

Alpha-lipoprotein Cholesterol, Mg./100 cc.

Age	Male and Female				Male				Female			
			Range				Range				Range	
Yr. Mo.	N	Mean	Min.	Max.	N	Mean	Min.	Max.	N	Mean	Min.	Max.
3 - 0	12	39.0	23.2	58.0								
4 - 0	19	41.4	24.0	59.4	10	40.7	24.0	59.4	9	42.1	27.7	53.2
5 - 0	30	42.7	27.6	64.2	14	40.5	27.6	63.6	16	44.7	34.6	64.2
6 - 0	25	45.6	20.4	62.2	13	42.6	20.4	58.6	12	48.7	34.1	62.2
7 - 0	34	44.3	26.8	72.5	16	44.5	26.8	72.5	18	44.1	31.2	63.4
8 - 0	30	45.8	28.0	74.6	15	44.1	29.0	55.7	15	47.5	28.0	74.6
9 - 0	34	48.5	26.6	68.5	17	48.8	26.6	68.5	17	48.2	33.2	64.5
10 - 0	35	47.2	35.1	69.8	20	49.3	39.0	69.8	15	44.5	35.1	57.7
11 - 0	39	48.2	34.7	79.7	21	50.3	37.2	79.7	18	45.8	34.7	58.0
12 - 0	37	47.7	35.4	73.4	20	48.9	35.8	73.4	17	46.4	35.4	68.3
13 - 0	36	47.2	31.3	72.8	19	48.0	32.1	71.0	17	46.2	31.3	72.8
14 - 0	31	48.4	27.9	66.6	16	47.9	27.9	66.6	15	49.0	31.7	61.0
15 - 0	29	45.7	25.0	64.6	14	48.3	25.0	64.6	15	43.2	29.6	64.0
16 - 0	31	41.6	23.0	69.4	16	37.9	23.0	58.0	15	45.6	27.0	69.4
17 - 0					16	38.5	26.1	54.4	18	43.8	27.8	77.8
18 - 0					13	34.7	25.4	42.2	17	51.3	31.1	97.8
19 - 0					12	34.1	25.1	48.1	19	43.8	28.5	69.0
20 - 0					12	37.7	26.9	59.4	16	46.5	33.2	69.4
21 - 0					14	41.4	24.2	59.9	12	45.5	24.8	63.0
22 - 0					9	36.9	27.9	53.4	12	43.3	29.6	67.2
23 - 0					10	39.5	27.4	52.8	10	45.9	27.9	69.3
24 - 0					13	35.4	25.8	53.6	7	43.0	34.9	50.4
25 - 0					8	45.5	29.6	74.7	10	56.6	37.1	78.0
28 - 6					20	41.0	23.7	63.8	14	51.0	36.8	75.0
33 - 6					24	41.5	26.8	58.4	11	57.2	26.7	97.9
38 - 6					14	41.4	16.0	79.4	8	61.5	42.4	79.6

Beta-lipoprotein Cholesterol, Mg./100 cc. TABLE J-4

Age Yr. Mo.	N	Mean	Min.	Max.	N	Mean	Min.	Max.	N	Mean	Min.	Max.
3 - 0	12	110.1	65.2	159.0								
4 - 0	19	131.3	93.6	196.2	10	131.2	101.1	196.2	9	131.4	93.6	161.4
5 - 0	30	124.7	91.2	160.6	14	122.8	96.1	157.8	16	126.3	91.2	160.6
6 - 0	25	121.2	88.0	170.2	13	119.4	92.8	170.2	12	123.2	88.0	148.0
7 - 0	34	118.4	87.5	181.4	16	120.2	88.5	181.4	18	116.8	87.5	143.4
8 - 0	30	123.0	86.4	181.8	15	127.6	103.1	167.0	15	118.5	86.4	181.8
9 - 0	34	117.9	88.0	160.1	17	116.0	88.0	160.1	17	119.7	91.5	147.6
10 - 0	35	118.0	81.3	177.0	20	118.2	81.3	177.0	15	117.8	82.6	170.6
11 - 0	39	121.8	67.6	207.9	21	121.3	80.2	164.9	18	122.4	67.6	207.9
12 - 0	37	119.0	75.2	164.0	20	118.7	75.2	164.0	17	119.3	88.6	155.8
13 - 0	36	118.6	84.9	172.2	19	117.5	85.6	172.2	17	119.9	84.9	171.6
14 - 0	31	114.8	68.5	176.0	16	112.8	68.5	176.0	15	117.0	83.8	156.5
15 - 0	29	116.6	74.0	203.6	14	109.1	74.0	150.4	15	123.6	86.8	203.6
16 - 0	30	117.2	70.8	180.7	16	111.7	70.8	157.9	14	123.4	74.0	180.7
17 - 0					16	112.8	82.3	149.7	18	119.8	78.4	177.0
18 - 0					13	111.7	88.0	150.0	17	119.7	81.2	191.0
19 - 0					12	118.7	96.4	145.4	19	120.7	77.8	172.8
20 - 0					12	131.9	80.6	164.6	16	131.7	99.3	167.8
21 - 0					14	137.7	92.0	184.4	12	119.9	69.2	151.2
22 - 0					9	126.3	105.4	193.2	12	124.4	87.4	164.4
23 - 0					10	139.3	99.5	166.8	10	116.9	60.6	181.6
24 - 0					13	137.8	78.3	208.6	7	124.0	99.6	163.8
25 - 0					8	152.4	112.6	198.6	10	118.9	44.3	160.9
28 - 6					20	148.0	85.3	239.6	14	117.7	62.8	184.4
33 - 6					24	159.4	90.0	235.4	11	130.4	90.4	183.4
38 - 6					14	175.7	110.8	265.9	8	134.0	79.8	207.4

EPILOGUE

THE purposes for which this volume is offered serve two separate needs. For those who require group data on growth, such as physical educators, health educators, scientists dealing with children with growth problems, clothing manufacturers, etc., the data supply ranges and distributions of many measurements taken on children and young adults whose health is documented and who probably represent a large part of the United States population. For research workers whose interests are in growth of individuals, this material supplies descriptions of the methods used in measurement, the specific measurements taken, the age range over which measurements have been recorded and the number of subjects of each sex for whom they are available. The fact that these data are organized in a data system on magnetic tape makes it possible to retrieve them in total or in any fraction desired at relatively low cost. Expense involved must be borne by those requesting them, but the staff of the Child Research Council hopes that any interested scientist will accept the invitation to make use of them. Questions that can be approached by use of them are so many that this staff cannot possibly do the analyses necessary to answer even those we have identified. We suspect that the fertile minds of our fellow scientists can devise many we have not considered.

The material presented in this volume should be regarded as the framework against which growth, nutritional change, biochemical and hematologic composition and health performance of the individual subject may be projected to see how he compares with and differs from his peers. To attain the sorts of wisdom, understanding and knowledge that longitudinal research is designed to provide we must ultimately return to the study of the individual and his total function. It is the unique character of his genetic endowment, the environmental events to which he is subjected, and his adaptive responses that promise to explain much of his particular fate. One additional essential factor is knowing the final outcome in subjects who have been followed so carefully for so long. Forty years is barely more than half the life span of these people, so the job undertaken by Child Research Council is not yet half complete. Without the second half, the first cannot possibly fulfill its promise of new insight into the natural history of health and disease.

The studies of this program have had a strong medical orientation throughout, but the perspectives are different from those of clinical research. Interest has been in the individual and in health rather than in disease and its cure. Longitudinal research views acute illness as but a brief environmentally-induced state to which the individual must adapt, no more important than acute emotional stress or social pressures in shaping a person toward his mature state. Acute conditions of any origin to which the individual successfully adapts do not change his status of being a "healthy" subject. Completion of the study of the life span in healthy subjects which has advanced to the half-way mark gives a primary objective to our struggle to remain in existence. No such study has yet been achieved to match in man the fruitful life-span studies in insects and animals. Other objectives, as outlined below, carry more apparent immediate appeal, but the study of healthy growth and development will not be complete until equally intensive knowledge of the second half of the life span is added to studies such as these.

When chronic disease, and particularly degenerative disease, is considered, it is impossible to doubt that its origins occur long before clinical symptoms appear. In our present state of ignorance of the etiology of most of these conditions it seems entirely reasonable to regard the long succession of adaptations that begins before birth and continues throughout life as significantly contributing factors if not truly etiological in such diseases. Certainly the origins from which aging and degeneration spring are complex and operate through long periods of time. The effort to understand and gain the ability to modify them must be as complex and enduring as the processes being studied.

The staff of the Child Research Council has been privileged to carry out the longest continuous intensive investigation of human subjects ever accomplished. The program started with the upsweep of enthusiasm about understanding man that characterized the years around 1930. By reason of financial and moral support afforded by the University of Colorado and major private foundations such as the Commonwealth Fund and the Rockefeller Foundation as well as smaller foundations and many individuals the study was able to survive the years of the depression and World War II. After the war there was expansion of the disciplines involved, with addition of such vital studies as nutritional intake and much more sophisticated psychological investigations. In the immediate postwar years there was growing excitement in an expanding staff about what was being learned. The great promise of being able to follow the life span of healthy individuals as partners with other investigators in different disciplines in a truly single-minded effort to understand the individual and how he functions attracted the needed investigators with ease. The fulfillment of that promise kept them on the staff. By the mid-1950's the first efforts could be made to investigate the importance of psychological development on nutritional intake and acquisition of fat or rate of growth.* Questions gradually became interdisciplinary in type and effort turned more and more toward reassembling the individual from the fragments represented by discipline-oriented measurements. That enthusiasm in the staff and promise in the data still exist, but shrinking funding threatens both.

Present scientific attitudes in this country, and indeed in the western world, militate against successful completion of the program of the Child Research Council or any study of the life span of man. Influenced by the dramatic success of experimental approaches in the physical sciences, in the conquest of bacterial infection, in untangling the genetic code, and in manipulating the mechanisms of immunity, scientists demand hypotheses and controls not feasible in the study of healthy human subjects. Little stature is granted to research that describes in detail rather than altering conditions and drawing conclusions from evoked

*See Appendix B for publication list from Child Research Council.

responses. Yet, if we are to match the accomplishments in treatment of acute disease with equal control of degenerative processes, we must first understand the human events involved throughout the years degeneration is progressing. Longitudinal research with human subjects must be carried out to gain this knowledge. If present subject populations, including that of the Child Research Council, are not studied for the rest of their life spans, a new start will ultimately be necessary. Critics of long-term research are sure to cite the gradual attrition in longitudinal programs over the past decade in support of their contention that life-span research in man is impossible. The success of Child Research Council through 40 years bears witness that the scientific aspects of such programs are both possible and practical.

Appendix A

FAMILY PEDIGREES AND DEMOGRAPHIC DATA

A PEDIGREE has been constructed for each of 334 subjects in 162 "families" including 160 kinships and two (A #992 and B #980) in which the family units are related by marriage with no genetic relationship between the enrolled Child Research Council subjects involved. These are presented in approximately numerical order within three groups: Group A includes families in which at least one enrolled subject was seen in 1965-1966, and data were obtained for all enrolled subjects and their parents; Group B includes those not seen in 1965-1966, but some family contact was made - one subject, family B #963, was lost to his family and no information was available for him; Group C includes all families on whom there is no information since the subject was last seen.

The pedigrees include data as follows:

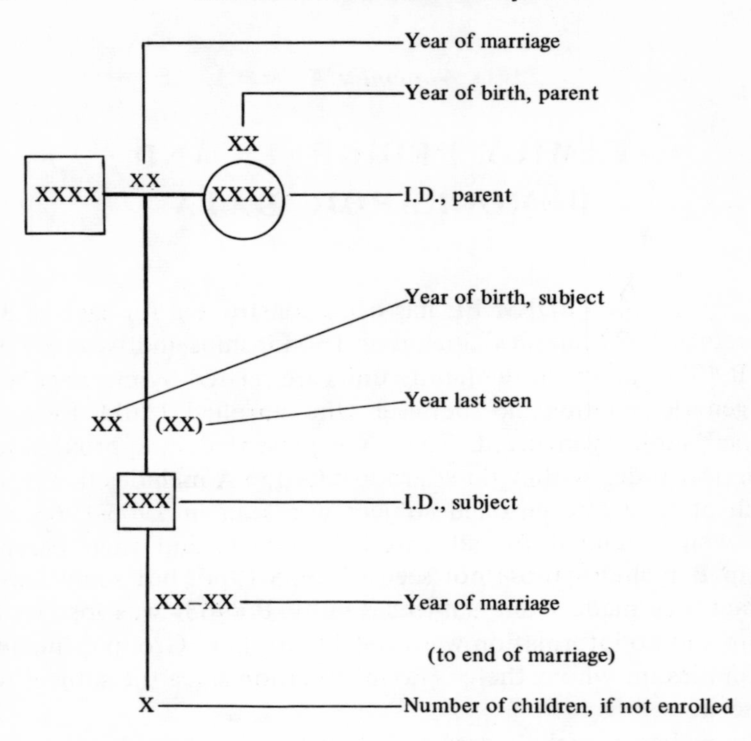

Special designations are:

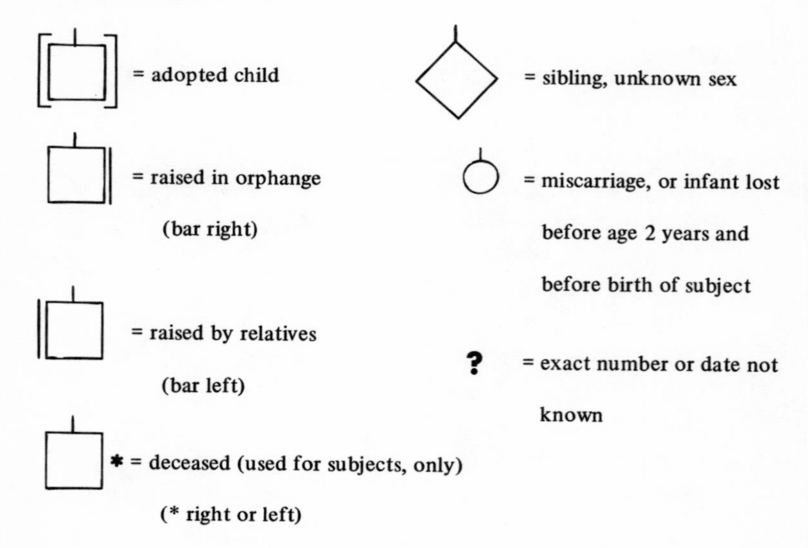

Groups A and B . . No entry for marriage or children of subjects indicates that the subject states he was not married and/or had no children as of December 31, 1966.
Group C. . . . . No entry indicates a lack of information.
All groups . . . . . . "?" indicates the number is unknown, that is, a "?" in position for year of marriage indicates that the subject *is* married but did not state the year of marriage.
Dates "61" through "66" pertinent to parents' birth are 1861-1866.
Dates "61" through "66" for all other entries are 1961-1966.

Additional "Demographic" Data on Tape But Not Shown on Pedigree

1. *Data on Subjects:*
   Type of delivery: Caesarean, high forceps, mid forceps, low forceps, spontaneous.
   Exact date of birth: Month, day, year.
   Birth weight: Kg.
   Birth status: Premature, full term, one of twins.
   Year first seen at Child Research Council.
   ABO type.
   Haptoglobin type.
   Last IQ, age of IQ, type of IQ test.
   Education, if complete.
   Occupation, if 25 years of age or older.
   Age at death and primary cause of death.
2. *Miscarriage or Child lost.* Classified as:
   Fetal death, age unknown.
   Lost before 6 months fetal age.
   Stillborn.
   Death in first 2 weeks.
   Death between 2 weeks and 1 year.
   Death between 1 and 2 years.
3. *Data on Parents:*
   Height and weight just prior to conception of first enrolled

subject, as stated by the parents.
Education.
Last IQ, type of IQ test.
Father's occupation.
Previous marriage, no children in family of subject.
Divorce, death of spouse, remarriage.
Citizenship at birth (U.S.A. or not U.S.A.).
Citizenship of subject's grandparents at birth.
Family national background.
Family religion and church attendance.
Age and cause of death of subject's parents and grandparents, or age and date when last known to be living.

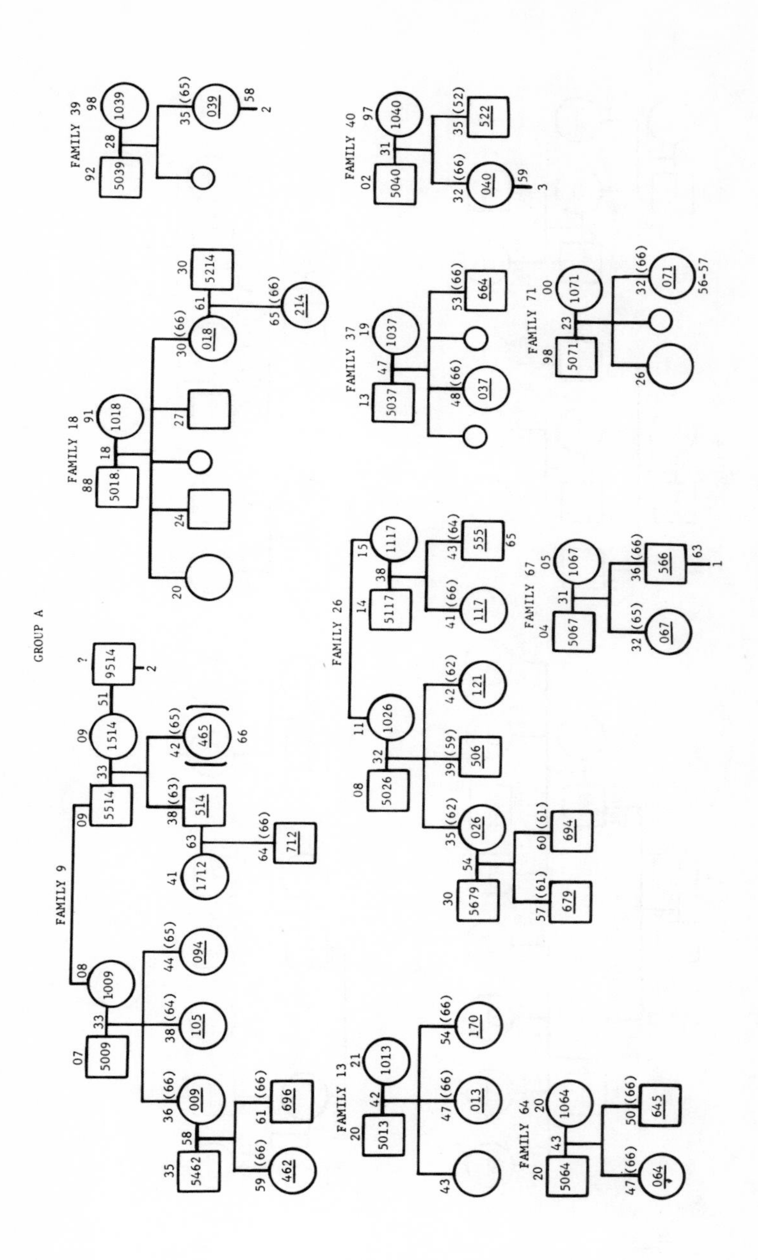
GROUP A
FAMILY 9
FAMILY 18
FAMILY 39
FAMILY 26
FAMILY 37
FAMILY 40
FAMILY 13
FAMILY 64
FAMILY 67
FAMILY 71

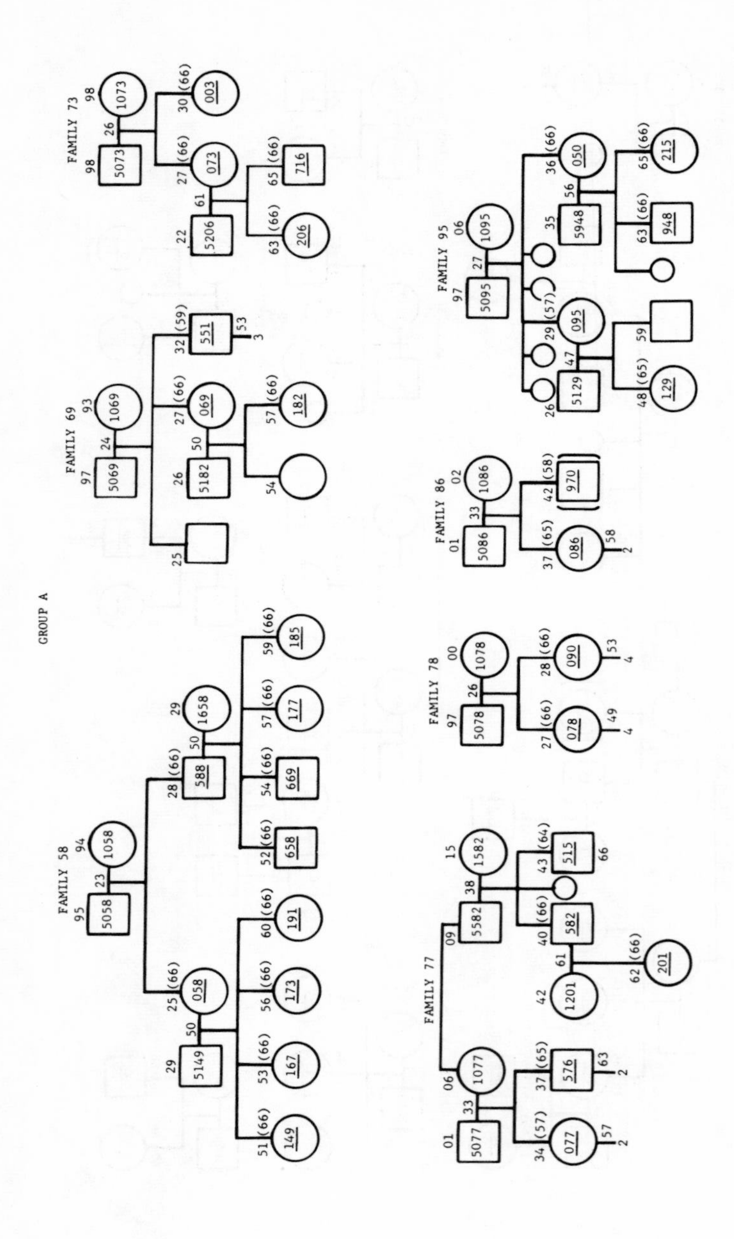
GROUP A
FAMILY 58
FAMILY 69
FAMILY 73
FAMILY 77
FAMILY 78
FAMILY 86
FAMILY 95

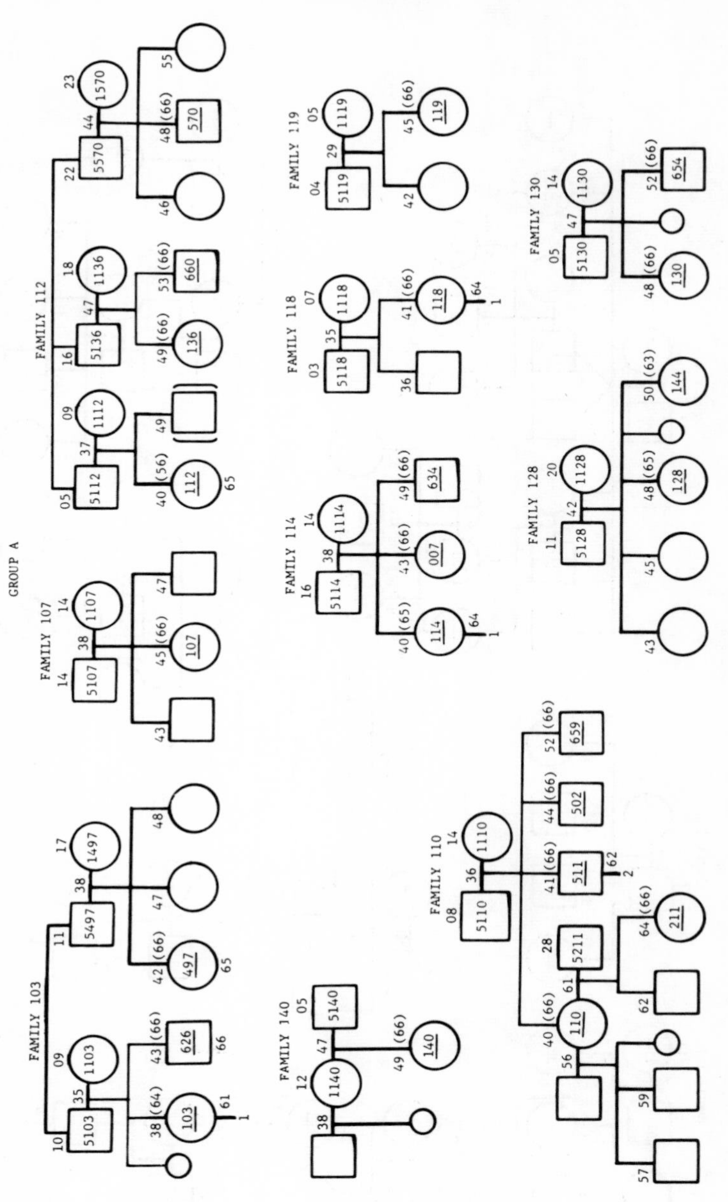

GROUP A
FAMILY 103
FAMILY 107
FAMILY 112
FAMILY 140
FAMILY 114
FAMILY 118
FAMILY 119
FAMILY 110
FAMILY 128
FAMILY 130

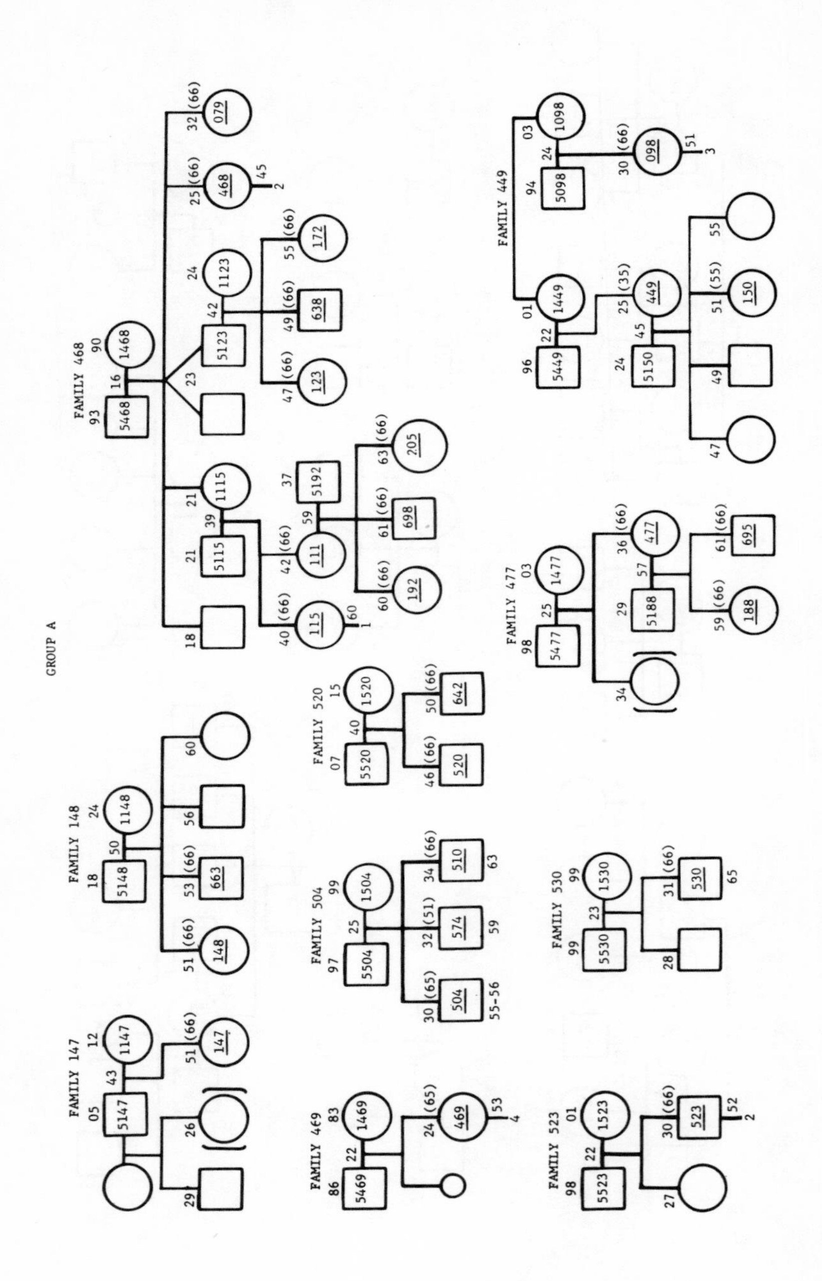

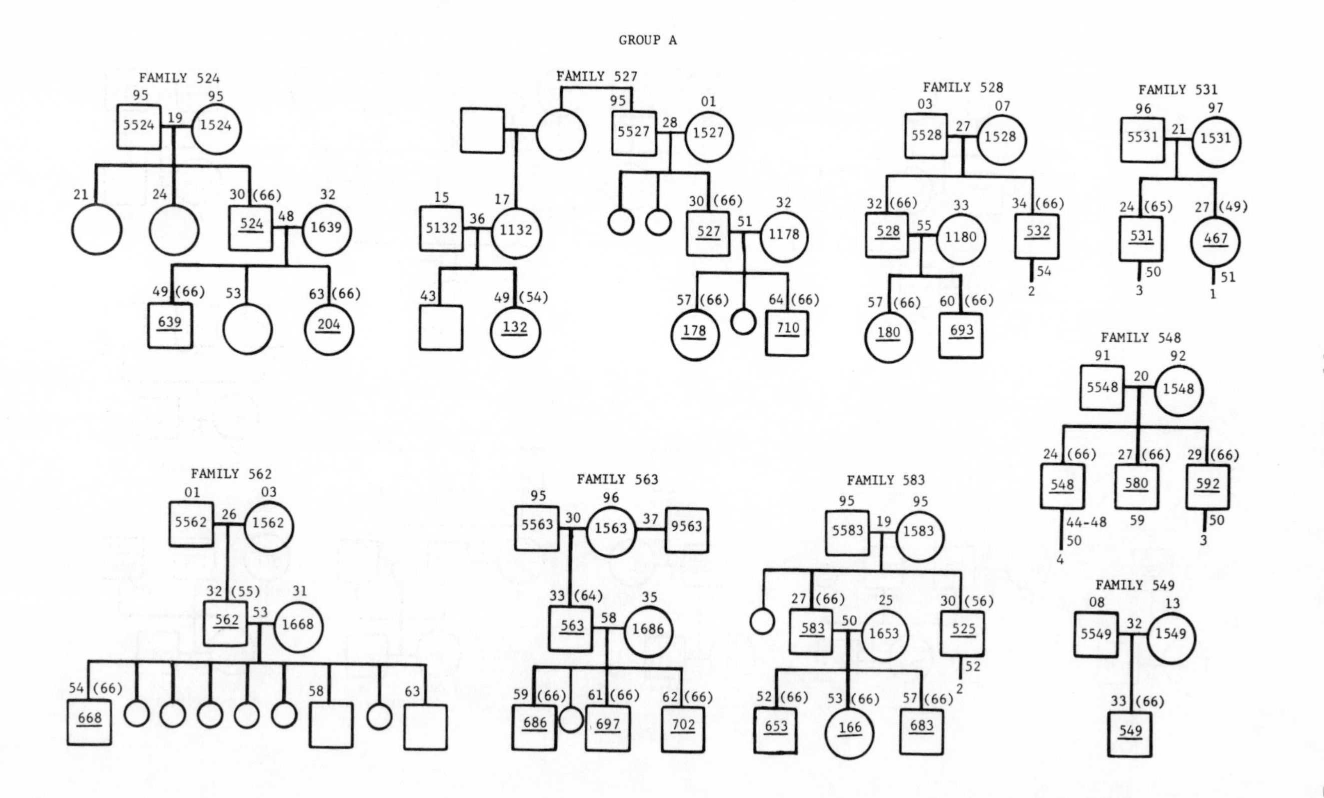
GROUP A
FAMILY 524
FAMILY 527
FAMILY 528
FAMILY 531
FAMILY 548
FAMILY 549
FAMILY 562
FAMILY 563
FAMILY 583

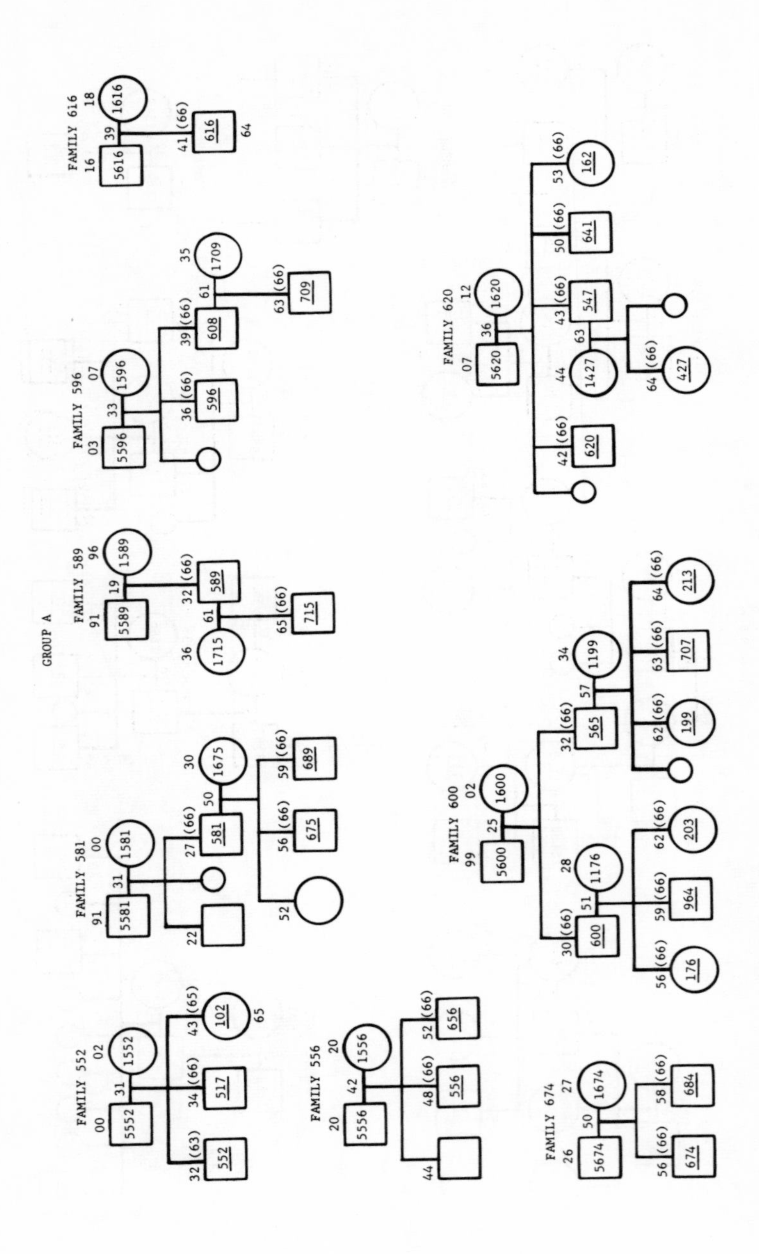
GROUP A
FAMILY 552
FAMILY 556
FAMILY 674
FAMILY 581
FAMILY 600
FAMILY 589
FAMILY 596
FAMILY 620
FAMILY 616

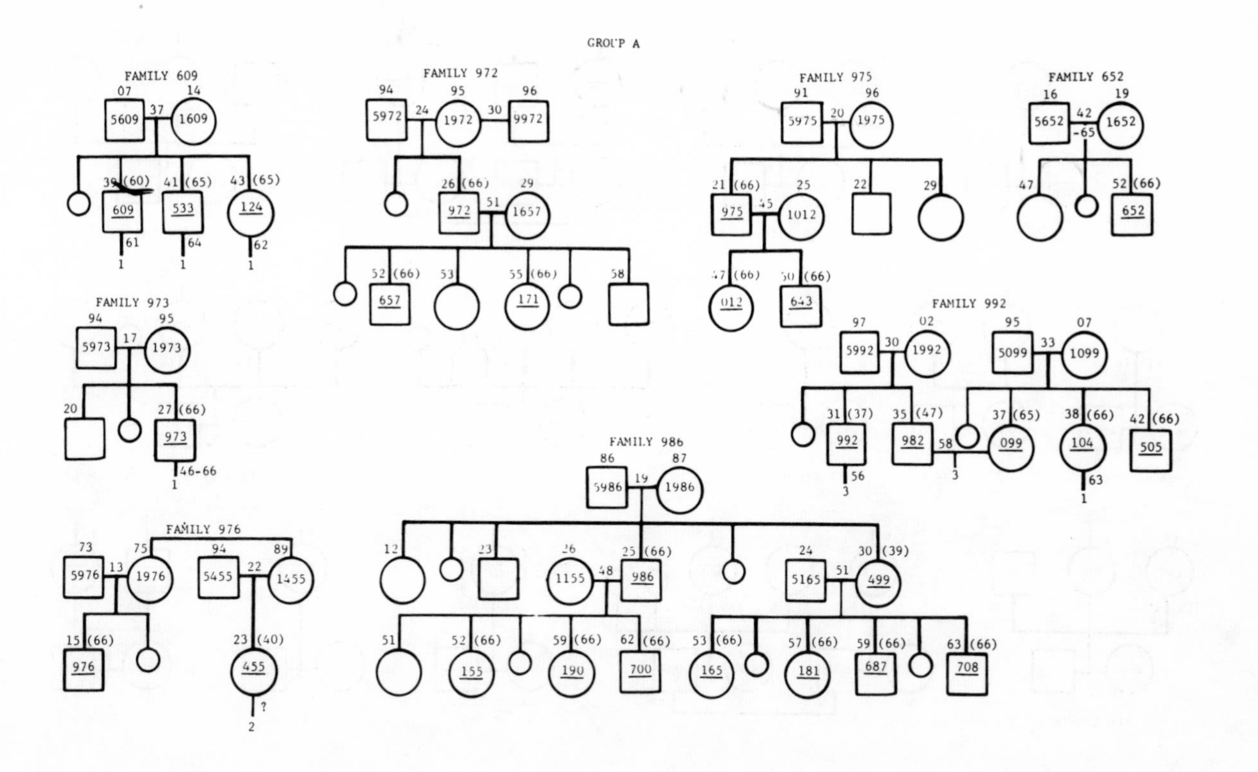
GROUP A
FAMILY 609
FAMILY 972
FAMILY 975
FAMILY 652
FAMILY 973
FAMILY 992
FAMILY 986
FAMILY 976

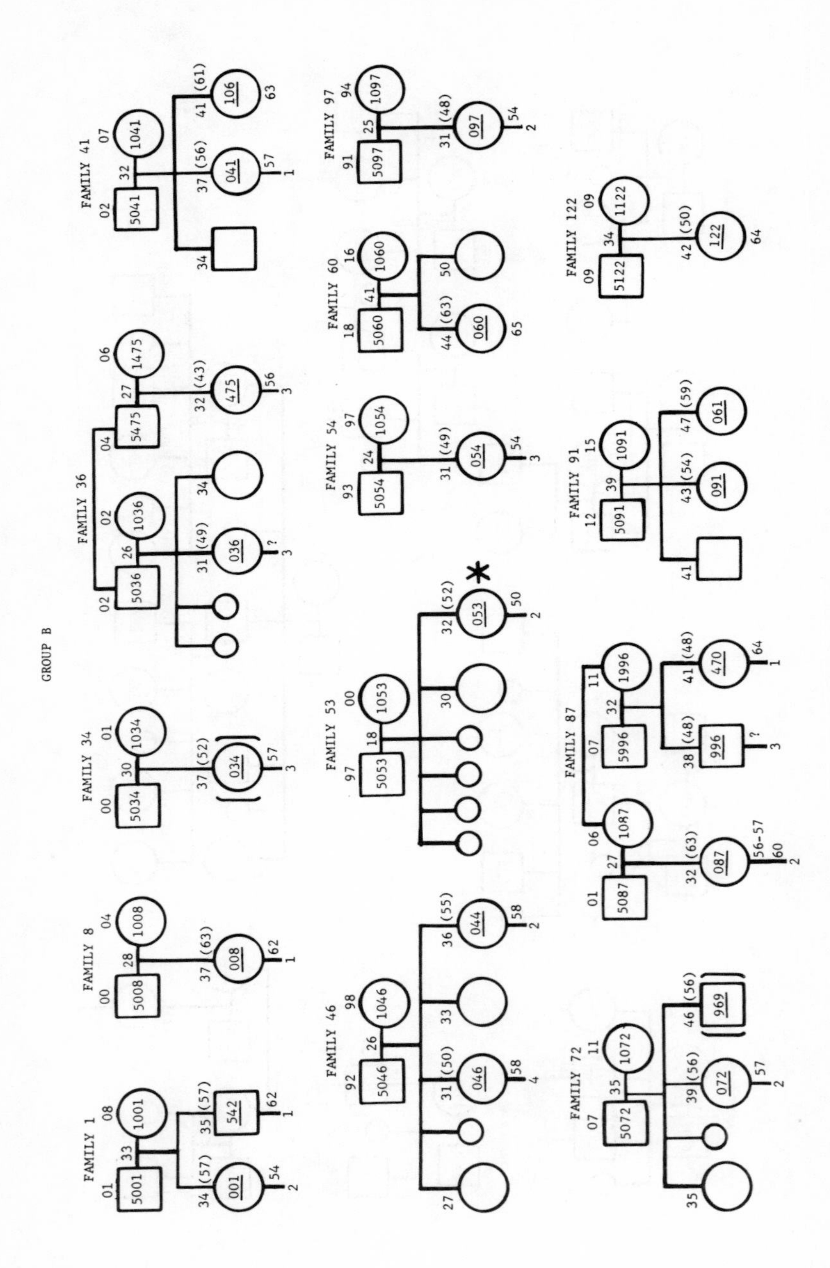

GROUP B
FAMILY 1
FAMILY 8
FAMILY 34
FAMILY 36
FAMILY 41
FAMILY 46
FAMILY 53
FAMILY 54
FAMILY 60
FAMILY 97
FAMILY 72
FAMILY 87
FAMILY 91
FAMILY 122

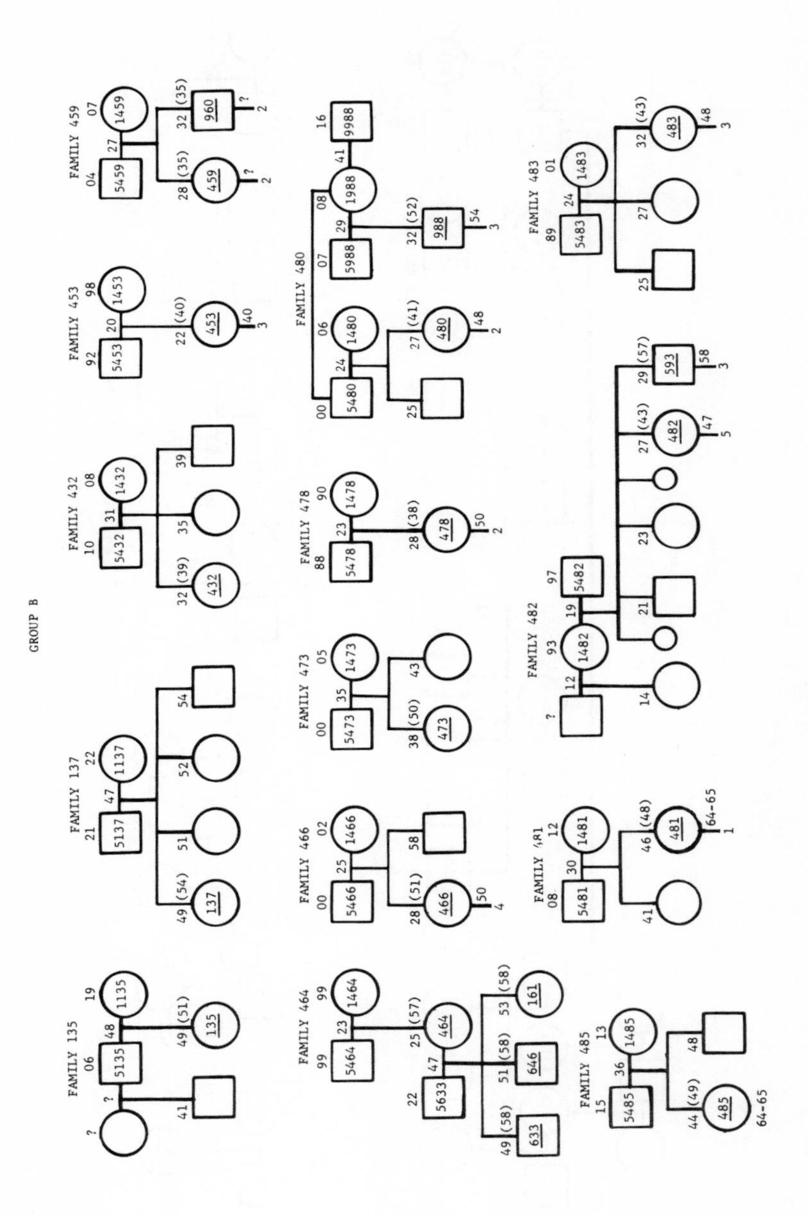

GROUP B
FAMILY 135
? ? 06 5135 48 19 1135
41 49 (51) 135
FAMILY 137
21 5137 47 22 1137
49 (54) 137 51 52 54
FAMILY 432
10 5432 31 08 1432
32 (39) 432 35 39
FAMILY 453
92 5453 20 98 1453
22 (40) 453 40 3
FAMILY 459
04 5459 27 07 1459
28 (35) 459 ? 2 32 (35) 960 ? 2
FAMILY 464
99 5464 23 99 1464
25 (57) 464
22 5633 47
49 (58) 633 51 (58) 646 53 (58) 161
FAMILY 466
00 5466 25 02 1466
28 (51) 466 50 4 58
FAMILY 473
00 5473 35 05 1473
38 (50) 473 43
FAMILY 478
88 5478 23 90 1478
28 (38) 478 50 2
FAMILY 480
00 5480 24 06 1480
25 27 (41) 480 48 2
07 5988 29 08 1988 41 16 9988
32 (52) 988 54 3
FAMILY 481
08 5481 30 12 1481
41 46 (48) 481 64-65 1
FAMILY 482
? 12 93 1482 19 97 5482
14 21 23 27 (43) 482 47 5 29 (57) 593 58 3
FAMILY 483
89 5483 24 01 1483
25 27 32 (43) 483 48 3
FAMILY 485
15 5485 36 13 1485
44 (49) 485 64-65 48

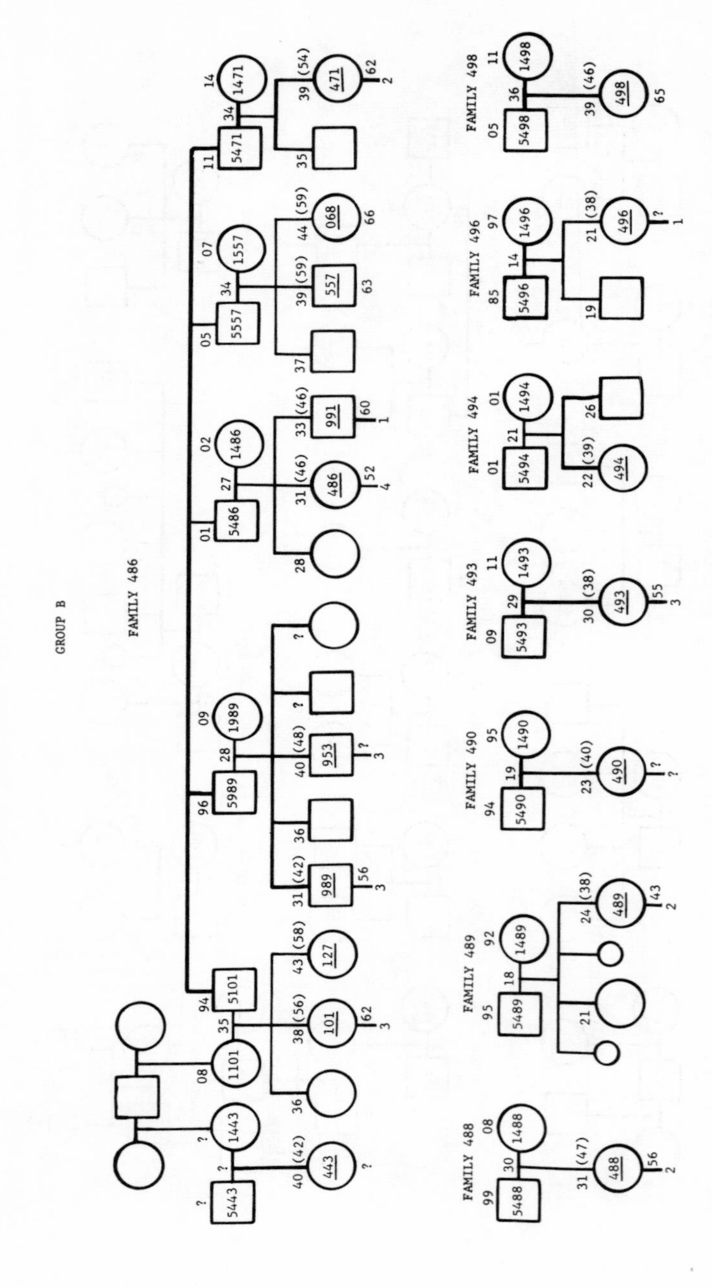
GROUP B
FAMILY 486
FAMILY 488
FAMILY 489
FAMILY 490
FAMILY 493
FAMILY 494
FAMILY 496
FAMILY 498

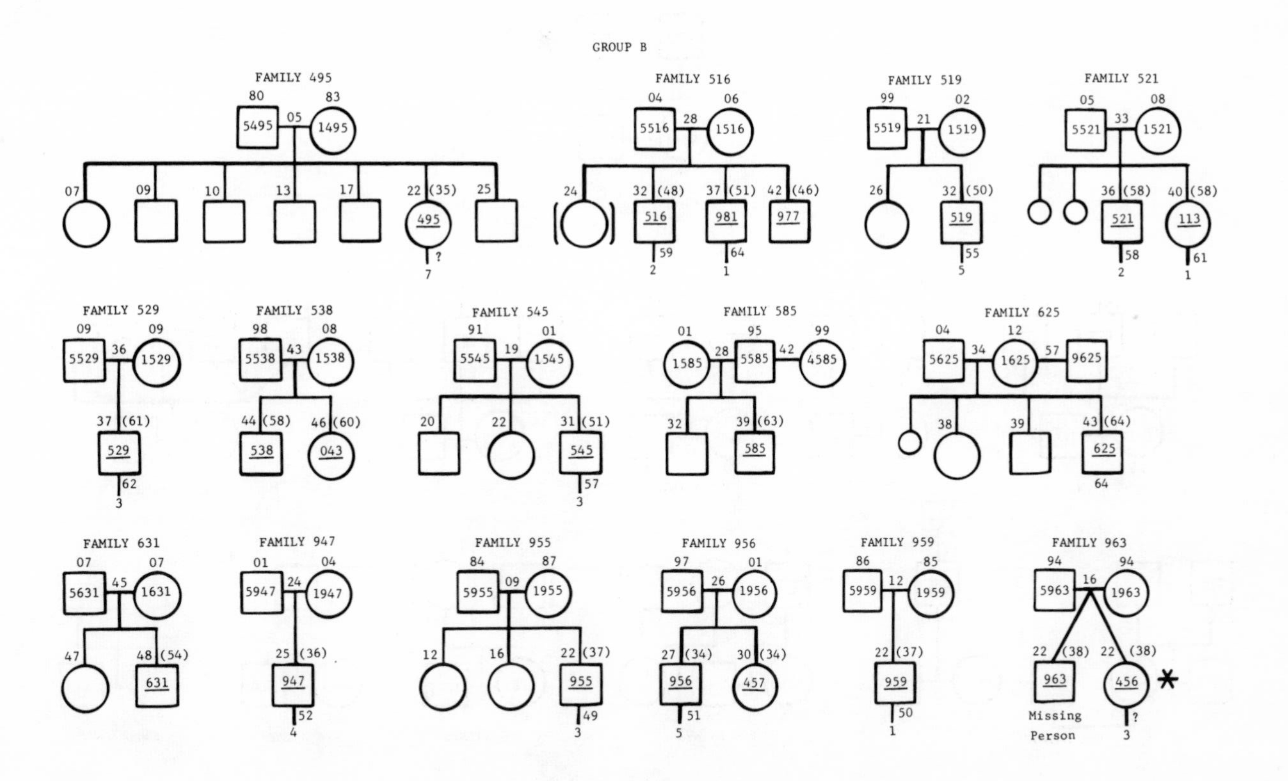
GROUP B
FAMILY 495
FAMILY 516
FAMILY 519
FAMILY 521
FAMILY 529
FAMILY 538
FAMILY 545
FAMILY 585
FAMILY 625
FAMILY 631
FAMILY 947
FAMILY 955
FAMILY 956
FAMILY 959
FAMILY 963
Missing
Person

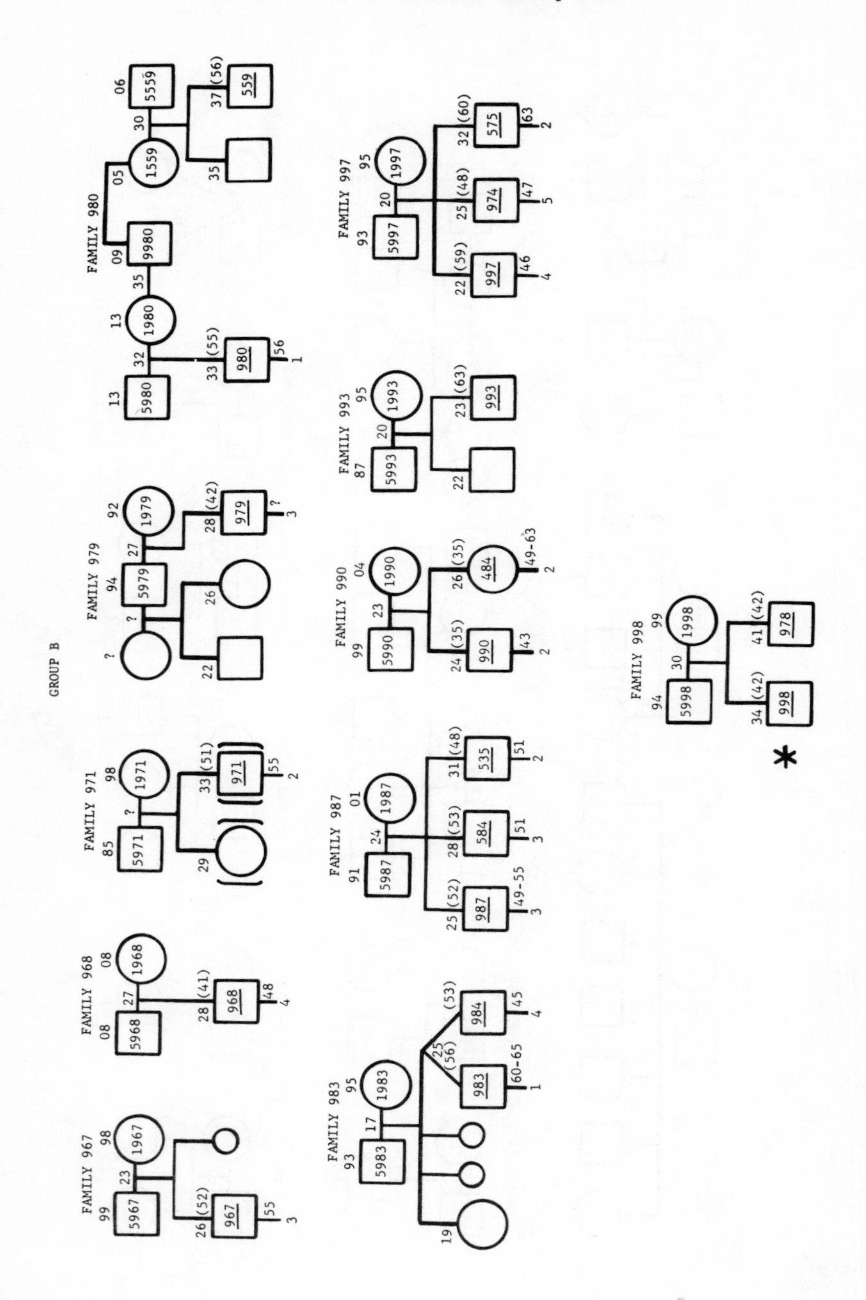
GROUP B
FAMILY 967
FAMILY 968
FAMILY 971
FAMILY 979
FAMILY 980
FAMILY 983
FAMILY 987
FAMILY 990
FAMILY 993
FAMILY 997
FAMILY 998

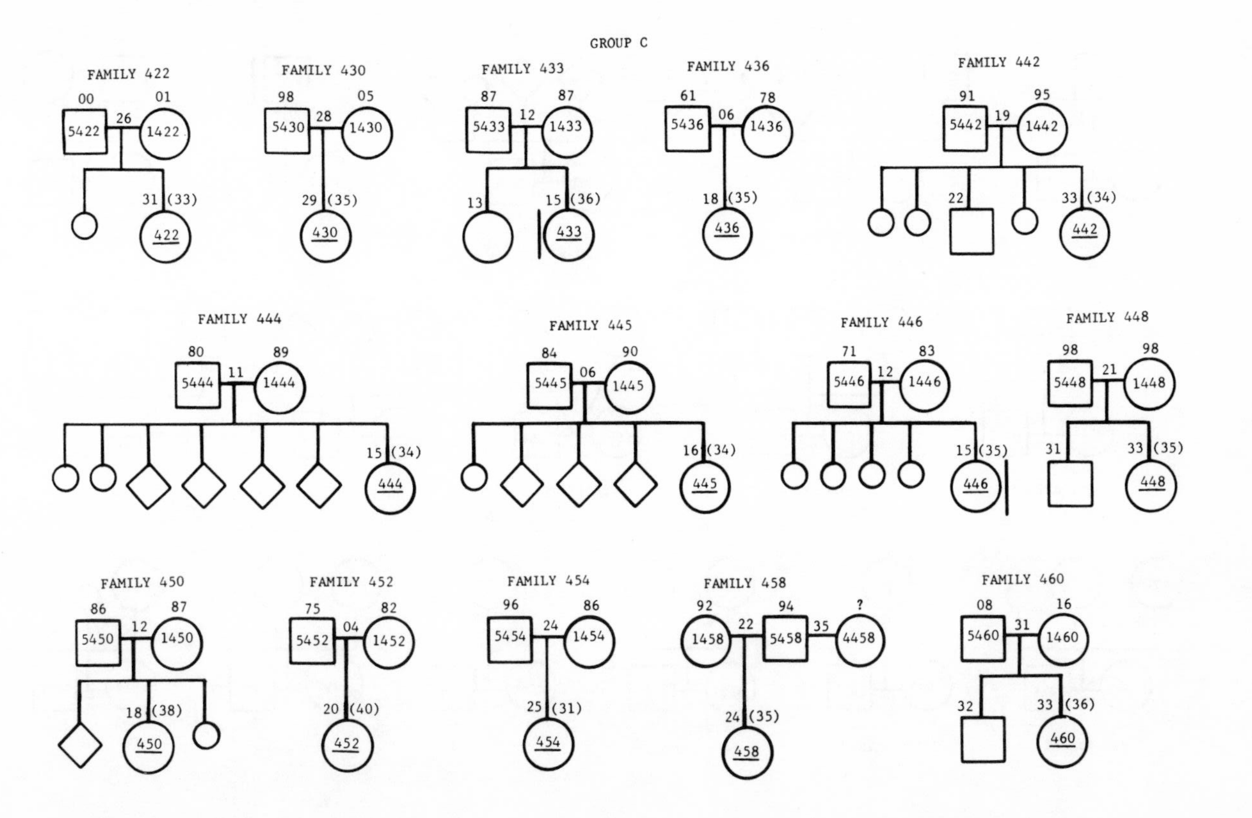
GROUP C
FAMILY 422
FAMILY 430
FAMILY 433
FAMILY 436
FAMILY 442
FAMILY 444
FAMILY 445
FAMILY 446
FAMILY 448
FAMILY 450
FAMILY 452
FAMILY 454
FAMILY 458
FAMILY 460

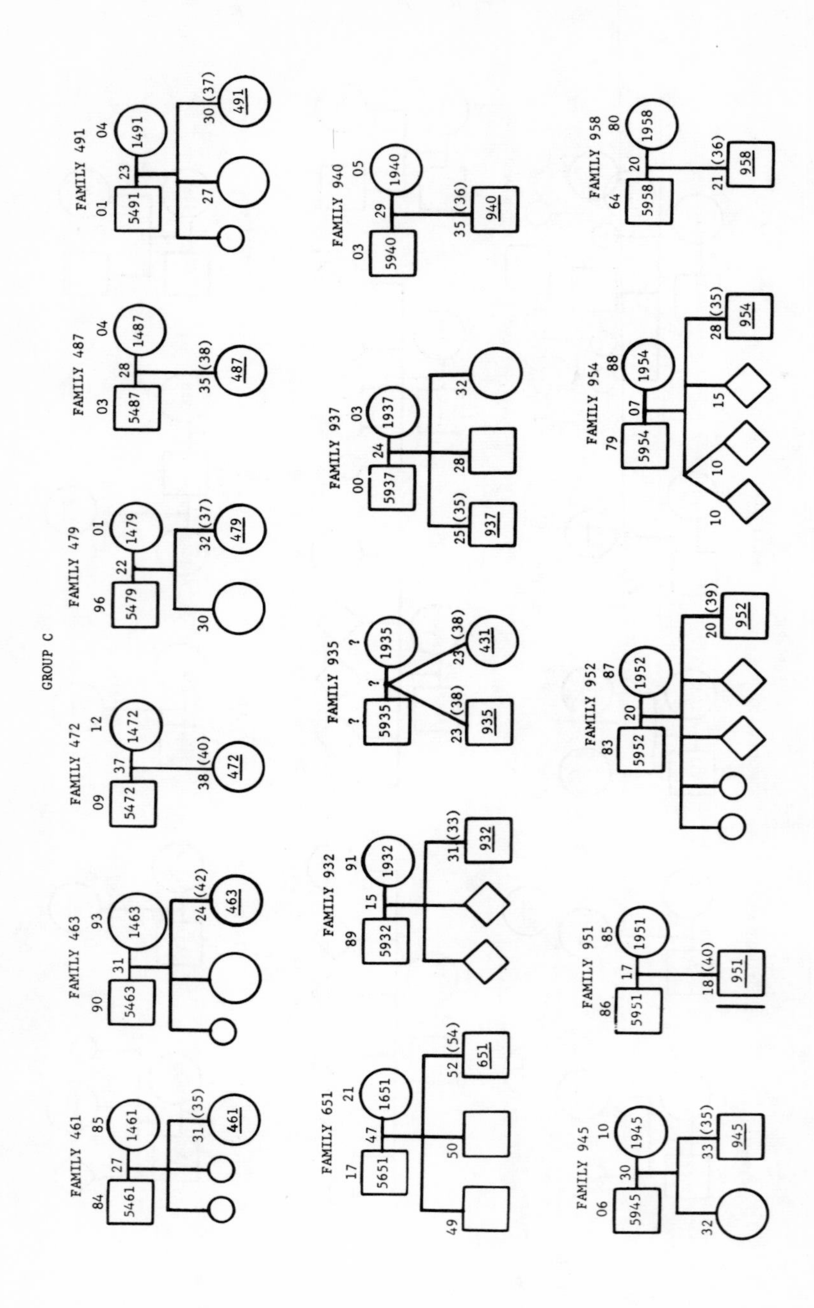
GROUP C
FAMILY 461
FAMILY 463
FAMILY 472
FAMILY 479
FAMILY 487
FAMILY 491
FAMILY 651
FAMILY 932
FAMILY 935
FAMILY 937
FAMILY 940
FAMILY 945
FAMILY 951
FAMILY 952
FAMILY 954
FAMILY 958

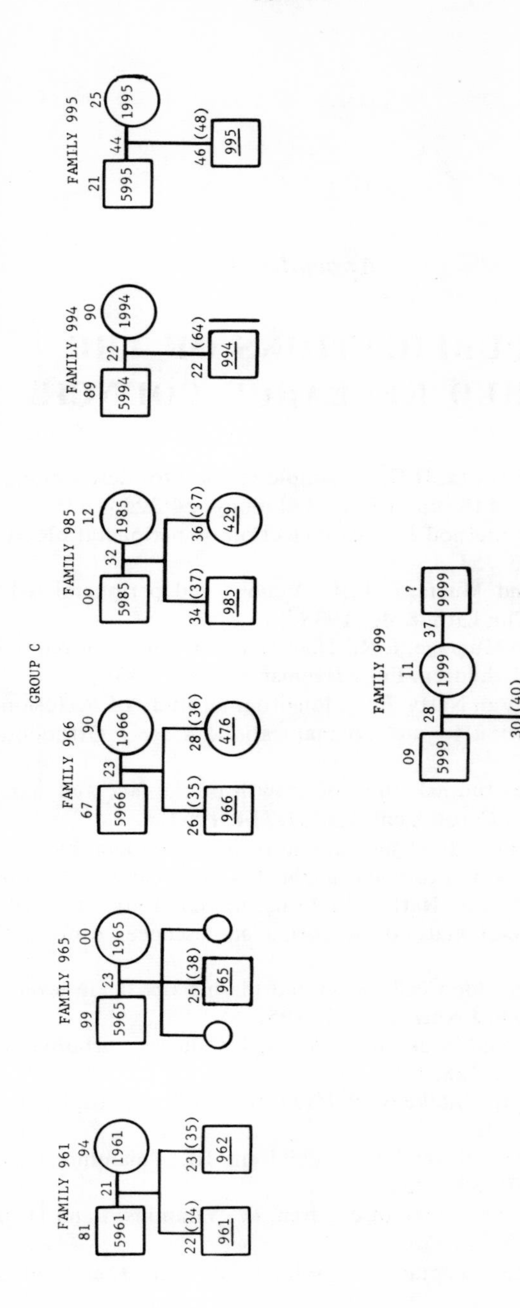
GROUP C
FAMILY 961
81
5961
21
94
1961
22 (34)
961
23 (35)
962
FAMILY 965
99
5965
23
00
1965
25 (38)
965
FAMILY 966
67
5966
23
90
1966
26 (35)
966
28 (36)
476
FAMILY 985
09
5985
32
12
1985
34 (37)
985
36 (37)
429
FAMILY 994
89
5994
22
90
1994
22 (64)
994
FAMILY 995
21
5995
44
25
1995
46 (48)
995
FAMILY 999
09
5999
28
11
1999
37
?
9999
30 (40)
999

Appendix B

PUBLICATIONS OF THE CHILD RESEARCH COUNCIL

Allen, K.D.A., and Waltz, H.D.: A simple method for determining the degree of inspiration from the chest film. Radiology, 24:225, 1935.

Andresen, M.I.: A method for the collection of peripheral blood samples. J Lab Clin Med, 23:751, 1938.

Andresen, M.I., and Mugrage, E.R.: Venous and peripheral red blood cell values. Amer J Clin Path, 8:46, 1938.

Andresen, M.I., and Mugrage, E.R.: Diameter and volume of red blood cells in infants and small children. Folia Haemat, 61:201, 1938.

Bambha, J.K., and Van Natta, P.: A longitudinal study of occlusion and tooth eruption in relation to skeletal maturation. Amer J Orthodont, 45:847, 1959.

Bambha, J.K.: Longitudinal study of growth of the face and cranium during preschool years. J Canad Dent Ass, 27:714, 1961.

Bambha, J.K.: Longitudinal cephalometric roentgenographic study of face and cranium in relation to body height. J Amer Dent Ass, 63:776, 1961.

Bambha, J.K., and Van Natta, P.: Longitudinal study of facial growth in relation to skeletal maturation during adolescence. Amer J Orthodont, 49:481, 1963.

Bartlett, M.N.: Red blood cell niacin and plasma riboflavin levels in a group of normal children. J Nutr, 57:157, 1955.

Beal, V.A.: Nutritional intake of children. I. Calories, carbohydrate, fat and protein. J Nutr, 50:223, 1953.

Beal, V.A.: Nutritional intake of children. II. Calcium, phosphorus and iron. J Nutr, 53:499, 1954.

Beal, V.A.: Nutritional intake of children. III. Thiamine, riboflavin and niacin. J Nutr, 57:183, 1955.

Beal, V.A.: Nutritional intake of children. IV. Vitamins A and D and ascorbic acid. J Nutr, 60:335, 1956.

Beal, V.A.: On the acceptance of solid foods and other food patterns of infants and children. Pediatrics, 20:448, 1957.

Beal, V.A., and Van Buskirk, J.J.: Riboflavin in red blood cells in relation to dietary intake of children. Amer J Clin Nutr, 8:841, 1960.

Beal, V.A.: Dietary intake of individuals followed through infancy and childhood. Amer J Public Health, 51:1107, 1961.

Beal, V.A.; Meyers, A.J., and McCammon, R.W.: Iron intake, hemoglobin, and physical growth during the first two years of life. Pediatrics, 30:518, 1962.

Beal, V.A.: Patterns and variations in nutritional requirements of individuals during growth. Bull Amer Ass Maternal Infant Health, 9:19, 1962.

Beal, V.A.: Nutrition in a longitudinal growth study. J Amer Diet Ass, 46:457, 1965.

Beal, V.A.: The nutritional history in longitudinal research. J Amer Diet Ass, 51:426, 1967.

Beal, V.A.: Feeding your baby. Amer Baby, 29:18, 1967.

Beal, V.A.: Calcium and phosphorus in infancy. J Amer Diet Ass, 53:450, 1968.

Beal, V.A.: Breast- and formula-feeding of infants. J Amer Diet Ass, 55:31, 1969.

Beal, V.A.: Termination of night feedings in infancy. J Pediat, 75:690, 1969.

Benjamin, J.D.: Approaches to a dynamic theory of development round table, 1949. 2. Methodological considerations in the validation and elaboration of psychoanalytical personality theory. Amer J Orthopsychiat, 20:139, 1950.

Benjamin, J.D.: Prediction and psychopathological theory. In Jessner, L., and Pavenstedt, E. (Ed.): Dynamic Psychopathology in Childhood. New York, Grune & Stratton, 1959, pp. 6-77.

Benner, M. C.: Technical studies on normal lungs. Amer J Med Techn, 5:152, 1939.

Bouslog, J.S.; Cunningham, T.D.; Hanner, J.P.; Walton, J.B., and Waltz, H.D.: Roentgenologic studies of the infant's gastrointestinal tract. J Pediat, 6:234, 1935.

Boyd, E.: Major Patterns of Human Growth. Vol. I. Origins of the Study of Human Growth. In preparation.

Boyd, E.: Pictorial and graphic analysis of the body build of one boy. Amer J Dis Child, 89:332, 1955.

Burnett, C.T., and Taylor, E.: Electrocardiograms on 167 average healthy infants and children. Amer Heart J, 11:185, 1936.

Deming, J., and Washburn, A.H.: Respiration in infancy. I. A method of studying rates, volume and character of respiration with preliminary report of results. Amer J Dis Child, 49:108, 1935.

Deming, J., and Hanner, J.P.: Respiration in infancy. II. A study of rate, volume and character of respiration in healthy infants during the neonatal period. Amer J Dis Child, 51:823, 1936.

Deming, J.: Application of the Gompertz curve to the observed pattern of growth in length of 48 individual boys and girls during the adolescent cycle of growth. Hum Biol, 29:83, 1957.

Deming, J., and Washburn, A.H.: Application of the Jenss curve to the observed pattern of growth during the first eight years of life in forty boys and forty girls. Hum Biol, 35:484, 1963.

Dunlop, D.: The families of the Child Research Council. A study of families whose children are similar to those in urban pediatric practice. J Pediat, 22:111, 1943.

Halpern, S.R.: Quantitative cytological studies of the anterior lobe of the hypophysis of fetuses and children, correlated with sexual and skeletal development. Endocrinology, 22:173, 1938.

Hanner, D.D.: Chest radiography in infants and uncooperative children. X-ray Techn, 7:62, 1935.

Hansman, C.F., and Maresh, M.M.: A longitudinal study of skeletal maturation. Amer J Dis Child, 101:305, 1961.

Hansman, C.F.: Appearance and fusion of ossification centers in the human skeleton. Amer J Roentgen, 88:476, 1962.

Hansman, C.F.: Variations in physical growth. J Amer Med Wom Ass, 19:953, 1964.

Hansman, C.F.: Growth of interorbital distance and skull thickness as observed in roentgenographic measurements. Radiology, 86:87, 1966.

Hilden, A.H.: A presentation of data on the mental growth curve, with some implications for longtime prediction, Proc. Fall Meet. Rocky Mts. Branch Amer. Psychol. Ass. Psychol Bull, 42:749, 1945.

Hilden, A.H.: A Rorschach succession chart. J Psychol, 22:53, 1946.

Hilden, A.H.: A longitudinal study of intellectual development. J Psychol, 28:187, 1949.

Hill, R.M., and Trevorrow, V.: Plasma albumin, globulin, and fibrinogen in healthy individuals from birth to adult life. I. A system of microanalysis. J Lab Clin Med, 26:1838, 1941.

Hill, R.M., and Trevorrow, V.: Normal variation in the concentration of fibrinogen, albumin and globulin in blood plasma. J Phys Chem, 46:1117, 1942.

Iliff, A.; Kinsman, G.M.; Hill, R.M., and Lewis, R.C.: A simple method for the approximate analysis of carbon dioxide and oxygen in gas samples. J Lab Clin Med, 28:1380, 1943.

Iliff, A.; Gordon, H.H.; McNamara, H., and Bell, W.R.: Basal metabolic rate in obese children with a note on the basal metabolic rate in dwarfs. Pediatrics, 4:744, 1949.

Iliff, A.; Lee, V., and Lewis, R.C.: Interpretation of the basal metabolic rate of children of unusual body build. Pediatrics, 8:616, 1951.

Iliff, A., and Lee, V.A.: Pulse rate, respiratory rate, and body temperature of children between two months and eighteen years of age. Child Develop, 23:237, 1952.

Lee, V.A., and Iliff, A.: The energy metabolism of infants and young children during postprandial sleep. Pediatrics, 18:739, 1956.

Lee, V.A.: Individual trends in the total serum cholesterol of children and adolescents over a ten-year period. Amer J Clin Nutr, 20:5, 1967.

Lewis, R.C.; Kinsman, G.M., and Iliff, A.: The basal metabolism of normal boys and girls from two to twelve years old, inclusive. Amer J Dis Child, 53:348, 1937.

Lewis, R.C.; Iliff, A.; Duval, A.M., and Kinsman, G.M.: The effect of change of altitude on the basal metabolism of human subjects. J Lab Clin Med, 28:851, 1943.

Lewis, R.C.; Iliff, A.; Duval, A.M., and Kinsman, G.M.: The effect of change of altitude on the blood of human subjects. J Lab Clin Med, 28:860, 1943.

Lewis, R.C.; Duval, A.M., and Iliff, A.: Basal metabolism of normal children from thirteen and fifteen years old, inclusive. Amer J Dis Child, 65:845, 1943.

Lewis, R.C.; Duval, A.M., and Iliff, A.: Basal metabolism of normal boys and girls from two to twelve years old, inclusive. Report of a further study. Amer J Dis Child, 65:834, 1943.

Lewis, R.C.; Duval, A.M., and Iliff, A.: Standards for the basal metabolism of children from 2 to 15 years of age, inclusive. J Pediat, 23:1, 1943.

Lewis, R.C.; Iliff, A., and Duval, A.M.: The comparative accuracy of the closed circuit bedside method and the open circuit chamber procedure for the determination of basal metabolism. J Lab Clin Med, 28:1238, 1943.

Lewis, R.C.; Iliff, A., and Duval, A.M.: Further consideration of the effect of altitude on basal metabolism. A study on young women residents of Denver. J Nutr, 26:175, 1943.

Lewis, R.C.; Duval, A.M., and Iliff, A.: Effect of adolescence on basal metabolism of normal children. Amer J Dis Child, 66:396, 1943.

Lewis, R.C.; Duval, A.M., and Iliff, A.: The effect of repeated determinations on the basal metabolism of children. Amer J Physiol, 140:461, 1944.

Lubchenco, L.O.; Hansman, C.; Dressler, M., and Boyd, E.: Intrauterine growth as estimated from liveborn birth-weight data at 24 to 42 weeks of gestation. Pediatrics, 32:793, 1963.

Lubchenco, L.O.; Hansman, C., and Boyd, E.: Intrauterine growth in length and head circumference as estimated from live births at gestational ages from 26 to 42 weeks. Pediatrics, 37:403, 1966.

Lubchenco, L.O., and Hansman, C.: Factors influencing fetal growth. Aspects of prematurity and dysmaturity. Second Nutricia Symposium. Leiden, Holland, H. E. Stenfert Kroese N.V., 1967, and Springfield, Thomas, 1967.

Maresh, M.M., and Washburn, A.H.: Size of the heart in healthy children. Roentgen measurements of the cardiac area and transverse diameter for sixty-seven children between birth and the age of six years. Amer J Dis Child, 56:33, 1938.

Maresh, M.M., and Deming, J.: The growth of the long bones in 80 infants. Roentgenograms versus anthropometry. Child Develop, 10:91, 1939.

Maresh, M.M.: Paranasal sinuses from birth to late adolescence. I. Size of the paranasal sinuses as observed in routine posteroanterior roentgenograms, Amer J Dis Child, 60:55, 1940.

Maresh, M.M., and Washburn, A.H.: Paranasal sinuses from birth to late adolescence. II. Clinical and roentgenographic evidence of infection. Amer J Dis Child, 60:841, 1940.

Maresh, M.M.: Growth of major long bones in healthy children: A preliminary report on successive roentgenograms of the extremities from early infancy to twelve years of age. Amer J Dis Child, 66:227, 1943.

Maresh, M.M.: Growth of the heart related to bodily growth during childhood and adolescence. Pediatrics, 2:382, 1948.

Maresh, M.: Linear growth of long bones of extremities from infancy through adolescence. Amer J Dis Child, 89:725, 1955.

Maresh, M.M.: Linear body proportions. A roentgenographic study. Amer J Dis Child, 98:27, 1959.

Maresh, M.M.: Bone, muscle and fat measurements. Longitudinal measurements of the bone, muscle and fat widths from roentgenograms of the extremities during the first six years of life. Pediatrics, 28:971, 1961.

Maresh, M.M.: Tissue changes in the individual during growth from x-rays of the extremities. Ann NY Acad Sci, 110:465, 1963.

Maresh, M.M.: Variations in patterns of linear growth and skeletal maturation. J Amer Phys Ther Ass, 44:881, 1964.

Maresh, M.: Changes in tissue widths during growth. Amer J Dis Child, 111:142, 1966.

Maresh, M., and Groome, D.S.: Potassium-40: Serial determinations in infants. Pediatrics, 38:642, 1966.

McCammon, R.W.: Preliminary report on the developmental aspects of the P-R interval in the electrocardiograms of healthy children. Pediatrics, 16:873, 1955.

McCammon, R.W., and Sexton, A.W.: Implications of longitudinal research in fitness programs. JAMA, 168:1440, 1958.

McCammon, R.W.: A longitudinal study of electrocardiographic intervals in healthy children. Acta Paediat, 50:Supplement 126, 1961

McCammon, R.W.: Some aspects of physical and physiological individual variation, Symposium of The Nutrition Society on Individual Variation, 17 March 1962. Proc Nutr Soc, 21:144, 1962.

McCammon, R.W.: Are boys and girls maturing physically at earlier ages? Amer J Public Health, 55:103, 1965.

McCammon, R.W.: The concept of normality. (Presented at conference entitled The Biology of Human Variation held by The New York Academy of Sciences on Feb. 11, 12, and 13, 1965.) Ann NY Acad Sci, 134:559, 1966.

McDowell, R.M.: The use of lateral head radiographs for evaluating orthodontic results as distinguished from growth changes. Part I. Technique and statement of problem. Amer J Orthodont Oral Surg, 27:59, 1941.

Meyers, A.J.; Trevorrow, V.; Washburn, A.H., and Mugrage, E.R.: Quantitative studies of the influence of plasma proteins and hematocrit on the erythrocyte sedimentation rate. Blood, 8:893, 1953.

Mugrage, E.R., and Andresen, M.I.: Values for red blood cells of average infants and children. Amer J Dis Child, 51:775, 1936.

Mugrage, E.R., and Andresen, M.I.: Red blood cell values for normal men and women. Arch Intern Med, 58:136, 1936.

Mugrage, E.R., and Andresen, M.I.: Normal standards for red blood cell values in Colorado. Colorado Med, 34:473, 1937.

Mugrage, E.R., and Andresen, M.I.: Red blood cell values in adolescence. Amer J Dis Child, 56:997, 1938.

Nanda, R.S.: The rates of growth of several facial components measured from serial cephalometric roentgenograms. Amer J Orthodont, 41:658, 1955.

Nanda, R.S.: Cephalometric study of the human face from serial roentgenograms. Ergebn Anat Entwicklungsgesch, 35:359, 1956.

Nanda, R.S.: Eruption of human teeth. Amer J Orthodont, 46:363, 1960.

Reeve, R., and DeBoer, K.: Sinus arrhythmia. I. Data and patterns from groups of individuals followed from 1 month to 23 years of age. Pediatrics, 26:402, 1960.

Ricciuti, H.N.: Use of the Rorschach test in longitudinal studies of personality development. J Project Techn, 20:256, 1956.

Sexton, A.W.: Value of longitudinal studies of exercise fitness tests. Pediatrics, 32:730, 1963.

Snyder, M.L., and Hall, I.C.: Bacillus capitovalis, a new species of obligate anaerobe encountered in post mortem materials, in a wound infection, and in the feces of infants. Zbl Bakt, 135:290, 1935.

Snyder, M.L., and Hanner, J.P.: Bacilluria caused by bacterium alkalescens. J Infect Dis, 60:51, 1937.

Snyder, M.L.: Bacterium alkalescens in the stools of normal infants. J Pediat, 14:341, 1939.

Snyder, M.L.: The normal fecal flora of infants between two weeks and one year of age. I. Serial studies. J Infect Dis, 66:1, 1940.

Szymanski, B.B., and Longwell, B.B.: Plasma vitamin A and carotene determinations in a group of normal children. J Nutr, 45:431, 1951.

Tennes, K.H., and Lampl, E.E.: Stranger and separation anxiety in infancy. J Nerv Ment Dis, 139:247, 1964.

Tennes, K.H., and Lampl, E.E.: Some aspects of mother-child relationship pertaining to infantile separation anxiety. J Nerv Ment Dis, 143:426, 1966.

Trevorrow, V.; Kaser, M.; Patterson, J.P., and Hill, R.M.: Plasma albumin, globulin, and fibrinogen in healthy individuals from birth to adulthood. II. "Normal" values. J Lab Clin Med, 27:471, 1942.

Trevorrow, V.E.: Longitudinal study of plasma fibrinogen in children. Hum Biol, 29:354, 1957.

Trevorrow, V.E.: Concentration of gamma-globulin in the serum of infants during the first three months of life. Pediatrics, 24:746, 1959.

Trevorrow, V.E.; Merrill, D., and Claman, H.N.: Immunoglobulin components of "gamma" globulin in human serum. Clin Chem, 11:527, 1965.

Trevorrow, V.E.: Intra-individual gamma globulin changes with age from 4 to 20 years. Hum Biol, 39:1, 1967.

Waldo, C.M.: Teeth and jaws of infants. Bull Colorado State Dent Ass, 12:3, 1933.

Waldo, C.M.: Orthodontic research as a component part of a balanced longitudinal study of 100 children. Int J Orthodont Oral Surg, 22:659, 1936.

Washburn, A.H.: Blood pictures in average healthy infants during the first six months. Colorado Med, 30:413, 1933.

Washburn, A.H.: Blood cells in healthy young infants. I. The leukocytic picture during the first three months with special reference to hourly and daily variations. Amer J Dis Child, 47:993, 1934.

Washburn, A.H.: Blood cells in healthy young infants. II. A comparison of routine and special technics in the differentiation of leukocytes. Amer J Dis Child, 50:395, 1935.

Washburn, A.H.: Blood cells in healthy young infants. III. A study of 608 differential leukocyte counts, with a final report on 908 total leukocyte counts. Amer J Dis Child, 50:413, 1935.

Washburn, A.H.: The significance of individual variations. J Pediat, 8:31, 1936.

Washburn, A.H.: Opportunities for a liaison between psychiatry and pediatrics in a child research institute. Proc. of the Third Conference on Psychiatric Educ., 1936, pp. 24-31.

Washburn, A.H.: Diverse attributes of healthy children. A report of progress in understanding the "normal child." J Pediat, 11:37, 1937.

Washburn, A.H.: The place of child research in medicine. Some contributions to medical thought suggested by a study of the growth and development of the individual child. Proc Inst Med Chicago, 12:30, 1938.

Washburn, A.H.: Blood cells in healthy young infants. IV. Postnatal readjustments of the red blood cells in individual babies. Amer J Dis Child, 62:530, 1941.

Washburn, A.H.: Presidential address: Society for Research in Child Development, New York, Dec. 29, 1949. Child Develop, 21:61, 1950.

Washburn, A.H.: Growth; its significance in medicine viewed as human biology. Pediatrics, 5:765, 1950.

Washburn, A. H.: Pediatric potpourri, Pediatrics, 8:299, 1951.

Washburn, A.H.: Medicine as human biology. J Med Educ, 28:9, 1953.

Washburn, A.H.: Human growth, development, and adaptation. Amer J Dis Child, 90:2, 1955.

Washburn, A.H., and Meyers, A.J.: The sedimentation of erythrocytes at an angle of 45 degrees. J Lab Clin Med, 49:318, 1957.

Washburn, A.H.: The child as a person developing. I. A philosophy and program of research. Amer J Dis Child, 94:46, 1957.

Washburn, A.H.: The child as a person developing. II. More questions raised than answered. Amer J Dis Child, 94:54, 1957.

Washburn, A.H.: Influences of early development upon later life. In Birren, James E. (Ed.): Relations of Development and Aging. Springfield, Thomas, 1964.

Washburn, A.H.: All human beings start life as babies. Pediatrics, 37:828, 1966.

Washburn, A.H.: Plasma cells in the circulation in infants and children. Amer J Dis Child, 113:633, 1967.

Wasson, W.W.: The hilus of the lung. Boston Med Surg J, 197:1492, 1928.

Wasson, W.W.: Changes in the nasal accessory sinuses after birth. Arch Otolaryng, 17:197, 1933.

Wasson, W.W., and Waltz, H.D.: The relationship of sinus disease to chest disease in children. Radiology, 22:432, 1934.

Yarrow, L.J.: The relationship between nutritive sucking experiences in infancy and non-nutritive sucking in childhood. J Genet Psychol, 84:149, 1954.